MANUAL OF MATHEMATICAL PHYSICS

MANUAL OF
MATHEMATICAL PHYSICS

by

PAUL I. RICHARDS
Technical Operations, Inc., Burlington, Massachusetts, U.S.A

PERGAMON PRESS
NEW YORK · LONDON · PARIS · LOS ANGELES
1959

PERGAMON PRESS INC.
122 *East 55th Street, New York 22, N.Y.*
P.O. Box 47715, Los Angeles, California

PERGAMON PRESS LTD.
4 & 5 *Fitzroy Square, London W.*1.

PERGAMON PRESS S.A.R.L.
24 *Rue des Écoles, Paris V^e^*

PHYSICS

Library of Congress Card Number 58–12659

Printed in Northern Ireland at The Universities Press, Belfast

CONTENTS

PREFACE

THE goal of this book is to condense established theoretical physics, its applications and its mathematical equipment into a single reference volume of reasonable size without sacrificing either logical continuity or fundamentals. In this way, each formula appears in its deductive context and its origin, as well as any approximations or assumptions which it may entail, can readily be determined.

To render this ideal more approachable the Physics section has been limited to theories which have been well established by experiment, and their deductive ramifications have been terminated while the results still maintain a wide utility in applications. Likewise, the Mathematics section has been economized by omitting much material which can be found in tables of integrals or in compilations of the properties of the classical functions of analysis.

To facilitate rapid extraction of information, an attempt was made either to define or to cross-reference every special concept and every symbol within at least a few pages preceding its every appearance, although some exceptions necessarily occur with the more standard symbols.

Three guides for finding information have been provided: (1) The table of contents displays the overall organization of the material and lists the major subjects within each chapter. (The chapter number forms the first half of each equation number.) (2) The left-hand page headings designate the major subject area, while the right-hand page headings mention individual items which appear on the corresponding pair of pages. (3) The index is as complete as the author could make it and should suffice to locate any item contained in the book.

The index has also been designed for use as a dictionary of terms and concepts, by including even items which are merely mentioned or parenthetically defined in the text.

Any suggestions or comments which users may feel would add to the general utility of the book, either as a reference or as a study guide, will be gratefully received.

PART 1

PHYSICS

PHILOSOPHY

UNLIKE mathematics, physics has as its prime purpose the description of the real world. The mathematician need only assure himself that his theorems follow from his axioms, but the physicist must continually ask Nature to pass judgement on the smallest facet of his theories. The *facts* of the world alone are the final judges of the usefulness and truth of any theoretical model. Ideally, there should be no disagreement whatever, but we must frequently make do with imperfect theories, being fully cognizant of their limitations.

Yet physics (especially of all the sciences) is not a mere listing of data. Rather physics is mainly a set of mathematical models of Nature. These models serve the dual purpose of describing the logical interrelations of various facts and at the same time of summarizing great masses of data *which can then be discarded.*

Unlike the mathematician, the physicist must stand ready at all times to abandon previously "established" theories. However many and varied may be the experiments which have "verified" a theory, it has never been proved; a new fact of Nature can always arise to contradict it. Yet "well established" theories are never wholly wrong; if they properly describe a wide range of data, they must be good approximations and, indeed, must appear as special cases of any more general theory. Thus Newtonian Mechanics, while now known to be wrong in a philosophic sense, remains a respected and indispensable tool of physics. Under appropriate conditions, it gives to high accuracy the same answers as the more ponderous and inconvenient theories of Quantum Mechanics or of Relativity, of each of which it is a special case. Not to use it would be mere pedantry.

CHAPTER 1

MECHANICS

A. POINT MASSES AND RIGID BODIES

Point Particles; Fundamental Concepts

DENOTE the position of a "small" particle (mass point) by the vector, $\mathbf{r}$, relative to any convenient origin.

It is found experimentally that the acceleration, $\mathrm{d}^2\mathbf{r}/\mathrm{d}t^2$, of a mass point is, in many circumstances, independent of its previous motion and depends only on its position (and sometimes on the time). Moreover, different mass points are usually found to suffer proportional accelerations under the same circumstances. It is therefore useful to introduce concepts of "mass" and "force" *defined* by

$$\mathbf{F} = m\frac{\mathrm{d}^2\mathbf{r}}{\mathrm{d}t^2} \tag{1–1}$$

where m is a constant characteristic of each particle and called the mass of the particle (chosen as unity for some standard particle) and $\mathbf{F}$ is the force which is then *defined* by (1–1) (as applied to the standard particle or one whose mass has been determined by comparison with the standard under identical conditions).

Newton's Third Law* states that if a body A exerts a force, $\mathbf{F}$, on body B then, conversely, body B exerts an equal and opposite force, $-\mathbf{F}$, on body A. ("To *every* action, there is an equal and opposite reaction.")

Unlike the definition (1–1), this is a statement of *fact* which withstood 200 years experimental investigation (but is now known to have exceptions—at least with the simple definition, (1–1)).

The term "body" used above ultimately refers to mass-points but, by summation or integration, may also be interpreted as a physical system of any degree of complexity.

Note finally the implication that the forces can be regarded as "caused" by other agencies.† This, too, is a question of fact and has been well borne out by experience. In greater detail, experiment indicates that forces "from" different agencies, which act on the same particle, may be added vectorially:

$$\mathbf{F}_{\text{total on } A} = \sum_i \mathbf{F}_{\text{on } A \text{ due to } i}$$

From Newton's Third Law it follows that if a system of particles is "isolated" in the sense that all forces are produced within the system‡ ("no external forces act") and are independent of external conditions, then $0 = \sum \mathbf{F}_i = \frac{\mathrm{d}}{\mathrm{d}t}\left(\sum m_i \frac{\mathrm{d}\mathbf{r}_i}{\mathrm{d}t}\right)$ or if $\mathbf{v}_i = \mathrm{d}\mathbf{r}_i/\mathrm{d}t$ (velocity) then

$$\sum_i m_i\mathbf{v}_i = \mathbf{P}, \text{ a constant} \tag{1–2}$$

---

* The first two are contained in (1–1) and are really a definition of "force."

† Philosophically better: certain forces are present when and only when the associated agencies are present (correlation, not causation).

‡ More precisely, if the Lagrangian function of the system is independent of translations of the coordinates describing the system.

(The law of conservation of "*momentum*", **P**.) Correspondingly, if we define the momentum of a particle as $\mathbf{p}_i = m_i\mathbf{v}_i$ then $\sum_i \mathbf{p}_i =$ constant if no external forces act.

The "*work*" done between times t_1 and t_2 by the force **F** acting on a particle which undergoes displacements d**r** (whether "due to" the force or not) is defined by

$$W = \int_{t_1}^{t_2} \mathbf{F}\cdot \mathrm{d}\mathbf{r} \tag{1–3}$$

From (1–1)

$$W = \tfrac{1}{2}mv^2\Big|_{t_1}^{t_2} = T_2 - T_1 \tag{1–4}$$

where

$$T = \tfrac{1}{2}mv^2 \tag{1–5}$$

is known as the "*kinetic energy*" of the particle. The work done on a particle is always equal to the change in its kinetic energy, according to (1–4).

The change in momentum $\mathbf{p} = m\mathbf{v}$ of a particle is always equal to

$$\mathbf{I} = \int_{t_1}^{t_2} \mathbf{F}\,\mathrm{d}t = (m\mathbf{v})_2 - (m\mathbf{v})_1 \tag{1–6}$$

which is called the "*impulse*".

Moving Coordinates, Coriolis Forces

All of the above relations are valid in general (since, indeed, most of them are definitions) but in moving coordinates one must remember that the "basis vectors", $\mathbf{e}_i$, in $\mathbf{r} = x_1\mathbf{e}_1 + x_2\mathbf{e}_2 + x_3\mathbf{e}_3$ are also moving so that their time derivatives enter along with those of the "components", x_i. Since (1–1) involves a double time derivative, some of the extra terms will appear multiplied by the (local, apparent) velocity of the particle, $\mathrm{d}x_i/\mathrm{d}t$. These extra "forces", which have the property that they appear only when the particle is in motion (as seen from the moving coordinates), are known as "Coriolis forces".

Potential Fields, Conservative Forces

In many circumstances **F** can be expressed as the gradient of a simple scalar function:

$$\mathbf{F} = -\nabla\phi(\mathbf{r}, t) \tag{1–7}$$

(evaluated at the position of the particle). Here $\phi(\mathbf{r}, t)$ is known as the "potential energy". If ϕ is actually independent of t, then from (1–4), (1–7) and (1–1),

$$\frac{\mathrm{d}}{\mathrm{d}t}(T + \phi) = 0; \qquad T + \phi = E, \text{ a constant} \tag{1–8}$$

Here E is called the total energy of the particle. Forces which keep E constant are called "conservative forces".

Conversely, if the total energy is conserved, the forces must be derivable from some ϕ via (1–7). [Thus, if $|\mathbf{v}|$ depends only on **r**—for any orbit—then ϕ *defined* by (1–8) satisfies (1–7).]

Example: (Newton's law of gravity). The gravitational force which each of two "particles" exerts on the other is experimentally found to be

$$m_1 m_2 G\,\frac{\mathbf{r}_1 - \mathbf{r}_2}{|\mathbf{r}_1 - \mathbf{r}_2|^3} = \text{force on \#2 "due to" \#1}$$

Here G is a universal constant of Nature. Both forces are simply obtained from (1–7) if we take

$$-\phi = \frac{m_1 m_2 G}{|\mathbf{r}_1 - \mathbf{r}_2|} \tag{1–9}$$

Orbit-Tracing in Potential Fields

Let $U = (\text{constant} - \phi)$ so that $\mathbf{F} = +\nabla U$ and adjust the constant so that, for the orbit desired, $\frac{1}{2}mv^2 = U$. Then if the independent variable, t, in (1–1) is replaced by the path-length, s, the result is

$$2U \frac{\mathrm{d}^2\mathbf{r}}{\mathrm{d}s^2} = \frac{\mathrm{d}\mathbf{r}}{\mathrm{d}s} \times \left[(\nabla U) \times \frac{\mathrm{d}\mathbf{r}}{\mathrm{d}s} \right] \tag{1–10}$$

That is,

$$\text{Curvature vector} = \text{Projection of } \left(\frac{\mathbf{F}}{mv^2}\right) \text{ perpendicular to the orbit} \tag{1–11}$$

This relation can be made the basis of a numerical or graphical method for tracing the path of a particle under the influence of conservative static forces.

Constraints

In some cases, a particle is required to satisfy such conditions as $g_\alpha(\mathbf{r}, t) = 0$. (EXAMPLE: motions of a particle over a surface.) Such cases are often most easily treated by substituting these conditions directly in the equations of motion (or by using the Lagrange equations; see later).

Occasionally, however, Lagrange's method of undetermined multipliers is more convenient: We have $\nabla g_\alpha = 0$; multiply these by unspecified functions, $\lambda_\alpha(\mathbf{r}, t)$ and add to (1–1),

$$m \frac{\mathrm{d}^2\mathbf{r}}{\mathrm{d}t^2} = \mathbf{F} + \sum_\alpha \lambda_\alpha \nabla g_\alpha \tag{1–12}$$

These equations may often conveniently be solved by algebraically eliminating the λ_α and picking out solutions of the resulting relations which satisfy $g_\alpha(\mathbf{r}, t) = 0$. [If the constraining forces, $\lambda_\alpha \nabla g_\alpha$, are desired, they may then be found by returning to (1–12).]

Systems of Mass Points

As already hinted, a system of many mass points, m_i, is described by a set of equations (1–1), one for each particle, along with a prescription, perhaps of the form (1–7), for the forces. The total momentum and total kinetic energy of the system are defined as the sum of those of the individual particles:

$$m_i \frac{\mathrm{d}^2\mathbf{r}_i}{\mathrm{d}t^2} = \mathbf{F}_i \qquad (i = 1, \cdots, n;\ 3n \text{ equations}) \tag{1–13}$$

$$\mathbf{P} = \sum_i m_i \mathbf{v}_i; \qquad T = \sum_i \tfrac{1}{2} m_i v_i^2 \tag{1–14}$$

and if $\mathbf{F}_i = -\nabla_i \phi$ (that is, if $(\mathbf{F}_i)_x = \frac{\partial}{\partial x_i} \phi(\mathbf{r}_1, \mathbf{r}_2, \cdots, \mathbf{r}_n)$, etc.) then

$$T + \phi = E, \text{ a constant, the energy of the system}$$

Note that the concept of potential of *a* particle of the system need not have meaning.

Center of Mass

If we define

$$\mathbf{r}_c = \frac{1}{M} \sum_i m_i \mathbf{r}_i \qquad (M = \sum_i m_i) \tag{1-15}$$

as the position of the "center of mass" of the system, then $\mathbf{P} = M(\mathrm{d}\mathbf{r}_c/\mathrm{d}t)$ and from (1–13) and (1–14),

$$\frac{\mathrm{d}\mathbf{P}}{\mathrm{d}t} = \sum_i \mathbf{F}_i\,; \qquad \text{or:} \qquad \mathbf{F} = M\,\frac{\mathrm{d}^2\mathbf{r}_c}{\mathrm{d}t^2} \tag{1-16}$$

where $\mathbf{F}$ is the total *external* force acting on all the particles. (By Newton's third law, the overall sum of internal forces is zero.) Thus *the center of mass of a system moves as if all the mass and all external forces were concentrated there.* Thus macroscopic bodies, whether rigid or not, can be treated as point particles, if we wish to know only the motion of the center of mass.

Kinetic Energy

From (1–14) and (1–15) it follows immediately that

$$T = \tfrac{1}{2}M|\mathbf{v}_c|^2 + \sum_i \tfrac{1}{2}m_i|\mathbf{v}_i - \mathbf{v}_c|^2 \tag{1-17}$$

(where $\mathbf{v}_c = \mathrm{d}\mathbf{r}_c/\mathrm{d}t$). That is, the kinetic energy of the system can be expressed as that of a mass point $M = \sum_i m_i$ concentrated at the center of mass plus the kinetic energy due to motions of the particles *relative* to the center of mass.*

Angular Momentum; Torque

To indicate gross features of the additional motions of the system around its center of mass, define†

$$\mathbf{J} = \sum_i m_i \mathbf{r}_i \times \mathbf{v}_i \qquad \mathbf{L} = \sum_i \mathbf{r}_i \times \mathbf{F}_i \tag{1-18}$$

called respectively the total "angular momentum" and total "torque" (or "moment") on the system. From (1–13), it follows that

$$\frac{\mathrm{d}\mathbf{J}}{\mathrm{d}t} = \mathbf{L} \tag{1-19}$$

as a "gross" equation for the motion about the center of mass.

Equation (1–19) is the anti-symmetric part of the more general dyadic relation (for each particle)

$$\frac{\mathrm{d}}{\mathrm{d}t}\, m\mathbf{r}\mathbf{v} = \mathbf{r}\mathbf{F} + m\mathbf{v}\mathbf{v} \tag{1-20}$$

which is also an immediate consequence of (1–1). The symmetric part of this relation is

$$-\mathbf{r}\cdot\mathbf{F} = 2T - \frac{\mathrm{d}}{\mathrm{d}t}(\mathbf{r}\cdot\mathbf{p})$$

---

* In view of (1–16), it might appear that the extra term in (1–17) violates the general principle (1–4). It does not, of course, and the reason is that, despite (1–16), the external forces do not actually act *on* $\mathbf{r}_c$ and this must be taken into account in computing the work done by them.

† Note that the order of the factors in (1–18) is purely a matter of *convention*; the corresponding sign-ambiguity indicates that $\mathbf{J}$ and $\mathbf{L}$ are "axial" vectors.

If the system is such that $\mathbf{r} \cdot \mathbf{p}$ is bounded, then taking time averages $\left[(1/t_0)\int_0^{t_0} \cdots dt;\ t_0 \to \infty\right]$ gives the "virial theorem"; summing over all the particles of the system:

$$2\langle T\rangle_{\text{Av}} = -\langle \sum_i \mathbf{r}_i \cdot \mathbf{F}_i \rangle_{\text{Av}} \tag{1–21}$$

If both the positions and the velocities are taken relative to the center of mass, one obtains the same equation. Thus if

$$\mathbf{J}_c = \sum_i m_i(\mathbf{r}_i - \mathbf{r}_c) \times (\mathbf{v}_i - \mathbf{v}_c) = \mathbf{J} - \mathbf{r}_c \times \mathbf{P} \tag{1–22}$$

and if

$$\mathbf{L}_c = \sum_i (\mathbf{r}_i - \mathbf{r}_c) \times \mathbf{F}_i = \mathbf{L} - \mathbf{r}_c \times \mathbf{F} \tag{1–23}$$

then from (1–16) and (1–19)

$$\frac{d\mathbf{J}_c}{dt} = \mathbf{L}_c \tag{1–24}$$

quite independent of the motion of $\mathbf{r}_c$.

In particular, *if no external forces act* and the mutual (equal and opposite) forces between two particles lie on a line joining them,* then $\mathbf{L}_c = 0$ so that $\mathbf{J}_c$ *is constant.*

Rigid Bodies

For a *rigid* system of mass points, equations (1–16) and (1–24) completely determine the entire motion:

First, define the following tensor ("moment of inertia tensor"—relative to the center of mass),

$$\mathfrak{I}_c = \sum_i m_i[|\mathbf{r}_i - \mathbf{r}_c|^2\, \mathbf{1} - (\mathbf{r}_i - \mathbf{r}_c)(\mathbf{r}_i - \mathbf{r}_c)] \tag{1–25}$$

(the last term is *not* a dot product) where $\mathbf{1}$ is the unit tensor and $\mathbf{r}_c$ is the position of the center of mass.

Note that, just as $\mathbf{r}_c$ is defined independently of the coordinate system, so the tensor $\mathfrak{I}_c$ is completely defined by (1–25) quite independently of whether the body is in motion or not. If it is moving, the *components* of $\mathfrak{I}_c$ in a fixed coordinate system may change (as do those of $\mathbf{r}_c$) but the tensor "changes" only in the same sense that $\mathbf{r}_c$ changes.

For a rigid body, it follows from (10–26) that

$$\mathbf{v}_i - \mathbf{v}_c = \boldsymbol{\omega} \times (\mathbf{r}_i - \mathbf{r}_c) \tag{1–26}$$

where $\boldsymbol{\omega}$ (which can be time-varying) is known as the instantaneous angular velocity of the body. From (1–26), (1–25), (1–22) and (1–17) it then follows that

$$\mathbf{J}_c = \mathfrak{I}_c \cdot \boldsymbol{\omega} = \boldsymbol{\omega} \cdot \mathfrak{I}_c \tag{1–27}$$

and that†

$$T = \tfrac{1}{2}M|\mathbf{v}_c|^2 + \tfrac{1}{2}\boldsymbol{\omega} \cdot \mathfrak{I}_c \cdot \boldsymbol{\omega} \tag{1–28}$$

The main advantage of these relations appears upon transforming to a *coordinate system fixed in the body.* Then the components of $\mathfrak{I}_c$ become constants and, moreover,

---

* More generally: if the Lagrangian function of the system is independent of rotations of the coordinates describing the system.

† Note the identity, $|\boldsymbol{\omega} \times \mathbf{a}|^2 = (\boldsymbol{\omega} \times \mathbf{a}) \cdot (\boldsymbol{\omega} \times \mathbf{a}) = [(\boldsymbol{\omega} \times \mathbf{a}) \times \boldsymbol{\omega}] \cdot \mathbf{a} = -\mathbf{a} \cdot [\boldsymbol{\omega}(\boldsymbol{\omega} \cdot \mathbf{a}) - \mathbf{a}(\boldsymbol{\omega} \cdot \boldsymbol{\omega})] = \omega^2 a^2 - (\boldsymbol{\omega} \cdot \mathbf{a})^2$.

because these components form a symmetric (and thus Hermitian) matrix, there is one set of (orthogonal) coordinates, x, y, z in which $\mathfrak{J}_c$ is diagonal:

$$(\mathfrak{J}_c)_{jk} = I_j\,\delta_{jk} \qquad \text{(constants)} \tag{1–29}$$

The three constants, I_j, are known as the "principal" moments of inertia. It is easily shown [by taking the origin at $\mathbf{r}_c$ and writing out explicitly the "xx" component of (1–25)] that these constants are given by

$$I_{xx} = \sum_i m_i(y_i^2 + z_i^2), \quad \text{etc.} \tag{1–30}$$

Thus the principal moments of inertia are necessarily positive.

From (10–27) it follows that, even though the coordinates are fixed in the rotating body, the equations of motion (1–24) take, with the help of (1–29) and (1–27), the form

$$\mathbf{L}_c = \frac{d\mathbf{J}_c}{dt} = \frac{d_r\mathbf{J}_c}{dt} + \boldsymbol{\omega} \times \mathbf{J}_c = \mathfrak{J}_c \cdot \frac{d_r\boldsymbol{\omega}}{dt} + \boldsymbol{\omega} \times [\mathfrak{J}_c \cdot \boldsymbol{\omega}] \tag{1–31}$$

or, in components:

$$\left.\begin{aligned} L_x &= I_{xx}\frac{d\omega_x}{dt} + (I_{zz} - I_{yy})\omega_y\omega_z \\ L_y &= I_{yy}\frac{d\omega_y}{dt} + (I_{xx} - I_{zz})\omega_z\omega_x \\ L_z &= I_{zz}\frac{d\omega_z}{dt} + (I_{yy} - I_{xx})\omega_y\omega_z \end{aligned}\right\} \tag{1–32}$$

These equations completely determine the motion of the rigid body about its center of mass. Note that the simple form (1–32) is obtained *only* if *principal* axes *fixed* to the body are used. Note also that if $\mathbf{L} = 0$, $\boldsymbol{\omega}$ is still not constant unless two of its three components (in *this* system) vanish; that is, the only stable axes of rotation for a free body are the three principal axes.

Rigid Body with One Fixed Point

If a body is "anchored" at one point* but is otherwise free, it becomes useful to take that point as the coordinate origin, $\mathbf{r} = 0$, and *then* define a moment of inertia tensor:

$$\mathfrak{J} = \sum_i m_i[r_i^2\mathbf{1} - \mathbf{r}_i\mathbf{r}_i] \tag{1–33}$$

Unlike $\mathfrak{J}_c$, this tensor does depend on the position of the coordinate *origin* but, of course, is otherwise independent of the coordinates or motion of the body.

Since $\mathbf{v} \equiv 0$ at $\mathbf{r} = 0$, it follows from (10–26) that $\mathbf{v}_i = \boldsymbol{\omega} \times \mathbf{r}_i$ for some (time-varying) $\boldsymbol{\omega}$, the instantaneous angular velocity. Then, as above,

$$\mathbf{J} = \boldsymbol{\omega} \cdot \mathfrak{J} = \mathfrak{J} \cdot \boldsymbol{\omega} \tag{1–34}$$

$$T = \tfrac{1}{2}\boldsymbol{\omega} \cdot \mathfrak{J} \cdot \boldsymbol{\omega} \tag{1–35}$$

Note that (1–35) includes the term, $\frac{1}{2}Mv_c^2$ of (1–28) and that both (1–34) and (1–35) are special consequences of the fact that $\mathbf{v} \equiv 0$ when $\mathbf{r} = 0$.

---

* The point need not be actually a part of the body; in some special cases (gyro top in a cage, for example) an imaginary extension of the body may be used.

Again, the relations are especially simple in coordinate axes fixed to the body. In such coordinates, the components of $\mathfrak{J}$ become constants and as before (compare (1–31)) the equations of motion take the form,*

$$\mathfrak{J} \cdot \frac{d_r\boldsymbol{\omega}}{dt} + \boldsymbol{\omega} \times (\mathfrak{J} \cdot \boldsymbol{\omega}) = \mathbf{L}_f \tag{1–36}$$

which also takes a very simple explicit form, essentially identical to (1–32), if "principal axes", in which $\mathfrak{J}$ is diagonal, are employed. These will in general be different from the coordinates which diagonalize $\mathfrak{J}_c$.

Rotation About a Fixed Axis

If a body is constrained to rotate about a fixed axis then $\boldsymbol{\omega} = \omega\mathbf{a}$ where $\mathbf{a}$ is a constant *unit* vector. If we also choose the *coordinate origin on the axis* then $\mathbf{v}_i = \omega\mathbf{a} \times \mathbf{r}_i$ and from (1–18)

$$\mathbf{a} \cdot \mathbf{J} = \omega \sum_i m_i \, |\mathbf{a} \times \mathbf{r}_i|^2 \tag{1–37}$$

whence by (1–19) the equation of motion may be taken simply as

$$I_a \frac{d\omega}{dt} = \mathbf{L} \cdot \mathbf{a} = L_a \tag{1–38}$$

where the constant,

$$I_a = \sum_i m_i \, |\mathbf{a} \times \mathbf{r}_i|^2 \tag{1–39}$$

is called the moment of inertia about the axis, $\mathbf{a}$. Note that $\mathbf{r}_i$ must be measured from a point on the axis; $|\mathbf{a} \times \mathbf{r}_i|$ is then the distance of m_i from the axis. Note also that the constraining forces (at the "axle bearings") do not contribute to the component, L_a.

This simple numerical "moment of inertia" constant, I_a, is obtained *only* when the axis of rotation is constrained to be constant in both direction and points of passage through the body. Otherwise, the full (six-component) concept of an inertia tensor must be used and even its components are functions of time when coordinates fixed in space are employed.

Parallel Axes

If I_0 is the moment of inertia about a second axis, parallel to $\mathbf{a}$ but passing through the center of mass, $\mathbf{r}_c$, then (recalling that the origin must lie on the axis in question in each case) we have, in the same coordinates used for (1–39)

$$\begin{aligned} I_0 = \sum_i m_i \, |\mathbf{a} \times (\mathbf{r}_i - \mathbf{r}_c)|^2 &= I_a + M|\mathbf{a} \times \mathbf{r}_c|^2 - 2(\mathbf{a} \times \mathbf{r}_c) \cdot \sum_i m_i(\mathbf{a} \times \mathbf{r}_i) \\ &= I_a - M|\mathbf{a} \times \mathbf{r}_c|^2 \end{aligned}$$

(the last step by definition of $\mathbf{r}_c$). Hence

$$I_a = I_0 + M|\mathbf{a} \times \mathbf{r}_c|^2 \tag{1–40}$$

or: The moment of inertia about any axis is equal to the moment of inertia about a parallel axis through the center of mass plus the moment of the total mass (considered concentrated at the center of mass) about the chosen axis. I_0 may, of course, be computed from either the analogue of (1–39) or by $I_0 = \mathbf{a} \cdot \mathfrak{J}_c \cdot \mathbf{a} = (\mathfrak{J}_c)_{aa}$.

---

* We have written $\mathbf{L}_f$ in (1–36) to emphasize that, in evaluating $\mathbf{L}$, the coordinate origin must be chosen at the fixed point.

Lagrange's Equations

Notation

To simplify non-vector expressions, it is common to label the components of the various position vectors consecutively (and they are commonly denoted by q_i); thus $q_1 = x_1$, $q_2 = y_1$, $q_3 = z_1$, $q_4 = x_2$, etc. Further, time differentiation is denoted by a dot; thus $\dot{q}_5 = \dot{y}_2 = v_{2y}$, the y-component of the velocity of particle #2. Equations (1–13) and (1–14) then read

$$m_i \ddot{q}_i = F_i \tag{1–41}$$

$$T = \sum_i \tfrac{1}{2} m_i \dot{q}_i^2 \tag{1–42}$$

(Here m_i takes the same value for three consecutive values of i, and the F_i have been labeled in a manner paralleling that of the q's.)

Conditions

Lagrange's equations are less general than (1–1) but cover the great majority of cases of interest and have the advantage of being easily written down in whatever coordinates may seem desirable.

If the forces F_i in (1–41) can be expressed by means of a "generalized potential", $\psi(q_i, \dot{q}_i, t)$, in the form*

$$F_i = -\frac{\partial \psi}{\partial q_i} + \frac{\mathrm{d}}{\mathrm{d}t}\left(\frac{\partial \psi}{\partial \dot{q}_i}\right) \tag{1–43}$$

Define (with T given by (1–42)),

$$L(q_i, \dot{q}_i, t) = T - \psi \tag{1–44}$$

Then (1–41) and (1–43) are equivalent to

$$\boxed{\frac{\mathrm{d}}{\mathrm{d}t}\left(\frac{\partial L}{\partial \dot{q}_i}\right) = \frac{\partial L}{\partial q_i}} \tag{1–45}$$

Note, however, that L is not unique; (1–45) remains equivalent to (1–41) and (1–43) if we add to L any (total) time derivative of an arbitrary function of q_i, t (but *not* $\dot{q}_i$); that is,

$$L' = T - \psi + \sum_i \dot{q}_i \frac{\partial f}{\partial q_i} + \frac{\partial f}{\partial t} = T - \psi + \frac{\mathrm{d}}{\mathrm{d}t} f(q_i, t) \tag{1–44a}$$

also satisfies (1–45).

Equation (1–45) has been derived for Cartesian coordinates but it is actually quite general. Namely, (1–45) is also equivalent [for fixed $q_i(t_1)$ and $q_i(t_2)$] to

$$\delta\left[\int_{t_1}^{t_2} L(q_i, \dot{q}_i, t)\,\mathrm{d}t\right] = 0 \tag{1–46}$$

but, in this form, it is evidently *immaterial what coordinates are used* to describe the positions. Moreover (1–45) will then also hold as a direct consequence of (1–46).

It is this feature which makes the Lagrangian formulation so powerful. The functions T and ψ can usually be written down immediately, whereas acceleration

---

* The notation implies that $q_1, \cdots, q_n, \dot{q}_1 \cdots, \dot{q}_n, t$ are to be considered independent in forming the partial derivatives in (1–43). The time derivative in (1–43) is taken *after* evaluating the partials. These conventions hold in all that follows.

vectors are often difficult to evaluate in unusual coordinate systems. Equations (1–45) may then be used immediately to obtain the equations of motion. In practice, constrained systems are best handled in this way, simply ignoring "impossible" motions.

Charged Particle in an Electromagnetic Field

The force can be written in the form (1–43) if ψ is defined as [see (3–3), (3–29), (3–30)]

$$\psi = e\phi - (e/c)\mathbf{v} \cdot \mathbf{A}$$

Thus

$$L = \tfrac{1}{2}mv^2 - e\phi + (e/c)\mathbf{v} \cdot \mathbf{A}$$

The motion of a charged particle in a magnetic field is in general very complex. If the particle is not too energetic, it spirals about the magnetic field lines with constant speed, v (even when $\partial B/\partial t \neq 0$ or when weak forces are acting *perpendicular* to $\mathbf{B}$). The following approximate rules help to visualize the motion.

(1) Radius of curvature $= R = |\mathbf{p} \times \mathbf{B}|\,(c/|e|\,B^2) = (pc \sin\theta)/|e|\,B$.

(2) Flux enclosed by the spiral path, $\pi R^2 B \doteq$ constant. Thus $B/\sin^2\theta \doteq$ constant, and regions of intense B can "reflect" the particle.

(3) A weak force, $\mathbf{F}$, perpendicular to $\mathbf{B}$ causes the spiral-center to drift across the field lines with velocity, $\mathbf{v}_d = (c/eB^2)(\mathbf{F} \times \mathbf{B})$. In particular if the field lines curve with radius R_B the centrifugal force, $m(\mathbf{v} \cdot \mathbf{B})^2/B^2R_B$, causes a drift of magnitude, $v_d = (R/R_B)v\cos^2\theta/\sin\theta$.

(4) A gradient of B causes a drift given by $(e/|e|)\,\mathbf{v}_d = (v\sin\theta)(R/2B^2)(\mathbf{B} \times \nabla B)$.

Rigid Bodies

Lagrange's equations may be applied directly to a rigid body by expressing T and ψ for the body in terms of any convenient variables. This is physically obvious since rigid body motions are a consequence of the laws for particles; formally, one may readily verify that this statement is correct for Cartesian coordinates and it then follows from (1–46) that it is generally true.

Quite generally for any mechanical system, if one (a) chooses variables $q_1, \cdots, q_n$ whose values, along *with* the constraints, are sufficient to characterize the position of the system and (b) writes ψ and T in terms of the q_i and $\dot{q}_i$, then Lagrange's equations *are* the equations of motion.

Note, that if while $\dot{q}_I$ appears, q_I is missing in L, then an immediate consequence is $\partial L/\partial \dot{q}_I =$ constant. ("Ignorable coordinate".)

Normal Coordinates; Small Vibrations of Conservative Systems

At an equilibrium point $F_i = 0 = -\partial\phi/\partial q_i$ for a conservative system. Thus when ϕ is expanded in a Taylor's series about such a position, taken as coordinate origin,

$$\phi = \phi_0 + \sum_{ij} q_i q_j U_{ij} + \cdots \tag{1–47}$$

where, if the equilibrium in stable, $U_{ij} = \partial^2\phi/\partial q_i\,\partial q_i$ is a positive definite matrix. (The position is a true minimum of ϕ and not merely a stationary point or saddle point.)

Since T is a positive definite form, there exists a (not necessarily orthogonal) linear transformation of the q_i coordinates which will convert it to $T = \sum_i \dot{Q}_i^2$. Then a further (orthogonal) linear transformation will diagonalize U_{ij}, leaving T unchanged. Thus it is possible to convert (1–45) to the simple form $\ddot{Q}_i = \lambda_i Q_i$ and such coordinates are called "normal". The motions, $Q_i = A\sin(t\sqrt{\lambda_i} + \alpha)$—which are mutually independent and superposable—are called "normal" vibrations.

Dissipative Systems

While (1–43) will treat certain types of dissipative systems (and $L' \rightarrow Le^{t/T}$ for some T will also introduce dissipation), a common method of handling such cases destroys both the variational principle (1–46) and the invariance of (1–45) under arbitrary coordinate transformations.

The method is to write down (1–45) for the corresponding lossless system and then add to the right side of (1–45) a term,

$$\frac{\partial F}{\partial \dot{q}_i} \quad ; \quad \text{where} \quad F = \sum_{ij} R_{ij}\dot{q}_i\dot{q}_j \tag{1–48}$$

F is the rate at which the system converts mechanical energy into heat. This is only an approximation to the behavior of most actual systems.

Hamilton's Equations

These are usually less expedient than (1–45) for computation, but are commonly used as a basis for quantum mechanical modifications.

Define

$$H(q_i, p_i, t) = \sum_i p_i\dot{q}_i - L(q_i, \dot{q}_i, t) \tag{1–49}$$

where the "conjugate momenta":

$$p_i = \frac{\partial L}{\partial \dot{q}_i} \tag{1–50}$$

are taken as new "independent" variables, replacing $\dot{q}_i$. For a *conservative* system

$$H = T + \phi = E \tag{1–51}$$

(expressed as functions of q_i, p_i of course). It follows* from (1–49) and (1–50) that, for any system,

$$\frac{dp_j}{dt} = -\frac{\partial H}{\partial q_j} \quad ; \quad \frac{dq_j}{dt} = \frac{\partial H}{\partial p_j} \tag{1–52}$$

are equivalent to (1–45).

Note that H, like L, is not unique. The effect of changing L from (1–44) to (1–44a) is to replace H by

$$H'(q_i, p_i, t) = H\left(q_i, p_i - \frac{\partial f}{\partial q_i}, t\right) - \frac{\partial f}{\partial t} \tag{1–53}$$

B. MECHANICS OF CONTINUOUS MEDIA

The particles in a "continuous" medium also follow the laws of mechanics, but the forces between particles are mainly molecular in origin and can be described on a macroscopic scale only by somewhat approximate relations.

It becomes convenient to shift attention from the particles themselves and deal with local averages such as mass-density, ρ, mean flow velocity, $\mathbf{v}$, etc., which are regarded as functions of the independent variables x, y, z, t.

One consequence of this approach is that we acquire an additional (formerly

---

* An excellent exercise in the meaning and manipulation of partial derivatives.

trivial) equation of motion, the *conservation equation*, expressing the fact that mass cannot be created or destroyed:

$$\boxed{\frac{\partial \rho}{\partial t} + \nabla \cdot (\rho \mathbf{v}) = 0} \tag{1–54}$$

Ways of satisfying (1–54):

1. If $\mathbf{G}(\mathbf{r}, t)$ is an *arbitrary* vector function, then

$$\rho = \nabla \cdot \mathbf{G} \quad ; \quad \rho \mathbf{v} = -\frac{\partial}{\partial t}\mathbf{G} \tag{1–55}$$

satisfy (1–54). If further it is known that the motion is irrotational, $\nabla \times \rho\mathbf{v} = 0$, one may further set $\mathbf{G} = -\nabla\phi(\mathbf{r}, t)$.

2. If ρ is an *arbitrary* function of $\mathbf{r}$, t then *one* solution of (1–54)—the solution satisfying $\nabla \times (\rho\mathbf{v}) = 0$—is

$$\mathbf{v} = \frac{1}{4\pi\rho}\nabla\left[\oint\!\!\oint\!\!\oint \frac{\partial\rho/\partial t}{|\mathbf{r} - \mathbf{r}'|}\,\mathrm{d}V'\right] \tag{1–56}$$

A Convention

As might be expected, it is often convenient to consider the time-changes in various quantities as seen by an "observer" who *moves with the fluid*—i.e. whose velocity is always $\mathbf{v}(\mathbf{r}, t)$ whatever position he may have been brought to. We therefore *define*

$$\boxed{\frac{\mathrm{d}}{\mathrm{d}t} = \frac{\partial}{\partial t} + \mathbf{v} \cdot \nabla} \tag{1–57}$$

Note that all functions still have four independent variables, x, y, z, t, and that the symbol $(\mathrm{d}/\mathrm{d}t)$ would in general be meaningless without this *convention*, (1–57).

Consequences of this convention are

$$\frac{\mathrm{d}\mathbf{v}}{\mathrm{d}t} = \frac{\partial \mathbf{v}}{\partial t} + \tfrac{1}{2}\nabla(\mathrm{v}^2) - \mathbf{v} \times (\nabla \times \mathbf{v}) \tag{1–58}$$

and for *any* function, $g(\mathbf{r}, t)$, using (1–54)

$$\rho\frac{\mathrm{d}g}{\mathrm{d}t} = \frac{\partial}{\partial t}(\rho g) + \nabla \cdot (\rho g \mathbf{v}) = \frac{\mathrm{d}}{\mathrm{d}t}(\rho g) + \rho g\, \nabla \cdot \mathbf{v} \tag{1–59}$$

In particular (set $g = 1$) the conservation equation (1–54) can also be written

$$\frac{\mathrm{d}\rho}{\mathrm{d}t} + \rho\nabla \cdot \mathbf{v} = 0 \tag{1–60}$$

Let δ be the volume of a small part of the fluid (that is, δ contains a certain fixed set of particles at all times). Either from (1–60) (with the observation that $\delta \sim 1/\rho$) or directly from first principles, it may be seen that

$$\frac{\mathrm{d}\delta}{\mathrm{d}t} = \delta\nabla \cdot \mathbf{v} \tag{1–61}$$

Forces

1. A so-called "*volume force*" may be present, which acts "at a distance" on every particle independent of its surroundings. Example: gravitation. It is expedient to specify the force per unit volume (hence the name) rather than per particle. Thus the earth's field exerts a volume force $= g\rho(\mathbf{r}, t)$.

2. The remaining local (molecular, statistical) forces must be described by an ("averaged") macroscopic relation whose origin can only be traced by statistical or quantum mechanics. All of the useful relations for this purpose fall under the following type. The central idea is that these local molecular forces can act only on the *surfaces* of any volume element. (When this is not true, much of classical fluid dynamics and elasticity theory lose their usefulness.)

The Stress Tensor

Consider a small (plane) *cut* in the interior of the medium. The (equal and opposite) forces, which must be applied to the faces of the cut in order to restore all material to its former state, will be proportional to the area of the cut and will also depend on its orientation. (Note that these forces are not usually normal to the plane of the cut.) The dependence on orientation may be shown* to be linear:

$$\mathbf{df} = \mathfrak{P} \cdot \hat{n}\, dA \qquad [df_i = \sum_j \mathscr{P}_{ij}\, n_j\, dA] \tag{1–62}$$

where $\hat{n}$ is a unit normal vector directed from the face in question into the cut (area dA). The coefficients $\mathscr{P}_{ij}$ of this "stress tensor" $\mathfrak{P}$ will be some function of the state of deformation (strain) of the material as well as of temperature, etc. For the moment, we do not need this information.

Properties of the Stress Tensor

(1) The pressure in the medium is the negative of the average of the diagonal elements of $\mathfrak{P}$:

$$p = -\tfrac{1}{3}\sum_i \mathscr{P}_{ii} = -\tfrac{1}{3}\,\text{Trace}\,\mathfrak{P} \tag{1–63}$$

(2) $\mathfrak{P}$ is symmetric†:

$$\mathscr{P}_{ij} = \mathscr{P}_{ji} \tag{1–64}$$

* If the medium is in the same state over a finite volume, then any small part of that volume is in equilibrium with its neighbors: $\sum_\alpha \mathbf{df}_\alpha = 0$ where $\mathbf{df}_\alpha$ are the forces on the faces of any small polyhedron. For a polyhedron, $\sum_\alpha \hat{n}_\alpha\, dA_\alpha = 0$. [If $\mathbf{a} = \sum_\alpha \hat{n}_\alpha\, dA_\alpha = \oint\!\!\oint \hat{n}\, dS$, then for *any* constant $\mathbf{b}$, $\mathbf{a} \cdot \mathbf{b} = \oint\!\!\oint\!\!\oint (\nabla \cdot \mathbf{b})\, dV = 0$.] Hence $\sum_\alpha \hat{n}_\alpha\, dA_\alpha = 0$ must entail $\Sigma\, \mathbf{df}_\alpha = 0$. Apply this to a tetrahedron with three mutually perpendicular faces (which can be chosen as coordinate planes) and a fourth, arbitrarily oriented face. Then

$$\hat{n}_4\, dA_4 - \hat{\imath}\, dA_x - \hat{\jmath}\, dA_y - \hat{k}\, dA_z = 0$$

whence $dA_x = (\hat{n}_4 \cdot \hat{\imath})\, dA_4$ etc.

Thus if $\mathbf{df}_x = \mathbf{P}_x\, dA_x$, etc., it follows that

$$\mathbf{df}_4 = -(\mathbf{P}_x\hat{\imath} + \mathbf{P}_y\hat{\jmath} + \mathbf{P}_z\hat{k}) \cdot \hat{n}_4\, dA_4$$

which is (1–62) with $-\mathfrak{P} = \mathbf{P}_x\hat{\imath} + \mathbf{P}_y\hat{\jmath} + \mathbf{P}_z\hat{k}$.

† Consider a uniformly stressed region of the medium in equilibrium with its neighbors and let $\mathbf{f} = 0$. The total torque (exerted by its neighbors), acting on an arbitrary part, V, of this region of the medium, must vanish: $0 = \oint\!\!\oint \mathbf{r} \times \mathfrak{P} \cdot \mathbf{dS}$. If $\mathbf{a}$ is an *arbitrary* constant vector, $0 = \mathbf{a} \cdot \oint\!\!\oint \mathbf{r} \times \mathfrak{P} \cdot \mathbf{dS} = \oint\!\!\oint \mathbf{a} \times \mathbf{r} \cdot (\mathfrak{P} \cdot \mathbf{dS}) = \iiint_V \nabla \cdot (\mathbf{a} \times \mathbf{r} \cdot \mathfrak{P})\, dV = -\mathbf{a} \cdot \iiint \nabla \times \mathbf{r} \cdot \mathfrak{P})\, dV$ or, since $\mathbf{a}$ and V are arbitrary, $\nabla \times (\mathbf{r} \cdot \mathfrak{P}) = 0$. Since $\mathfrak{P}$ is a constant over the small region, the three components of this equation immediately yield (1–64).

(3) The total force on a finite volume V is

$$\mathbf{F}_v = \iiint\limits_V \mathbf{f}\,\mathrm{d}V + \oint\!\!\oint \mathfrak{P}\cdot \mathrm{d}\mathbf{S} = \iiint\limits_V [\mathbf{f} + \nabla\cdot\mathfrak{P}]\,\mathrm{d}V \tag{1–65}$$

where $\mathbf{f}$ is the volume force and $(\nabla\cdot\mathfrak{P})_j = \sum_i \frac{\partial \mathscr{P}_{ij}}{\partial x_i}$.

Equations of Motion

From (1–65) the equation of motion of a small volume element δ, containing certain fixed particles of the fluid, is $\frac{\mathrm{d}}{\mathrm{d}t}(\mathbf{v}\rho\delta) = \delta[\mathbf{f} + \nabla\cdot\mathfrak{P}]$ and from (1–61) and (1–60) this reduces to

$$\boxed{\rho\frac{\mathrm{d}\mathbf{v}}{\mathrm{d}t} = \mathbf{f} + \nabla\cdot\mathfrak{P}} \tag{1–66}$$

wherein, it must be mentioned, much of the apparent simplicity comes from the convention (1–57). (Note that the "local forces" as expressed by $\mathfrak{P}$ contribute to the motion only when $\mathfrak{P}$ varies from point to point of the fluid.)

Energy Relations

The rate at which the mechanical forces do work on a volume is

$$\frac{\mathrm{d}W}{\mathrm{d}t} = \iiint \mathbf{f}\cdot\mathbf{v}\,\mathrm{d}V + \oint\!\!\oint \mathbf{v}\cdot\mathfrak{P}\cdot\mathrm{d}\mathbf{s} = \iiint [\mathbf{f}\cdot\mathbf{v} + \nabla\cdot(\mathbf{v}\cdot\mathfrak{P})]\,\mathrm{d}V \tag{1–67}$$

while from (1–66), with the help of (1–60) and then (1–61), for a "fluid volume" δ

$$\mathbf{v}\cdot(\mathbf{f} + \nabla\cdot\mathfrak{P})\delta = \frac{\mathrm{d}}{\mathrm{d}t}(\tfrac{1}{2}\rho v^2\delta) \tag{1–68}$$

Comparing (1–68) with (1–67), we see that the quantity

$$\nabla\cdot(\mathbf{v}\cdot\mathfrak{P}) - \mathbf{v}\cdot(\nabla\cdot\mathfrak{P}) = \mathfrak{P}\colon\nabla\mathbf{v} = \sum_{ij}\mathscr{P}_{ij}\partial v_i/\partial x_j$$

must (when multiplied by δ) represent the rate at which energy other than kinetic (which is $\frac{1}{2}\rho v^2\delta$) enters or leaves the fluid volume δ. At this point, we must appeal to concepts which are ultimately thermodynamic in nature. If $\mathbf{Q}$ is the heat-flow ("current density") vector and e the internal energy per unit *mass* of the fluid, then we require:

$$(\delta)\mathfrak{P}:\nabla\mathbf{v} = (\delta)\nabla\cdot\mathbf{Q} + \frac{\mathrm{d}}{\mathrm{d}t}(e\rho\delta) \tag{1–69}$$

from (1–68) with (1–59) and (1–61) one then derives

$$\boxed{\rho\frac{\mathrm{d}e}{\mathrm{d}t} + \nabla\cdot\mathbf{Q} = \mathfrak{P}:\nabla\mathbf{v}} \tag{1–70}$$

Another form is

$$\mathbf{v}\cdot\mathbf{f} + \nabla\cdot(\mathfrak{P}\cdot\mathbf{v}) = \nabla\cdot\mathbf{Q} + \rho\frac{\mathrm{d}}{\mathrm{d}t}(e + \tfrac{1}{2}v^2) \tag{1–71}$$

For a non-viscous liquid or gas, there can be no shearing forces, so that

$$\mathscr{P}_{ij} = -p\delta_{ij} \qquad (\mathfrak{P} = -p\mathbf{1})$$

and (1–70) may be written in the sometimes more useful forms,

$$\rho\left(\frac{\mathrm{d}e}{\mathrm{d}t} + p\,\frac{\mathrm{d}(1/\rho)}{\mathrm{d}t}\right) = -\boldsymbol{\nabla}\cdot\mathbf{Q} = \rho T\,\frac{\mathrm{d}s}{\mathrm{d}t} \tag{1–72}$$

where s is the entropy per unit *mass* and T the absolute temperature; the second half of (1–72) assumes no changes in local composition of the fluid.

Shock Waves

If viscosity and heat conduction are both neglected, then, because high pressures generally propagate (spread) more rapidly than low pressures, "shock waves" involving *discontinuous* pressure changes always eventually form from any finite disturbance. Despite the inconvenience of such (idealized) discontinuities, the mathematical description is considerably simplified by neglect of dissipative effects and the approximation to reality is exceedingly good for very large amplitude waves.

At such discontinuities, the differential equations (1–54), (1–66) and (1–70) must be replaced by boundary (or "jump") conditions equivalent to them. These are known as:

Rankine–Hugoniot Relations

To derive these, first re-write (1–66) and (1–71) with the aid of (1–59); then integrate the resulting relations over a "pill box" volume whose two large faces lie on either side of the shock-discontinuity but whose height is "vanishingly small". Note that all velocities must be taken *relative* to the shock wave since the pill box must move with the shock. One finds that *the following quantities are continuous across a shock front*:

$$\left.\begin{array}{l} \rho\mathbf{v}_R\cdot\hat{n} \\ \rho\mathbf{v}_R(\mathbf{v}_R\cdot\hat{n}) - \mathfrak{P}\cdot\hat{n} \\ \mathbf{Q}\cdot\hat{n} + [\tfrac{1}{2}\rho v^2 + \rho e](\mathbf{v}_R\cdot\hat{n}) - \mathbf{v}_R\cdot\mathfrak{P}\cdot\hat{n} \end{array}\right\} \tag{1–73}$$

where

$\mathbf{v}_R = \mathbf{v} - \mathbf{U}$ where $\mathbf{U}$ is the velocity of the shock surface

$\hat{n}$ = unit vector normal to the shock surface

Magnetohydrodynamics

For a conducting fluid in an electromagnetic field, the previous equations apply simply by setting the volume-force [see also (3–6)],

$$\mathbf{f}_e = \rho_e\mathbf{E} + (1/c)\,\mathbf{J}\times\mathbf{B}$$

where ρ_e is the electric charge density in the fluid and $\mathbf{J}$ is the electric current density. If σ is the conductivity of the fluid, then (non-relativistic),

$$\mathbf{J} = \rho_e\mathbf{v} + \sigma\left[\mathbf{E} + \frac{\mathbf{v}}{c}\times\mathbf{B}\right]$$

where the last term accounts for the additional electric field "seen" by the fluid due to its motion in the magnetic field, $\mathbf{B}$. In addition, of course, Maxwell's equations govern the connections between $\mathbf{E}$, $\mathbf{B}$, ρ_e, $\mathbf{J}$. (The charge-continuity equation, $\partial\rho_e/\partial t + \nabla\cdot\mathbf{J} = 0$, is a consequence of these.)

B.1 Elastic Media

To characterize elastic media (in terms of the relation between $\mathfrak{P}$ and the strain) we must first describe possible deformations of the medium. Let a deformation carry any point $\mathbf{r}$ into the point $\mathbf{r} + \mathbf{s}$ and consider a small neighborhood of some original point $\mathbf{r}_0$ which now lies at $\mathbf{r}_0 + \mathbf{s}_0$. The displacement, $\mathbf{s}$, of sufficiently close neighboring points may be expressed in terms of $\mathbf{s}_0$ and a power series in $\delta\mathbf{r} = \mathbf{r} - \mathbf{r}_0$ of which the first terms may be written:

$$\mathbf{s} = \mathbf{s}_0 + \tfrac{1}{2}\delta\mathbf{r} \times [\nabla \times \mathbf{s}]_0 + \mathfrak{S} \cdot \delta\mathbf{r} \tag{1–74}$$

where* the tensor:

$$\mathfrak{S}_{ij} = \frac{1}{2}\left(\frac{\partial s_i}{\partial x_j} + \frac{\partial s_j}{\partial x_i}\right) \tag{1–75}$$

The first term in (1–74) expresses merely a translation of the neighborhood about $\mathbf{r}_0$ and the second term is merely a (first order) rotation [see (10–19)] of the neighborhood. Both, of course, lead to no actual deformation of the material. Thus (1–75) alone describes the intrinsic deformation (first order) and, if the deformation is continuous, its entire course could be constructed from given values of $\mathfrak{S}$ for every point.

The tensor $\mathfrak{S}$ can be given further intuitive meaning by noting that the volume change is given by $\nabla \cdot \mathbf{s} = \sum_i \mathfrak{S}_{ii}$. The remainder of $\mathfrak{S}$, namely,

$$\mathfrak{S}' = \mathfrak{S} - \mathbf{1}(\tfrac{1}{3}\nabla \cdot \mathbf{s}) \tag{1–76}$$

$$\left[\text{or} \qquad \left[\mathfrak{S}_{ik}' = \frac{1}{2}\left(\frac{\partial s_i}{\partial x_k} + \frac{\partial s_k}{\partial x_i}\right) - \tfrac{1}{3}(\nabla \cdot \mathbf{s})\delta_{ik}\right] \qquad \text{thus} \quad \sum_i \mathfrak{S}_{ii}' = 0\right]$$

must then represent a deformation without change of volume, that is, a *shear*.

Since $\mathfrak{S}$ is symmetric (i.e. its components form a real-Hermitian matrix) it can be diagonalized by changing to suitable Cartesian coordinates ("strain ellipsoid"). The same is true of $\mathfrak{P}$ ("stress ellipsoid") but the coordinates are in general different from those for $\mathfrak{S}$.

Definition

An elastic medium (non-viscous) may now be defined as a medium wherein $\mathfrak{P}$ *and* $\mathfrak{S}$ *are linearly related* (Hooke's law). Empirically, this relation holds for actual substances only up to certain limits of deformation. (Beyond these limits, most media behave more like a highly viscous fluid—"plastic flow region".) Since both $\mathfrak{P}$ and $\mathfrak{S}$ are symmetric (have only six independent components), it is common to write $\mathcal{P}_1 = \mathcal{P}_{xx}$, $\mathcal{P}_2 = \mathcal{P}_{yy}$, $\mathcal{P}_3 = \mathcal{P}_{zz}$, $\mathcal{P}_4 = \sqrt{2}\mathcal{P}_{yz}$, $\mathcal{P}_5 = \sqrt{2}\mathcal{P}_{zx}$, $\mathcal{P}_6 = \sqrt{2}\mathcal{P}_{xy}$ and similarly for $\mathfrak{S}$. Then

$$\mathcal{P}_i = \sum_j c_{ij}\mathfrak{S}_j \tag{1–77}$$

which apparently involves 36 constants; however, only 21 of these are actually independent even in the most general anisotropic medium. This follows from:

---

* $\mathfrak{S}$ is the symmetric part of $\nabla\mathbf{s}$; its anti-symmetric part constitutes (as an "axial vector") the middle term in (1–74).

Energy of Deformation

From (1–69) with no heat flow ($\mathbf{Q} = 0$) it follows that the *internal* energy per unit volume (that is, aside from kinetic energy), $e\rho$, is equal to $\frac{1}{2}\mathfrak{P} : \nabla \mathbf{s}$ which* is also equal to $\frac{1}{2}\mathfrak{P} : \mathfrak{S}$ since $\mathfrak{P}$ is symmetric.

$$2e\rho = \mathfrak{P} : \mathfrak{S} = \sum_{ij} c_{ij}\, \mathfrak{S}_i \mathfrak{S}_j \tag{1–78}$$

in the terminology of (1–77). From (1–78), $c_{ij} = \frac{1}{2}\partial^2(e\rho)/\partial\mathfrak{S}_i\partial\mathfrak{S}_j = c_{ji}$ which means that only 21 of the c_{ij} are distinct.

For certain crystal classes, additional symmetries are present which further reduce the number of independent elastic constants.† For isotropic media (see below) only two are independent.

Equation (1–78) is used as a basis for calculating elastic constants from quantum solid state theory.

Isotropic Media

By symmetry, the principal axes of $\mathfrak{P}$ and $\mathfrak{S}$ must coincide. In these diagonalizing coordinates, symmetry further shows that the relation (1–77) can only take the form:

$$\mathscr{P}_1 = a\mathfrak{S}_1 + b(\mathfrak{S}_2 + \mathfrak{S}_3)$$
$$\mathscr{P}_2 = a\mathfrak{S}_2 + b(\mathfrak{S}_3 + \mathfrak{S}_1)$$
$$\mathscr{P}_3 = a\mathfrak{S}_3 + b(\mathfrak{S}_1 + \mathfrak{S}_2)$$

(with all other components vanishing). Setting $a = \frac{1}{3}(\alpha + 2\beta)$, $b = \frac{1}{3}(\alpha - \beta)$, this may be written in a tensor form which is therefore independent of these special coordinates and holds generally:

$$\left.\begin{aligned} &\sum_1^3 \mathscr{P}_{ii} = \text{Trace } \mathfrak{P} = \alpha \text{ Trace } \mathfrak{S} \\ &\left(p = -\frac{\alpha}{3}\nabla \cdot \mathbf{s}\right) \\ \text{and} \quad &\mathfrak{P}' = \beta\mathfrak{S}' \end{aligned}\right\} \tag{1–79}$$

where $\mathfrak{S}'$ is defined by (1–76) and similarly $\mathfrak{P}' = \mathfrak{P} - \mathbf{1}(\frac{1}{3}\sum_i \mathscr{P}_{ii})$. In terms of components:

$$\mathscr{P}_{ij} = \frac{\alpha - \beta}{3}\left(\sum \mathfrak{S}_{ll}\right)\delta_{ij} + \beta\mathfrak{S}_{ij} \tag{1–80}$$

By consideration of special physical situations, one sees that

$$\alpha = 3k = \frac{E}{1 - 2\nu} \quad ; \quad \beta = 2G = \frac{E}{1 + \nu} \tag{1–81}$$

where k is the bulk modulus, G is the shear modulus, E is Young's modulus (linear modulus), and ν is Poisson's ratio. (The first equality in each half of (1–81) is almost obvious from (1–80).)

---

* $\mathfrak{A} : \mathfrak{B}$ signifies $\sum_i \sum_j A_{ij}B_{ji} = \text{Trace } (\mathfrak{A} \cdot \mathfrak{B})$.

† For cubic crystals, there are three independent components: $c_{11} = c_{22} = c_{33}$; $c_{44} = c_{55} = c_{66}$; $c_{12} = c_{13} = c_{23}$; and all others vanish.

For hexagonal crystals, there are five: c_{12}; $c_{13} = c_{23}$; $c_{11} = c_{22}$; c_{33}; $c_{44} = c_{55}$; $c_{66} = \frac{1}{2}(c_{11} - c_{12})$ while all others vanish.

For isotropic media, the equation of motion (1–66) becomes, after substituting (1–75) and (1–80) therein,

$$\rho \frac{d^2\mathbf{s}}{dt^2} = \mathbf{f} + \tfrac{1}{2}\beta\, \nabla^2\mathbf{s} + \tfrac{1}{6}(2\alpha + \beta)\nabla(\nabla \cdot \mathbf{s})$$

$$= \mathbf{f} + \tfrac{1}{3}(\alpha + 2\beta)\nabla(\nabla \cdot \mathbf{s}) - \tfrac{1}{2}\beta\, \nabla \times \nabla \times \mathbf{s} \qquad (1\text{–}82)$$

If $\nabla \cdot \mathbf{s} = 0$ (no volume changes), then

$$\rho \frac{d^2\mathbf{s}}{dt^2} = \frac{\beta}{2}\nabla^2\mathbf{s} \qquad \text{(transverse or shear waves)} \qquad (1\text{–}83)$$

while if $\nabla \times \mathbf{s} = 0$,

$$\rho \frac{d^2\mathbf{s}}{dt^2} = \tfrac{1}{3}(\alpha + 2\beta)\nabla^2\mathbf{s} \qquad \text{(longitudinal or compression waves)} \qquad (1\text{–}84)$$

Since any vector $\mathbf{s}$ can be split into $\mathbf{s}_1 + \mathbf{s}_2$ where $\nabla \cdot \mathbf{s}_1 = 0$ and $\nabla \times \mathbf{s}_2 = 0$, any general wave motion in such media can be built up out of these two types. (Only the second type can occur in fluids.) See also (15–80)–(15–82).

Static Loading of an Isotropic Elastic Medium

In many practical problems $\mathbf{f} = 0$ and static solutions of (1–82) are desired. That is,

$$\nabla^2\mathbf{s} + \frac{1}{1 - 2\nu}\nabla(\nabla \cdot \mathbf{s}) = 0 \qquad (1\text{–}85)$$

or:

$$\nabla \times \nabla \times \mathbf{s} - 2\frac{1 - \nu}{1 - 2\nu}\nabla(\nabla \cdot \mathbf{s}) = 0 \qquad (1\text{–}86)$$

which must be matched to the boundary conditions imposed by the loading. In practice, this is often approximated by judicious superposition of many special solutions of (1–85) or (1–86).

Such solutions are:

$$\mathbf{s} = A\mathbf{r};\ \mathbf{s} = B\mathbf{r}/r^3;\ \mathbf{s} = \mathbf{a} \times \mathbf{r};\ \mathbf{s} = \frac{\mathbf{a} \times \mathbf{r}}{r^3}$$

$$\mathbf{s} = (\mathbf{a} \cdot \mathbf{r})\mathbf{r} - \frac{3 - 2\nu}{4 - 6\nu} r^2\mathbf{a}$$

$$\mathbf{s} = (3 - 4\nu)\frac{\mathbf{a}}{r} + \frac{(\mathbf{a} \cdot \mathbf{r})}{r^3}\mathbf{r}$$

From any solution, others can also be generated by (repeated) applications of the operator $\mathbf{A} \cdot \nabla$ where $\mathbf{A}$ is any constant vector. See also (15–78)–(15–79).

B. 1a Visco-Elastic Media

When the strains become large, a better approximation to real materials is obtained by replacing the constants on both sides of (1–77) or (1–80) by differential operators of the form,

$$\sum_n c_n \frac{\partial^n}{\partial t^n}$$

A useful technique* for solving such problems consists in noting that the elastic constants may be replaced by a ratio of operators in the *solutions* of standard elastic problems, thereby yielding a differential equation in t only, which may then be solved to obtain the modifications of the simple elastic solution due to visco-elastic effects.

A commonly used model is the "Voigt material" defined by

$$3k = C; \quad 2G = A\frac{\partial}{\partial t} + B$$

With $B = 0$, this model becomes a viscous fluid with constant compressibility.

B.2 Fluids

A fluid, by definition, can support no *static* shearing forces, but changing, non-static shears may give rise to resisting forces. The properties of most fluids are well described† by:

$$\mathfrak{P} = -p\mathbf{1} + 2\eta\mathfrak{V}' \tag{1-87}$$

where $\mathfrak{V}'$ is the symmetric (*shear*) part of $\nabla\mathbf{v}$, that is (compare (1–76)):

$$\mathscr{V}_{ij}' = \frac{1}{2}\left(\frac{\partial v_i}{\partial x_j} + \frac{\partial v_j}{\partial x_i}\right) - \tfrac{1}{3}\delta_{ij}(\nabla \cdot \mathbf{v}) \tag{1-88}$$

The constant η in (1–87) is the "coefficient of viscosity". Substituting in (1–66), we obtain the Navier-Stokes equation: assuming $\nabla\eta$ is negligible,

$$\begin{aligned}\rho\frac{\mathrm{d}\mathbf{v}}{\mathrm{d}t} &= \mathbf{f} - \nabla p + \eta[\nabla^2\mathbf{v} + \tfrac{1}{3}\nabla(\nabla\cdot\mathbf{v})] \\ &= \mathbf{f} - \nabla p + \eta[\tfrac{4}{3}\nabla(\nabla\cdot\mathbf{v}) - \nabla\times(\nabla\times\mathbf{v})]\end{aligned} \tag{1-89}$$

This equation of motion must, of course, be supplemented by the continuity equation (1–54) and by (1–70) as well as equations of state and equations determining $\mathbf{Q}$ and η in terms of the state. Generally, however, one assumes $\mathbf{Q} = 0$ and $\eta = $ constant.

The only practically important body forces $\mathbf{f}$ are gravitational:

$$\mathbf{f} = -\rho\nabla\Phi \tag{1-90}$$

If $\mathrm{d}\mathbf{v}/\mathrm{d}t = 0$ (no acceleration of fluid masses; straight flow lines) then (1–89) becomes similar to the elastic equations, (1–85), and similar techniques can be used. In particular, in steady flow through a round pipe of radius R, (Poiseuille's law)

$$-(\nabla p)\frac{\pi R^4}{8\eta}\rho = \frac{\mathrm{d}M}{\mathrm{d}t} \tag{1-91}$$

where $\mathrm{d}M/\mathrm{d}t$ is the mass flow per unit time through any cross section. If the fluid is incompressible, $\nabla p = (p_1 - p_2)/l$. For an ideal gas ($p = \rho RT/A$) one obtains from (1–91) (provided $\lambda \ll R$)

$$\frac{\mathrm{d}M}{\mathrm{d}t} = \rho_1\frac{\pi R^4}{16\eta}\frac{p_1^2 - p_2^2}{p_1 l}$$

Empirically, these solutions are found to hold for small velocities only (see below).

* Due to J. R. M. Radok (*Quart. Appl. Math.* **15**, 198 (1957)).

† A bulk-viscosity, which adds a term of the form $(-\mathbf{1}a\rho\ \mathrm{d}\rho/\mathrm{d}t)$ to (1–87), is given by kinetic theory but is usually negligible.

Similitude ("Scaling Laws"); Reynolds' Number

If in (1–89) we introduce dimensionless or normalized variables, $\rho = \xi\rho_0$, $\mathbf{v} = \mathbf{u}v_0$, $\mathbf{r} = L\mathbf{R}$, $t = (L/v_0)\tau$ where ρ_0, v_0, L are "standard" values of density, velocity, and length then (1–89) becomes

$$\xi \frac{d\mathbf{u}}{d\tau} = \left(\frac{\eta}{\rho_0 v_0 L}\right)[\nabla^2\mathbf{u} + \tfrac{1}{3}\nabla(\nabla \cdot \mathbf{u})] - \xi\nabla \frac{\Phi}{v_0^2} - \nabla \frac{p}{\rho_0 v_0^2}$$

so that the entire equation is dimensionless (∇ refers to derivatives with respect to **R**). Two problems which are geometrically similar will thus be completely similar provided the body forces are changed in the ratio v_0^2, the pressures in the ratio $\rho_0 v_0^2$, and provided the dimensionless characteristic constant,

$$R_e = L\rho_0 v_0/\eta \tag{1–92}$$

has the same value in the two cases. It is known as "Reynolds' number".

If we think of ρ_0, v_0, L in (1–92) as being magnitudes defining a given problem (for example, L = diameter of a pipe or the span of a wing; ρ_0 and v_0 the density and velocity in the "main stream") we see that: *Reynolds' number essentially characterizes the type of flow.* (In particular, turbulence in a pipe sets in for $R_e \geqslant 2000$ approximately, depending on the smoothness of the walls, etc.)

Note that small velocities are thus equivalent to *large* viscosities, η, and that small viscosities have the same effect as *large* velocities.

Turbulence

The simple results, such as (1–91), which essentially assume "uniform" flow are only the simplest solutions of (1–89). By numerical computation, it has recently been verified that (1–89) predicts the experimental result that, as $\nabla\mathbf{v}$ becomes large, *turbulence* sets in and the character of the flow changes completely. Completely turbulent flow has not been treated by (1–89) except for a few numerically computed results. In engineering practice, a number of empirical relations have been developed. Some of these are:

For approximately round tubes, turbulent flow of either gases or liquids follows the relation (D = average diameter, L = length):

Pressure difference $= p_1 - p_2 = B(\frac{1}{2}\rho v^2)(L/D)$ where v = mean flow velocity = average volume flow/area and B = (1/20) to (1/100) with the latter occurring only for very smooth-walled pipes and for $R_e \doteqdot 10^6$. The effects of discontinuities in the straight pipe can be equated to an effective change, ΔL, in the total length: (1) diameter change, $\Delta L = 40\ D$ if abrupt, $\Delta L = 20\ D$ for 10% slope of walls; (2) inlet, $\Delta L = 50\ D$; (3) outlet, $\Delta L = -20\ D$; (4) elbow, $\Delta L = 20\ D$ (for 90°, mean radius $= D$); (5) Tee joint $\Delta L = 45\ D$.

Approximations

1. *Acoustic (Small Wave) Theory*

For sufficiently small disturbances, the equation of state for a fluid may be approximated by the first term of a series

$$p - p_0 = \left.\frac{\partial p}{\partial \rho}\right|_{s_0} (\rho - \rho_0) = c_0^2(\rho - \rho_0)$$

where $1/\rho_0 c_0^2$ is the adiabatic compressibility (c_0 is the speed of sound). Also for sufficiently small disturbances, the second term of (1–87) may be neglected; using (1–58) and neglecting second order terms, (1–89) and (1–54) reduce to

$$\frac{\partial \mathbf{v}}{\partial t} + \frac{1}{\rho_0} \nabla p = 0; \qquad \frac{1}{c_0^2} \frac{\partial p}{\partial t} + \rho_0 \nabla \cdot \mathbf{v} = 0$$

which may be solved by setting

$$v = -\nabla \phi; \qquad p = \rho_0 \frac{\partial \phi}{\partial t}; \qquad \nabla^2 \phi - \frac{1}{c_0^2} \frac{\partial^2 \phi}{\partial t^2} = 0 \tag{1–93}$$

To these same approximations, the energy per unit volume is

$$\tfrac{1}{2}\rho_0 \left[|\nabla \phi|^2 + \frac{1}{c_0^2} \left(\frac{\partial \phi}{\partial t} \right)^2 \right] \tag{1–94}$$

and the energy flux ("current") vector is

$$-\rho_0 (\nabla \phi) \left(\frac{\partial \phi}{\partial t} \right) = p\mathbf{v} \tag{1–95}$$

2. *Stokes' Approximation*

With very low velocities but large displacements, the term, $(\mathbf{v} \cdot \nabla)\mathbf{v}$, (from $d\mathbf{v}/dt$) in (1–89) may be neglected. For the problem of a sphere falling through an incompressible viscous fluid, this procedure leads to Stokes' law:

$$F_d = 6\pi\eta a v \tag{1–96}$$

where F_d is the drag force, a the radius and v the velocity of the sphere.

For a cylinder, however, the same procedure leads to results that are not at all reasonable. This can be traced to the fact that, while for a sphere neglect of $(\mathbf{v} \cdot \nabla)\mathbf{v}$ leads to a solution which indeed makes this term small*, the case of a cylinder leads to a solution whose correction terms, arising from $(\mathbf{v} \cdot \nabla)\mathbf{v}$, are larger than the "first" order terms.

3. *Modified Stokes' Approximation*

A better approximation for low flow velocities is to replace $(\mathbf{v} \cdot \nabla)\mathbf{v}$ by $(\mathbf{v}_0 \cdot \nabla)\mathbf{v}$ where $\mathbf{v}_0$ is the "main stream" velocity of a flow.

When $R_e < 1$, this procedure leads to results in good accord with experiment. As R_e approaches unity, the method begins to converge very slowly and becomes of little practical use in that region.

For a cylinder of radius a in a uniform flow field of velocity v_0, the resulting drag force per unit length is

$$F_d = \frac{4\pi\eta v_0}{\ln (\eta/\rho a v_0) + \frac{1}{2} + 2 \ln 2 - 0.577215 \cdots}$$

valid for small $\rho a v_0/\eta$. ($C = 0.577215 \cdots$ is Euler's constant.)

4. *Incompressibility Approximations*

If ρ cannot change then, from (1–60), $\nabla \cdot \mathbf{v} = 0$.

* Provided the Reynolds' number, $2av\rho/\eta \lessdot \frac{1}{2}$, approximately.

4a. *Incompressible potential flow*

If we *also* assume $\nabla \times \mathbf{v} = 0$ then $\mathbf{v} = \nabla\psi$ where ψ is called the "velocity potential". By $\nabla \cdot \mathbf{v} = 0$ and by (1–89) (with $\mathbf{f}/\rho = -\nabla\phi$)*

$$\left.\begin{aligned} &\nabla^2\psi = 0 \\ &\frac{p}{\rho} = F(t) - \phi - \frac{\partial\psi}{\partial t} - \tfrac{1}{2}|\nabla\psi|^2 \end{aligned}\right\} \qquad (1\text{–}97)$$

where η has dropped out completely since $\nabla^2\mathbf{v} = 0$ also. In (1–97), $F(t)$ is an arbitrary function of t. The first of equations (1–97) is readily solved under various boundary conditions and the second relation then gives p as a function of position and time.

"Circulation" about a closed curve, $\mathbf{r} = \mathbf{s}(\lambda)$ is defined as

$$k = \oint \mathbf{v} \cdot d\mathbf{s} \qquad (1\text{–}98)$$

It might appear that, by Stokes' theorem, $k = \oint\oint(\nabla \times \mathbf{v}) \cdot d\boldsymbol{\sigma} = 0$, but if the curve surrounds an obstacle, $\mathbf{v}$ and $\nabla \times \mathbf{v}$ are undefined inside the obstacle and Stokes' theorem need not apply. Consequently the circulation, k, as distinct from $\nabla \times \mathbf{v}$, need not vanish over such closed curves. It does follow from Stokes' theorem that k is the same for all curves which enclose the same obstacles.

By straightforward application of complex-variable integration theory to the first half of (1–97) for two-dimensional flow about an infinite "cylindrical" obstacle aligned along $\hat{z}$, one finds that the force ($= \oint \hat{n} p\, ds$) on the obstacle (per unit length) is

$$\mathbf{F} = \rho k \mathbf{v}_\infty \times (\hat{x} \times \hat{y}) \qquad (1\text{–}99)$$

where $\mathbf{v}_\infty$ is the flow velocity at large distances (i.e. the main-stream velocity) and $\hat{x}$ and $\hat{y}$ are unit vectors along the x and y axes. (Kutta-Joukowski lift formula.)

In practice, however, even for simple situations and even for low velocities, the assumption $\nabla \times \mathbf{v} = 0$ is too restrictive. First, the condition, "$\mathbf{v} = 0$ at the surfaces of obstacles", cannot be used; the order of equations (1–97) is only sufficient to allow the obstacle-surface condition, $\mathbf{v} \cdot \hat{n} = 0$, plus one other requirement (which sets the value of k in (1–99)) such as "no flow around the trailing edge of a wing" etc. These solutions for cylindrical geometry lead to lifting forces† on objects in an infinite flow field but, quite generally, there is then no drag force. Compare (1–99).

Thus the assumptions leading to (1–97) are too restrictive to give accurate results. Nevertheless, they indicate correctly gross features of the flow and give order-of-magnitude approximations for the lifting forces.

4b. *Boundary-Layer Theory of Incompressible Flow*

This theory is essentially a "point of view" which has proven very useful for obtaining approximate solutions of (1–89), more realistic than those found from (1–97). It is based on the following picture: With $\mathbf{f} = -\rho\nabla\phi$, taking the curl of (1–89) and setting $\boldsymbol{\omega} = \nabla \times \mathbf{v}$ (still assuming $\nabla\rho = 0$)

$$\frac{\partial\boldsymbol{\omega}}{\partial t} + (\mathbf{v} \cdot \nabla)\boldsymbol{\omega} = \frac{\eta}{\rho}\nabla^2\boldsymbol{\omega} \qquad (1\text{–}100)$$

---

* Note $\dfrac{d}{dt}\nabla\psi \neq \nabla\dfrac{d\psi}{dt}$ because of the convention (1–57); rather $\dfrac{d}{dt}\nabla\psi = \dfrac{\partial}{\partial t}\nabla\psi + (\nabla\psi \cdot \nabla)\nabla\psi = \nabla\left(\dfrac{\partial\psi}{\partial t} + \tfrac{1}{2}|\nabla\psi|^2\right)$

† Perpendicular to the flow field; a "drag" is a force parallel to the fluid flow system.

Thus (each component of) $\boldsymbol{\omega}$ is propagated in the same manner as a temperature-perturbation in a moving, heat-conducting fluid. The effective "diffusivity" is η/ρ (often called the kinematic viscosity).

The basic idea is then that an obstacle generates vortices ("eddies"), $\boldsymbol{\omega} = \nabla \times \mathbf{v} \neq 0$, which, however, are quickly damped out as they start to spread and travel with the stream. From (1–100), we may expect that this spread will be approximately given by $\sqrt{\eta x/\rho v_0}$ where x is distance along the stream lines from the point of generation and v_0 is the velocity of the flow near the obstacle. Thus one is led to expect:

(a) Flow of the potential type (1–97) at large distances from any obstacles.

(b) A "boundary layer" of fluid adjacent to obstacles where $\nabla \times \mathbf{v} \neq 0$ over a transverse region of order $\sqrt{\eta x/\rho v_0}$ where v_0 = flow velocity and x is distance to the leading edge of the obstacle. (In particular, the "boundary layer" also includes a "wake" behind the obstacle.)

In practice, approximate solutions of considerable utility have been obtained by applying these expectations to (1–89). At very high flow velocities, the boundary layer can become truly turbulent (rather than merely containing a "smooth" flow with $\nabla \times \mathbf{v} \neq 0$).

Example. For a thin flat plate of width w oriented parallel to a uniform flow field, the drag force per unit length found by this method is

$$F_d = 1.328\sqrt{\eta \rho w {v_0}^3}$$

valid for velocities that are not too small.

For more complicated shapes, a method giving drag forces in good agreement with experiment consists in *assuming* a velocity-flow field in general agreement with the boundary-layer concepts but subject to conditions such that the momentum loss of successive cross-sectional slices of fluid be balanced by the resulting (viscous, shear) force over the corresponding section of the obstacle. In a sense, this is a variational procedure wherein an assumed form of solution is forced to satisfy certain gross (integral) relations; although the flow assumed may not approximate the actual flow very well, the drag forces seem fairly accurate.

B.3 Non-Viscous Fluids

For studying violent fluid motions which do not interact with obstacles (or for obtaining gross features of flow analogous to (1–97) as a first approximation for boundary-layer theories in very rapid flows), it is a better approximation to neglect the viscosity but preserve other features.

With $\eta = 0$ in (1–89), the equations of continuity, motion, and energy balance (1–72) are:

$$\boxed{\begin{aligned} &\frac{\partial \rho}{\partial t} + \nabla \cdot (\rho \mathbf{v}) = 0 \\ &\rho \frac{d\mathbf{v}}{dt} = \mathbf{f} - \nabla p \\ &\rho T \frac{ds}{dt} = -\nabla \cdot \mathbf{Q} \end{aligned}} \qquad (1\text{–}101)$$

which can, of course, be written in many other ways by using (1–59) etc. In addition to (1–101), *equations of state and heat flow* are needed to complete the description.

Commonly, one takes $\mathbf{Q} = 0$ so that $ds/dt = 0$. However, $\nabla s \neq 0$ in general: especially if shock waves are present, the fluid need not have uniform entropy even though it may have started in a uniform state.

If $\mathbf{Q} = 0$ and a shock is proceeding with velocity U into a portion of fluid at rest ($\mathbf{v} = 0$), then the Rankine–Hugoniot conditions (1–73) can be manipulated into the more convenient forms:

$$e_1 - e_0 = \tfrac{1}{2}(p_1 + p_0)\left(\frac{1}{\rho_0} - \frac{1}{\rho_1}\right)$$

$$v_1 = \sqrt{(p_1 - p_0)\left(\frac{1}{\rho_0} - \frac{1}{\rho_1}\right)} \qquad (1\text{–}102)$$

$$U = \frac{1}{\rho_0}\sqrt{(p_1 - p_0)\Big/\left(\frac{1}{\rho_0} - \frac{1}{\rho_1}\right)}$$

where subscript 0 denotes the fluid at rest and subscript 1 denotes values just behind the shock. Note also that the last two conditions can be written

$$v_1 U = \frac{p_1 - p_0}{\rho_0}; \quad \frac{v_1}{U} = 1 - \frac{\rho_0}{\rho_1}$$

The first of the relations (1–102) is, *for fixed* ρ_0 *and* p_0, an "equation of state" for the material behind the shock. It is known as the "*Hugoniot curve*" and serves to delineate those states of the fluid which can be reached by a shock wave traveling into a fluid at rest in the state ρ_0, p_0.

Equations (1–101) and (1–102), even with $ds/dt = 0$, are exceedingly difficult to solve and analytic results are known only for a few very simple plane-wave situations and for spherical or cylindrical shocks of constant energy-content expanding into an infinite medium with $p_0 = 0$, $\rho_0 =$ constant. Other results have been obtained numerically. To the author's knowledge, no problem of (even isentropic—$s \equiv$ constant) non-linear flow (1–101) which involves more than two independent variables has ever been solved analytically (except for cases which differ only by small perturbations from simpler problems).

Von Mises Transformation

For one dimensional motions, this is equivalent to taking coordinates fixed to the fluid (so-called Lagrange or co-moving coordinates). The general transformation is:

1. Define ρ and $\mathbf{v}$ by means of (1–55); this automatically satisfies (eliminates) the continuity equation.

2. Take as new independent variables t and the vector $\mathbf{G}$ from (1–55). The corresponding relations for the partial derivatives are:

$$\left.\frac{\partial}{\partial t}\right|_{\mathbf{r}} = \left.\frac{\partial}{\partial t}\right|_{G} + \sum_i \frac{\partial G_i}{\partial t}\frac{\partial}{\partial G_i}$$

$$\frac{\partial}{\partial x_i} = \sum_j \frac{\partial G_j}{\partial x_i}\frac{\partial}{\partial G_j}$$

In *one* dimension, these also imply $\dfrac{d}{dt} = \left.\dfrac{\partial}{\partial t}\right|_{G}$.

B.4 Isentropic Flow of Non-Viscous Fluids

Isentropic flow (as distinguished from adiabatic flow) is characterized not only by $\mathrm{d}s/\mathrm{d}t = 0$ but also by $\nabla s = 0$. That is,

$$s(\mathbf{r}, t) = s_0, \text{ a constant} \tag{1–103}$$

Under this condition, p and ρ are uniquely related; a value of either implies the value of the other (through the equations of state of the fluid, combined with (1–103)). Note that (1–103) can be true only in a non-viscous fluid.

The relation $\rho = \rho(p, s_0)$ implied by (1–103) enables us to define

$$h = \int_{(s=s_0)} \frac{\mathrm{d}p}{\rho} \tag{1–104}$$

which is, in fact, the enthalpy (per unit mass).

From (1–101) and (1–104)

$$\frac{\mathrm{d}\mathbf{v}}{\mathrm{d}t} = -\nabla(\phi + h)$$

That is, using $\mathbf{v} \times \nabla \times \mathbf{v} = \frac{1}{2}\nabla v^2 - (\mathbf{v} \cdot \nabla)\mathbf{v}$, equivalently,

$$\frac{\partial \mathbf{v}}{\partial t} = -\nabla(\phi + \tfrac{1}{2}v^2 + h) + \mathbf{v} \times (\nabla \times \mathbf{v}) \tag{1–105}$$

If the flow is *steady* ($\partial/\partial t \equiv 0$) then this gives

Bernoulli's Theorem:

$$\left.\begin{aligned} &\frac{\mathrm{d}}{\mathrm{d}t}(\tfrac{1}{2}v^2 + \phi + h) = 0 \\ \text{or:}\quad &\tfrac{1}{2}v^2 + \phi + h = \text{constant along any stream line} \end{aligned}\right\} \tag{1–106}$$

Note that if the fluid is incompressible as well as non-viscous, then $h = p/\rho$ and (1–106) is essentially the same as (1–97) for steady flow. Thus Bernoulli's theorem holds for steady flow either (a) in non-viscous or (b) in viscous but incompressible fluids.

If a steady flow also has the property $\nabla \times \mathbf{v} = 0$ (or merely $\mathbf{v} \times \nabla \times \mathbf{v} = 0$) then by (1–105) since $\frac{\partial}{\partial t} \equiv 0$ we obtain directly

$$\tfrac{1}{2}v^2 + \phi + h = C \tag{1–107}$$

where now C is constant throughout the region of flow (where $\nabla \times \mathbf{v} = 0$); that is, the constant in (1–106) is independent of the individual stream line.

Equation (1–107) along with mass conservation and the equation of state can also be regarded as specifying a cross-section-versus-distance relation which will allow smooth high-speed flow—"Laval nozzle".

Again for *steady* flows, (1–106) may be written in a more useful form by observing that, by the continuity equation, $\mathbf{v} \cdot \nabla h = (\mathrm{d}h/\mathrm{d}\rho)\mathbf{v} \cdot \nabla\rho = (-\mathrm{d}h/\mathrm{d}\rho)\rho\nabla \cdot \mathbf{v} = (-\mathrm{d}p/\mathrm{d}\rho)\,\nabla \cdot \mathbf{v}$. Thus defining (speed of sound):

$$c^2(\rho) = \frac{\mathrm{d}p}{\mathrm{d}\rho} \qquad \left(\text{better: } c^2 = \left.\frac{\partial p}{\partial \rho}\right|_{s_0}\right) \tag{1–108}$$

equation (1–105) yields for steady flow

$$\mathbf{v}\cdot\nabla(\tfrac{1}{2}v^2+\phi)=c^2\nabla\cdot\mathbf{v} \tag{1–109}$$

For many fluids, the approximation, $c \doteqdot$ constant is adequate under a wide range of conditions.

The assumption, $\nabla\times\mathbf{v}=0$ (that is $\mathbf{v}=\nabla\psi$) in (1–109) leads to the so-called "equation of compressible flow" (isentropic, steady *and* curl-free). For two-dimensional flows of this type, the result is:

$$\left[\left(\frac{\partial\psi}{\partial x}\right)^2-c^2\right]\frac{\partial^2\psi}{\partial x^2}+2\frac{\partial\psi}{\partial x}\frac{\partial\psi}{\partial y}\frac{\partial^2\psi}{\partial x\partial y}+\left[\left(\frac{\partial\psi}{\partial y}\right)^2-c^2\right]\frac{\partial^2\psi}{\partial y^2}=-\nabla\psi\cdot\nabla\phi$$

wherein it is usual to assume $c=$ constant and $\phi=0$. For the "hodograph" method of generating solutions under such assumptions, see (15–91)–(15–93). Important special solutions are "simple waves" for which $\partial\psi/\partial x=f(\partial\psi/\partial y)$. (The above is then an ordinary differential equation for $f(z)$.) It can be shown that only simple waves can adjoin a region of uniform flow.

Riemann's Method of Characteristics

This is applicable only for one-dimensional, isentropic,* non-viscous flow but is otherwise quite general; it can handle non-steady flows and is well-adapted to numerical computation.

The basic idea is to use the relation between p and ρ, implied by (1–103), to introduce as new dependent variables c (defined by (1–108)) and:

$$\sigma=\int c(\rho)\frac{d\rho}{\rho}=\int_{s=s_0}\frac{1}{\rho}\sqrt{\left.\frac{\partial p}{\partial\rho}\right|_{s_0}}\,d\rho \tag{1–110}$$

From (1–101) with $\mathbf{f}=0=\mathbf{Q}$ and one-dimensional motion, there follow ($v=v_x$):

$$\left.\begin{aligned}\left[\frac{\partial}{\partial t}+(v+c)\frac{\partial}{\partial x}\right](v+\sigma)=0\\ \left[\frac{\partial}{\partial t}+(v-c)\frac{\partial}{\partial x}\right](v-\sigma)=0\end{aligned}\right\} \tag{1–111}$$

(Recall that σ and c are related; a value of either implies the value of the other.) By the further substitution $f=v+\sigma$, $g=v-\sigma$ these are easily integrated graphically. If the fluid is an ideal gas (specific heat ratio γ: $p=K\rho^\gamma$ for $s=s_0$) then $\sigma=2c/(\gamma-1)$. A (singular) solution of (1–111) is then

$$(\gamma+1)c=(\gamma-1)(x/t)+2c_0;\qquad (\gamma+1)v=2\left(\frac{x}{t}-c_0\right)$$

where c_0 is arbitrary and represents the value of c in the undisturbed fluid. The solution corresponds to an expansion wave such as that in a vessel one wall of which is suddenly removed.

A more general singular solution of (1–111) is obtained by assuming $v=\pm\sigma+$ constant. The results are called "simple waves": (like signs must be chosen in the two equations)

$$x=(v\pm c)t+\Psi(\sigma);\qquad v=\pm\sigma+A \tag{1–112}$$

---

* Thus the instant a shock wave appears, the method is no longer applicable except in very special cases.

where Ψ is arbitrary and obviously describes the variation of σ with x when $t = 0$. The steepening of the wave with time is then clear from these relations by considering the motion of the position where $\sigma =$ some constant value.

Simple waves (1–112) are always generated when external pressure is applied to the boundary of a fluid originally at rest. When the wave "crests" a shock must develop and (1–112) is then strictly applicable only in regions not yet traversed by the shock. But a good approximation for moderate pressures is to retain (1–112), cutting it off by a shock-front so located as to conserve the total momentum.

For an ideal gas, if further $\gamma = (2m + 1)/(2m - 1)$ ($m =$ integer) then, with F and G arbitrary functions, the "general" solution of (1–111) is*

$$\left.\begin{aligned} t &= \left.\frac{\partial Z}{\partial v}\right|_\sigma; \qquad x = v\left.\frac{\partial Z}{\partial v}\right|_\sigma - \frac{\sigma}{2m-1}\left.\frac{\partial Z}{\partial \sigma}\right|_v - Z \\ \text{where} \quad Z &= \left(\frac{1}{\sigma}\left.\frac{\partial}{\partial \sigma}\right|_v\right)^{m-1}\left\{\frac{1}{\sigma}F(v+\sigma) + \frac{1}{\sigma}G(v-\sigma)\right\} \end{aligned}\right\} \tag{1–113}$$

Most of the known analytic results have been obtained by combining (1–112) and (1–113) with algebraic consequences of (1–102). Solutions often take very different analytic forms in different regions of space-time for a single problem.

C. SURFACE TENSION

Consideration of attractive forces between molecules leads to the experimentally confirmed fact that energy must be expended to increase the surface area of a volume of fluid, even when the density is unchanged. Simple theory and experiment both show that fluids are well described as possessing a surface energy, U_s, which is proportional to the surface area:

$$U_s = \alpha S \tag{1–114}$$

By applying this to a thin film of fluid (say on an expandable wire frame), it is easily shown that 2α is the force per unit length of boundary curve (required to prevent the fluid from collapsing to a sphere). It is thus convenient to think of α as the "surface tension", that is, the force which acts across an imaginary cut of unit length in ("one face of") the film. [Strictly, this interpretation holds only for adiabatic (zero heat-flow) changes of film area. For a more general treatment, see (2–72)].

With this concept, it is easily shown that an extra pressure δp (in addition to "atmospheric", externally applied pressure) must be present under a *curved* surface of the fluid:

$$\delta p = \alpha\left(\frac{1}{R_1} + \frac{1}{R_2}\right) \tag{1–115}$$

---

* PROOF: Take x, t as dependent variables and v, σ as independent. Then if $1/a = 2m - 1$, (1–111) becomes

$$\frac{\partial x}{\partial \sigma} = v\frac{\partial t}{\partial \sigma} - a\sigma\frac{\partial t}{\partial v} \quad ; \quad \frac{\partial x}{\partial v} = v\frac{\partial t}{\partial v} - a\sigma\frac{\partial t}{\partial \sigma}$$

whence $(2m/\sigma)\dfrac{\partial t}{\partial \sigma} = \dfrac{\partial^2 t}{\partial v^2} - \dfrac{\partial^2 t}{\partial \sigma^2}$ and by induction on m, one shows that $t = Z$ is a solution of this and hence so is $t = \partial Z/\partial v$. The remainder follows easily.

where R_1 and R_2 are the principal* radii of curvature of the surface of the fluid. If the surface is concave, δp is negative.

From (1–115), the differential equation for an unclosed film (e.g. supported by a closed wire loop of any shape) is

$$\frac{1}{R_1} + \frac{1}{R_2} = 0 \tag{1–116}$$

In Cartesian coordinates, this reads,

$$0 = \frac{\partial^2 z}{\partial x^2}\left[1 + \left(\frac{\partial z}{\partial y}\right)^2\right] - 2\frac{\partial z}{\partial x}\frac{\partial z}{\partial y}\frac{\partial^2 z}{\partial x \partial y} + \frac{\partial^2 z}{\partial y^2}\left[1 + \left(\frac{\partial z}{\partial x}\right)^2\right] \tag{1–117}$$

which, of course, is the equation for a surface of least area for a given boundary.

With constant external pressure, the surface of a liquid must satisfy $\nabla(\delta p) = \mathbf{f} = -\rho\nabla\phi$ if the body force $\mathbf{f}$ is due to a gravitational field. If the liquid is incompressible, the equation of its surface is therefore,

$$\alpha\left(\frac{1}{R_1} + \frac{1}{R_2}\right) + \rho\phi = \text{constant} \tag{1–118}$$

Boundary conditions depend on the (molecular) attraction of the walls of the vessel for the molecules of the liquid. If this "mutual" or "interaction" surface tension is expressed by another constant α_m, the condition for static boundary position becomes

$$\alpha \cos\theta = \alpha_m \tag{1–119}$$

where θ is the "angle of contact"—the dihedral angle between the liquid surface and wall surface. If $\alpha_m < 0$, $\theta > \pi/2$. If $\alpha_m > \alpha$, the liquid spreads in a thin film over the wall (e.g. water and glass).

* Respectively, the maximum and minimum radius of curvature (of the curves which the surface cuts) in a plane containing the normal vector, as the plane is rotated about the normal. The extreme values always occur 90° apart.

CHAPTER 2

THERMODYNAMICS

THERMODYNAMICS is an abstract, economical theory of physical and chemical systems; from a few phenomenological premises it derives far-reaching relationships and results, which are *independent of any postulated molecular mechanisms.** Classical thermodynamics deals with *equilibrium states* and relations between them. (Hence, the name, "thermostatics" has recently been urged.)

A. GENERAL RELATIONS

"Zeroth Law"

Two systems in thermal equilibrium with a third are in thermal equilibrium with each other. [That is, any "thermometer" with any construction (and any arbitrary scale, θ) reads the same when coupled to any part of a complex system at equilibrium. This empirical fact justifies the concept of temperature, but the "functional form" of θ is arbitrary.]

Heat

Experiments on temperature equilibration (calorimetry) are, by themselves, consistent with the existence of a "heat substance", the amount† of which determines the temperature and chemical state of a body; however, experiments with friction, heat engines, etc., show that mechanical (or electric, etc.) energy and "heat substance" can often be interconverted, *always quantitatively.*

In modern (strict) terminology, the concepts are therefore:

1. *Internal energy,* U, of a system. It represents mainly (but not always entirely) "invisible" energy, macroscopically detectable only by changing the state of the system.

2. *Heat "flow"*, δQ, which represents energy *exchanged* by any non-mechanical (and non-electrical) means. It is the thermal analogue of mechanical *work* (rather than energy). Like $\delta W = \mathbf{F} \cdot \mathbf{ds}$, it is *not a perfect differential.* That is, $\int \delta Q$ by itself has no meaning; physical conditions during the integration must be specified (and then the value depends on those conditions as well as the initial and final states).

First Law

Energy is always conserved.‡ Thus, if δW represents work done *by* the system and δQ the heat flow into the system,

$$\boxed{\delta Q = dU + \delta W} \tag{2-1}$$

* The *concept* of a molecule (or of a mole $= N_0$ molecules) is required, however, to deal quantitatively with systems involving chemical reactions (simply because chemical reaction equations themselves involve the concept). This concept, of course, can be developed from purely phenomenological data.

† Defined, say, by referring all measurements to a temperature rise of 1° C of one gram of water initially at 14.5° C. (The unit of "heat" is then the calorie.)

‡ Conservation of *mass* might be termed the "minus first law." Relativity shows that, strictly, these two conservation laws cannot be expected to hold separately but must be combined. This is discussed in (4–51)–(4–57).

Equations of State

For each external "force" (pressure, electric or magnetic field, shearing forces, etc.) applied to a system, there are "equations of state" giving the corresponding "response" of the system and usually involving the temperature as well as other variables. Typical forms are:

$$F(p, V, \theta) = 0; \qquad 4\pi\mathbf{P} = [\epsilon(p, \theta) - 1]\mathbf{E}; \qquad \text{etc.}$$

Such relations need hold only for equilibrium states. In essence, specification of all external forces and the temperature completely determines the equilibrium state.

The "response" parameters (volume, polarization, magnetization, strain, etc.) are said to be *conjugate* to the forces when the work done (*by* the system), δW, can be expressed in the form,*

$$\delta W = p\,\mathrm{d}V + f_1\,\mathrm{d}R_1 + \cdots + f_n\,\mathrm{d}R_n \tag{2–2}$$

(Since V, R_i vary with the mass or "extent" of the system they are often called "*extensive parameters*" while θ, p, f_i are independent of (the size of) the system and are called "*intensive parameters*".)

With conjugate parameters, the first law becomes,

$$\delta Q = \mathrm{d}U + p\,\mathrm{d}V + \sum f_i\,\mathrm{d}R \tag{2–3}$$

(Note that $\mathrm{d}U$, while determined by the state, cannot in general be *calculated* from information contained in the equations of state alone; for example, C_p is not specified by $F(p, \theta, V) = 0$.)

Reversible (Quasi-Static, Quasi-Equilibrium) Processes

"Reversible" processes are (finite) changes of state which take place *through a succession of equilibria*, so that all equations of state remain valid at all times during the process.† Classical thermodynamics can deal quantitatively with such processes; it can only place limitations on others.

Entropy and Thermodynamic Temperature

It is found experimentally that the adiabatic condition, $\delta Q = 0$, always imposes a definite functional restriction on attainable equilibrium states of a system:

$$\phi(\theta, p, V, f_1, R_1, \cdots, f_n, R_n) = \text{constant} \tag{2–4}$$

(adiabatic equation). Equation (2–3), with $\delta Q = 0$, must *therefore* be equivalent‡ to $\mathrm{d}\phi = 0$ and thus δQ must have an integrating factor,

$$(1/h)\,\delta Q = \mathrm{d}\phi \tag{2–5}$$

where ϕ is a definite function of the state and could be used as a state-variable (in place of V, for example).

* The notation is not meant to draw any fundamental distinction between p and the other f_i but merely emphasizes more clearly the common case where p is the only external force.

† "Continuous equilibrium" is the basic *concept* here, but "reversibility" is its best experimental test. Many systems to which the theory is applied are, strictly speaking, metastable (for example, a "cool" mixture of H_2 and O_2 or even H_2 itself, which could change to D_2 by a nuclear reaction). Provided, however, that the behavior of a system follows equations of state independent of the direction of change throughout some region, the theory remains valid in that region.

‡ The mere form of (2–3) does not itself mathematically guarantee this; compare (14–73)–(14–79). This method of developing the concepts is due essentially to Carathéodory. Other methods are mentioned following (2–14).

Consider next a complex system made up of many *separate* sub-systems in contact, and take $\phi_1, \cdots, \phi_n$ and θ (and any others if necessary) as independent state variables. Since $\delta Q = \sum_\alpha \delta Q_\alpha$,

$$h\,\mathrm{d}\phi = \sum_\alpha h_\alpha\,\mathrm{d}\phi_\alpha \tag{2–6}$$

With the above independent variables, this implies

$$\frac{\partial \phi}{\partial \theta} = 0; \quad \frac{\partial \phi}{\partial \phi_\alpha} = \frac{h_\alpha}{h}; \quad \frac{\partial}{\partial \theta}\left(\frac{h_\alpha}{h}\right) = \frac{\partial^2 \phi}{\partial \phi_\alpha\,\partial \theta} = 0$$

so that

$$\left.\begin{aligned} \phi &= \Phi(\phi_1, \phi_2, \cdots, \phi_n) \\ h_\alpha &= G(\theta) H_\alpha(\phi_\alpha) \\ h &= G(\theta) H(\phi_1, \phi_2, \cdots, \phi_n) \end{aligned}\right\} \tag{2–7}$$

where $G(\theta)$ is the same function for *all* of the subsystems (and hence for *all* physical systems).

Thermodynamic temperature is defined by

$$T = C\,G(\theta) \tag{2–8}$$

(where C is a constant scale-factor). The empirical determination of the function, G, is considered later; see (2–31).

The entropy of subsystem α is defined by

$$T\,\mathrm{d}S_\alpha = \delta Q_\alpha = h_\alpha\,\mathrm{d}\phi_\alpha = (T/C) H_\alpha(\phi_\alpha)\,\mathrm{d}\phi_\alpha$$

(where the last form shows that $\mathrm{d}S_\alpha$ is indeed the differential of a state-function). Thus,

$$S_\alpha = \int \frac{\delta Q_\alpha}{T} = \int \frac{\mathrm{d}U_\alpha + \delta W_\alpha}{T} \tag{2–9}$$

where the integral must be taken through equilibrium states ("reversible path") but need not be otherwise specified (unlike $\int \delta Q$). That is, since S_α is completely determined (to an additive constant) by the state of subsystem α, the integral over any closed (cyclic) path vanishes:

$$\oint \frac{\delta Q_\alpha}{T} = 0 \tag{2–10}$$

and (2–9) depends only on the end points of the integration (one of which is regarded as standardized).

Moreover, the entropy of the full complex system also exists, for by substituting (2–7) into (2–6), it is easy to show that

$$\frac{\partial H}{\partial \phi_\beta}\frac{\partial \phi}{\partial \phi_\alpha} = \frac{\partial H}{\partial \phi_\alpha}\frac{\partial \phi}{\partial \phi_\beta}$$

so that* actually $H = H[\phi(\phi_1, \cdots, \phi_n)]$ and thus $h = G(\theta)H(\phi)$ and $\delta Q = (T/C)H(\phi)\,\mathrm{d}\phi = T\,\mathrm{d}S$ (say), or

$$\boxed{S_1 - S_0 = \int_0^1 \frac{\delta Q}{T}} \tag{2–11}$$

* for then $$\mathrm{d}H = \sum_\alpha \frac{\partial H}{\partial \phi_\alpha}\mathrm{d}\phi_\alpha = \frac{\partial H/\partial \phi_\beta}{\partial \phi/\partial \phi_\beta}\sum_\alpha \frac{\partial \phi}{\partial \phi_\alpha}\mathrm{d}\phi_\alpha = \mathrm{d}\phi\,\frac{\partial H/\partial \phi_\beta}{\partial \phi/\partial \phi_\beta}$$

Since $\delta Q = \sum_{\alpha} \delta Q_{\alpha}$

$$dS = \sum_{\alpha} dS_{\alpha} \tag{2–12}$$

where it must be recalled that the subsystems, α, may be in contact but *must not be mixed*. (Individual terms in (2–12) may be influenced in value by the presence of the others if surface energies, etc., are important.) Since also $\delta W = \sum_{\alpha} \delta W_{\alpha}$, it follows from (2–1) that

$$dU = \sum_{\alpha} dU_{\alpha} \tag{2–13}$$

This also holds only if the systems are *not mixed*.

The Second Law

The state-function, S, exists for all physical systems and *for an isolated system* ($\delta Q = 0$):

$$\boxed{\frac{dS}{dt} \geqslant 0} \qquad (\delta Q = 0) \tag{2–14}$$

for all processes, with equality only for reversible processes and equilibrium states. (By sufficient extension of the "system" considered, the law may be applied to any situation.)

ALTERNATIVE FORMULATIONS:

1. There can be no (net) flow of heat from a colder to a hotter body without the absorption of external work. (Clausius) (Note the analogy to the "zeroth law".)
2. No device can *continuously* deliver mechanical work and produce no effect other than abstraction of heat from a reservoir. (Kelvin)

These formulations may be connected with (2–14) through the concept of:

A *Carnot engine* is any *cyclic, reversible* engine which exchanges heat only at two (constant) temperatures.

An *example* is a fluid (*not* necessarily "ideal") performing the following steps cyclically:

(a) Adiabatic ($\delta Q = 0$) expansion from T_1 to $T_2 < T_1$.
(b) Isothermal ($T = T_2$) compression (giving out heat, $|\Delta Q_2| > 0$)
(c) Adiabatic compression from T_2 to T_1.
(d) Isothermal ($T = T_1$) expansion (taking in heat $|\Delta Q_1| > 0$).

All steps for any Carnot engine are quasi-static (reversible) and since the states repeat after every cycle, (2–10) asserts,

$$\frac{|\Delta Q_1|}{T_1} - \frac{|\Delta Q_2|}{T_2} = 0 = \Delta S$$

By the first law, the external work delivered per cycle is $\Delta W = |\Delta Q_1| - |\Delta Q_2|$ and the efficiency may be defined as

$$\text{Efficiency} \equiv \frac{\Delta W}{|\Delta Q_1|} = 1 - \frac{T_2}{T_1} \tag{2–15}$$

This efficiency is therefore the same for *all* cyclic, two-temperature, reversible engines (i.e. Carnot engines).

[DIRECT PROOF: Run two Carnot engines off the same two heat-reservoirs with the mechanical output of one driving the other in reverse.]

For a *non*-reversible, cyclic engine, $\Delta S_e = 0$ (because the states repeat) but ΔS_e is no longer calculable by (2-11). However, for the two reservoirs, $\Delta S_r = -|\Delta Q_1|/T_1 + |\Delta Q_2|/T_2$, and applying (2-14) to the system, "engine plus reservoirs", we find $\Delta S_r + \Delta S_e \geqslant 0$; thus the efficiency is necessarily less than $1 - (T_2/T_1)$.

Equation (2–15) may be used to define the thermodynamic temperature when developing the concepts from the Clausius or Kelvin statement of the second law. By various ingenious interconnections of Carnot and other engines, the equivalence of the various formulations of the second law may then be proven. A key step is the proof of (2–10)—in order to define S—by regarding any cycle as a "sum" of many smaller Carnot cycles.

Other Thermodynamic Functions

Other state-functions are of importance in practical systems which are not isolated (as is required in (2–14)!) but rather are coupled to an "environment" so large that its T, V, p, etc., may be considered constant. Then, by (2–14) and (2–11) applied to "system plus environment":

$$dS + dS_e = dS - \frac{\delta Q}{T} = dS - \frac{dU + \delta W}{T} \geqslant 0 \tag{2–16}$$

In particular:

(1) If T is constant, then

$$\delta W \leqslant -d(U - TS) \tag{2–17}$$

and defining, the *Helmholtz free energy*,

$$\boxed{F = U - TS} \tag{2–18}$$

we see that (2–17) states that the work obtained in an isothermal process is never more than the decrease in F.

(2) If T, p and all external "forces" are constant, then $\delta W = d(pV + \sum_i f_i R_i)$. If we define the *Gibbs free energy** (or *Gibbs potential*),

$$\boxed{G = U + pV + \sum_i f_i R_i - TS} \tag{2–19}$$

equation (2–16) specializes to

$$\boxed{\frac{dG}{dt} \leqslant 0} \quad \text{(fixed } T, p, f_i) \tag{2–20}$$

The condition, constant T, p, f_i, is the usual one under which chemical experiments are carried out.

(3) If only p and all f_i are constant, then by (2–3) and (2–16),

$$\delta Q = dH \qquad \text{(fixed } p, f_i) \tag{2–21}$$

---

* The term, "free energy," without further specification, usually denotes G in chemical literature, where it is often denoted by F. In physics literature, it is more likely to denote F.

where H is the *enthalpy*, defined by

$$\boxed{H = U + pV + \sum_i f_i R_i = G + TS} \tag{2–22}$$

According to (2–21), ΔH is the "heat of reaction" usually measured in physical and chemical experiments at constant p, f_i.

By (2–12) and (2–13) (and the analogous relations, $\mathrm{d}V = \sum_\alpha \mathrm{d}V_\alpha$, $\mathrm{d}R_i = \sum_\alpha \mathrm{d}R_{i\alpha}$) we have, for systems *side-by-side* (not intermixed):

$$F = \sum_\alpha F_\alpha; \qquad G = \sum_\alpha G_\alpha; \qquad H = \sum_\alpha H_\alpha \tag{2–23}$$

All of the thermodynamic functions U, S, F, G, H are completely determined by the state of the system* and are independent of the manner in which that state was attained. Any of them may be used as state-variables to replace p, T, V, etc.

Differential Relations

Relations between the total differentials are the most convenient summary of the interrelations of the various functions and their partial derivatives. From (2–3) and (2–11),

$$\boxed{\mathrm{d}U = T\,\mathrm{d}S - p\,\mathrm{d}V - \sum_i f_i\,\mathrm{d}R_i} \tag{2–24}$$

and then from (2–18)–(2–22),

$$\boxed{\mathrm{d}F = -S\,\mathrm{d}T - p\,\mathrm{d}V - \sum_i f_i\,\mathrm{d}R_i} \tag{2–25}$$

$$\boxed{\mathrm{d}G = -S\,\mathrm{d}T + V\,\mathrm{d}p + \sum_i R_i\,\mathrm{d}f_i} \tag{2–26}$$

$$\boxed{\mathrm{d}H = T\,\mathrm{d}S + V\,\mathrm{d}p + \sum_i R_i\,\mathrm{d}f_i} \tag{2–27}$$

Total-differential relations are *always valid whether the quantities appearing are independent or not*†. This fact is the key to deriving and manipulating the almost endless ($>10^{10}$) relations between various partial derivatives.

All quantities in (2–24)–(2–27) are on an equal footing and the values of any $n + 2$ of them determine the values of all others (—even though some may not be directly calculable from equations of state alone; thus $F(p, V, T) = 0$ does not specify C_V or C_p).

---

* Except (see (2–11)) for an arbitrary additive constant in S (and also in U and hence in H) and therefore an additive arbitrary function of the form, $a + bT$, in F and G. These indeterminancies are a matter of *definition*, however, and are not concerned in any way with the physical behavior of the system. (These constants, of course, are related for those systems which can be inter-converted one to another. This is discussed in greater detail below.)

† Provided the system does not exchange mass with its environment. This possibility is considered later and adds extra terms in (2–24)–(2–27); here, these terms are tacitly understood to vanish. Compare (2–74) ff.

Notation

There are so many possible sets of independent variables and these are changed so frequently that context cannot be used to indicate the meaning of the partial derivatives. Therefore (modern) thermodynamics always indicates the remaining independent variables by subscripts. Thus, for example, from (2–25),

$$S = -\left.\frac{\partial F}{\partial T}\right|_{V,R_i} \tag{2–28}$$

(Read: "at constant V and R_i".)

Differential Equations

From (2–18) and (2–28),

$$U = F - T\left(\frac{\partial F}{\partial T}\right)_{V,R_i}$$

(Gibbs–Helmholtz equation). From (2–22) and (2–26),

$$H = G - T\left(\frac{\partial G}{\partial T}\right)_{p,f_i}$$

and if p is the only external force

$$F = G - p\left(\frac{\partial G}{\partial p}\right)_T$$

These relations, in integrated form, are sometimes useful for numerical computation of thermodynamic functions from empirical data.

Examples

1. Determining T in terms of (empirical) θ: From (2–24),

$$\left.\frac{\partial U}{\partial V}\right|_{T,R_i} = T\left.\frac{\partial S}{\partial V}\right|_{T,R_i} - p$$

but from (2–28) and a second application of (2–25),

$$\left.\frac{\partial S}{\partial V}\right|_{T,R_i} = -\left.\frac{\partial^2 F}{\partial T\,\partial V}\right|_{R_i} = \left.\frac{\partial p}{\partial T}\right|_{V,R_i} \tag{2–29}$$

Thus

$$\boxed{\left.\frac{\partial U}{\partial V}\right|_{T,R_i} = T\left.\frac{\partial p}{\partial T}\right|_{V,R_i} - p} \tag{2–30}$$

(This equation connects U with the equation-of-state and is often of use in its own right.) Setting $\frac{\partial}{\partial T} = \frac{d\theta}{dT}\frac{\partial}{\partial \theta}$

$$\ln T = \int^{\theta} \frac{(\partial p/\partial \theta)_{V,R_i}}{p + (\partial U/\partial V)_{\theta,R_i}}\, d\theta \tag{2–31}$$

Other methods of obtaining T in terms of θ are also available (see "ideal gases" and also (2–118) below).

2. All thermodynamic properties of a system are contained in a *single* equation of the form,

$$F = F(T, V, R_1, \cdots, R_n).$$

For, (2–28) gives S while, from (2–25),

$$p = -\left.\frac{\partial F}{\partial V}\right|_{T,R_i}; \qquad f_i = -\left.\frac{\partial F}{\partial R_i}\right|_{T,V,R_j}$$

(equations of state) and finally,

$$U = F + TS; \quad G = F + pV + \sum_i f_i R_i; \qquad H = G + TS$$

Other "all powerful" relations have the forms (compare (2–24)–(2–27)),

$$U = U(S, V, R_i) \qquad G = G(p, T, f_i)$$
$$H = H(S, p, f_i) \qquad S = S(U, V, R_i) \qquad \text{etc.}$$

3. Two-variable systems ("no f_i"):
If (say) p, T completely determine the state, then defining,

$$\left.\begin{aligned}
C_V &= \text{``}\left.\frac{\delta Q}{\partial T}\right|_V\text{''} = \left.\frac{\partial U}{\partial T}\right|_V \\
C_p &= \text{``}\left.\frac{\delta Q}{\partial T}\right|_p\text{''} = \left.\frac{\partial U}{\partial T}\right|_p + p\left.\frac{\partial V}{\partial T}\right|_p = \left.\frac{\partial H}{\partial T}\right|_p \qquad \text{(specific heats)} \\
\alpha &= \frac{1}{V}\left.\frac{\partial V}{\partial T}\right|_p \qquad \text{(thermal expansion coefficient)} \\
\sigma &= \frac{1}{p}\left.\frac{\partial p}{\partial T}\right|_V \qquad \text{(thermal pressure coefficient)} \\
K &= -\frac{1}{V}\left.\frac{\partial V}{\partial p}\right|_T \qquad \text{(isothermal compressibility)} \\
K_S &= -\frac{1}{V}\left.\frac{\partial V}{\partial p}\right|_S \qquad \text{(adiabatic compressibility)}
\end{aligned}\right\} \tag{2–32}$$

Some of the relations among these are:

$$\alpha = p\sigma K \tag{2–33}$$

$$C_p/C_V = K/K_S \tag{2–34}$$

$$C_p - C_V = TpV\sigma\alpha = TV\alpha^2/K \tag{2–35}$$

(The last may be proved by equating (2–37) and (2–39) below and solving for dT.) The right side of (2–35) is very nearly constant (empirically) for any given substance—"Grueneisen's law."

4. Relations for estimating δQ.

($\delta Q = T\,dS$ only if the process is quasi-static.)

(a) If we define,

$$C_{V,R_i} = \left.\frac{\partial U}{\partial T}\right|_{V,R_i} = T\left(\frac{\partial S}{\partial T}\right)_{V,R_i} \tag{2–36}$$

where we have used (2–24), then because (by definition of partial derivatives),

$$dS = \left.\frac{\partial S}{\partial T}\right|_{V,R_i} dT + \left.\frac{\partial S}{\partial V}\right|_{T,R_i} dV + \sum_i \left.\frac{\partial S}{\partial R_i}\right|_{T,V,R_j} dR_i$$

it follows from (2–29)—and analogous relations with f_i—that

$$T\,\mathrm{d}S = C_{V,R_i}\,\mathrm{d}T + T\left.\frac{\partial p}{\partial T}\right|_{V,R_i}\mathrm{d}V + \sum_i T\left.\frac{\partial f_i}{\partial T}\right|_{V,R_j}\mathrm{d}R_i \tag{2–37}$$

(b) Similarly, define

$$\left.\begin{aligned} C_{p,f_i} &= \left.\frac{\partial U}{\partial T}\right|_{p,f_i} + p\left.\frac{\partial V}{\partial T}\right|_{p,f_i} + \sum f_i\left.\frac{\partial R_i}{\partial T}\right|_{p,f_j} \\ &= \left.\frac{\partial H}{\partial T}\right|_{p,f_i} \qquad \text{(by (2–22))} \\ &= T\left.\frac{\partial S}{\partial T}\right|_{p,f_i} \qquad \text{(by (2–27))} \end{aligned}\right\} \tag{2–38}$$

then, writing dS in terms of dT, dp, df_i analogously and using relations such as

$$\left.\frac{\partial S}{\partial f_i}\right|_{T,p,f_j} = \frac{\partial}{\partial f_i}\left(-\left.\frac{\partial G}{\partial T}\right|_{p,f_j}\right) = -\left.\frac{\partial^2 G}{\partial T\partial f_i}\right|_{p,f_j} = -\left.\frac{\partial R_i}{\partial T}\right|_{p,f_j}$$

(which follow from (2–26)), one finds,

$$T\,\mathrm{d}S = C_{p,f_i}\,\mathrm{d}T - T\left.\frac{\partial V}{\partial T}\right|_{p,f_i}\mathrm{d}p - \sum T\left.\frac{\partial R_i}{\partial T}\right|_{p,f_j}\mathrm{d}f_i \tag{2–39}$$

5. Heats of reaction (at constant T, p, f_i):
By (2–21), the heat absorbed or liberated in a reaction of any type at constant p, f_i is

$$Q_{21} = H_{(2)} - H_{(1)}$$

where the subscripts refer to the states of the system before and after the reaction. Differentiating this relation with respect to T and using (2–38).

$$\left.\frac{\partial Q_{21}}{\partial T}\right|_{p,f_i} = C_{pf_i(2)} - C_{pf_i(1)} \tag{2–40}$$

Likewise, differentiation with respect to p shows,

$$\left.\frac{\partial Q_{21}}{\partial p}\right|_{T,f_i} = -T^2\frac{\partial}{\partial T}\left.\left(\frac{V_2 - V_1}{T}\right)\right|_{p,f_i} \tag{2–41}$$

since

$$-\left.\frac{\partial V}{\partial T}\right|_{p,f_i} = \left.\frac{-\partial^2 G}{\partial p\,\partial T}\right|_{f_i} = \left.\frac{\partial S}{\partial p}\right|_{T,f_i} = \frac{1}{T}\left(\left.\frac{\partial H}{\partial p}\right|_{T,f_i} - V\right).$$

B. SPECIAL SUBSTANCES AND SYSTEMS

Ideal Gases

At sufficiently low density, all substances approximate an ideal gas, which is macroscopically characterized* by:

$$pV = f(\theta) = \Theta \qquad \text{(say)} \tag{2–42}$$

$$U = g(pV) = g(\Theta) \tag{2–43}$$

* Microscopic characterization: no interaction (energy) between molecules.

where Θ can be employed as an empirical temperature. These relations imply, by (2–31) that

$$\Theta = (\text{constant}) \cdot T \tag{2–44}$$

Ideal gas temperature is therefore identical with thermodynamic temperature* (to within a scale factor).

With a standard scale for T, (2–42) takes the following form (where ρ = mass density; M = total mass of gas considered),

$$p = \frac{\rho}{m} RT; \qquad \text{or} \qquad pV = \frac{M}{m} RT = NRT \tag{2–45}$$

where R is a universal constant† (1.987 cal/mole °K), where m (grams/mole) is known as the "molecular weight" of the substance, and where N is the number of "moles" of gas considered.

By (2–32) and (2–43), $c_v = C_V/N$ (the specific heat per mole) is a function of T only:

$$c_v = c_v(T) \tag{2–46}$$

and by (2–45), $H = U(T) + NRT$, so that $C_p = C_V + NR$, or per mole,

$$c_p = c_v(T) + R \tag{2–47}$$

By (2–3), (2–11) and (2–45)

$$\frac{S}{N} = s_0 + \int^T c_v(T) \frac{dT}{T} + R \ln V \tag{2–48}$$

or

$$s = \frac{S}{N} = \phi(T) - R \ln p \tag{2–49}$$

A "*polytropic*" ideal gas has constant c_v and hence

$$\gamma = \frac{c_p}{c_v} = 1 + \frac{R}{c_v} \tag{2–50}$$

is also constant. Then

$$\left.\begin{aligned} \frac{U - U_0}{V} = \frac{p}{\gamma - 1}; \qquad \frac{H - U_0}{V} &= \frac{\gamma p}{\gamma - 1} \\ S/N = s_0' + c_p \ln T - R \ln p& \\ = s_0'' + c_v \ln (p/\rho^\gamma)& \end{aligned}\right\} \tag{2–51}$$

(The constant, U_0, usually includes chemical binding energy.) Thus the *isentropic*‡ condition for a polytropic ideal gas is

$$p/\rho^\gamma = \text{constant} \quad (\text{or } pV^\gamma = \text{constant}) \tag{2–52}$$

* This shows that true (equilibrium) thermodynamic temperatures are never negative. However, "negative temperature" is a useful concept for dealing with certain metastable systems (namely those which cannot accept more than a definite limit of internal energy without completely changing their nature—notably nuclear spin systems). See remarks following (6–148).

† In these equations, it is especially useful to remember that *pressure has the dimensions of energy density*; some conversion factors are:

$$1.013 \text{ megadyne/cm}^2 = 1 \text{ atmosphere} = \frac{1}{41.32} \text{ cal/cm}^3$$

‡ Strict terminology is

Adiabatic $\leftrightarrow \delta Q = 0$

Isentropic $\leftrightarrow dS = 0$

Only for reversible (quasi-static) processes are these conditions equivalent.

Expressions (in abundance) for F, G, H follow from their definitions and the above results.

Some results *not* derivable from phenomenological thermodynamics alone (see Chapter 6):

$$c_v/R = \tfrac{1}{2}f; \qquad \gamma = 1 + (2/f) \tag{2–53}$$

where:

> f = number of degrees of freedom of the molecules [monatomic, 3; diatomic, 5; polyatomic, 6; plus any "active" internal degrees of freedom (vibrational or electronic)].

(From (6–50).)

For a monatomic gas with no "active" internal excitations* (p in atm; natural logarithms)

$$s = \frac{S}{N} = -2.314\left(\frac{\text{cal}}{\text{mole °K}}\right) + R[\tfrac{3}{2}\ln m + \tfrac{5}{2}\ln T - \ln p] \tag{2–54}$$

(From (6–76).)

For linear-top (e.g. diatomic) gases, add to (2–54) the following, in which I = moment of inertia and $\sigma = 2$ for symmetric molecules, $\sigma = 1$ otherwise:

$$s^{(\text{rot})} = R\left[1 + \ln\left(\frac{2IkT}{\sigma\hbar^2}\right)\right] \tag{2–55}$$

(From (6–78); further results are given there.)

"Black-Body" Radiation

Black-body radiation† is electromagnetic radiation in *thermal equilibrium* (with any substance). Since such radiation is stationary in time and randomly directed, Maxwell's theory (esp. (3–8)) shows $p = U/3V$ where U is the field energy in volume, V. Moreover, the energy density U/V, must be completely determined by T alone, for otherwise there could be a net flow of energy from one to another of two ovens, connected by an orifice and at the same (or negligibly different) temperature—in violation of the second law (Clausius' form). Thus $p = U/3V = p(T)$ and from (2–30), $\mathrm{d}p/\mathrm{d}T = 4p/T$, whence,

$$\frac{U}{V} = 3p = \frac{4}{c}\sigma T^4 \tag{2–56}$$

where σ is known as the Stefan–Boltzmann constant ($\sigma = 5.67 \times 10^{-5}$ c.g.s.). From (2–56) and (2–24)–(2–27), there follow,

$$\left.\begin{aligned} S &= \tfrac{16}{3}\frac{\sigma}{c}T^3V \\ F &= -\tfrac{4}{3}\frac{\sigma}{c}T^4V \\ G &\equiv 0 \\ H &= \tfrac{16}{3}\frac{\sigma}{c}T^4V \end{aligned}\right\} \tag{2–57}$$

* The constant term in (2–54) has been fixed by a "universally consistent" standard which emerges from statistical theory, Chapter 6.

† The German term, "Hohlraumstrahlung" ("cavity radiation"), is more suggestive of the concept actually involved.

[If kT is expressed in electron volts,

$$(kT)_{\text{ev}} = T/(11{,}605^\circ \text{ K})$$

then

$$U/V = 4\sigma T^4/c = 137[(kT)_{\text{ev}}]^4 \quad \text{erg/cm}^3$$

which is conveniently remembered as "$137T^4$ with T in ev".]

Van der Waals Gas

This idealized substance is a good qualitative approximation to almost any substance in *both* its liquid and gaseous states.*

The equation of state is

$$\left(p + \frac{A}{V^2}\right)(V - B) = \frac{MR}{m}T; \qquad \text{or } (p + a\rho^2)\left(\frac{1}{\rho} - b\right) = \frac{R}{m}T \tag{2–58}$$

The critical point (where $(\partial p/\partial V)_T = 0 = (\partial^2 p/\partial V^2)_T$) is given by

$$\rho_c = \frac{1}{3b}; \qquad p_c = \frac{a}{27b^2}; \qquad T_c = \frac{8a}{27b}\frac{m}{R} \tag{2–59}$$

[Empirically, $T_c \doteqdot 1.7 \times$ (boiling temp. at 1 atm).]

The constant, B, may be envisaged as the total volume of the molecules themselves (so $V \geqslant B$). The term, A/V^2, crudely represents an "extra pressure" due to mutual

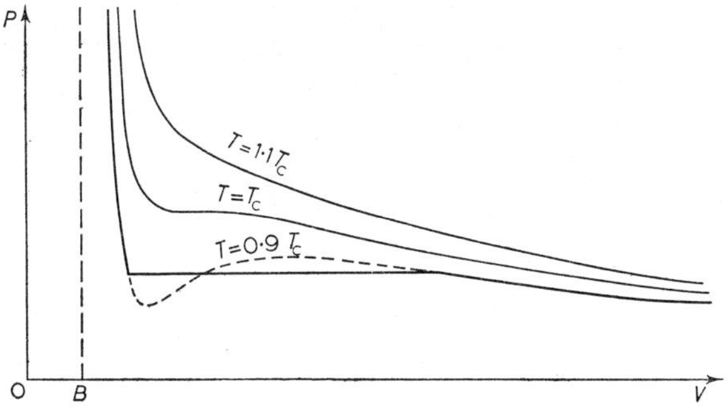

attraction of molecules. For a mixture of gases, A and B are very roughly equal to averages of their values for the individual constituents.

When $T < T_c$, the isotherms predicted by (2–58) have extrema which actually are not traversed by any substance.† Rather, (2–58) is to be modified by cutting off the extrema with a line of constant pressure (= the vapor-pressure at that T). The unmodified sections of the isotherm then correspond to pure vapor and to pure liquid, while the central, horizontal portion represents *condensation* (or vaporization); both liquid and vapor are present.

Rigorous discussion of this modification requires concepts developed later in this chapter, but, anticipating these: As the substance traverses the isotherm, it follows smoothly along (2–58) until one of the other branches of (2–58) [at the same T, p] has equal Gibbs potential (per unit mass). The thermodynamically stable state is then

* Of course, no simple equation can be expected to describe any substance with high accuracy over large ranges of temperature.

† Except in part, during (metastable) supercooling or superheating.

(see (2–87) below) a mixture of two parts of the substance and remains so until all of the substance is converted to one form or the other. (Note that, in the figure, V represents the total volume of the system; the individual volumes of vapor and liquid, however, are completely determined by V and the end points of the horizontal segment.) The horizontal (vapor) pressure line is determined thus: From (2–26), $(\partial G/\partial p)_T = V$ and hence* by (2–87) below,

$$\int_{\text{Vap.}}^{\text{Liq.}} V\Big|_{T=\text{const}} \mathrm{d}p = G_{\text{vap}} - G_{\text{liq}} = 0 \tag{2–60}$$

Thus the vapor-pressure line must be drawn to cut off equal areas from the two loops of (2–58) (dotted in the figure).

The actual analytic forms of G, U, S, F are only partly determined by (2–58); from (2–58) and (2–30), $(\partial U/\partial V)_T = A/V^2$, so that

$$\mathrm{d}U = C_V\,\mathrm{d}T + (A/V^2)\,\mathrm{d}V \tag{2–61}$$

Thus, since $\mathrm{d}U$ and $\mathrm{d}V/V^2 = -\mathrm{d}(1/V)$ are complete differentials, $C_V\,\mathrm{d}T$ must also be a perfect differential and hence,

$$C_V = f(T) \tag{2–62}$$

From (2–24) and (2–61),

$$\mathrm{d}S = C_V \frac{\mathrm{d}T}{T} + \frac{R}{m}\frac{M\,\mathrm{d}V}{(V-B)} \tag{2–63}$$

Also from (2–35),

$$C_p - C_V = \frac{MR}{m}\left[1 - \frac{2A(V-B)^2}{(MR/m)\,TV^3}\right]^{-1} \tag{2–64}$$

It is frequently assumed that $C_V =$ constant (as is approximately true for most substances). In this case, for example,

$$U = U_0 + C_V T - A/V \tag{2–65}$$

$$S = S_0 + C_V \ln T + \frac{MR}{m}\ln(V-B) \tag{2–66}$$

$$G = C_V T(1 - \ln T) - \frac{MRT}{m}\ln(V-B) - \frac{A}{V} + (U_0 - TS_0) + pV \tag{2–67}$$

(These, and all formulas generally, are easily written in terms of ρ by considering one gram of substance and setting $V = 1/\rho$.)

The Tait Equation

The Tait equation is widely used as a simple approximation for nearly incompressible fluids. The equation of state is

$$[p + P_0(S)]\,V^{\nu} = P_0(S)[V_0(S)]^{\nu} \tag{2–68}$$

---

* The fact that the dotted loops in the figure are not physically attainable is immaterial in (2–60). If G is related to p and V by an *analytic* relation like (2–58), ΔG may then be *evaluated* by using such mathematical relations even though the "path" involved has no physical meaning.

This general situation, involving an analytic mathematical equation of state which must be modified in a non-analytic way to satisfy thermodynamics, is typical of any theory which encompasses changes of phase.

where $\nu > 1$ is a constant, V_0 is the volume at "zero" pressure, and $P_0(S)$ (often assumed constant) is related to the adiabatic compressibility:*

$$K_S = \frac{1/\nu}{p + P_0(S)} \tag{2–69}$$

From (2–24), $(\partial U/\partial V)_S = -p$ which, with (2–68), implies

$$U = U_0(S) + \frac{V}{\nu - 1}[p + \nu P_0(S)] \tag{2–70}$$

(and, conversely, (2–70) implies (2–68)). T can be determined from $(\partial U/\partial S)_V = T$.

Electric Cells

The electrical work done by a chemical cell is $\mathscr{E}\,\mathrm{d}q$ where the "force", $\mathscr{E}$, is the cell voltage (an intensive parameter) and the "response", q, is the electric charge which has flowed (an extensive—size proportional—parameter). From (2–26),

$$S = -\frac{\partial}{\partial T}(G - \mathscr{E}q)\Big|_{p,q}; \qquad \mathscr{E} = -\frac{\partial}{\partial q}(G - \mathscr{E}q)\Big|_{p,T}$$

so that

$$\frac{\partial S}{\partial q}\Big|_{T,p} = \frac{\partial \mathscr{E}}{\partial T}\Big|_{p,q}$$

and hence from (2–27),

$$\frac{\partial(H - \mathscr{E}q)}{\partial q}\Big|_{T,p} = \frac{\partial(U + pV)}{\partial q}\Big|_{T,p} = T\frac{\partial \mathscr{E}}{\partial T}\Big|_{p,q} - \mathscr{E} \tag{2–71}$$

which provides a means of measuring the enthalpy ("heat") of chemical reactions, $U + pV$, by electrical measurements at a variety of ambient temperatures. When available, this method is exceedingly accurate.

Surface Energy

An expansion of the surface area, A, of a fluid entails mechanical work, $\delta W = -\beta\,\mathrm{d}A$, (done by the system), where β is the surface tension, By (2–37), for reversible changes,

$$\delta Q = C_{V,A}\,\mathrm{d}T + T\frac{\partial p}{\partial T}\Big|_{V,A}\mathrm{d}V - T\frac{\partial \beta}{\partial T}\Big|_{V,A}\mathrm{d}A$$

and by the first law,

$$\mathrm{d}U = \delta Q - \delta W = C_{V,A}\,\mathrm{d}T + T\frac{\partial p}{\partial T}\Big|_{V,A}\mathrm{d}V + \left(\beta - T\frac{\partial \beta}{\partial T}\Big|_{V,A}\right)\mathrm{d}A$$

Thus

$$\frac{\partial U}{\partial A}\Big|_{T,V} = \beta - T\frac{\partial \beta}{\partial T}\Big|_{V,A} \tag{2–72}$$

which relates the *surface* energy change (at constant T) to the surface tension, β. (For water, the second term is comparable in value to the first.)

---

* and hence to the velocity of sound: $P_0 = c^2\rho/\nu$ at "zero" pressure. For water, $P_0 \doteqdot 3 \times 10^9$ cgs, $\nu \doteqdot 7$; for aluminum at high pressures ("plastic region"), $\nu \doteqdot 5$, $P_0 \doteqdot 1.5 \times 10^{11}$ cgs.

C. INTERNAL EQUILIBRIUM (Specified T, p, f_i):

Previous sections dealt with systems as a whole and therefore assumed no mass exchange with the environment. When either restriction is lifted, it is necessary to introduce the masses of the constituents as additional variables. None of the foregoing is affected but the partial derivatives (and (2–24)–(2–27)) are, of course, *understood to have been written for the special case of constant mass-variables.*

General Relations

Let the system consist of c *chemical substances,** distributed among ϕ physically homogeneous regions† ("phases"). Let there be $N_{i\alpha}$ moles of the ith chemical in the αth phase. The quantity,

$$\mu_{i\alpha} = \left.\frac{\partial G}{\partial N_{i\alpha}}\right|_{T,p,f,N_{j\beta}} \tag{2–73}$$

is called the "*chemical potential*" of the ith constituent in the αth phase.

From (2–26) and (2–73), if the $N_{i\alpha}$ are no longer constant,

$$\mathrm{d}G = -S\,\mathrm{d}T + V\,\mathrm{d}p + \sum_j R_j\,\mathrm{d}f_j + \sum_{\alpha=1}^{\phi}\sum_{i=1}^{c} \mu_{i\alpha}\,\mathrm{d}N_{i\alpha} \tag{2–74}$$

For any changes of the system as a whole, there are auxiliary conditions: Let

$$\sum_{\alpha=1}^{\phi} N_{i\alpha} = N_i \tag{2–75}$$

(the total number of moles of the ith chemical). If the ith substance cannot react chemically, $\mathrm{d}N_i = 0$, but a chemical reaction, such as,

$$n_1N_1 + n_2N_2 \rightleftharpoons n_3N_3 + n_4N_4$$

requires instead

$$-\frac{\mathrm{d}N_1}{n_1} = -\frac{\mathrm{d}N_2}{n_2} = +\frac{\mathrm{d}N_3}{n_3} = +\frac{\mathrm{d}N_4}{n_4} = \mathrm{d}\epsilon$$

(where ϵ is a measure of the extent to which the reaction proceeds), and similarly for reactions between phases (freezing, vaporization, etc.) with or without chemical changes.

If there are r *reactions*, all of the auxiliary conditions may be combined:

$$\mathrm{d}N_i = \sum_{\alpha=1}^{\phi} \mathrm{d}N_{i\alpha} = \sum_{\alpha=1}^{\phi}\sum_{k=1}^{r} \nu_{i\alpha}{}^{(k)}\,\mathrm{d}\epsilon^{(k)} \tag{2–76}$$

where $\nu_{i\alpha}{}^{(k)} = 0$ if $N_{i\alpha}$ does not take part in the kth reaction and $\nu_{i\alpha}{}^{(k)}$ is otherwise the $N_{i\alpha}$ coefficient in the chemical-equation for the kth reaction, $\pm n_{i\alpha}{}^{(k)}$, according to the side of the kth reaction on which $N_{i\alpha}$ appears.

---

* Strictly, different isotopes etc. should be regarded as different substances, but this is actually done only in special cases because the entropy of mixing cancels in all processes if the isotopic ratios do not change. Compare (2–91).

† In practical applications (notably in metallurgy) a macroscopically uniform solid may actually be a fine-grained mixture of several solid *phases*, mutually dispersed as very small (but not molecular) "grains" of the several materials. All such subregions which are physically identical are usually regarded, in common, as a single "phase" (for each *type* of "grain").

Conditions (2–76) and the vanishing of (2–74) for constant external conditions ($dT = dp = 0 = df$'s)—namely, according to (2-20), $\sum_\alpha \sum_i \mu_{i\alpha}\, dN_{i\alpha} = 0$—imply (use the method of Lagrange multipliers),

$$\mu_{i\alpha} = \mu_{i\beta} = \mu_i \quad \text{(say)} \tag{2–77}$$

and

$$\sum_\alpha \sum_j \mu_j \, \nu_{j\alpha}{}^{(k)} = 0 \tag{2–78}$$

that is:

Each chemical has the same "potential" in all phases and these potentials are further related through the coefficients of any reaction-equations, as in (2–78).

Gibbs' Phase Rule

If we seek the equilibrium *composition* of the phases (ignoring the total mass in each), there are $c\phi$ concentrations (or "mole fractions"),

$$c_{i\alpha} = \frac{N_{i\alpha}}{\sum_{j=1}^{c} N_{j\alpha}} \tag{2–79}$$

of which at most* $(c\phi - \phi)$ are independent (since $\sum_i c_{i\alpha} = 1$), while (2–77) represents $c(\phi - 1)$ equations and (2–78) represents r non-vacuous equations. If there are n external forces, f_i, (in addition to p), we have at most $(c\phi - \phi + n + 2)$ variables, and the number which can be assigned arbitrary values is limited:

$$\text{"Variance"} \leqslant c - r - \phi + 2 + n \tag{2–80}$$

(*The phase rule*). The difference of the two sides, of course, is the number, z, of restricting relations* on the $c_{i\alpha}$. The quantity,

$$c' = c - r - z \tag{2–81}$$

is called the "number of (independent) components"; it is independent of the presence or absence of dissociations, dimerizations, etc., and, with experience, can be evaluated by inspection of the system. Then

$$\text{Variance} = \text{degrees of freedom} = c' - \phi + 2 + n \tag{2–82}$$

In particular, a single substance ($c' = 1$) whose state depends only on p, T ($n = 0$) can exist in two phases only along a curve, $p = p(T)$ (vapor pressure or sublimation pressure) and can exist in three phases (solid, liquid, vapor) only at a single point, $p = p_0$ and $T = T_0$ (triple point). (The triple point, therefore, is an excellent temperature standard.) With binary mixtures ($c' = 2$; interacting or not) the situation is more complex, but if it is assumed that the pressure is constant (one atmosphere if not otherwise specified) and that there is no ("important") vapor phase, a two dimensional diagram, with temperature and concentration axes ("phase diagram") suffices to present all information; again, $\phi \leqslant 2$ except at a single point, and in regions where $\phi = 2$ the relative masses of the two phases are readily obtained from the "gross" concentration and that of the two phases.

---

* Additional restricting relations can arise during the specification of the system. Thus, in the dissociation of H_2O vapor, the concentration of O_2 determines that of H_2 (and vice versa), IF the system initially contains only H_2O; here $c = 3$, $r = 1$, $z = 1$ and $c' = 1$.

Properties of Chemical Potentials

By (2–23), $G = \sum_\alpha G_\alpha$ and since* only G_β involves $N_{i\beta}$, (2–73) may be written more simply:

$$\mu_{i\alpha} = \frac{\partial G_\alpha}{\partial N_{i\alpha}}\bigg|_{T,p,f,N_{k\alpha}} \tag{2–83}$$

Thus there is no loss of generality in considering a *single phase.**

If all masses are multiplied by a common factor, λ, then* $G' = \lambda G$, and Euler's theorem, with (2–83), states that

$$G = H - TS = \sum \mu_i N_i \tag{2–84}$$

(Gibbs-Duhem equation).

Substitution of (2–74) into $dH = dG + T\,dS + S\,dT$ then shows,

$$\mu_i = \frac{\partial H}{\partial N_i}\bigg|_{p,f,S,N_j} \tag{2–85}$$

Similarly,

$$\mu_i = \frac{\partial F}{\partial N_i}\bigg|_{T,V,R_k,N_j} = \frac{\partial U}{\partial N_i}\bigg|_{S,V,R_k,N_j} = -T\,\frac{\partial S}{\partial N_i}\bigg|_{U,V,R_k,N_j} \tag{2–86}$$

When only a single chemical substance is present, (2–84) shows that

$$\mu = G/N \tag{2–87}$$

and (2–77) states that the Gibbs potential per mole (or per unit mass) must be the same in all coexisting phases of the substance.

Mass Action Laws

Mass action laws are equilibrium equations,† equivalent to (2–78), but written in the form (for each reaction),

$$\prod_{i,\alpha} [c_{i\alpha}]^{\nu_{i\alpha}} = K(T, p, \cdots) \tag{2–88}$$

(where the $c_{i\alpha}$ are the mole fractions, (2–79)).

Since the *heat of reaction*, L, (at constant T, p, f_i) is,‡ by definition of the coefficients $\nu_{i\alpha}$,

$$L = \sum_{i,\alpha} \nu_{i\alpha} \frac{\partial H}{\partial N_{i\alpha}}\bigg|_{T,p,f_i,N_{k\beta}} \tag{2–89}$$

and since $G = H - TS$, (2–78) and (2–83) are equivalent to (note $\delta Q = T\,dS$)

$$\boxed{\frac{L}{T} = \sum_{i,\alpha} \nu_{i\alpha} \frac{\partial S}{\partial N_{i\alpha}}\bigg|_{T,p,f_i,N_{j\beta}}} \tag{2–90}$$

Further reduction of (2–90) requires additional experimental information concerning mixtures of substances.

---

* To the extent that surface and interface effects can be neglected.

† In physics literature. Chemical literature often employs this term for formulas giving the speeds of reactions, such as (6–206)–(6–208).

‡ Also "at constant $c_{i\alpha}$"—that is, although L is expressed per $\nu_{i\alpha}$ ($\gtrless 0$) moles of substance i in phase α created during the reaction, nevertheless (2–89) should be regarded as a differential relation since L may in general change when the concentrations change.

1. **Ideal gas phases.** The required information in this case is:

(a) Dalton's law of partial pressures*.

(b) The empirical existence of semi-permeable membranes (which confine one gas and are porous to another).

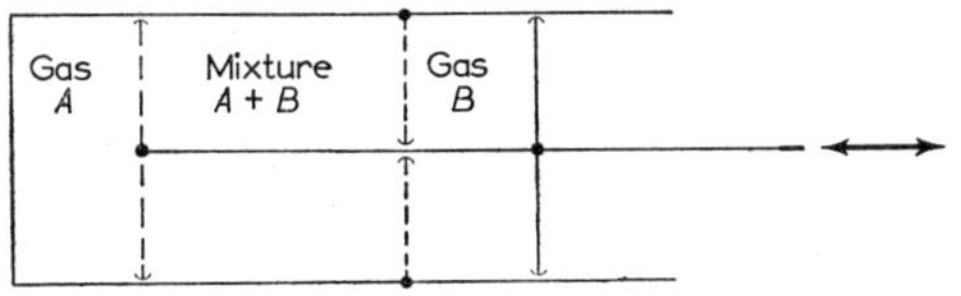

With these facts, one can envisage and analyze a device (see figure) which can *reversibly* ($dS = 0$) mix and unmix two (or more) gases; since $dS = 0 = \delta W = \delta Q$ this implies for ideal gases (with $c_i p = p_i$, the partial pressure of gas i, and using (2–49)),

$$S_{\text{mixture}} = \sum_i S_i(T, p_i)$$
$$= \sum_i N_i s_i(T, p) - R \sum_i N_i \ln c_i \tag{2–91}$$

(Gibbs' theorem;† this might be adjoined as another principle of thermodynamics; compare the "third law" below.)
Inserting (2–91) into (2–90) and using (2–49),

$$\frac{L}{RT} = \sum_i (\nu_i/R) s_i(T, p) - \sum \nu_i \ln c_i$$
$$= \psi(T) - (\sum_i \nu_i) \ln p - \sum \ln (c_i^{\nu_i}) \tag{2–92}$$

Or, setting $B(T) = \exp(\psi)$,

$$\prod_i (c_i)^{\nu_i} = e^{-L/RT} p^{-(\Sigma \nu_i)} B(T) \tag{2–93}$$

Note that, for any T, sufficiently low pressures will cause dissociation (and even ionization; see (2–115) below). For the signs of the ν_i and of L, compare (2–89).

From (2–91), the Gibbs function for a mixture of ideal gases is,

$$G_{\text{mixture}} = \sum_i N_i g_i(T, p_i) = \sum N_i g_i(T, p) + RT \sum_i N_i \ln c_i \tag{2–94}$$

where g_i is the Gibbs potential for one mole of the ith gas at T, p.

For polytropic ideal gases, (2–51) shows that in (2–93), $B(T) = \exp [\sum \nu_i s_{0i}' + (\ln T) \sum \nu_i c_{pi}]/R$ and moreover since $H_i = U_{0i} + C_{pi} T$ we also have $L = L_0 + T \sum \nu_i c_{pi}$, where L_0 is the "heat of reaction at $T = 0$" [or the molecular binding energy; for the sign-convention, compare (2–89)].

$$\prod_i (c_i)^{\nu_i} = A p^{-\Sigma \nu_i} T^{\Sigma \nu_i c_{pi}/R} e^{-L_0/RT} \tag{2–95}$$

where (the coefficient of ν_i is called the "chemical constant" of gas i):

$$A = \exp [\sum \nu_i (s_{0i}' - c_{pi})/R] \tag{2–96}$$

* Namely: Each gas in a mixture exerts the same pressure that it would if it alone were present, and the total pressure (of the mixture) is the sum of these partial pressures.

† Gibbs' paradox: There is nothing in (2–91) that obviously requires the gases to be chemically distinct. This may be regarded as an example of discontinuous behavior with respect to "the chemical variable".

Here all quantities are calculable (compare (2–51)–(2–55)). From (2–92) in the notation (2–88),

$$\ln K = -\frac{\text{“}\Delta G\text{”}}{RT} = \frac{-1}{RT}\sum_i \nu_i\, g_i(T, p) \tag{2–97}$$

where "ΔG" is the difference between the (sums of) the Gibbs potentials for ($|\nu_i|$ moles of): (a) *unmixed* reactants, all at T, p and (b) *unmixed* reaction-products, all at T, p. This relation is valid only for ideal gases.

From (2–97) and $(\partial g_i/\partial T)_p = -s_i$, it follows that

$$\frac{\partial}{\partial T}\ln K\bigg|_p = \frac{L}{RT^2} \tag{2–98}$$

Similarly,

$$\frac{\partial}{\partial p}\ln K\bigg|_T = -\frac{\sum \nu_i v_i}{RT} = -\frac{\Delta v}{RT} \tag{2–99}$$

where Δv is the volume change accompanying the reaction (of ν_i moles). These relations actually have wider validity than (2–97).

2. **Dilute "solutions".** If, in a (solid, liquid, or gas) single phase, one component chemical is present in great excess ($c_0 \doteqdot 1$), then the internal energy and volume* of the "solution" may be expanded in a Taylor's series†

$$\left.\begin{aligned} U &= U_0 + \sum_i N_i\,\alpha_i \\ V &= V_0 + \sum_i N_i\,\beta_i \end{aligned}\right\} \tag{2–100}$$

where the coefficients, α_i and β_i, are *independent of the* N_i since they are derivatives evaluated with all $N_i = 0$.

Then

$$dS = \frac{dU_0 + p\,dV_0}{T} + \sum N_i \frac{d\alpha_i + p\,d\beta_i}{T}$$

The first term is simply dS_0 (for the pure "solvent") and, because the N_i are *independent*, each of the remaining terms must also be a perfect differential (regarding the N_i as parameters of the system):

$$(d\alpha_i + p\,d\beta_i)/T = d\,\phi_i(T, p) \tag{2–101}$$

Thus, integrating,

$$S = S_0(T, p) + \sum_i N_i\,\phi_i(T, p) + C$$

where C must be independent of p and T but may depend on the N_i. But if the density is sufficiently decreased the system will approach a mixture of ideal gases and this observation determines C from (2–91):

$$S = N_0 s_0 + \sum_{i=1}^{n} N_i\phi_i(T, p) - R\sum_{i=0}^{n} N_i \ln c_i \tag{2–102}$$

and (2–90) becomes

$$\sum_{i=0}^{n} \nu_i \ln c_i = \frac{\nu_0 s_0}{R} + \sum_{i=1}^{n}\frac{\nu_i\phi_i}{R} - \frac{L}{RT} = \ln K(T, p) \tag{2–103}$$

which is (2–88), with K dependent on the chemical nature of the components but independent of the c_i. For sign conventions, compare (2–89).

---

* And, similarly, any other extensive "response" parameters, R_k.

† The functions G, S, F cannot be so expanded because they are non-analytic (though finite) when $N_i = 0$; compare (2–102).

Taking (total) differentials in (2–103), using (2–101) and using,

$$L = \nu_0(u_0 + pv_0) + \sum \nu_i(\alpha_i + p\beta_i)$$

(a form of (2–89) and (2–100)), we find,

$$\mathrm{d}(\ln K) = \frac{L}{RT^2}\,\mathrm{d}T - \frac{\Delta v}{RT}\,\mathrm{d}p \qquad (2\text{–}104)$$

where Δv is the volume change accompanying the reaction (of ν_i moles). Thus (2–98) and (2–99) hold also for dilute "solutions".

For solutions of finite concentration, the most important practical breakdown of (2–103) occurs for electrolytes in water (or similar systems containing free ions). Quantitative correction* of (2–103) for these cases requires a detailed molecular statistical theory, but the main qualitative features are predictable by observing that dissociation of the salts will double the effective number of dissolved moles.

From (2–100) and (2–102), the Gibbs potential of a dilute solution has the form,

$$G = G_0(T, p) + \sum_{i=1}^{n} N_i\gamma_i(T, p) + RT \sum_{i=0}^{n} N_i \ln c_i \qquad (2\text{–}105)$$

where G_0 is the Gibbs function of the pure solvent and $\gamma_i = \alpha_i + p\beta_i - T\phi_i$ depends only on T and p.

3. **Several phases: Ideal gases and dilute "solutions".** Since entropies and other thermodynamic functions for the different *phases* are additive (see (2–23)), it easily follows from the foregoing that

$$\boxed{\prod_{i\alpha} (c_{i\alpha})^{\nu_{i\alpha}} = K(T, p)} \qquad (2\text{–}106)$$

where K is independent of the $c_{i\alpha}$ and

$$\boxed{\left.\frac{\partial \ln K}{\partial p}\right|_T = \frac{-\Delta v}{RT}\,; \qquad \left.\frac{\partial \ln K}{\partial T}\right|_p = \frac{L}{RT^2}} \qquad (2\text{–}107)$$

4. For general systems, K can always be defined by (2–106), but, since it will usually depend on the $c_{i\alpha}$, this observation would be of little value without further information. For this, the phenomenological theory requires an additional general principle:

The Third Law of Thermodynamics

The third law† has been deferred to this point since it is still subject to some controversy, though there is little doubt of its main consequences. (The difficulty lies in obtaining a proper phenomenological, "macroscopic" statement.) It will not be used after (2–114) without explicit mention.

Note also that the formulation given below avoids the semi-permeable membrane arguments used above to evaluate entropies of mixing.

---

* In chemical literature, this correction is often made by replacing c_i by (a_ic_i) in (2–103); the a_i are called "activity coefficients" and a_ic_i, the "activities". (When a_ic_i refers to a gas, it is sometimes called the "fugacity," f_i.)

† Due mainly to W. Nernst. Sometimes called the Nernst heat "theorem", but it is a law or hypothesis to be tested against experiment like all physical "laws".

STATEMENT: At $T = 0$, the entropy of a (one-phase) mixture of pure* substances may be taken as†

$$S_{T=0} = -R \sum_i N_i \ln c_i \tag{2–108}$$

(On the basis of molecular statistical theory, (2–108) states that a system of indistinguishable particles always has a single (non-degenerate) ground state.)

In particular, for any system, (2–11) and (2–108), imply

$$S = \int_0^T \left(\frac{C_{pf}}{T}\right)_{p,f} \mathrm{d}T - R \sum_i \sum_\alpha N_{i\alpha} \ln c_{i\alpha} \tag{2–109}$$

(the subscripts indicate that the integration is to be carried out at constant p and f's). Insert (2–109) into (2–90) and use (2–38) and (2–89) to find:

$$\boxed{\begin{aligned} \ln K &\equiv \sum_i \sum_\alpha \nu_{i\alpha} \ln c_{i\alpha} \\ &= \int_0^T \left(\frac{\partial L}{\partial T}\right)_{p,f} \frac{\mathrm{d}T}{RT} - \frac{L}{RT} \\ &= \int_0^T \left(\frac{L - L_0}{RT^2}\right)_{p,f} \mathrm{d}T - \frac{L_0}{RT} \end{aligned}} \tag{2–110}$$

where L_0 is the heat of reaction at $T = 0$ (that is, the molecular binding energy per $\nu_{i\alpha}$ moles). K depends on $c_{i\alpha}$ as well as T, p, f_l and the nature of the system, but (2–110) gives an explicit expression for it. By (2–110) and (2–41),

$$\boxed{\left.\frac{\partial \ln K}{\partial T}\right|_{p,f,N} = \frac{L}{RT^2}\,; \quad \left.\frac{\partial \ln K}{\partial p}\right|_{T,f,N} = -\frac{\Delta v}{RT}} \tag{2–111}$$

Other consequences of the third law:

Since (2–108) states that $S \neq -\infty$ at $T = 0$, the integral in (2–109) must converge, and similarly for an integral at constant volume; hence,

$$C_{p,f} = 0 = C_{V,R} \quad \text{at} \quad T = 0 \tag{2–112}$$

Moreover (from (2–26)) with f_k, N_j constant

$$\left.\frac{\partial V}{\partial T}\right|_p = -\left.\frac{\partial S}{\partial p}\right|_T = -\int_0^T \frac{\partial^2 S}{\partial T\,\partial p}\,dT = \int_0^T \left.\frac{\partial^2 V}{\partial T^2}\right|_p dT = \left.\frac{\partial V}{\partial T}\right|_p\Big|_0^T$$

and hence

$$\left.\frac{\partial V}{\partial T}\right|_{p,f,N} = 0 \quad \text{at} \quad T = 0 \tag{2–113}$$

* Strictly, different isotopes, crystal orientations, nuclear spins, etc., should all be considered different "pure substances", but in practice this is done only in special studies since the additional entropy of mixing cancels out in almost all processes.

† That is, the law does not remove the arbitrariness in the original definition of S; it states a principle for obtaining a universally consistent assignment of the arbitrary constants for various systems. The law does implicitly assert that S remains finite as T approaches zero.

Similarly,

$$\left.\frac{\partial p}{\partial T}\right|_{V,R,N} = 0 \quad \text{at} \quad T = 0 \tag{2–114}$$

and, in fact, all temperature coefficients vanish* at $T = 0$. In particular, ideal gas equations must fail at sufficiently low temperatures. All these results are borne out both by experiment and by modern molecular-statistical theories.

Examples of Equilibria

1. **Stereoisomers** ("mirror image" molecules, macroscopically detectable by optical rotation): If the heat of reaction, L, is identically zero, then according to (2–110) (ultimately, the third law),

$$\sum \nu_i \ln c_i = 0$$

Thus (since all $\nu_i = \pm 1$), the thermodynamically stable state contains all stereo modifications in equal amounts (is optically inactive).

2. **Ionization (Saha equation).** For the gas-phase reaction, $A \rightleftharpoons A^+ + e^-$, if (2–54) is substituted in (2–95) and (2–96), the result may be written,

$$\frac{\alpha^2}{1-\alpha^2} = \frac{(1\text{ atm})\, T^{3/2}}{\rho R/m}\, 10^{-[(L_0/4.57T)+6.48]} \tag{2–115}$$

where m is the atomic weight of the atom or ion, $\alpha = N_e/(N_A + N_{A^+}) = c_e/(1 - c_e)$ is the percentage ionization, and L_0 is the ionization potential in cal/mole (1 eV/molecule $= 23.06$ kilocal/mole). Note that the ionization becomes complete as $\rho \to 0$ for any fixed T, however low.

This might appear to violate Boltzmann's statistical distribution law: $N_i/N_j = \exp[(E_j - E_i)/kT]$ for any two *states* i, j. However, recall that $N(E_i)/N(E_j) = (g_i/g_j)(N_i/N_j)$ where g_k is the number of states with energy E_k. If g_i refers to dissociated states and g_j to non-dissociated states, then $g_i \doteqdot (g_j)^2$ and (see remarks after (6–28)) $g_j = \exp(S/k) = [\exp(S/R)]^{N_0}$ which is an exceedingly large number. Consequently, $N(E_i)/N(E_j)$ can be comparable to unity even though $kT \ll E_i - E_j \doteqdot L_0$. In essence, the "greater randomness" (entropy) of the dissociated state has a strong "attraction" for the system.

3. **Clausius–Clapeyron equation.** By (2–77) and (2–87), if two phases of a single substance are in equilibrium,

$$G_1/N_1 = g_1 = g_2 = G_2/N_2 \tag{2–116}$$

(lower case symbols denote quantities per mole). Differentiating†,

$$s_1 - s_2 = (v_1 - v_2)\frac{dp}{dT} \tag{2–117}$$

where the total derivative has meaning because (by the phase rule) T completely determines p (the vapor pressure, sublimation pressure, or pressure for a given melting-point—as the case may be). Since $T\Delta s = L$, the "latent heat" (per mole) for the phase-change in question,

$$\boxed{\frac{dp}{dT} = \frac{L}{T(v_1 - v_2)}} \tag{2–118}$$

---

* Hence, the condition $T = 0$ cannot be attained by any finite experimental procedure.

† Assuming either that other external forces, f_i, have no effect on the substance or else that they are held constant throughout.

This relation may also be used to determine the thermodynamic temperature scale, T, from empirical measurements $[T\,\mathrm{d}p/\mathrm{d}T = (\mathrm{d}p/\mathrm{d}\theta)\,\mathrm{d}\theta/\mathrm{d}(\ln T)]$. Note also that $p(v_1 - v_2)/L$, the fraction of the latent heat used for external work, may also be evaluated from experiment by using (2–118); for most substances under ordinary conditions, this is small.

By differentiating $L = T(s_1 - s_2)$ [with $p \equiv p(T)$] and using the above, we obtain,

$$\frac{\mathrm{d}L}{\mathrm{d}T} = c_{p1} - c_{p2} + \frac{L}{T} - \frac{L}{v_1 - v_2}\left[\left.\frac{\partial v_1}{\partial T}\right|_p - \left.\frac{\partial v_2}{\partial T}\right|_p\right] \tag{2–119}$$

for the variation of L along the change-of-phase curve.

If one of the phases is a vapor of low density, then approximately, $v_2 \ll v_1 = RT/pm$, and

$$\frac{\mathrm{d}\ln p}{\mathrm{d}T} \doteqdot \frac{mL}{RT^2} \tag{2–120}$$

and if it is further assumed* that $L = L_0 + aT$, then

$$\ln p \doteqdot C - \frac{mL_0}{RT} + B\ln T \tag{2–121}$$

Effect of surface curvature: In (2–116), the pressures on the liquid and vapor are assumed equal. If the interface has a radius of curvature, r, the pressure on the liquid is greater by $2\beta/r$ where β is the surface tension. Thus, $g = g(p + 2\beta/r) \doteqdot g(p) + v(2\beta/r)$. The final result for vapor pressures is

$$\ln(p/p_\infty) = \frac{2\beta m}{r\rho_l RT}$$

where ρ_l is the density of the liquid and m the molecular weight. Note that large droplets will always tend to grow at the expense of small ones.

4. **Second-order phase transitions.** In (2-117) it may happen that $L = T\Delta s = 0$; empirically it is found that in such cases, $v_1 = v_2$ as well.† Thus (totally) differentiating: $T\,\mathrm{d}s_1 = T\,\mathrm{d}s_2$ and $\mathrm{d}v_1 = \mathrm{d}v_2$. Using (2–32) and (2–39),

$$\frac{\mathrm{d}p}{\mathrm{d}T} = \frac{c_{p1} - c_{p2}}{Tv(\alpha_1 - \alpha_2)} = \frac{\alpha_1 - \alpha_2}{K_1 - K_2} \tag{2–122}$$

where $v = v_1 = v_2$. (Ehrenfest's equations.)

5. **Lowering of freezing point.** Consider a dilute solution in equilibrium with a *solid phase of pure solvent*,‡ and consider a freezing "reaction" whereby liquid solvent is converted to solid. If $c_0 = 1 - \sum c_i$ is the mole fraction of solvent in the liquid, then by (2–106), $c_0/c_{\text{solid}} = c_0 = K$ and by (2–107),

$$\left.\frac{\partial T}{\partial(\sum c_i)}\right|_p = -\frac{RT^2}{c_0|L|} \doteqdot -\frac{RT^2}{|L|} \tag{2–123}$$

where L is the heat of fusion (>0) of pure solvent.

---

* A very rough "rule of thumb" is $L_0 \doteqdot 10\,RT_b$ for vaporization, where T_b is the boiling point at 1 atmosphere. (Trouton's rule.)

† Note that s_i and v_i are the two partial derivatives of $g_i(T, p)$.

‡ If the solutes freeze out in the solid phase also, the result (2–123) does not hold; the freezing point may even rise with increasing concentration.

The right side of (2–123) involves only properties of the pure solvent. The impurity mole-fraction, $\sum_i c_i$, and consequently the *molecular weight* of an "impurity" (when in the solvent*) may therefore by determined by freezing-point measurements, even when the chemical nature of the "impurity" is unknown. Similarly (2–124) and (2–125) below may be used for the same purpose; in all cases it is necessary to verify that the unknown does not enter one phase.

6. **Elevation of boiling point.** Similarly, *provided* the solutes do not enter the vapor phase,

$$\left.\frac{\partial T}{\partial(\sum c_i)}\right|_p = \frac{RT^2}{c_0\,|L|} \doteq \frac{RT^2}{|L|} \tag{2–124}$$

where L is now the heat of vaporization (>0) of the pure solvent.

7. **Osmotic pressure.** Two liquid phases, separated by a semi-permeable membrane, must have different pressures (for there must be the same number of solvent atoms per unit volume on both sides of the membrane if the latter does not affect their motions, whereas solutes occur only on one side). Denote the "solvent" (it need not be chemically pure) by subscript, o. Then on the "pure solvent" side,

$$\mu_o = \frac{\partial G}{\partial N_o} = \frac{G_o}{N_o} = g_o(p)$$

and on the (dilute) "solution" side, using (2–105) and denoting the osmotic (excess) pressure by Π,

$$\mu_o = \frac{\partial G}{\partial N_o'} = g_o(p+\Pi) + RT\ln c_o = g_o(p+\Pi) + RT\ln(1-\sum c_i)$$

where $\sum c_i$ is the total mole-fraction of substances unable to pass the membrane. By (2–77),

$$RT\ln(1-\sum c_i) = g_o(p) - g_o(p+\Pi)$$

or, approximately,

$$RT\sum c_i \doteq \Pi\left.\frac{\partial g_o}{\partial p}\right|_T = \Pi\frac{V_o}{N_o}$$

$$\Pi \doteq \frac{RT}{V}\sum_1^n N_i \tag{2–125}$$

where the sum extends only over substances unable to pass the membrane (van't Hoff equation). [This relation is often used for molecular weight determination in biology since it is easy to find membranes (e.g. cellophane) which will not pass very large molecules, and the substances need not be subject to extreme temperatures or pressures.] Note the analogy between (2–125) and the ideal gas equation.

D. IRREVERSIBLE (OFF-EQUILIBRIUM) THERMODYNAMICS

This is a macroscopic formalism which deals with (quasi-steady but) *non*-equilibrium situations. (Examples: steady gas diffusion, thermal or electrical conduction, thermo-electric effects and various cross-coupling phenomena between these.)

* Thus electrolytes (NaCl, etc.) dissociate in H_2O and hence lower its freezing point by twice the "expected" amount (at infinite dilution); electrical effects from electrolytes further modify (2–123) at moderate concentrations; see (6–149) ff.

Although originally developed from statistical models, the theory can be cast in the following phenomenological form.

The formalism applies only when the phenomena can be described by *linear* relations ("small deviations from equilibrium"):

$$\boxed{J_i = \sum_k L_{ik} X_k} \tag{2–126}$$

where J_i are "currents" or "fluxes" (heat flow, mass flow, etc.) and the X_k are the "forces" which drive them (temperature gradients, etc.).

Entropy production is a central concept for setting up the analysis of any system. In accord with (2–16), an off-equilibrium situation is characterized by an entropy increase over and above the increase, (2–11), due to externally introduced heat. The difference between the two sides of (2–16), or its time derivative, is called the (internal) entropy production.

The main content of the formalism is expressed by the following postulates.

1. The steady state of an externally constrained system is characterized by minimum entropy production.

2. *Onsager's reciprocal relations.* If the fluxes and forces in (2–126) are so chosen that the entropy production is

$$\frac{dS_I}{dt} = \sum_i J_i X_i \geqslant 0 \tag{2–127}$$

then in (2–126)

$$L_{ik}(\mathbf{B}) = L_{ki}(-\mathbf{B}) \tag{2–128}$$

where $\mathbf{B}$ is any applied magnetic field.

Corollary: By the linearity of (2–126), if the fluxes and forces are instead so chosen that

$$f\frac{dS_I}{dt} = \sum_i J_i X_i \tag{2–129}$$

where f is any function independent of $\mathbf{B}$ and the J_i and X_j, then (although the L_{ik} are altered) equation (2–128) remains valid.

Corollary: By (2–126) and (2–127), L_{ik} is *positive definite*:

$$\sum_{ik} L_{ik} X_i X_k \geqslant 0 \tag{2–130}$$

for all values of X_i; in particular,

$$L_{ii} L_{kk} \geqslant L_{ik} L_{ki} \tag{2–131}$$

3. In isotropic media, those cross-coefficients, L_{ik}, vanish if they would otherwise connect forces to fluxes of different tensor type; that is, scalar to vector, tensor to vector, etc. (Curie's principle; a consequence of the independence of physical effects and the choice of coordinates).

(Example: a chemical reaction rate cannot be coupled to a heat flux.)

4. Gibbs' relation is assumed to remain valid in local regions:

$$T\,dS = dU + p\,dV + \Sigma f_i\,dR_i - \Sigma \mu_i\,dN_i \tag{2–132}$$

where μ_i are chemical potentials; compare (2–74) and (2–86). (Note that (2–132) asserts that S does not depend, explicitly, on J_i or X_j.)

The main results of the theory are various explicit forms of (2–128) and (2–131). (Sometimes (2–126) is also regarded as a postulate—"for small deviations"—and its explicit forms are then regarded as results.)

Examples

1. *Thermoelectricity*

Applying (2–132), $T\,dS = dU + \phi\,dq$, to the two reservoirs and the capacitor (see figure):

$$dS = dS_{I} + dS_{II} + dS_{c} = -\frac{dU}{T} + \frac{dU}{T + \Delta T} + \frac{\Delta\phi\,dq}{T}$$

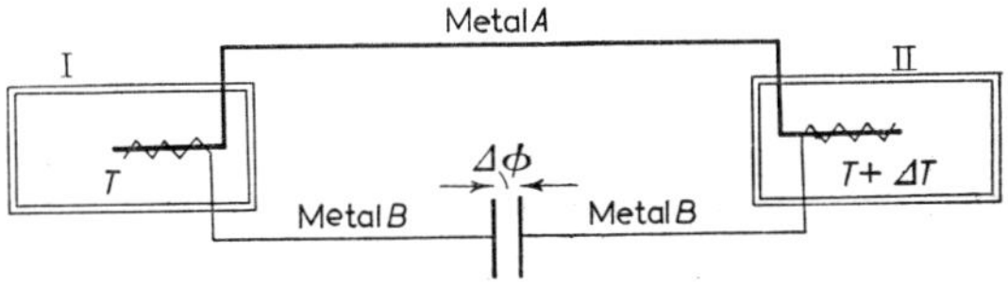

where $\Delta\phi$ is the voltage on the capacitor and dU is the energy carried from *I* to *II* when a charge, dq, flows. To first order ($dQ_{\text{ext}} = 0$),

$$\frac{dS}{dt} = -\frac{dU}{dt}\left(\frac{\Delta T}{T^2}\right) + \frac{dq}{dt}\left(\frac{\Delta\phi}{T}\right)$$

If the currents are taken as

$$J = dU/dt; \qquad I = dq/dt$$

then the forces may be taken to be

$$X_J = -\Delta T/T^2; \qquad X_I = \Delta\phi/T$$

The linear relations (2–126) then read

$$I = L_{11}(\Delta\phi/T) - L_{12}(\Delta T/T^2)$$
$$J = L_{21}(\Delta\phi/T) - L_{22}(\Delta T/T^2) \qquad (2\text{–}133)$$

where the coefficients have the interpretations:

for $I = 0$:

thermoelectric power, $$\epsilon = \frac{\Delta\phi}{\Delta T} = \frac{L_{12}}{TL_{11}}$$

for $\Delta T = 0$:

Peltier heat, $$\Pi = \frac{dU}{dq} = \frac{J}{I} = \frac{L_{21}}{L_{11}}$$

and (2–128) then asserts,

$$\frac{d\phi}{dT} = \epsilon = \frac{\Pi}{T} \qquad (2\text{–}134)$$

From conservation of energy, if σ_A, σ_B are the Thomson heats ($\sigma_A\,dT$ = heat absorbed when a unit charge passes from T to $T + dT$ in metal A),

$$-d\Pi + (\sigma_B - \sigma_A)dT = -d\phi \qquad (2\text{–}135)$$

Combining (2–134) and (2-135),

$$\sigma_B - \sigma_A = T\frac{d^2\phi}{dT^2} = \frac{d\Pi}{dT} - \frac{\Pi}{T} \qquad (2\text{–}136)$$

2. *Electrical Conduction*

In anisotropic media, $\mathbf{J} = \sigma \cdot \mathbf{E}$ where σ is a conductivity tensor. Since the internal heat production is $\mathbf{J} \cdot \mathbf{E} = T\, \mathrm{d}S$, (2–128) therefore asserts that the conductivity tensor in unmagnetized media is *symmetric* (despite crystal anisotropies!), while in general

$$\sigma_{ij}(\mathbf{B}) = \sigma_{ji}(-\mathbf{B}) \tag{2–137}$$

(as in the ionosphere).

3. *Heat Conduction*

Energy conservation states*:

$$\rho \frac{\mathrm{d}u}{\mathrm{d}t} = -\nabla \cdot \mathbf{Q} \tag{2–138}$$

where u is the internal energy per unit mass and $\mathbf{Q}$ is the heat flux. From $\mathrm{d}u = T\, \mathrm{d}s$ (neglecting volume expansion),

$$\rho \frac{\mathrm{d}s}{\mathrm{d}t} = -\frac{1}{T} \nabla \cdot \mathbf{Q} = -\nabla \cdot (\mathbf{Q}/T) + \mathbf{Q} \cdot \nabla(1/T)$$

Here, the first term is merely an entropy change due to divergence or convergence of the "entropy current," $\mathbf{Q}/T$, and does not represent internal *production*, which is given by the last term alone. If (2–126) is regarded as a postulate, we conclude

$$\mathbf{Q} = \mathfrak{L} \cdot \nabla(1/T) = -\mathfrak{K} \cdot \nabla T$$

where, by (2–128), the heat conductivity tensor, $\mathfrak{K}$, is *symmetric*, despite any crystal anisotropy (as is found experimentally).

4. *Galvanomagnetic Effects*

Within a metal subject to electrical and/or thermal gradients, (2–138) expresses conservation of energy and

$$\rho \frac{\mathrm{d}M}{\mathrm{d}t} = -\nabla \cdot (\mathbf{J}/e) \tag{2–139}$$

expresses conservation of electrons (where M is the mass of conduction electrons per unit mass of metal). By (2–132), $T\, \mathrm{d}s = \mathrm{d}u - \mu\, \mathrm{d}M$ (neglecting volume expansion; μ is the chemical potential of electrons per unit mass, effectively $e\phi$ in this case). By (2–138) and (2–139),

$$\rho \frac{\mathrm{d}s}{\mathrm{d}t} = -\nabla \cdot \left(\frac{\mathbf{Q}}{T} - \frac{\phi \mathbf{J}}{T}\right) + \mathbf{Q} \cdot \nabla\left(\frac{1}{T}\right) - \mathbf{J} \cdot \nabla\left(\frac{\phi}{T}\right) \tag{2–140}$$

It is convenient to introduce the entropy flux (total "heat" flux divided by T),

$$\Sigma = (\mathbf{Q} - \phi \mathbf{J})/T$$

in terms of which (2–140) reads,

$$\rho \frac{\mathrm{d}s}{\mathrm{d}t} = -\nabla \cdot \Sigma + \frac{1}{T}[-\Sigma \cdot \nabla T - \mathbf{J} \cdot \nabla \phi] \tag{2–141}$$

Thus the "forces" may (see (2–129)) be taken as

$$\mathbf{X}_\Sigma = -\nabla T \quad ; \quad \mathbf{X}_J = -\nabla \phi \tag{2–142}$$

* In (2–138) and frequently below, $\mathrm{d}/\mathrm{d}t$ is a "co-moving" derivative (see (1–57)); if the medium is not moving, $\mathrm{d}/\mathrm{d}t = \partial/\partial t$.

If a *magnetic field*, **B**, *is present*, it establishes a preferred direction and, even considering only components transverse to **B**, we must use the most general form of (2–126). Isotropy of the metal, however, reduces the matrix to the following form.

$$\left\| \begin{matrix} J_x \\ \Sigma_x \\ J_y \\ \Sigma_y \end{matrix} \right\| = \left\| \begin{array}{cc|cc} L_{11} & L_{12} & L_{13} & L_{14} \\ L_{21} & L_{22} & L_{23} & L_{24} \\ \hline -L_{13} & -L_{14} & L_{11} & L_{12} \\ -L_{23} & -L_{24} & L_{21} & L_{22} \end{array} \right\| \times \left\| \begin{matrix} -\dfrac{\partial\phi}{\partial x} \\ -\dfrac{\partial T}{\partial x} \\ -\dfrac{\partial\phi}{\partial y} \\ -\dfrac{\partial T}{\partial y} \end{matrix} \right\| \quad \text{(2–143}$$

where, moreover, L_{11}, L_{12}, L_{21} and L_{22} are even functions of **B** and the remaining L's are odd functions of **B** (which has been taken along the z-axis).

Then Onsager's relations (2–128) assert

$$L_{12} = L_{21}; \qquad L_{14} = L_{23} \tag{2–144}$$

Equations (2–143) predict the following effects:

Nernst effect:

$$-\frac{\partial\phi}{\partial y} = \nu B \frac{\partial T}{\partial x} \quad \text{when} \quad \mathbf{J} = 0, \frac{\partial T}{\partial y} = 0 \tag{2–145}$$

Ettingshausen effect:

$$\frac{\partial T}{\partial y} = \epsilon B J_x \quad \text{when} \quad J_y = 0 = \Sigma_y, \frac{\partial T}{\partial x} = 0 \tag{2–146}$$

Hall effect:

$$\frac{\partial\phi}{\partial y} = -RBJ_x \quad \text{when} \quad \nabla T = 0, J_y = 0 \tag{2–147}$$

Righi–Leduc effect:

$$\frac{\partial T}{\partial y} = \alpha B \Sigma_x \quad \text{when} \quad \mathbf{J} = 0, \Sigma_y = 0 \tag{2–148}$$

"Isothermal" heat conduction:

$$T\Sigma_x = -\lambda_i \frac{\partial T}{\partial x} \quad \text{when} \quad \mathbf{J} = 0, \frac{\partial T}{\partial y} = 0 \tag{2–149}$$

"Adiabatic" heat conduction:

$$T\Sigma_x = -\lambda_a \frac{\partial T}{\partial x} \quad \text{when} \quad \mathbf{J} = 0, \Sigma_y = 0 \tag{2–150}$$

Isothermal electrical conduction:

$$J_x = -\sigma_i \frac{\partial\phi}{\partial x} \quad \text{when} \quad \nabla T = 0, \Sigma_y = 0 \tag{2–151}$$

Upon evaluating the coefficients defined in (2–145)–(2–151) in terms of the L_{ij} of (2–143), it is found that the Onsager relations (2–144) imply,

$$T\nu = \epsilon\lambda_i \tag{2–152}$$

(Bridgman's relation) and another relation which is too complicated to be of practical use in its general form.

5. *Thermal Diffusion Effects*

For a mixture of two non-viscous liquids or gases, the equation (1–72) must be altered to allow for local changes in composition:

$$\frac{-1}{\rho}\nabla\cdot\mathbf{Q} = \frac{du}{dt} + p\frac{d(1/\rho)}{dt} = T\frac{ds}{dt} + \mu_1\frac{dw_1}{dt} + \mu_2\frac{dw_2}{dt} \tag{2–153}$$

where $w_k = \rho_k/\rho$ are the local concentrations (by weight) and μ_k are the chemical potentials (per unit mass* as are also u, s). The co-moving derivative is taken with respect to the mean mixture velocity:

$$\frac{d}{dt} = \frac{\partial}{\partial t} + \mathbf{v}\cdot\nabla \qquad \text{where} \qquad \mathbf{v} = \sum_k \rho_k\mathbf{v}_k/\rho = \sum_k w_k\mathbf{v}_k \tag{2–154}$$

If the component fluids do not react chemically, the mass of each, as well as the total mass, is conserved:

$$\frac{\partial\rho_k}{\partial t} = -\nabla\cdot(\rho_k\mathbf{v}_k); \qquad \frac{\partial\rho}{\partial t} = -\nabla\cdot(\rho\mathbf{v}) \tag{2–155}$$

From these,

$$\rho\frac{dw_k}{dt} = -\nabla\cdot\mathbf{J}_k \tag{2–156}$$

where

$$\mathbf{J}_k = \rho_k(\mathbf{v}_k - \mathbf{v}); \qquad \mathbf{J}_1 + \mathbf{J}_2 = 0 \tag{2–157}$$

are the fluxes of the component fluids relative to the "local center of mass" (or "barycentric") motion of the fluid. From (2–153), (2–156) and (2–157),

$$\rho\frac{ds}{dt} = -\nabla\cdot\left(\frac{\mathbf{Q} - \sum_k \mu_k\mathbf{J}_k}{T}\right) + \frac{1}{T}\left[-\frac{\nabla T}{T}\cdot\mathbf{Q} - \mathbf{J}_1\cdot\left(T\nabla\frac{\mu_1-\mu_2}{T}\right)\right] \tag{2–158}$$

Since the first term represents entropy changes due only to convection, (see (2–126), (2–129)),

$$\left.\begin{aligned} -\mathbf{Q} &= L_{11}\frac{\nabla T}{T} + L_{12}\left(T\nabla\frac{\mu_1-\mu_2}{T}\right) \\ -\mathbf{J}_1 &= L_{21}\frac{\nabla T}{T} + L_{22}\left(T\nabla\frac{\mu_1-\mu_2}{T}\right) = \mathbf{J}_2 \end{aligned}\right\} \tag{2–159}$$

(a) *Ordinary diffusion:* With $\nabla T = 0$,

$$-\mathbf{J}_1 = L_{22}\nabla(\mu_1-\mu_2) = L_{22}\left[\left.\frac{\partial(\mu_1-\mu_2)}{\partial p}\right|_{w,T}\nabla p + \left.\frac{\partial(\mu_1-\mu_2)}{\partial w_1}\right|_{T,p}\nabla w_1\right]$$

* To convert from more usual relations, it is convenient to use (2–84) in the form, $G/M = u + (p/\rho) - Ts = \sum_k \mu_k\rho_k/\rho = \sum_k \mu_k w_k$, recalling that M is variable.

(recalling $w_2 = 1 - w_1$ is not independent). Then using $w_1\,d\mu_1 + w_2\,d\mu_2 = dg = 0$ at constant T, p

$$\mathbf{J}_2 = -\mathbf{J}_1 = L_{22}\left[\left(\frac{1}{\rho_1} - \frac{1}{\rho_2}\right)\nabla p + \left.\frac{\partial\mu_1}{\partial w_1}\right|_{T,p}\frac{\nabla w_1}{w_2}\right] \tag{2–160}$$

Thus if $\nabla p = 0$ (mechanical equilibrium, $d\mathbf{v}/dt = 0$)

$$\mathbf{J}_2 = -\mathbf{J}_1 = \rho D\nabla w_1 \qquad \text{where} \qquad D = \frac{L_{22}}{\rho w_2}\left.\frac{\partial\mu_1}{\partial w_1}\right|_{T,p} \tag{2–161}$$

In any case, directly from (2–159) with $\nabla T = 0$,

$$\mathbf{Q} = \frac{L_{12}}{L_{22}}\mathbf{J}_1 = q^*\mathbf{J}_1 \tag{2–162}$$

where q^* is called the "heat of transfer."

(b) *Thermal diffusion* (*Soret effect*): If the mixture is enclosed in a vessel with an externally maintained thermal gradient, the final steady state is characterized by $\mathbf{J}_1 = 0 = \mathbf{J}_2$ and $\nabla p = 0$; from (2–159), using the Onsager relation, $L_{12} = L_{21} = q^* L_{22}$, we find

$$q^*\frac{\nabla T}{T} = \frac{\mu_1 - \mu_2}{T}\nabla T - \left[\left(\frac{1}{\rho_1} - \frac{1}{\rho_2}\right)\nabla p - (s_1 - s_2)\nabla T - \left.\frac{\partial(\mu_1 - \mu_2)}{\partial w_1}\right|_{T,p}\nabla w_1\right]$$

or, if $h_k = g_k + Ts_k = \mu_k + Ts_k$ are the enthalpies per unit mass of the components (*in* the mixture), the final result is (again using $w_1 d\mu_1 + w_2 d\mu_2 = 0$ under constant T and p):

$$\nabla w_1 = (\nabla T)\,\frac{w_2(q^* - h_1 + h_2)}{T(\partial\mu_1/\partial w_1)_{T,p}} \tag{2–163}$$

which gives the mass-separation due to the thermal gradient.

(c) *Dufour effect:* By (2–159), a concentration gradient sets up an energy current, $\mathbf{Q}$, and thus if two fluids, originally at the same temperature, are allowed to mix, a temperature gradient is set up (the inverse of the Soret effect). The details involve substituting (2–159) back into (2–153) and (2–155) and solving a dynamic problem. (The effect amounts to a few degrees centigrade for hydrogen and nitrogen, for example.)

CHAPTER 3

ELECTROMAGNETIC THEORY

A Note on Units

We use *Gaussian Units* throughout this book. These are equivalent to electrostatic units for all quantities except **H**, **B**, **M** for which magnetostatic units are used. Factors of 4π then occur, as usual, in the source terms of the differential equations and the factor c is always associated with t (time). Also E and B have the same numerical value in a radiation wave in vacuum.

To convert to practical units,* convenient relations are:

$$300 \text{ volts} = 1 \text{ statvolt}$$

$$\frac{10}{c} \text{ amps} = 1 \text{ statamp} \qquad \left(\frac{\mathbf{J}}{c} = \frac{\mathbf{J}_{\text{amp}}}{10}\right)$$

$$1 \text{ gauss} = 1 \text{ gauss}$$

$$\frac{10}{9}\,\mu\mu\text{fd} = 1 \text{ cm}$$

$$1 \text{ ohm cm} = \frac{10}{9}\,\mu\mu\text{sec}$$

MKS Units (rationalized) are another very commonly used system. To convert an equation from *MKS to Gaussian* units:

1. Replace $(\mathbf{D}, \mathbf{H}, \epsilon, 1/\mu)$ by $\left(\frac{\mathbf{D}}{4\pi}, \frac{\mathbf{H}}{4\pi}, \frac{\epsilon}{4\pi}, \frac{1}{4\pi\mu}\right)$

2. Replace t by ct and hence also $(\mathbf{J}, \mathbf{S}, \sigma, \omega, \mathbf{v})$ by $(\mathbf{J}/c, \mathbf{S}/c, \sigma/c, \omega/c, \mathbf{v}/c)$ (Note that **E**, **B** are unaffected as are **P**, **M**; only the "anthropomorphic" fields **D**, **H** and the constants relating them to **E**, **B** are changed. The locations of factors, c, are readily deduced from the association with time, t.) All other quantities (such as **F**, U, ρ, Q, ϕ, **A**) are not to be changed.

Maxwell's Equations (The Postulates of Electromagnetic Theory)

From a *microscopic* point of view, whereby for example a dielectric in a non-uniform electric field "can be seen" to have non-zero volume-charge-density and the changing polarization as that field changes is "seen" to involve motions of charge and hence a current—from such an atomic viewpoint, Maxwell's equations involve the true (actual, physical) electric charge density, ρ_t, and net charge-flux (current density), $\mathbf{J}_t$.

$$\left.\begin{aligned} \nabla \times \mathbf{B} &= \frac{4\pi}{c}\mathbf{J}_t + \frac{1}{c}\frac{\partial \mathbf{E}}{\partial t} \\ \nabla \times \mathbf{E} &= -\frac{1}{c}\frac{\partial \mathbf{B}}{\partial t} \end{aligned}\right\} \tag{3–1}$$

* Volts, amperes, ohms, cm, gram, sec.

with the initial conditions:*

$$\nabla \cdot \mathbf{B} = 0; \qquad \nabla \cdot \mathbf{E} = 4\pi\rho_t \tag{3-2}$$

Forces

The electric and magnetic fields may be interpreted as forces through the laws (which are, effectively, the definitions of **E** and **B**)†:

For a point-charge, e,

$$\mathbf{F} = e\mathbf{E} + e\frac{\mathbf{v}}{c} \times \mathbf{B} \tag{3-3}$$

Hence the force per unit volume for a charge density, ρ_t, and (net) current density, $\mathbf{J}_t$ is

$$\mathbf{F}/\mathrm{Vol} = \rho_t\mathbf{E} + \frac{\mathbf{J}_t}{c} \times \mathbf{B} \tag{3-4}$$

or:

$$4\pi\mathbf{F}/\mathrm{Vol} = \mathbf{E}(\nabla \cdot \mathbf{E}) - \mathbf{B} \times (\nabla \times \mathbf{B}) - \frac{1}{c}\frac{\partial \mathbf{E}}{\partial t} \times \mathbf{B} \tag{3-5}$$

Using the identity $\mathbf{A} \times (\nabla \times \mathbf{A}) = \nabla(\frac{1}{2}A^2) - (\mathbf{A} \cdot \nabla)\mathbf{A}$, one obtains as an alternative form for (3–5):

$$\mathbf{F}/\mathrm{Vol} = \frac{-1}{4\pi c}\frac{\partial}{\partial t}(\mathbf{E} \times \mathbf{B}) + \nabla \cdot \mathfrak{T} \tag{3-6}$$

where the tensor,

$$\mathfrak{T} = -\frac{E^2 + B^2}{8\pi}\mathbf{1} + \frac{\mathbf{EE} + \mathbf{BB}}{4\pi} \tag{3-7}$$

is the Maxwell electromagnetic stress-tensor. On the basis of (3–6), the vector $\mathbf{G} = \mathbf{E} \times \mathbf{B}/4\pi c = \mathbf{S}/c^2$ is often called the (electromagnetic) momentum-density vector.‡

Radiation Pressure: For a stationary electromagnetic field (wherein the first term of (3–6) averages to zero), $\mathbf{F}/\mathrm{Vol} = \nabla \cdot \mathfrak{T}$ and the field exhibits some properties of a fluid (compare (1–65)). The force on a surface (normal vector, $\hat{n}$) immersed in the field is $-\hat{n} \cdot \mathfrak{T}$ per unit area, and if this is independent of orientation ($\hat{n}$), it is proper to speak of an isotropic "radiation pressure" (see (1–63)):

$$p = -\tfrac{1}{3}\sum_i \mathfrak{T}_{ii} = \frac{E^2 + B^2}{24\pi} = \tfrac{1}{3}U \tag{3-8}$$

(where U is the energy density of the field; compare (3–28) below).

For incident plane waves, $-\hat{n} \cdot \mathfrak{T}$ is not independent of orientation, but the force can be expressed as an "effective pressure" which depends on the angle of incidence, θ, and the reflectivity, R:

$$\text{“}p\text{”} = \frac{1 + R}{4\pi}E_{\mathrm{inc}}B_{\mathrm{inc}}\cos^2\theta = \frac{1 + R}{c}|\mathbf{S}_{\mathrm{inc}}|\cos^2\theta \tag{3-9}$$

This particular result is much more easily derived from the quantum picture or from momentum (**G**) considerations. If $\theta \neq 0$ there is also a shearing force.

---

* From (3–1) alone plus the continuity equation, $\frac{\partial\rho_t}{\partial t} + \nabla \cdot \mathbf{J}_t = 0$ it follows that $\frac{\partial}{\partial t}(\nabla \cdot \mathbf{B}) = 0$ and $\frac{\partial}{\partial t}(\nabla \cdot \mathbf{E} - 4\pi\rho_t) = 0$.

† Formerly, **H** was often written for **B** in (3–3)–(3–5); only recently have experiments on neutrons traveling in magnetized iron shown unequivocally that **B** determines the force.

‡ It is difficult to avoid this concept of momentum "in transit," because of the finite propagation-time of electromagnetic fields (forces). The relation, $\mathbf{G} = \mathbf{S}/c^2$ is also in accord with the quantum picture of radiation.

Historical Origin of (3–1) and (3–2)

If the physical situation is "static" $\left(\frac{\partial}{\partial t} = 0\right)$, *then* the integral forms of (3–1) and (3–2) (compare (10–51)) are *Coulomb's law* and *Ampere's law*. Quite generally, the second part of (3–1) can be written (by Stokes' theorem) in the integral form

$$\oint_C \mathbf{E} \cdot \mathrm{d}\mathbf{s} = \frac{-1}{c} \frac{\mathrm{d}}{\mathrm{d}t} \oint\!\!\oint_S \mathbf{B} \cdot \mathrm{d}\mathbf{S} \tag{3–10}$$

which is *Faraday's law* of induction.* Finally, the term $\frac{1}{c} \frac{\partial \mathbf{E}}{\partial t}$ is necessary (as pointed out by Maxwell) to make the equations consistent with the indestructibility of charge, namely $\frac{\partial \rho_t}{\partial t} + \nabla \cdot \mathbf{J}_t = 0$.

The Tensor Nature of (E, B) (taken together)

Consider a point charge in motion in the laboratory. The (only physically observable quantity) force on it is given by (3–3). Now transform to *uniformly* moving coordinates, momentarily moving at the same velocity as the particle; its acceleration (namely $\mathbf{F}/m$) is unchanged and hence so is $\mathbf{F}$. But now $\mathbf{v} = 0$, and the only way (3–3) can remain true is for $\mathbf{E}$ and $\mathbf{B}$ to change—to "look different" from the moving system. In fact (for $v \ll c$)

$$\mathbf{E}' = \mathbf{E} + \frac{\mathbf{v}}{c} \times \mathbf{B}; \qquad \mathbf{B}' = \mathbf{B} - \frac{\mathbf{v}}{c} \times \mathbf{E} \tag{3–11}$$

Thus $\mathbf{E}$ and $\mathbf{B}$ are "vectors" (have "geometric reality") only for *space* coordinate changes; as soon as the coordinate system is moving, $\mathbf{E}$ and $\mathbf{B}$ become "mixed" together and only the *pair* of fields maintains some sort of physical reality.† Further discussion is given in Chapter 4, Relativity.

Macroscopic Equations

Note that no material constants (ϵ, μ, σ) have entered into (3–1) to (3–11)—as indeed they should not in a microscopic "true" picture. As a consequence, the form (3–1) is often of use for fundamental work when trying to work "behind" the macroscopic phenomena. Compare (3–87) ff.

However, an ammeter measures only macroscopic charge flows and not "displacement currents", and an electroscope is unable to detect charges which do not leave a dielectric. Hence for practical, macroscopic work, it is convenient to define two new field vectors, $\mathbf{D}$ and $\mathbf{H}$, in such a way as to convert ρ_t and $\mathbf{J}_t$ to their macroscopic counterparts. In this way, one can, for example, regard the charge density ρ and current density $\mathbf{J}$ as *always* zero inside a dielectric and a (d.c.) magnet can be regarded as having no (effective) d.c. currents flowing on its surface. These points of view are *conveniences* rather than truths. By introducing the "material constants", ϵ and μ, one can avoid having to take into account such basically atomic effects.

The introduction of ϵ and μ is really only a rather good approximation. Under extreme conditions this procedure may fail; that is, ϵ and μ may appear to depend

---

* Strictly, (3–10) follows from (3–1) only for a circuit, C, (wire) at rest; the fact that (3–10) also holds for a moving circuit ($v \ll c$) is an additional assertion; it is connected physically with the second term in (3–3). Compare footnote to (3–100).

† This also is the content of the statement that (3–10) holds for moving circuits.

on field strength or the rates-of-change of fields, etc. Finally, of course, there are substances where ϵ and μ must be replaced by tensors and even this is only a rather good approximation in the above sense.

Empirically, and not surprisingly, an electric field induces in a dielectric an array of dipoles. If **P** is the dipole moment per unit volume,* the charge and current densities due to the (bound) charges in the dielectric are

$$\rho_{\text{diel}} = -\nabla \cdot \mathbf{P}; \qquad \frac{1}{c}\,\mathbf{J}_{\text{diel}} = \frac{1}{c}\frac{\partial \mathbf{P}}{\partial t} \tag{3–12}$$

(**P** is called the "polarization".)
Similarly, a magnetized material is composed of tiny magnets (magnetic dipoles) which, in a given magnetic field partially aline to produce a net magnetic-dipole-moment per unit volume, **M**. There is no charge-density from this effect, but (see (3–1)) the currents must be (effectively)

$$\frac{1}{c}\,\mathbf{J}_{\text{mag}} = \nabla \times \mathbf{M} \tag{3–13}$$

(**M** is called the "magnetization".)
We therefore define

$$\left.\begin{aligned} \rho &= \rho_t + \nabla \cdot \mathbf{P} \\ \frac{1}{c}\,\mathbf{J} &= \frac{1}{c}\,\mathbf{J}_t - \frac{1}{c}\frac{\partial \mathbf{P}}{\partial t} - \nabla \times \mathbf{M} \end{aligned}\right\} \tag{3–14}$$

Note that the continuity equation holds for ρ, **J** as well as for ρ_t, $\mathbf{J}_t$. Note also that, while (3–4) involves ρ_t and $\mathbf{J}_t$, the forces can nevertheless be evaluated from (3–5) or (3–6) without explicitly re-introducing **P** or **M**.
If we then define

$$\left.\begin{aligned} \mathbf{D} &= \mathbf{E} + 4\pi\mathbf{P} \\ \mathbf{H} &= \mathbf{B} - 4\pi\mathbf{M} \end{aligned}\right\} \tag{3–15}$$

then it follows that (3–1) may be written,†

$$\left.\begin{aligned} \nabla \times \mathbf{H} &= \frac{4\pi}{c}\,\mathbf{J} + \frac{1}{c}\frac{\partial \mathbf{D}}{\partial t} \\ \nabla \times \mathbf{E} &= -\frac{1}{c}\frac{\partial \mathbf{B}}{\partial t} \end{aligned}\right\} \tag{3–16}$$

with the initial conditions,

$$\left.\begin{aligned} \nabla \cdot \mathbf{B} &= 0 \\ \nabla \cdot \mathbf{D} &= 4\pi\rho \end{aligned}\right\} \tag{3–17}$$

---

* That is, a small volume, dV, of the dielectric acts like a pair of charges $+q$ and $-q$ separated by a small distance $\boldsymbol{\delta}$ such that $q\boldsymbol{\delta} = \mathbf{P}\,dV$.

† Strictly speaking, the field vectors must also be averaged over regions of atomic extent when passing from (3–1) and (3–2) to (3–16) and (3–17). That is, the former hold on an atomic level, where the rapid variation of E etc., over regions of the atom, is kept in view. On the other hand (3–14) to (3–17) represent averages over such atomic variations (in both time and space) and contain only macroscopically observable quantities; indeed, **P, M, D, H**, can only be defined in a macroscopic sense and for wavelengths long compared to atomic dimensions.

The importance of this distinction arises when non-linear media are considered. Thus two solutions of (3–1) and (3–2) can always be added to give a third solution, but this is not true of (3–16) and (3–17) in all cases. Thus two sine waves can give rise, in some media, to sum, difference and harmonic frequencies as well.

These equations are now incomplete; one must also specify the dependence of **D** on **E** and of **H** on **B**. Also the dependence of **J** on the fields is required.

It turns out for most substances (except certain crystal dielectrics and certain ferrites, etc.) that **P** is parallel to and proportional to **E** and the same is true of **M** and **H**. Then we may write (for stationary media)

$$\mathbf{D} = \epsilon \mathbf{E}; \qquad \mathbf{H} = \frac{1}{\mu} \mathbf{B} \tag{3–18}$$

Where ϵ and μ are "constants" characteristic of the substance in question; as this constancy of ϵ and μ begins to break down, equation (3–18) can often be salvaged by allowing certain types of variation in ϵ and μ.

Since **J** involves only free charges now, it is almost solely dependent on **E** and (allowing for atomic scattering, etc.) the average motion is to good approximation parallel to and proportional to **E**,

$$\mathbf{J} = \sigma \mathbf{E} \tag{3–19}$$

Moving Media

The relations (3–18) and (3–19) hold for materials which are at rest with respect to the coordinate system to which the fields are referred. According to (3–11) such relations *cannot* remain valid if the media are moving. Arguments (which are more readily summarized in Chapter 4 on Relativity) based essentially on (3–11) lead to the general relationships,

$$\mathbf{J} = \rho \mathbf{v} + \frac{\sigma}{\sqrt{1 - (v/c)^2}} \left[\mathbf{E} + \frac{\mathbf{v}}{c} \times \mathbf{B} - \frac{\mathbf{v}}{c} \left(\frac{\mathbf{v}}{c} \cdot \mathbf{E} \right) \right] \tag{3–20}$$

$$\mathbf{D} = \frac{\epsilon - (1/\mu)}{1 - (v/c)^2} \left[\mathbf{E} + \frac{\mathbf{v}}{c} \times \mathbf{B} - \frac{\mathbf{v}}{c} \left(\frac{\mathbf{v}}{c} \cdot \mathbf{E} \right) \right] + \frac{1}{\mu} \mathbf{E} \tag{3–21}$$

$$\mathbf{H} = \frac{(1/\mu) - \epsilon}{1 - (v/c)^2} \left[\mathbf{B} - \frac{\mathbf{v}}{c} \times \mathbf{E} - \frac{\mathbf{v}}{c} \left(\frac{\mathbf{v}}{c} \cdot \mathbf{B} \right) \right] + \epsilon \mathbf{B} \tag{3–22}$$

where **v** is the local velocity of the medium in question, relative to the coordinates in which the fields are described. Usually, the second and higher powers of v/c can be neglected.

Boundary Conditions

At a "discontinuous" boundary, where ϵ, μ, σ suddenly change in value, (3–16) and (3–17) must be replaced by *corresponding* boundary conditions. These are derived by integrating (3–17) over a "pill-box" volume of negligible thickness, which straddles the boundary and by integrating (3–16) over a strip-shaped surface whose two long edges lie on either side of the boundary. The results are ($\hat{n}$ is a unit vector normal to the boundary and pointing into medium 1):

$$\left.\begin{aligned} &\hat{n} \times \mathbf{E}_1 = \hat{n} \times \mathbf{E}_2; \qquad &&\hat{n} \cdot \mathbf{B}_1 = \hat{n} \cdot \mathbf{B}_2 \\ &\hat{n} \cdot (\mathbf{D}_1 - \mathbf{D}_2) = 4\pi \rho_{\text{surf}}; \qquad &&\hat{n} \times (\mathbf{H}_1 - \mathbf{H}_2) = \frac{4\pi}{c} \mathbf{J}_{\text{surf}} \end{aligned}\right\} \tag{3–23}$$

where ρ_{surf} and $\mathbf{J}_{\text{surf}}$ are charge and current densities of charges *on* the surface. For media with finite σ, if **v** is the (local) velocity of material particles in the surface,

$$\mathbf{J}_{\text{surf}} = \mathbf{v} \rho_{\text{surf}} \qquad (\text{if } \sigma \neq \infty)$$

(Otherwise, **B** or **E** $= \infty$ at the surface as may be seen from (3–20).)

Poynting's Theorem; Energy of a Field

Directly from (3–16),

$$\mathbf{J}\cdot\mathbf{E}+\frac{1}{4\pi}\left(\mathbf{E}\cdot\frac{\partial\mathbf{D}}{\partial t}+\mathbf{H}\cdot\frac{\partial\mathbf{B}}{\partial t}\right)=\frac{-c}{4\pi}\nabla\cdot(\mathbf{E}\times\mathbf{H}) \tag{3–24}$$

Here

$$\mathbf{S}=\frac{c}{4\pi}\mathbf{E}\times\mathbf{H} \tag{3–25}$$

is called Poynting's vector. In integral form (3–24) gives for any volume V bounded by the surface A,

$$\oint\!\!\oint_A \mathbf{S}\cdot d\boldsymbol{\sigma}+\oint\!\!\oint\!\!\oint_V \mathbf{J}\cdot\mathbf{E}\,dV+\frac{\partial}{\partial t}\oint\!\!\oint\!\!\oint_V U\,dV=0 \tag{3–26}$$

where

$$U=\frac{1}{4\pi}\int^{t}\left[\mathbf{E}\cdot\frac{\partial\mathbf{D}}{\partial t}+\mathbf{H}\cdot\frac{\partial\mathbf{B}}{\partial t}\right]dt \tag{3–27}$$

If ϵ and μ are independent of time and also independent of frequency (compare (3–41)) then,

$$U=\frac{1}{8\pi}\{\epsilon|\mathbf{E}|^2+\mu|\mathbf{H}|^2\}=\frac{1}{8\pi}\{\mathbf{E}\cdot\mathbf{D}+\mathbf{B}\cdot\mathbf{H}\} \tag{3–28}$$

The term, $\mathbf{J}\cdot\mathbf{E}=\sigma|\mathbf{E}|^2$, represents heat generated by flow of (free charge) currents in conductors and the (integral) terms in U can be shown in many cases to represent the (rate of change of) work which must be done to establish the field **E**, **B** within V. Thus **S** *may* be interpreted as a flow of energy, its integral over the boundary surface giving the flow out of V. (But so could $\mathbf{S}+\nabla\times\mathbf{F}$ for *arbitrary* $\mathbf{F}(\mathbf{r},t)$.)

This interpretation is exceedingly useful but is not without occasional difficulties.* In particular, it is only the integral of U over large volumes which can be proved to represent stored energy and even this is difficult to justify except for static fields (very slowly established).

Homogeneous Media

[Note that the "microscopic" equations (3–1) and (3–2) can always be regained by setting $\epsilon\equiv 1\equiv\mu$ (and replacing ρ by ρ_t and (3–19) by $\mathbf{J}_t$). Thus in particular all the manipulations given below for homogeneous media apply directly also to the more fundamental equations (3–1) and (3–2).]

If ϵ and μ are independent of position† (and time) within the (not necessarily infinite) medium, then the six components of **E** and **B** can be replaced by four potentials:‡

---

* Compare a static point charge located at the center of a static magnet (dipole)—or a battery connected to a simple resistor.

† Note that σ may vary with position (though this is not a very important case).

‡ If $\partial\mathbf{A}/\partial t=0$, then note that $\phi(\mathbf{r}_1)-\phi(\mathbf{r}_2)$ represents the mechanical work done against the field when a unit charge is moved from $\mathbf{r}_2$ to $\mathbf{r}_1$.

Set:*

$$\nabla \times \mathbf{A} = \mathbf{B} \tag{3-29}$$

$$\nabla \phi + \frac{1}{c}\frac{\partial \mathbf{A}}{\partial t} = -\mathbf{E} \tag{3-30}$$

$$\nabla \cdot \mathbf{A} = -\frac{\epsilon\mu}{c}\frac{\partial \phi}{\partial t} \tag{3-31}$$

Then two of equations (3–16) and (3–17) are automatically satisfied and the others become,

$$\left.\begin{aligned} \nabla^2\phi - \frac{\epsilon\mu}{c^2}\frac{\partial^2\phi}{\partial t^2} &= -\frac{4\pi\rho}{\epsilon} \\ \nabla^2\mathbf{A} - \frac{\epsilon\mu}{c^2}\frac{\partial^2\mathbf{A}}{\partial t^2} &= -\frac{4\pi\mu\mathbf{J}}{c} \end{aligned}\right\} \tag{3-32}$$

Some general solutions of equations of this type are discussed in Chapter 15 on linear partial differential equations; see especially (15–47) to (15–55).

The equations (3–32) can be further reduced to a set involving a single vector **Z** (Hertz vector). By virtue of the continuity relation, $\partial\rho/\partial t + \nabla \cdot \mathbf{J} = 0$, if we define

$$\frac{\mu}{c}\frac{\partial \mathbf{Z}}{\partial t} = \mathbf{A}$$

(for harmonic time dependence, $\mathbf{A} = (i\omega\mu/c)\mathbf{Z}$ and there is little distinction) then

$$\boxed{\nabla^2\mathbf{Z} - \frac{\epsilon\mu}{c^2}\frac{\partial^2\mathbf{Z}}{\partial t^2} = -4\pi\mathbf{q} = -4\pi\int^t \mathbf{J}\,dt} \tag{3-33}$$

and it is sufficient to take $\epsilon\phi = -\nabla \cdot \mathbf{Z}$. The fields are then given directly in terms of **Z**;

$$\boxed{\begin{aligned} \mathbf{B} &= \frac{\mu}{c}\frac{\partial}{\partial t}\nabla \times \mathbf{Z} \\ \mathbf{E} &= \frac{1}{\epsilon}\nabla(\nabla \cdot \mathbf{Z}) - \frac{\mu}{c^2}\frac{\partial^2\mathbf{Z}}{\partial t^2} = \frac{1}{\epsilon}\nabla \times (\nabla \times \mathbf{Z}) - \frac{4\pi}{\epsilon}\mathbf{q} \end{aligned}} \tag{3-34}$$

The relations (3–33) and (3–34) are especially useful for calculating fields when *all* charges and currents are specified. [The fields generated by an arbitrarily moving, charged point-particle can in principle be obtained from these equations. However, it is simpler to obtain these by further transformations which are discussed in Chapter 4, equations (4–7), (4–15) and (4–22).]

If, however, $\mathbf{J} = \sigma\mathbf{E} + \mathbf{J}_d$ where $\mathbf{J}_d$ is some "driving current" (not expressible as $\sigma\mathbf{E}$) then (3–33) and (3–34) lose their usefulness. The following is then sometimes useful. Retain (3–29) and (3–30) but replace (3–31) by

$$\nabla \cdot \mathbf{A} = -\frac{\epsilon\mu}{c}\frac{\partial \phi}{\partial t} - \frac{4\pi\sigma\mu}{c}\phi \tag{3-35}$$

* The vector **A** is not fully defined by (3–29) alone; see (10–51).

Then again (3–16), (3–17) reduce to two equations, provided $\nabla\sigma = 0$,

$$\left.\begin{aligned}\nabla^2\phi - (4\pi\sigma\mu/c^2)\frac{\partial\phi}{\partial t} - \frac{\epsilon\mu}{c^2}\frac{\partial^2\phi}{\partial t^2} &= -\frac{4\pi\rho}{\epsilon}\\ \nabla^2\mathbf{A} - (4\pi\sigma\mu/c^2)\frac{\partial\mathbf{A}}{\partial t} - \frac{\epsilon\mu}{c^2}\frac{\partial^2\mathbf{A}}{\partial t^2} &= -\frac{4\pi\mu\mathbf{J}_d}{c}\end{aligned}\right\} \tag{3–36}$$

(The Hertz vector is less useful in this case since the analogue of (3–34) is very complicated in general.)

A Variational Principle

Equations (3–32) are equivalent to

$$\delta\int_{t_1}^{t_2} L\left(\phi, \mathbf{A}, \frac{\partial\mathbf{A}}{\partial t}\right)\,dt = 0$$

where, with the auxiliary constraint (3–31),

$$L = \iiint_{-\infty}^{\infty} \mathscr{L}\,dV$$

$$\mathscr{L}\left(\phi, \mathbf{A}, \frac{\partial\mathbf{A}}{\partial t}\right) = \frac{\mathbf{J}\cdot\mathbf{A}}{c} - \rho\phi + \frac{\epsilon}{8\pi}\left|\nabla\phi + \frac{1}{c}\frac{\partial\mathbf{A}}{\partial t}\right|^2 - \frac{1}{8\pi\mu}|\nabla\times\mathbf{A}|^2 \tag{3–37}$$

To append the equations of motion of charged matter to these relations, merely add L_{mech}, set $\mathbf{J} = \rho_+\mathbf{v}_+ - |\rho_-|\mathbf{v}_-$, and vary the particle coordinates as well as $\mathbf{A}$ and ϕ. For electrostatic fields with ρ specified, L itself is a true minimum for the correct ϕ; for magnetostatic fields with $\mathbf{J}$ specified, L is a maximum for the correct $\mathbf{A}$.

"Gauge Transformations" are transformations of the potentials $\mathbf{A}$, ϕ which do not change the fields $\mathbf{E}$, $\mathbf{B}$; since the fields alone are physically observable, all final physical equations must be "gauge" invariant. For arbitrary $f(\mathbf{r}, t)$, a gauge transformation is

$$\mathbf{A}' = \mathbf{A} + \nabla f; \qquad \phi' = \phi - \frac{1}{c}\frac{\partial f}{\partial t} \tag{3–38}$$

1. If $\nabla^2 f = \varepsilon\mu\,\partial^2 f/\partial(ct)^2$, equations (3–31) and (3–32) remain valid. ("Lorentz gauges"; these have particularly simple relativistic properties.)
2. If $\nabla^2 f = -\nabla\cdot\mathbf{A}$, then (using (3–31) for $\mathbf{A}$, ϕ):

$$\begin{aligned}&\nabla^2\phi' = -4\pi\rho/\epsilon\\ &\nabla^2\mathbf{A}' - \frac{\epsilon\mu}{c^2}\frac{\partial^2}{\partial t^2}\mathbf{A}' - \frac{\epsilon\mu}{c}\nabla\frac{\partial\phi'}{\partial t} = -4\pi\mu\mathbf{J}/c\\ &\nabla\cdot\mathbf{A}' = 0\end{aligned} \tag{3–39}$$

Note that ϕ' is here the "instantaneous *electrostatic* potential" due to ρ. ("Coulomb gauge"; this has especially simple mechanical-force properties.)

Alternating (Harmonic) Fields in Homogeneous Materials

We assume here that all quantities have the form typified by $\mathbf{E} = \mathbf{E}_0(\mathbf{r})e^{i\omega t}$ where $\mathbf{E}_0$ can be complex and it is understood that only the real parts of all expressions represent the physical fields, charges and currents.* (It is because all field equations are both linear and real that this calculational convenience is possible.)

---

* Of course, the imaginary parts taken together also represent physically possible fields.

The "constants" ϵ, μ, σ are then also allowed to take complex values and to depend on the (angular) frequency, ω, This is tantamount to saying that the simple relations (3–18) and (3–19) are inadequate but that they can be replaced by "convolution integrals" (see (13–7), ninth line) such as

$$\mathbf{D}(\mathbf{r}, t) = \int_{-\infty}^{t} \epsilon(\tau)\mathbf{E}(t-\tau)\, d\tau, \quad \text{etc.} \tag{3–40}$$

Note that ϵ, μ, σ must nevertheless be independent of field strength. Otherwise, Maxwell's equations are no longer linear and the method fails. (Waves of different frequency interact in such media—"cross talk", "intermodulation"—and the general problem takes all the complexity of non-linear partial differential equations.)

Power Flow

Since the Poynting vector involves a product of fields (is non-linear), care must be used in substituting these complex variables into it; recall that only the real parts are physically significant. The proper result is that the *time average* power flow is given by

$$\mathbf{S}_{\text{avg}} = \frac{c}{8\pi\mu} \operatorname{Re}(\mathbf{E} \times \mathbf{B}^*) \tag{3–41}$$

where "*" denotes the complex conjugate and "Re" signifies "real part of". Note in particular that (3–41) is independent of time and contains no information on the instantaneous rate of power flow.

If *all* currents and charges are prescribed, the "complex" forms of (3–33) and (3–34) (set $\partial/\partial t = i\omega$ and $\int^{t} \cdots dt = 1/i\omega$) are useful.

More frequently, however, it is the *fields* (on certain boundaries) which are prescribed or subject to conditions. It is then common to set $\rho = 0$ everywhere within the medium on the basis that

$$\frac{\partial\rho}{\partial t} = -\nabla\cdot\mathbf{J} = -\sigma\nabla\cdot\mathbf{E} = -\frac{4\pi\sigma}{\epsilon}\rho$$

whence

$$\rho = \rho_0 e^{-4\pi\sigma t/\epsilon} \tag{3–42}$$

and this "time constant",

$$T = \frac{\epsilon}{4\pi\sigma} \tag{3–43}$$

is so short for most media (even for sea water, $T = 1.5 \times 10^{-10}$ seconds) at practical frequencies that the approximation $\rho = 0$ is entirely adequate under most circumstances. (Note that $\rho_t = -\nabla\cdot\mathbf{P} \neq 0$.)

Let:

$$n = \sqrt{\epsilon\mu}\sqrt{1 + \frac{1}{i\omega T}} = n_R - i n_I \tag{3–44}$$

(complex index of refraction) where the "phase" of the square root is given by*

$$n_{\substack{R\\I}} = +\sqrt{\frac{\epsilon\mu}{2}\left[\sqrt{1 + (1/\omega T)^2} \pm 1\right]} \tag{3–45}$$

* So that factors such as e^{-ikr} correspond to phase *delays* and (in lossy media) to *attenuation.* Note also that either one of n_R, n_I determines the other through the relations (3–140) and (3–141) below—the "dispersion theorem."

Also let:

$$k = \frac{\omega n}{c} = \omega\left(\frac{\sqrt{\epsilon\mu}}{c}\right)\sqrt{1 + \frac{1}{i\omega T}} \tag{3–46}$$

$$\left(\text{“Skin depth”}, \ \delta = \frac{c}{\omega n_I} = \frac{-1}{Im(k)}\cdot\right) \tag{3–47}$$

With these definitions and with $\mathbf{J} = \sigma\mathbf{E}$, $\rho = 0$ [by (3–42)] throughout the region of interest, the harmonic forms ($i\omega = \partial/\partial t$) of (3–16) and (3–17) for homogeneous media become simply

$$\left.\begin{aligned} \nabla\cdot\mathbf{E} = 0 = \nabla\cdot\mathbf{B} \\ \nabla\times(\mathbf{B}/in) = k\mathbf{E}; \qquad \nabla\times\mathbf{E} = k(\mathbf{B}/in) \end{aligned}\right\} \tag{3–48}$$

Whence we see that if $\mathbf{E}_0$, $\mathbf{B}_0$ is any solution then

$$\mathbf{E}_1 = C(\mathbf{B}_0/in); \qquad \mathbf{B}_1 = C(in\mathbf{E}_0) \tag{3–49}$$

is another ("dual") solution for any complex constant, C.

Solutions of (3–48) can be generated in profusion as follows. Let $\mathbf{R}$ be ANY solution of (compare (3–36)):

$$\boxed{\nabla^2\mathbf{R} + k^2\mathbf{R} = 0} \tag{3–50}$$

(That is $\nabla(\nabla\cdot\mathbf{R}) - \nabla\times\nabla\times\mathbf{R} + k^2\mathbf{R} = 0$.)
Then solutions of (3–48) are (any complex constant times):

$$\boxed{\mathbf{E} = \nabla\times\mathbf{R}; \quad \mathbf{B} = \frac{ic}{\omega}\nabla\times\nabla\times\mathbf{R}} = \frac{i\omega n^2}{c}\mathbf{R}, \quad \text{IF } \nabla\cdot\mathbf{R} = 0 \tag{3–51}$$

or, in accord with (3–49), equally well:

$$\boxed{\mathbf{B} = \nabla\times\mathbf{R}; \quad \mathbf{E} = \frac{1}{ikn}\nabla\times\nabla\times\mathbf{R}} = \frac{k}{in}\mathbf{R}, \quad \text{IF } \nabla\cdot\mathbf{R} = 0 \tag{3–52}$$

Finally, of course, these (or any) solutions can be multiplied by arbitrary constants and added in any manner (or integrated with respect to any parameters, etc.).

Vectors $\mathbf{R}$ satisfying (3–50) can, moreover, be easily generated. If $\psi(\mathbf{r})$ satisfies the scalar wave equation:

$$\nabla^2\psi + k^2\psi = 0 \tag{3–53}$$

then some solutions of (3–50), suitable for use in (3–51) are:

$$\begin{aligned} \mathbf{R}_1 &= \mathbf{a}\psi; & \mathbf{R}_2 &= \nabla\psi \\ \mathbf{R}_3 &= \mathbf{a}\times\nabla\psi; & \mathbf{R}_4 &= -\mathbf{r}\times\nabla\psi \end{aligned} \tag{3–54}$$

where $\mathbf{a}$ is any constant vector. ($\nabla\cdot\mathbf{R}_3 = 0 = \nabla\cdot\mathbf{R}_4$.) (Note that these procedures, in principle, require an appeal to uniqueness theorems to prove that the solution found is the only physically possible one.)

Examples

1. $\mathbf{R} = \mathbf{a}e^{-ik(\mathbf{r}\cdot\hat{n})}$: *Plane Waves* ($\mathbf{a}$ = constant vector; $\hat{n}$ = constant *unit* vector.)
2. $\mathbf{R} = \mathbf{a}e^{i(n\phi+mz)}Be_n(\rho\sqrt{k^2 - m^2})$: *Cylindrical Waves* ($\mathbf{a}$ = constant vector; n and m constants, usually integers; $Be_v(x)$ = any Bessel function of order v.)
3. $\mathbf{R} = \mathbf{r} \times \nabla\left[\frac{1}{\sqrt{r}}\, Be_{n+\frac{1}{2}}(kr)\, Y_{n,m}(\theta, \phi)\right]$: *Spherical Waves* ($Y_{n,m}$ spherical harmonic: other notation as in #2.)
4. Taking $\mathbf{R}(\mathbf{r}) = \mathbf{R}_0(x, y)e^{i\gamma z}$ gives "guided waves" which propagate along the z-axis with various patterns in the x, y plane.

These basic solutions may be used to solve many problems involving waveguides, resonators and antennas. The more complex problems are often solved by employing series-sums of these wave-types. In all cases, the object is to discover solutions in various homogeneous media which satisfy required boundary conditions (3–23) and, also by (3–23), are continuous at any interfaces between such media.

Practical Limit on Antenna Beam-Sharpness

Any current distribution of finite spatial extent is conveniently analysed by #3 above, where $H^{(1)}_{n+\frac{1}{2}}$ (Hankel functions) are chosen for $Be(kr)$. The function $H^{(1)}_{n+\frac{1}{2}}(z)$ approaches infinity very suddenly and rapidly for z (real) less than about $2n/e$. Hence, to launch such a wave from an antenna of "radius" less than $2n/ke$ (approximately), requires inordinately large amounts of stored (reactive) energy and very large currents (which imply large ohmic losses). With $H^{(1)}_{n+\frac{1}{2}}$ goes the angle factor $Y_{n,m}(\theta, \phi)$ whose "lobes" have angular width of about π/n.

Thus in all, if the antenna occupies a spherical volume of radius a, then (roughly):

$$\text{Beam width, radians} \geqslant \frac{2\pi}{eka} \sim \frac{\lambda}{3a} \tag{3–55}$$

This argument applies to either a "pencil" beam or a "platter" beam and (3–55) then implies corresponding limits on the power gain in these two cases.

Dipole Radiation

This is a special case of #3 with $n = 1$, $m = 0$ and the $H^{(2)}_{3/2}$ (Hankel) function for $Be_{3/2}$. That is, if $\mathbf{d} = \mathbf{d}_0 e^{i\omega t}$ is the dipole strength,*

$$\mathbf{R} = -\frac{\mathbf{d}}{\epsilon} \times \nabla\left(\frac{e^{-ikr}}{r}\right) \qquad [\text{note } \nabla \cdot \mathbf{R} = 0] \tag{3–56}$$

(The dipole is located at $\mathbf{r} = 0$.)

When substituted in (3–51), this gives directly the fields due to an electric dipole. The prescription (3–52) gives ($1/\epsilon\mu$ times) the fields due to an oscillating magnetic dipole, or a current loop. ($\mathbf{d} = \hat{n}(I/c)(\text{area})$.)

At great distances $\mathbf{r}$, the fields given by (3–51) approach

$$\mathbf{E} \doteq \frac{k^2}{\epsilon}\mathbf{r} \times (\mathbf{d} \times \mathbf{r})\frac{e^{-ikr}}{r^3}; \quad \mathbf{B} \doteq \frac{ck^3}{\omega\epsilon}(\mathbf{r} \times \mathbf{d})\frac{e^{-ikr}}{r^2} \tag{3–57}$$

(Other terms vanish faster than $1/r$ as $r \to \infty$.)

---

* $\mathbf{d} = q\mathbf{l}$ where $+q$ and $-q$ are the charges at the ends of the dipole and $\mathbf{l}$ (very small; $l \to 0$) is a vector drawn from $-q$ to $+q$.

Rayleigh Scattering (Dipole Scattering)

From (3–57) one readily derives (by Poynting's theorem (3–41)) that the power radiated is (when $\sigma = 0$ in the surrounding medium; if **d** is a magnetic dipole multiply by $\epsilon\mu$)

$$\text{Power} = \frac{(2\pi)^4}{3} \frac{(c/\sqrt{\epsilon\mu})}{\epsilon\lambda^4} |\mathbf{d}|^2 \tag{3–58}$$

where the wavelength, $\lambda = 2\pi c/(\omega\sqrt{\epsilon\mu})$. If **d**, the dipole moment, is induced by an incident field, $\mathbf{E}_{\text{inc}}$, then $\mathbf{d} = \alpha\mathbf{E}_{\text{inc}}$ where α is the "polarizability" of the scattering center. With these relations (by another application of Poynting's theorem, noting that $|\mathbf{B}_{\text{inc}}| = n\,|\mathbf{E}_{\text{inc}}|$ in a plane wave), the cross section for scattering is given by,

$$\text{Cross section} = \frac{128\pi^5\alpha^2}{3\epsilon^2\lambda^4} \tag{3–59}$$

Here, some values for α are:

1. For a very small dielectric sphere (radius, $a \ll \lambda$) of dielectric constant ϵ_d

$$\alpha = a^3 \frac{\epsilon_d - \epsilon}{\epsilon_d + 2\epsilon}$$

2. For a charged particle (effectively)

$$\alpha = \left(\frac{\lambda}{c}\right)^2 \frac{e^2}{4\pi^2 m}$$

(provided $\hbar\omega \ll$ rest energy, mc^2).

3. Rayleigh molecular scattering (Tyndall effect)

$$\alpha = (n_g - 1)/4\pi N$$

with $\epsilon = 1 = \mu$ in (3–59). Here n_g is the index of refraction of the gas (whose molecules do the scattering) and N is the number of molecules per unit volume.

Radiation Vector

This is a useful device for finding the radiated power versus direction *in an infinite, lossless medium* due to a given system of known currents confined to a finite region of space ($\mathbf{J} = 0$ elsewhere).

An ("infinitesimal") element of current $\mathbf{I}\,ds$ is equivalent to an electric dipole, $\mathbf{I}\,ds = i\omega\mathbf{d}$, the *distant* field of which is given by (3–57). An arbitrary distribution of currents (*if* confined to a finite region of space) will produce a distant field obtained by superposing the fields due to all its elements. If the medium is lossless ($k = \sqrt{\epsilon\mu}(\omega/c)$, real), this observation coupled with (3–41) gives the result (after some manipulation):

The power radiated in the direction of the unit vector $\hat{n}$ is (per unit solid angle),

$$P(\hat{n}) = \frac{k\mu\omega}{8\pi c^2} |\mathbf{N} \times \hat{n}|^2 \qquad [|\mathbf{a}|^2 = \mathbf{a} \cdot \mathbf{a}^*] \tag{3–60}$$

where

$$\mathbf{N}(\hat{n}) = \oint\!\!\oint\!\!\oint \mathbf{J} e^{ik\mathbf{r}' \cdot \hat{n}}\, dV' \tag{3–61}$$

is called the "radiation vector".

Mean Absorption Cross Section of an Antenna

If an antenna, of any shape or size whatever is matched* at frequency, f_0, then its (effective) power-absorption cross section *averaged* over all directions and polarizations of incoming waves (of frequency, f_0) is

$$\langle A \rangle = \lambda^2/4\pi.$$

This may be proved either (i) by direct calculation for (say) an infinitesimal loop antenna followed by an application of (3–71) or (ii) by considering the matched antenna in thermal equilibrium with black-body radiation [the radiated noise power is $4kT\,\mathrm{d}f$ by Nyquist's theorem, (6–163), and this must be balanced by received black-body radiation, namely $\langle A\rangle\langle \mathbf{S}\rangle\,\mathrm{d}f = \langle A\rangle 2cU\,\mathrm{d}f \doteq \langle A\rangle(16\pi/\lambda^2)kT\,\mathrm{d}f$, by Planck's law, (6–55)].

Transient Signals

If the various material media are linear (superposition valid), "transient" (non-harmonic) phenomena are most expeditiously handled by using Laplace Transforms. *If* all quantities are assumed to vanish ("almost everywhere") when $t = 0$, then the Laplace transforms of (3–16) and (3–17) may be obtained from their harmonic form merely by setting $(\partial/\partial t =)\ i\omega = p$, the transform variable. Solutions to (3–16) and (3–17) in "transform space" may then be obtained by simply performing the same substitution in any harmonic solutions. (If all quantities are not zero at $t = 0$, extra terms, not found in harmonic solutions, may enter the equations and their solutions.) Choosing the desired driving terms (such as $\mathbf{J}(p) = \mathscr{L}(\mathbf{J}(t))$ where $\mathbf{J}(t)$ is given, etc.) and then inverting the Laplace transform then gives the desired solution.

Čerenkov Radiation

From (3–60) or otherwise (by Laplace or Fourier transforms and some manipulation), a particle with charge q which travels through a dielectric ($\mu = 1$, ϵ real) with speed $v > c/\sqrt{\epsilon}$ for a distance L produces radiation in the (angular) frequency range, $\omega \pm \frac{1}{2}\,\mathrm{d}\omega$, in the amount:

$$P(\hat{n}, \omega)\,\mathrm{d}\omega = \frac{q^2\sqrt{\epsilon}}{\frac{1}{2}\pi^2 c^3}\left[1 - \left(\frac{\hat{n}\cdot\mathbf{v}}{v}\right)^2\right]\left\{\frac{\sin\left[\dfrac{\omega L}{2v}\left(1 - \sqrt{\epsilon}\hat{n}\cdot\dfrac{\mathbf{v}}{c}\right)\right]}{\dfrac{1}{v}\left(1 - \sqrt{\epsilon}\hat{n}\cdot\dfrac{\mathbf{v}}{c}\right)}\right\}^2 \mathrm{d}\omega \qquad (3\text{–}62)$$

which, for $v > c/\sqrt{\epsilon}$ is strongly peaked in the cone, $\hat{n}\cdot\mathbf{v}/v = \cos\theta = c/v\sqrt{\epsilon}$. The total radiation in the band, $\omega \pm \frac{1}{2}\,\mathrm{d}\omega$, is

$$P(\omega)\,\mathrm{d}\omega = L\frac{q^2}{c^2}\left(1 - \frac{c^2}{\epsilon v^2}\right)\omega\,\mathrm{d}\omega \qquad (\text{where } v > c/\sqrt{\epsilon}) \qquad (3\text{–}63)$$

(Note, $\epsilon \to 1$ at X-ray frequencies for all substances so that $\int_0^\infty P\,\mathrm{d}\omega < \infty$.) This radiation is not only experimentally verified but is often used to measure velocities of high energy particles.

* That is, loaded with an impedance equal to the complex conjugate of the impedance seen looking into the antenna terminals.

Fundamental Difficulties of Classical Electromagnetics

1. Quite generally, Maxwell's equations imply that a charged particle, even in a field-free region, must radiate energy if it is (a) accelerated (compare (3–58)) and/or (b) traveling at velocity greater than $c/\sqrt{\epsilon\mu}$ (compare (3–63)). Experimentally this radiated energy is observed* and the particle loses a compensating energy.

Yet the force law (3–3) does *not* predict any such energy loss;† the experimentally observed "self-force" is not included. Effect (a) above can be handled by adding to (3–3) a term, $(2e^2\mu^2\epsilon/3c^3)(d^2\mathbf{v}/dt^2)$, but this is seldom done except when discussing this question; moreover, it will not account for effect (b). Fortunately, this self-force is extremely small in practice, for no good solution to the paradox has yet been proposed.

2. Another (perhaps related) difficulty is that relativity requires that no sharp distinction be made between energy and mass (that is, "energy must have mass"), while a charged point particle has, by (3–28), an associated field-energy which is infinite. By the principles of relativity, this implies an infinite effective mass. Classically, of course, this difficulty can be avoided by postulating a finite size for all charged particles, but the difficulty seems to reappear in quantum field theory.

Anisotropic Media

From such mechanisms as hindered atomic deformation due to crystal structure or confinement of charge or spin motions due to applied d.c. magnetic fields, etc., certain media (birefringent crystals; ferrites; ionized gases) can fail to satisfy the simple relations (3–18). Either **D** may not be parallel to **E** or **H** not parallel to **B**. In most practical cases, only one of these alternatives occurs and (3–19) remains valid.‡

The assumption of harmonic time dependence ($e^{i\omega t}$) is usually made, and $\rho = 0$ is usually a very good approximation.

Maxwell's equations, of course, remain valid, but (3–18) is replaced by a tensor relation between **D** and **E** and/or between **H** and **B**. The type of complication to which this can lead is illustrated by:

Birefringent Media

The relation between **D** and **E** is still found experimentally to be linear but takes the form (for stationary media),

$$D_i = \sum_j A_{ij}E_j \quad \text{or} \quad \mathbf{D} = \mathfrak{A} \cdot \mathbf{E} \tag{3–64}$$

[where, because **D** and **E** are vectors for space-transformations, $\mathfrak{A}$ must be a tensor for space-transformations ("rigorous quotient theorem")].

Experimentally it is found that $\mathfrak{A}$ is symmetric§

$$A_{ij} = A_{ji} \tag{3–65}$$

A consequence of this is that $U_{\text{elec}} = (1/8\pi)\mathbf{E} \cdot \mathbf{D}$ (and conversely (3–65) follows from the latter). Also (3–65) implies that $\mathfrak{A}$ has an inverse and takes diagonal form in a suitable coordinate system.

* (a) is observed in betatrons, etc.; (b) is observed in Čerenkov counters.

† The fields in (3–3) are not those of the particle itself; $\mathbf{F} = 0$ in a field-free region.

‡ The Hall effect (though usually treated by successive "corrections") is really one of the more complicated situations wherein (3–18) and (3–19) can both be violated.

§ More generally, the tensors (e.g. in ferrites) are usually Hermitian; then $8\pi U = \mathbf{E} \cdot \mathbf{D}^*$ is real as are also the eigenvalues of the tensor.

If we assume that all field vectors have the form typified by

$$\mathbf{D} = \mathbf{D}_0 e^{i\omega[t-(\mathbf{r}\cdot\hat{n})/v]}$$

where $\mathbf{D}_0$ is constant and $\hat{n}$ is a unit vector (the wave-normal), then Maxwell's equations (3–16) yield,

$$\frac{v}{c}\mathbf{B} = -\mathbf{E}\times\hat{n}; \qquad \frac{\mu v}{c}\mathbf{D} = \mathbf{B}\times\hat{n} \tag{3–66}$$

From this it readily follows that $\mathbf{B}$, $\mathbf{D}$, $\hat{n}$ are mutually orthogonal:

$$\mathbf{B}\cdot\hat{n} = 0 = \mathbf{D}\cdot\hat{n} = \mathbf{B}\cdot\mathbf{D} \tag{3–67}$$

while $\mathbf{E}$ lies in the plane of $\mathbf{D}$ and $\hat{n}$:

$$\mu\frac{v^2}{c^2}\mathbf{D} - \mathbf{E} + \hat{n}(\hat{n}\cdot\mathbf{E}) = 0 \tag{3–68}$$

It follows that the Poynting vector, $\mathbf{S} = (\mathbf{E}\times\mathbf{H})(c/4\pi)$, is *not* normal to the wave surfaces (that is, $\hat{n}\times\mathbf{S}\neq 0$) but makes the same angle with $\hat{n}$ that $\mathbf{E}$ does with $\mathbf{D}$. The "rays" are therefore inclined to the "wave-fronts"; limited-area waves move with a yaw or "on the bias".

Equation (3–68), with (3–64) is a homogeneous equation for determining $\mathbf{D}$ for a given $\hat{n}$; the condition, that it have non-vanishing solutions, determines v^2. This condition would appear to have three roots for v^2, but actually there are only two. This is most easily seen *in the special coordinates where $\mathfrak{A}$ is diagonal* (principal axes): $A_{ij} = \delta_{ij}\epsilon_i$, say. Then, writing (3–68) in the form, $\hat{n}(\hat{n}\cdot\mathbf{E}) = \left(\mathfrak{A}^{-1} - \mu\frac{v^2}{c^2}\right)\cdot\mathbf{D}$, solving for D_x, D_y, D_z and finally expressing $\mathbf{D}\cdot\hat{n} = 0$ in terms of these solutions, one obtains the *Fresnel equations*:

$$\sum_{i=1}^{3}\frac{n_i^2}{\dfrac{1}{\epsilon_i} - \mu\dfrac{v^2}{c^2}} = 0 \tag{3–69}$$

(where n_i are the components of $\hat{n}$ in the coordinates which diagonalize $\mathfrak{A}$).

Equation (3–69) is a quadratic in v^2 so that, *for a given* $\hat{n}$ there can be two phase-velocities*, v_1 and v_2 and correspondingly two solutions of (3–68), $\mathbf{D}_1$ and $\mathbf{D}_2$. Since both are orthogonal to $\hat{n}$, it follows from (3–68) that $(\mu v_1^2/c^2)(\mathbf{D}_1\cdot\mathbf{D}_2) - (\mathbf{E}_1\cdot\mathbf{D}_2) = (\mu v_2^2/c^2)(\mathbf{D}_2\cdot\mathbf{D}_1) - (\mathbf{E}_2\cdot\mathbf{D}_1)$ or, because $\mathbf{E}_1\cdot\mathbf{D}_2 = \mathbf{E}_2\cdot\mathbf{D}_1$ by (3–65), $\mu(\mathbf{D}_1\cdot\mathbf{D}_2)(v_1^2 - v_2^2)/c^2 = 0$. The two solutions for each given $\hat{n}$ are therefore always perpendicular:

$$\mathbf{D}_1\cdot\mathbf{D}_2 = 0 \tag{3–70}$$

and *these mutually perpendicular polarizations are thus propagated with different velocities.*

As follows from the form of (3–69), there are two† particular directions $\hat{n}$ in which only one phase velocity, v, exists. These two directions are called the *optic axes* and lie in the plane of the two ("diagonalizing") principal axes with the largest and smallest associated ϵ_i and are symmetrically disposed (so that specifying a single angle—the optic angle—determines both optic axes completely; if the optic angle vanishes, the crystal is called "uniaxial.")

* When a plane wave falls normally on a plane boundary of the crystal, the waves inside the crystal (both) have the same $\hat{n}$ as the incident wave. Compare (3–73) below.

† Four if one counts sign-reversals, $\hat{n}\to -\hat{n}$.

Gyroelectric (or Gyromagnetic) Media

In media of this type either ϵ or μ is replaced by a (complex) Hermitian tensor. The theory (3–64)–(3–68) remains valid for the gyroelectric case. [The more common gyromagnetic case follows by replacing ($\mathbf{B}$, $\mu\mathbf{D}$, $\mathbf{E}$) by ($-\mathbf{E}$, $\mathbf{B}$, $\mathbf{H}/\epsilon$) respectively.] Then if ϵ_i and $\mathbf{e}_i$ are the eigenvalues and eigenvectors of $\mathfrak{A}$ so that $\mathfrak{A} \cdot \mathbf{e}_i = \epsilon_i \mathbf{e}_i$, expanding $\mathbf{E}$ in the form $\mathbf{E} = \Sigma\, c_i \mathbf{e}_i$ gives $\mathbf{D} = \Sigma\, c_i \epsilon_i \mathbf{e}_i$ and from (3–68), using the theorem that $\mathbf{e}_i{}^* \cdot \mathbf{e}_j = \delta_{ij}$, we find

$$c_j = (\hat{n} \cdot \mathbf{e}_j{}^*)(\hat{n} \cdot \mathbf{E})/[1 - (v/c)^2 \mu \epsilon_j]$$

Then from $\mathbf{D} \cdot \hat{n} = \Sigma\, c_j \epsilon_j (\hat{n} \cdot \mathbf{e}_j) = 0$ it follows that

$$\sum_{j=1}^{3} \frac{|(\hat{n} \cdot \mathbf{e}_j)|^2}{(1/\epsilon_j) - \mu(v/c)^2} = 0$$

Again there are two solutions for the phase velocity, v, with two corresponding solutions of (3–68), $\mathbf{D}_1$ and $\mathbf{D}_2$. Equation (3–70) is generalized to

$$\mathbf{D}_1 \cdot \mathbf{D}_2{}^* = 0$$

Since in general the vectors are no longer real, these "single velocity" solutions now correspond to elliptically polarized waves. The properties of media of this type often depend sensitively on the frequency, ω. See " ionized gases", Chapter 6.

Non-Homogeneous Media

The majority of problems actually solved for non-homogeneous media concern different regions, each of which is homogeneous, separated by sharp, "discontinuous" boundaries. This type of problem is handled by choosing from the many various solutions for homogeneous media those which match across the boundaries so as to assemble a consistent solution for the entire system.

There are two special cases where somewhat more general theories can be developed. These are: (1) for very high-frequency waves, the theory of *optics* and (2) for very low-frequency waves, the theory of *lumped electric* (and magnetic) *circuits.*

Some general results not restricted to these limiting cases are the following.

The Rayleigh–Carson Reciprocity Theorem

In a *linear* system with $\mu \equiv 1$, if an impressed electric field, $\mathbf{F}_1$, produces a *true* current distribution, $\mathbf{J}_{t1}$ (compare (3–14)) and another impressed electric field, $\mathbf{F}_2$, produces $\mathbf{J}_{t2}$ (all fields harmonic and of the same frequency), then

$$\oint\oint\oint [\mathbf{F}_1 \cdot \mathbf{J}_{t2} - \mathbf{F}_2 \cdot \mathbf{J}_{t1}]\, dV = 0 \tag{3–71}$$

where the $\mathbf{J}_{ti}$ are defined by (3–14) (with $\mathbf{M} = 0$ because $\mu = 1$) and the interpretation of the $\mathbf{F}_i$ is discussed below.

REMARKS AND DEFINITIONS:

(1) The "system" must contain all regions of space wherein the fields considered are non-zero. It may extend to infinity (as for two antennas alternately sending and receiving) but it must be linear (i.e. two fields may be simply added to give the result of their simultaneous presence) and μ must be equal to unity throughout.

(2) "Impressed" field $\mathbf{F}_i$ means that $\mathbf{E} = \mathbf{F}_i + \mathscr{E}$ where $\mathscr{E}$ may be computed as due solely to charges and currents *within* the system (and not due to charges or currents inside the "generators").

(3) The integration in (3–71) need extend only over portions of the system containing material media since $\mathbf{J}_{ti} = 0$ in vacuum.

APPLICATION:

The "generators" can be well-shielded boxes with terminals whose spacing is very much smaller than a wavelength. The corresponding $\mathbf{F}_i$ will then essentially be zero except across the terminals and the theorem then states

$$V_1 I_{\text{at 1, due to 2}} = V_2 I_{\text{at 2, due to 1}}$$

(V = voltage; I = current).

PROOF: By definition of the concept of "impressed" electric fields (and the hypothesis of linearity): $\mathbf{E}_1 = \mathbf{F}_1 - (i\omega/c)\mathbf{A}_1 - \nabla\phi_1$ (and similarly for $\mathbf{E}_2$) *where* $\mathbf{A}_i$ and ϕ_i satisfy (3–32) as written for microscopic fields, that is with $\epsilon = 1 = \mu$ and $\mathbf{J}_{ti}$ substituted for $\mathbf{J}$ and $\rho_{ti} = (-1/i\omega)\nabla\cdot\mathbf{J}_{ti}$ substituted for ρ. Since, by hypothesis, $\mathbf{M} \equiv 0$, we also have from (3–14) and (3–18), $\mathbf{J}_{ti} = \lambda\mathbf{E}_i$; thus

$$\oint\!\!\oint\!\!\oint (\mathbf{J}_{t1}\cdot\mathbf{F}_2 - \mathbf{J}_{t2}\cdot\mathbf{F}_1)\,dV = \frac{i\omega}{c}\oint\!\!\oint\!\!\oint (\mathbf{J}_{t1}\cdot\mathbf{A}_2 - \mathbf{J}_{t2}\cdot\mathbf{A}_1)\,dV + \oint\!\!\oint\!\!\oint (\mathbf{J}_{t1}\cdot\nabla\phi_2 - \mathbf{J}_{t2}\cdot\nabla\phi_1)\,dV$$

and by applications of Gauss' theorem along with the (modified) relations (3–32), the last two integrals may be reduced to integrals over a surface enclosing the system. Since all fields and currents vanish outside the system (or decrease sufficiently rapidly at very large distances), the result (3–71) follows.

Fresnel's Formulas

If a (harmonic) plane wave strikes a plane boundary between two homogeneous (and linear) media, the reflected and transmitted waves may be completely determined* by (3–23). If the incident wave comes from medium #1 and its wave-normal makes an angle θ with the normal to the boundary, and if

$$N = \frac{\mu_1}{\mu_2}\frac{n_2}{n_1} \tag{3–72}$$

(where n_1 and n_2 are the complex indices of refraction, (3–44), for the two media†) then the results are:

(a) Angle of incidence = angle of reflection.

(b) Angle of refraction (transmission), θ'', is given by (compare (3–45)):

$$\sin\theta'' = \frac{n_{R1}}{n_{R2}}\sin\theta \tag{3–73}$$

If $(n_{R1}/n_{R2})\sin\theta > 1$, there is no transmitted wave but only an exponentially damped wave which carries no power into the second medium if the latter is lossless ("total internal reflection"). [Equation (3–73) is also true for the wave-*normals* if one medium is birefringent; however, n_{R2} then depends on θ'' and there are two consistent solutions of (3–73) for each given n_{R1} and θ.]

* Both the wave-fronts and the boundary should, strictly, be infinite planes. In practice it is necessary only that they be at least several wavelengths broad.

† In the optical region, the conductivity cannot be measured so that (3–44) is not useful, but complex indices, n, occur and can be measured directly.

(c) If the **E** vector of the incident wave lies in the plane determined by the wave-normal and boundary-normal ("*parallel* (p) *polarization*") and if **E** in all waves is taken positive when directed toward the surface normal, then (t = transmitted; r = reflected)

$$\frac{E_{pt}}{E_{pi}} = \frac{-2\,N\cos\theta}{N^2\cos\theta + \sqrt{N^2 - \sin^2\theta}}\,;\quad \frac{E_{pr}}{E_{pi}} = \frac{N^2\cos\theta - \sqrt{N^2 - \sin^2\theta}}{N^2\cos\theta + \sqrt{N^2 - \sin^2\theta}} \tag{3–74}$$

(d) If the **E** vector of the incident wave points perpendicular to the surface normal ("*perpendicular*" *or sidewise* (s) *polarization*) and if **E** is taken positive for all waves when on the same side, then

$$\frac{E_{st}}{E_{si}} = \frac{2\cos\theta}{\cos\theta + \sqrt{N^2 - \sin^2\theta}}\,;\quad \frac{E_{sr}}{E_{si}} = \frac{\sqrt{N^2 - \sin^2\theta} - \cos\theta}{\sqrt{N^2 - \sin^2\theta} + \cos\theta} \tag{3–75}$$

The **B** fields are in all cases given by $\mathbf{B} = n\hat{k} \times \mathbf{E}$, where $\hat{k}$ is the wave-normal.

Of the four expressions in (3–74) and (3–75), E_{pr} is the only one which can vanish for $N \neq 1$. For real n_1, n_2 this occurs when $\tan\theta = N$ ("Brewster's angle").

However, by using (3–74) and (3–75) it can be shown that if a third medium with appropriate thickness and values of μ, n is inserted between the two main materials, *all* reflections can be eliminated for any given ω and θ. By resorting to multiple layers, reflections can be greatly reduced for a range of ω and θ. (Coated optics).

If one medium is a conductor, the above relations remain valid with complex values of the parameters, but the main practical result is that the fields inside the conductor are attenuated by a factor, $e^{-x/\delta}$, where δ is the "skin depth" given by (3–45) and (3–47); at not too high frequencies, this relation becomes

$$\delta = c\sqrt{\frac{1}{2\pi\mu\sigma\omega}} \qquad (\omega T \ll 1)$$

(For copper, $\delta = 6.6/\sqrt{f}$ centimeters, where f is the frequency in cycles per second.)

[*Anomalous skin effect*: When certain conductors are operated at very low temperatures, the mean free path of the conduction electrons can become greater than the diameter of the sample and the relation, $\mathbf{J} = \sigma\mathbf{E}$ becomes somewhat meaningless. Even low-frequency alternating fields cause the electrons to collide with the surface of the sample. The a.c. resistance is very much higher than the d.c. resistance and is very sensitive to the condition of the sample surface.]

OPTICS

This branch of the theory corresponds to the limit of very large ω or to $\lambda \to 0$. The full machinery of Maxwell's equations can then be usefully replaced by a series of approximations.

Geometric Optics

Geometric optics is the "zeroth" approximation in which the wave nature of light is essentially ignored and replaced by a set of rules which may be derived as follows. Considering only lossless media for the moment ("good dielectrics, $\mathbf{J} = 0$, $\rho = 0$), then **E** and **B** satisfy (by Maxwell's equations) $\nabla^2\mathbf{E} + (\omega^2\mu\epsilon/c^2)\mathbf{E} = 0$. Substituting

$$\mathbf{E} = \mathbf{F}(\mathbf{r})\exp\left[-\frac{i\omega}{c}S(\mathbf{r})\right]$$

and considering the limit as $\omega \to \infty$, one finds that the time-delay ("phase") function $S(\mathbf{r})$ satisfies

$$|\nabla S|^2 = \mu\epsilon = n^2 \tag{3–76}$$

Now the "path" of a light-ray (wave-normal) will lie everywhere perpendicular to the surfaces of constant phase, S; thus light paths lie along ∇S. Now by (3–76), for any line integral between two fixed points,

$$\int_1^2 n\, dl \geqslant \int_1^2 (\nabla S) \cdot d\mathbf{l}$$

So that the actual paths ($d\mathbf{l}$ parallel to ∇S) are determined by

$$\boxed{\int_1^2 n\, dl = \text{minimum}} \tag{3–77}$$

which is *Fermat's principle of least time.* The path of a light-ray therefore satisfies (compare (21–51) with $g_{ik} = \delta_{ik} n^2$)

$$n \frac{d^2\mathbf{r}}{dl^2} = \frac{d\mathbf{r}}{dl} \times \left[(\nabla n) \times \frac{d\mathbf{r}}{dl} \right]$$

which can be used for graphical ray-tracing in inhomogeneous media; see (1–11).

From the method of derivation, it follows that bundles of light-rays always continue to lie along the normals of some surface (which may be constructed when the rays are given) if they have done so at any one time; this then remains true after any number of reflections or refractions. (Law of Malus.)

From (3–77) itself there follow:

(a) Light-rays follow straight lines in homogeneous media (neglect of diffraction).

(b) Different light-rays are independent (neglect of interference*).

(c) Any light path can also be described in the reverse direction.

(d) For reflected rays, the angles of incidence and reflection are equal.

(e) Snell's law, $n_1 \sin \theta_1 = n_2 \sin \theta_2$ for refracted rays.

Another easily derived rule determines the amplitude function, $|\mathbf{F}(\mathbf{r})|$ above,

(f) Energy (power flow), as represented by $I = |\mathbf{F}|^2$ must be conserved in lossless media.

(g) For lossy media, an extra factor, $e^{-\alpha x}$, is inserted (more or less empirically, though it may also be obtained formally from (3–76) with complex n).

These rules (a)–(g) [which may also be derived from Huygens' principle, (15–55)] suffice for an approximate solution of many optical problems. Their most serious defect is neglect of diffraction effects.

Lens Systems

From the rules (a)–(g), it follows that a spherical interface between two media acts as a lens and focusses light-rays from one point into an image point, provided that all angles of incidence and refraction are small (in the sense that $\sin \theta \doteqdot \theta$). The relations are

$$\frac{n_1}{u} + \frac{n_2}{v} = \frac{n_2 - n_1}{R} \tag{3–78}$$

$$m = \text{magnification} = y'/y = -n_1 v / n_2 u \tag{3–79}$$

where the notation and sign-conventions are shown in the figure. A negative value

* With the exception: If rays from an "object" are reconverged to form an "image", then by (3–77) their optical path lengths must be equal. (For waves, this is obviously necessary.)

of m signifies an inverted image. Note especially the sign-convention for R. For a mirror, simply set $n_2 = -n_1$ (retaining the same sign-convention for R).

As mentioned, (3–78) is, in general, a good approximation only if all angles of

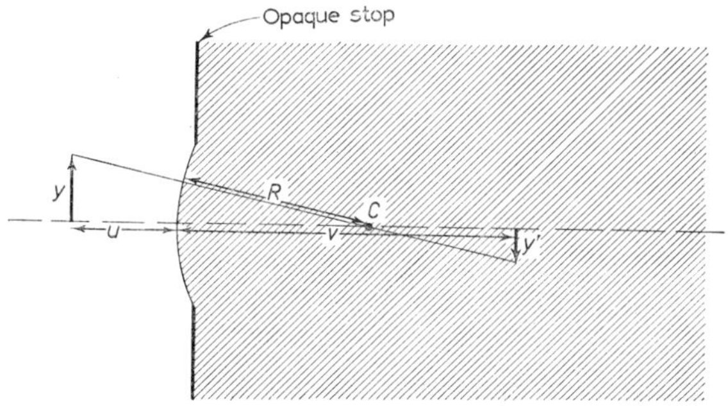

As here shown, $R > 0$. If the center of curvature, C, lies to the left of the figure, take $R < 0$. As drawn, u and v are also positive; negative values of u or v indicate an image or object on the opposite side of the interface.

incidence and refraction are small. However, if $u = -R\left(1 + \frac{n_2}{n_1}\right)$ and (hence) $v = R\left(1 + \frac{n_1}{n_2}\right)$ and if $y = 0 = y'$, then the focussing is perfect for all rays and arbitrarily large aperture (except, of course, for diffraction effects). The only other such case is the trivial one, $u = -R = -v$ and $y = 0 = y'$. In general, a (non-spherical) surface may be found which will image perfectly (except for diffraction) any pair of points—but no others.

In addition, n_1 and n_2 vary with wavelength in actual physical media so that any real lens exhibits different properties for different colors.

If a second spherical interface follows the first at a distance, t, then writing, in accord with (3–78):

$$\frac{n_1}{u} + \frac{n_2}{v} = \frac{1}{g_1} \quad \text{and} \quad \frac{n_2}{t - v} + \frac{n_3}{w} = \frac{1}{g_2}$$

After considerable algebraic reduction, these relations yield:

$$\left.\begin{aligned} &\frac{n_1}{u + a} + \frac{n_3}{w + b} = \frac{1}{g_1} + \frac{1}{g_2} - \frac{t}{n_2 g_1 g_2} \equiv \frac{1}{G}, \text{ (say)} \\ &\text{where} \\ &a = \frac{n_1 G}{n_2 g_2} t; \qquad b = \frac{n_3 G}{n_2 g_1} t \end{aligned}\right\} \qquad (3\text{–}80)$$

It then follows by induction on the number of spherical interfaces that:

Any system of coaxial spherical interfaces satisfies, as a system, the *thick lens equation*:*

$$\frac{F}{U} + \frac{F'}{V} = 1; \qquad F/F' = n/n' \qquad (3\text{–}81)$$

* Setting $X = U - F$ and $X' = V - F'$, the Newtonian form of the lens equation results:

$$XX' = FF' \qquad (N)$$

which is formally much simpler, but note the ambiguity that the signs of F and F' can be changed simultaneously without altering (N) whereas (3–81) shows that such a change indeed has a profound effect on the location of the image. The difficulty is purely formal in that the *meanings* of X and X' change with simultaneous sign-changes of F and F', but this circumstance makes (N) less convenient for most purposes.

where U and V are measured, not from a common point, but from two "suitable" points, known as the "principal points". (Planes through these points are known as the principal planes.) In this relation, n and n' are respectively the indices of refraction in the initial and final media; F and F' are called the focal lengths; the points $U = F$ (when $V = \infty$) and $V = F'$ (when $U = \infty$) are called the focal points of the system. See figure.

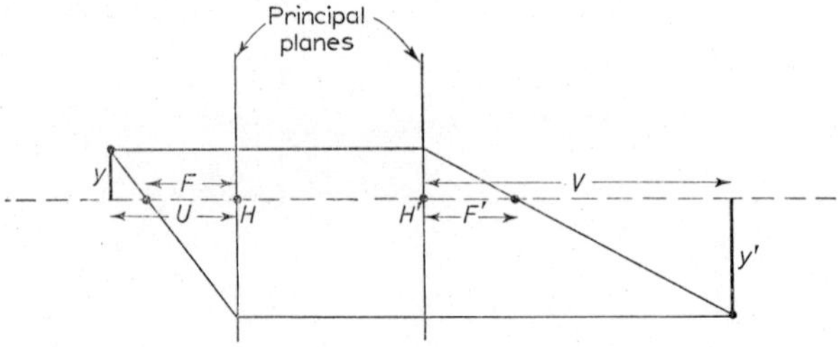

Notation for thick-lens optics. (Principal planes shown not crossed; U and V shown as positive as also are F and F'.) Any image-object combination may be located graphically by drawing two rays (as shown), one parallel to the axis and one passing through the "near" focal point. Between the principal planes, all rays travel (equivalently) parallel to the axis.

Equations (3–80) determine the focal points and principal points of any compound system when those of the components are known. The quantity $G = F/n = F'/n'$ can also be expressed as

$$G = \frac{-g_1g_2}{l} n_2 = \frac{-f'_1f_2}{ln_2} \tag{3–82}$$

where l is the (algebraic, "signed") separation of the focal *points* of the systems 1 and 2 and n_2 is the index of refraction of the intervening medium. For two thick lenses used in air, the relation becomes simply $F = -f_1f_2/l$.

The magnification is still given by (see figure above)

$$M = -nV/n'U \tag{3–83}$$

A more accurate form may be proved from (3–77) (see footnote to rule (b) above):

$$M = -n \sin \theta / n' \sin \theta'$$

where θ and θ' are the largest angles made by rays crossing the axis at U and V respectively.

The intensity in the image, formed by a system with $F = F'$ and used with U very large so that $V \doteqdot F = F'$, is easily computed to be

$$P_{\text{image}} = \frac{P_{\text{source}}}{16(F/D)^2} \tag{3–84}$$

where P represents erg/cm² sec and D is the diameter (effective*) of the optical assembly. Note that (3–84) is independent of the distance from the source to the first lens surface; the inverse square law cancels out completely because the magnification changes at the same rate.

* That is, (3–84) is derived by first ignoring lens stops and also reflections at the lens surfaces.

Note that, by the second law of thermodynamics (consider a black-body source),

$$F/D \geqslant 0.25$$

It has become common practice to denote D expressed as "F/α" as the "f-number" of the optical system. Thus "$f/8$" implies that $D = F/8$ and thus $F/D = 8$ is to be substituted in (3–84).

Aberrations of Lenses

Lens "defects" are simply due to the approximate nature of (3–78) and (3–79) and to the dependence of n on wavelength. Second-order theories (still based on geometric optics) may be developed as an aid to correcting the more important approximations for various specific instruments and applications. Some of the simplest results are:

1. Two thin lenses made of the same material and used with a separation, $t = \frac{1}{2}(f_1 + f_2)$ (that is, in (3–82), $l = -\frac{1}{2}(f_1 + f_2)$), form an "achromatic" thick lens, $df/d\lambda = 0$ (at the wavelength where f_1 and f_2 are measured).
2. Depth of field is greatest and geometric aberrations least when the aperture (effective diameter) of a system is least.
3. A parabolic *mirror* is completely achromatic and, for its axial direction, completely free of geometric aberrations.
4. As a general rule, geometric aberrations are least when the overall refraction of any ray is "divided equally" among the various interfaces of the system—a number of small deviations leads to less aberration than only a few large deviations.
5. An "immersion lens" used with $u = -R\left(1 + \frac{n_2}{n_1}\right)$ is completely free of geometric aberration; "immersion" can be avoided by using a first surface at $u = -R$ so located that $u' = -R\left(1 + \frac{n_2}{n_1}\right)$. ("Aplanatic lenses"—many microscope objectives.)

Despite all this, it should be remembered that the first microscopes were single glass beads mounted in a light shield; magnifications of 200 were obtained, though convenience left something to be desired.

Diffraction Optics

This theory is essentially a first-order correction to the simple approximations of geometric optics. The concepts of wave-spreading ("bending") and interference are re-introduced, but in a simplified manner which uses as a basic tool:

Huygens' principle: Every point on a wave-front can be regarded as a secondary source of waves; the full wave-front at a later time is given by the super-position of all such secondary wavelets.

This principle is rigorously correct for any field which satisfies the wave equation (see (15–55)) but its *application* is usually approximate in that only the incident waves are generally known. (For example, near a conducting screen, there must also be reflected waves which force the total tangential **E** field to vanish.)

Simple *interference arguments* (path difference of $\frac{1}{2}\lambda + N\lambda$ implies zero intensity; $N\lambda$ difference implies full intensity) when combined with Huygens' principle suffice to locate the maxima in the pattern of a grating, interferometer, etalon, etc. To compute continuous patterns (diffraction due to circular hole, slit, disc, knife-edge, etc.) requires more sophisticated integrations based on Huygens' principle.*

* The diffraction pattern for a knife-edge (conducting half-plane) illuminated by a plane wave is one of the few which have been rigorously computed (by analytic methods) directly from Maxwell's equations.

A result of importance for optical lens systems is that the first minimum in the diffraction pattern from a circular lens of diameter d lies in the direction,

$$\theta = \sin^{-1}(1.22\lambda/d) \tag{3-85}$$

(measured from the direction of the geometric ray; λ = wavelength of light in the medium where the image is formed).

Babinet's principle is essentially the observation that, to compute the diffraction pattern of an *obstacle*, it is convenient *not* to integrate "Huygens wavelets" coming from all points around the obstacle. Rather, from the unimpeded intensity pattern (i.e. with the obstacle removed), one may *subtract* the contribution of the Huygens wavelets which are *blocked* by the obstacle.

Thus it is seen that the diffraction pattern from an obstacle is the complement of the pattern due to a similarly shaped hole in an infinite plane screen illuminated by the same source.

Resolution of Optical Systems

From the result (3–85) it follows that two point objects will form over-lapping "images" (diffraction patterns) which cannot be distinguished if their angular separation is less than (about),

$$\Delta\theta \doteq 1.22\lambda/d \tag{3-86}$$

This fundamental limitation is due to the wave-nature of light and thus implies that although "magnifications" can be increased at will, the image will not distinguish any finer details at the same time unless either the diameter of the system (d) is increased or the wavelength (λ) of the light is decreased. (The human eye can resolve about 3 minutes of arc or about 10^{-3} radians.)

Color

Subjectively, color is roughly correlated with (average) wavelength of the light, but (empirically) *any* color can be matched by a proper mixture* of *any* three arbitrary different colors ("primaries"). Therefore, to define "color" objectively, three international primaries† have been adopted. Since only ratios of the amounts (X, Y, Z) of such primaries determine the mixture (their sum only specifies intensity), two numbers, $x = X(X + Y + Z)^{-1}$ and $y = Y(X + Y + Z)^{-1}$, suffice to specify a "color". The standard "tristimulus plot" of colors assigns each color to its point (x, y) in the Cartesian plane.

Pure spectral colors (single-frequency light waves) form an open-loop locus on this plot, and all colors are found to lie within the region bounded by this locus and a straight line joining its ends. (Purples appear near the latter.) When two colors are mixed, the result (necessarily!) lies on the line joining them. White (= gray) falls in a more or less central location ($x = 0.310$, $y = 0.316$) $= W$; any color, A, may also be specified by giving (1) the intersection, H, of the line AW with the spectrum locus (H = "hue" or "dominant wavelength", negative for purples) and (2) the fraction

* Provided (and only provided) "negative" amounts are available—that is provided addition of a primary to the *unknown* is allowed in seeking a match.

† Selected so that any color can be matched using only positive amounts of all three; hence they are not all physically realizable (the second, Y, is the average human visibility curve). However, any "practical" primary can be regarded as a certain mixture (superposition) of the standards.

$(\overline{AW})/(\overline{WH})$, usually expressed as a percentage and called "purity" or "saturation".

The "brightness" of an *object* is its (mean) spectral reflectivity, weighted by the human visibility curve. Thus brightness, an independent parameter, is closely related to color and serves to distinguish white from gray—or orange of low saturation from brown.

Photometry: In illumination engineering, it is obviously advantageous to measure radiation intensity in terms of *useful* power. Thus a family of units (lumen, lux, candle, lambert) have been adopted, all of which are units of integrated (spectral) power *weighted by the average human visibility curve.*

Unfortunately, these units are often very loosely employed. Since the proper correction of a detector (film, photocell, etc.), or source, for spectral response involves tedious numerical integrations. the difference between such instruments and the average human eye is often ignored in quoting data.

CIRCUIT THEORY

At very low frequencies, inhomogeneous physical systems can be analysed by neglecting (a) propagation delays* and (b) "displacement currents" (the term $\partial \mathbf{P}/\partial t$ in (3–14)).

If a typical length (l) of the system is small compared to the wavelength ($2\pi c/\omega$) of the electromagnetic fields, the propagation delays (l/c) will be small compared to the period ($2\pi/\omega$) of field-variations. Neglect of $\partial \mathbf{P}/\partial t$, on the other hand, is justified mainly on the empirical ground that *direct* experimental detection of this term in (3–14) is in fact exceedingly difficult.

The phenomena of primary interest are the flow of currents in wires, the production of mechanical motion, transmission of signals and power, etc.

All media are assumed to be linear;† non-linear devices require special detailed analysis, unless, of course, their use is restricted in such a way that linear approximations may be usefully employed.

Method

To analyse inhomogeneous systems, introduce the potentials (3–29) and (3–30) into the "*microscopic*" equations, (3–1) and (3–2), replacing (3–31) by its microscopic analogue:

$$\nabla \cdot \mathbf{A}_0 = -\frac{1}{c}\frac{\partial \phi_0}{\partial t} \tag{3–87}$$

where the subscript distinguishes these potentials from the potentials used earlier. The results are

$$\left.\begin{aligned} \nabla^2 \phi_0 - \frac{1}{c^2}\frac{\partial^2 \phi_0}{\partial t^2} &= -4\pi\rho_t \\ \nabla^2 \mathbf{A}_0 - \frac{1}{c^2}\frac{\partial^2 \mathbf{A}_0}{\partial t^2} &= -4\pi \mathbf{J}_t/c \end{aligned}\right\} \tag{3–88}$$

From a "microscopic" point of view, there are no "boundaries" between media and

---

* An exception is a long transmission line, but such delays can be re-introduced through circuit theory itself (provided any element of the circuit is directly influenced only by neighboring elements much closer than a wavelength, $2\pi c/\omega$).

† *Superposition*: The response to a sum of stimuli must be the sum of the responses to the separate stimuli when applied individually.

(3–88) is solved by (15–55). When the propagation delay, $|\mathbf{r} - \mathbf{R}|/c$, in that equation is neglected, the resulting ϕ_0 and $\mathbf{A}_0$ satisfy (3–88) only when the time derivatives are neglected. Finally, using (3–14) and neglecting the "displacement current", $\partial\mathbf{P}/\partial t$, the equations determining ϕ_0 and $\mathbf{A}_0$ under the two approximations of circuit theory are:

$$\left.\begin{aligned}\nabla^2\phi_0 &= -4\pi(\rho - \nabla\cdot\mathbf{P})\\ \nabla^2\mathbf{A}_0 &= -\frac{4\pi}{c}(\mathbf{J} + c\nabla\times\mathbf{M})\end{aligned}\right\} \tag{3–89}$$

In addition, recall (3–42) which, especially at low frequencies, implies, to an excellent approximation, that in bulk materials

$$\rho = 0, \qquad \nabla\cdot\mathbf{J} = 0 \tag{3–90}$$

so that the only charges (aside from $\nabla\cdot\mathbf{P}$) which need be considered are *surface charges* residing (almost) literally *on* the boundaries of conductors.

Capacitance

Consider first a set of conductors, S_i, carrying no currents and imbedded in an insulating dielectric medium ($\mu = 1$, $\sigma = 0$), wherein ϵ may vary arbitrarily. Since $\mathbf{J} = 0 = \nabla\times\mathbf{M}$ according to these hypotheses, $\mathbf{A}_0 = 0$ and $\mathbf{E} = -\nabla\phi_0$. Introducing ϵ into (3–89) by (3–15) we have, according to (3–90), within the medium,

$$\nabla\cdot(\epsilon\nabla\phi_0) = 0 \tag{3–91}$$

while at the surface of the conductor, since $0 = (1/\sigma)\mathbf{J} = \mathbf{E} = -\nabla\phi_0$ inside the conductors, (3–23) gives $\hat{n}\times\nabla\phi_0 = 0$. That is, on each conducting surface S_i, ϕ_0 is constant*

$$\phi_0 = V_i, \quad \text{on } S_i \tag{3–92}$$

The problem (3–91), (3–92) is solved by (15–32)–(15–34), namely,

$$\phi_0(\mathbf{r}) = \sum_i V_i \oint\!\!\oint_{S_i} \epsilon(\mathbf{r}_i)\left[\frac{\partial}{\partial n_i} G(\mathbf{r}_i, \mathbf{r})\right] dS_i \tag{3–93}$$

where $G(\mathbf{R}, \mathbf{r})$ [which is, in fact, the potential at $\mathbf{R}$ due to a point charge at $\mathbf{r}$ when all $V_i = 0$] is independent of the values of the V_i. Now according to (3–23), $-\hat{n}\cdot\nabla\phi_0$ evaluated near a conductor is equal to the (*surface*) charge density on the conductor, so that if q_i is the total (net) charge on S_i, we have from (3–93),

$$q_j = \sum_i V_i \left\{\oint\!\!\oint_{S_j} dS_j \frac{\partial}{\partial n_j} \oint\!\!\oint_{S_i} \epsilon \frac{\partial G}{\partial n_i} dS_i\right\} = \sum_i p_{ji} V_i \tag{3–94}$$

where the *constants p_{ij} depend only on the physical system and not on its state of electrical charge.*

By the physical meaning of ϕ_0 (since $\mathbf{A}_0 = 0$, the forces $\mathbf{F} = -e\nabla\phi_0$), the work required to change the charges q_i by amounts dq_i is $dW = \sum_j V_j\, dq_j = \sum_j \sum_i V_j p_{ji}\, dV_i$

* We are here regarding t as a parameter since no time derivatives enter into (3–91) or its boundary conditions.

whence the energy stored in the system by electrical charges* is

$$W = \tfrac{1}{2} \sum_{ij} V_j p_{ji} V_i \tag{3-95}$$

Thus $p_{ij} = 2\partial^2 W/\partial V_i \partial V_j = p_{ji}$ and the matrix p_{ij} is thus symmetric† and positive definite ($W \geqslant 0$). It therefore has a (symmetric) inverse and we may write

$$\boxed{V_k = \sum_j \left(\frac{1}{C_{kj}}\right) q_j; \qquad C_{kj} = C_{jk}} \tag{3-96}$$

while (3–95) becomes

$$W = \tfrac{1}{2} \sum_{ij} \frac{q_i q_j}{C_{ij}} = \tfrac{1}{2} \sum_j V_j q_j \tag{3-97}$$

These coefficients C_{ij} are known as the coefficients of capacity for the system. [They are best computed by solving (3–91) and (3–92) directly and comparing the result with (3–96), whose derivation merely shows that the concept is always valid.] Like the p_{ij}, of course, the C_{ij} depend only on the physical system and not on its state of charge.

Important Special Cases

If $q_1 = -q_2$ and all other $q_j = 0$ (other conductors "floating") then

$$W = \tfrac{1}{2} q_1^2 \left(\frac{1}{C_{11}} + \frac{1}{C_{22}} - \frac{2}{C_{12}}\right) = \frac{1}{2} \frac{q_1^2}{C} \tag{3-98}$$

(say) and then

$$\boxed{V_1 - V_2 = V = q_1/C} \tag{3-99}$$

where C is called the mutual capacity between S_1 and S_2 (with any other conductors "floating" if they are of importance), and V is the "voltage" or "potential difference" across the condenser.

The Case $\mathbf{J} \neq 0$

In this case, (3–92) will not be true in general. However, the conductors may be thought of as split into many small segments, on each of which ϕ_0 is constant ("distributed capacity"). Then, since by (3–89) ϕ_0 is completely determined by ρ and the boundary conditions (3–92), this "augmented circuit" can be analysed as before to obtain (many new) geometrically defined quantities C_{ik} with the same properties (3–96). [Equation (3–97) does not obviously hold except for slowly-varying charges since in general $\partial \mathbf{A}_0/\partial t \neq 0$. However, compare (3–109) below.] Usually (because of this difficulty) circuits are carefully designed so that (3–92) is true over large portions of conductors (plates of a condenser) while capacitative effects are nearly negligible elsewhere. An exception is a continuous transmission line where the subdivision process must be carried to the limit, $dl \to 0$.

---

* Not all of this energy need be in "electrical form"; for example, some may be in elastic distortion of the polarized dielectric (piezoelectric effect).

† This also follows from (3–94) since $G(\mathbf{r}_1, \mathbf{r}_2) = G(\mathbf{r}_2, \mathbf{r}_1)$; see (15–31).

Imperfect Dielectrics

Condensers with imperfect insulation can still be analysed under the condition (3–92), if the required currents are not too great. Then $\partial \mathbf{A}_0/\partial t = 0$ so that $E = -\nabla\phi_0$ as before and the only remaining alteration in the previous argument is that $q_i \neq -\oint\!\!\oint \hat{n} \cdot \nabla\phi \, dS$. If the leakage is small, however, this effect can be shown to be unimportant and the final result is simply to add resistors in parallel with the otherwise "perfect" condensers to allow for the necessary current flow.

If the leakage flow is large, these techniques fail, and the system must be more completely analysed in its own right.

Resistance and Inductance

Consider a length of conducting wire (possibly coiled) imbedded in an insulating medium. Take the line-integral ($\mathbf{dr}_0$) of (3–30) along (within) the wire from end to end. Because $\mathbf{E} = (1/\sigma)\mathbf{J}$ within the wire

$$\frac{1}{c}\frac{\mathrm{d}}{\mathrm{d}t}\int_a^b \mathbf{A}_0 \cdot \mathbf{dr}_0 + \frac{1}{\sigma}\int_a^b \mathbf{J} \cdot \mathbf{dr}_0 = \phi_0(a) - \phi_0(b) \tag{3–100}$$

(This form is also valid if the wire is moving, provided that either the points a and b are identical or both are fixed in position.*) By (3–90) and since no current can leave the wire,† Gauss' theorem shows that a constant net current,

$$I = \underset{\substack{\text{cross}\\ \text{section}}}{\oint\!\!\oint} \mathbf{J} \cdot \frac{\mathbf{dr}_0}{\mathrm{d}r_0}\, \mathrm{d}S \tag{3–101}$$

must flow through all cross sections. It follows that the quantity,

$$R = \frac{1}{I\sigma}\int_a^b \mathbf{J} \cdot \mathbf{dr}_0 = \frac{(1/\sigma)\int_a^b \mathbf{J} \cdot \mathbf{dr}_0}{\oint\!\!\oint \mathbf{J} \cdot \mathbf{dS}} \tag{3–102}$$

known as the resistance of the wire, depends only on (1) the conductivity and shape of the wire and (2) the *distribution* of the current I in the wire. (At very low frequencies,

---

* Compare (3–10) and (3–11). More completely: If the wire is moving, then by (3–20) the right side of (3–100) should read (for $v \ll c$)

$$\int_{a(t)}^{b(t)} \frac{1}{c}\frac{\partial \mathbf{A}_0}{\partial t} \cdot \mathbf{dr}_0 + \frac{1}{\sigma}\int_a^b \mathbf{J} \cdot \mathbf{dr}_0 - \int_{a(t)}^{b(t)} \frac{\mathbf{v}}{c} \times (\nabla \times \mathbf{A}_0) \cdot \mathbf{dr}_0$$

The first term represents only that part of the total time derivative which is due to changes in $\mathbf{A}_0$. The last term may be written

$$+\frac{1}{c}\int_a^b (\nabla \times \mathbf{A}_0) \cdot (\mathbf{v} \times \mathbf{dr}_0).$$

Multiply by $\mathrm{d}t$ and note that $(\mathbf{v}\,\mathrm{d}t) \times \mathbf{dr}_0$ is an elemental area, $\mathbf{dS}$, of the surface swept out by the wire in time $\mathrm{d}t$. By Stokes' theorem, this can be converted to a line integral about that area. On dividing by $\mathrm{d}t$ and taking the limit as $\mathrm{d}t \to 0$, using the definition of a derivative, one finds that

$$\frac{\mathrm{d}}{\mathrm{d}t}\int_{a(t)}^{b(t)} \mathbf{A}_0 \cdot \mathbf{dr}_0(t) = \int_a^b \frac{\partial \mathbf{A}_0}{\partial t} \cdot \mathbf{dr}_0 - \int_a^b \mathbf{v} \times (\nabla \times \mathbf{A}_0) \cdot \mathbf{dr}_0 - (\mathbf{v} \cdot \mathbf{A}_0)_a + (\mathbf{v} \cdot \mathbf{A}_0)_b$$

and thus (3–100) is obtained in general if a and b are identical or if $\mathbf{v}_a = 0 = \mathbf{v}_b$.

† The slight effects of "inter-turn capacitance" can be treated as a small perturbation.

J is uniform across the wire; at high frequencies, it is confined to a skin of thickness δ, given by (3–47), as follows from (3–50); strong magnetic fields can also affect the distribution.)

To evaluate the first term in (3–100), consider first that $\mu = 1$ everywhere so that $\mathbf{M} = 0$. Then the solution of (3–89), namely (15–55), gives

$$\int_a^b d\mathbf{r}_0 \cdot \mathbf{A}_0(\mathbf{r}_0) = \int_a^b d\mathbf{r}_0 \cdot \oint\oint\oint \frac{\mathbf{J}(\mathbf{r})\, dV}{c|\mathbf{r} - \mathbf{r}_0|} \tag{3–103}$$

If all currents of the system (or at least those which contribute significantly in (3–103)) are confined to various wires, $i = 0, 1, 2, \cdots$ and if the current distribution in each is always symmetric about its axis, then the "transverse" vector components of the triple integral in (3–103) cancel over any small length $d\mathbf{r}_i$ and we may write:

$$\frac{1}{c}\int_a^b \mathbf{A}_0(\mathbf{r}_0) \cdot d\mathbf{r}_0 = \sum_i \int_a^b d\mathbf{r}_0 \cdot \int_{a_i}^{b_i} \frac{d\mathbf{r}_i}{c^2|\mathbf{r}_0 - \mathbf{r}_i|} \left[\oint\oint \mathbf{J} \cdot \frac{d\mathbf{r}_i}{dr_i}\, dS_i\right]$$

$$= \sum_i I_i \int_a^b \int_{a_i}^{b_i} \frac{d\mathbf{r}_0 \cdot d\mathbf{r}_i}{c^2|\mathbf{r}_0 - \mathbf{r}_i|} \tag{3–104}$$

The coefficient:*

$$L_{ij} = \int_{a_i}^{b_i} \int_{a_j}^{b_j} \frac{d\mathbf{r}_i \cdot d\mathbf{r}_j}{c^2|\mathbf{r}_i - \mathbf{r}_j|} = L_{ji} \quad \text{(air core)} \tag{3–105}$$

(for MKS units, replace $1/c^2$ by $\mu/4\pi$; the formula (3–102) for R is unchanged). L_{ij} depends only on the geometric configuration of the wires i, j and is known as the (mutual) inductance between i and j.

When $i = j$, the more general integral (3–103) should be used, but a good approximation is: (1) take $d\mathbf{r}_0$ in (3–105) on the wire axis and $d\mathbf{r}'_0$ at its surface ("external inductance"—dV in (3–103) outside the wire) and (2) add to this result the "internal inductance (dV inside the wire) computed from (3–103) on the simple assumption that the internal $\mathbf{A}_0$ is the same as in an infinite straight cylindrical wire. [See (3–114), (3–115) below.]

If $\mu \neq 1$, there is no such simple formula as (3–105), but since, by (3–89)

$$\mathbf{A}_0(\mathbf{r}) = \oint\oint\oint \frac{\mathbf{J} + c\nabla \times \mathbf{M}}{c|\mathbf{r}' - \mathbf{r}|}\, dV'$$

and **M** is linear in the magnetic field (provided μ is independent of field strength), $\mathbf{A}_0$ is nevertheless linear in the various currents. Thus in any case, whether (3–105) is valid or not,

$$\boxed{\frac{1}{c}\frac{d}{dt}\int_a^b \mathbf{A}_0 \cdot d\mathbf{r}_0 = \sum_i \frac{d}{dt}(L_{0i}I_i)} \tag{3–106}$$

provided the media are linear.

---

* Note that the signs of the mutual inductance, L_{ij}, $i \neq j$ are determined by the (arbitrary) choice of direction for positive currents I_i and I_j.

Circuit Equations

Combining (3–100), (3–102) and (3–106) and denoting $\phi_0(a)$ by V_a etc., and the potential difference, $V_a - V_b$, by V:

$$V = V_a - V_b = RI + \sum_{i=0}^{n} \frac{d}{dt}[L_{0i}I_i] \tag{3–107}$$

Equations (3–99) and (3–107) are the basic relations of circuit theory and replace Maxwell's equations for low-frequency analysis, when combined with the conservation laws:

1. At any junction: $\sum_k I_k = 0 \qquad (\nabla \cdot \mathbf{J} = 0)$
2. About any closed path (metallic or not)

$$\sum V_{\text{drop}} = \sum (V_i - V_{i+1}) = 0.$$

("Kirchhoff's laws".) Note that V is defined in terms of ϕ_0, which satisfies (3–89) and *not* (3–32).

Power Flow

For quasi-static changes, (3–97) gives the energy stored in a condenser. By energy conservation and by (3–99) it then follows, at least for quasi-static changes, that the expression,

$$P(t) = (V_a - V_b)I = V(t)I(t) \tag{3–108}$$

must represent instantaneous electrical power flow in any circuit. It is usual to assume that (3–108) is generally valid under any circumstances (where V and I have meaning) and indeed this is in complete accord with experiment.

Direct justification from Maxwell's equations is rather difficult, partly because of many special cases which should be considered.* One rather general justification can be obtained as follows.

With no approximations whatever, it is easily shown that

$$\oiiint \mathbf{E} \cdot \mathbf{J}\, dV = \oiiint \left(\phi_0 \frac{\partial \rho}{\partial t} + \mathbf{J} \cdot \frac{\partial \mathbf{A}_0}{c\partial t}\right) dV + \oiint \phi_0 \mathbf{J} \cdot d\mathbf{s} \tag{3–109}$$

and this may be interpreted as an energy-conservation theorem with as much justification as for Poynting's theorem, (3–26). If circuit-theory approximations are applied to (3–109) (divide each wire into many small filaments each carrying a constant current, dI), the result is equivalent to (3–108).

Energy

A consequence of (3–108) is that (3–97) and (3–98) represent electrostatic stored energy while, if L_{ij} are constant,

$$W_m = \tfrac{1}{2}\sum_{ij} I_i L_{ij} I_j \tag{3–110}$$

is the magnetic stored energy. These relations, which may be established directly

* For example, if motors or generators are involved or if the boundary of the region of interest cuts through a condenser or a transformer core.

from (3–4) for "quasi-static" changes, are often used as a basis for deriving the circuit relations (3–99) and (3–107).*

Estimation of R, L, C

1. *Energy storage:*

$$\tfrac{1}{2}CV^2 = W = \oint\!\!\oint\!\!\oint \frac{\mathbf{E}\cdot\mathbf{D}}{8\pi}\,\mathrm{d}V \tag{3–111}$$

$$\tfrac{1}{2}LI^2 = \oint\!\!\oint\!\!\oint \frac{\mathbf{H}\cdot\mathbf{B}}{8\pi}\,\mathrm{d}V \tag{3–112}$$

(For MKS units, replace $1/8\pi$ by $\tfrac{1}{2}$.)

2. *Flux linkage:* If the ends of the circuit are close together and there are n turns,

$$LI = \oint \mathbf{A}_0\cdot \mathrm{d}\mathbf{r}_0 = n\oint\!\!\oint \mathbf{B}\cdot\mathrm{d}\mathbf{S} \tag{3–113}$$

(same in MKS units). This is most useful for iron-cored circuits where **B** is easily estimated from the relation, $\oint \mathbf{H}\cdot\mathrm{d}\mathbf{l} = \oint\!\oint \mathbf{J}\cdot\mathrm{d}\mathbf{A} = nI$, for MKS units.

3. *Skin effect:* (L_i = "internal" inductance; δ = skin depth)

(a) At low frequencies ($\delta \gg$ thickness; A = area of cross section)

$$R = l/(\sigma A); \qquad L_i = l\mu/(2c^2) \tag{3–114}$$

(MKS: replace $1/c^2$ by $1/4\pi$.)

(b) At high frequencies ($\delta \ll$ thickness; p = perimeter of cross section)

$$R = \frac{l}{\sigma p\delta}; \qquad L_i = R/\omega \tag{3–115}$$

(any units).

Moveable Circuits

In general (3–99) and (3–107) must be supplemented by mechanical equations of motion for the various parts of the circuit (and any other mechanical system to which they may be coupled). Coupling between the electrical and mechanical behaviors may arise either through basic properties of matter (piezoelectricity, magnetostriction) or through electromagnetic volume forces, (3–3)–(3–5).

Forces: Though in some cases direct space-integration of (3–4) or (3–5) will readily yield the desired forces, it is often more expedient to evaluate forces or torques by the *energy principle*:

$$-\delta W_{\text{mech}} = \tfrac{1}{2}\sum_{ij} q_i q_j\,\delta\!\left(\frac{1}{C_{ij}}\right) + \tfrac{1}{2}\sum_{kl} I_k I_l\,\delta(L_{kl}) \tag{3–117}$$

Thus, for example, the (electromagnetic) torque, T, on the rotor of a generator or motor is

$$T = \tfrac{1}{2}\sum_{kl} I_k I_l \frac{\partial L_{kl}}{\partial \theta} \tag{3–118}$$

where I_k are the currents in the various windings and θ measures the angular position of the rotor.

* If condenser-plates or coils are allowed to move, the work expended against mechanical forces *may* be included as "electromagnetic" stored energy if it can be fed back later (restoring springs in meters or electroscopes, etc.). It is more common, however, at least for magnetic circuits and especially for motors and generators, to regard such energy as non-electric. Equation (3–110) then holds in general (that is for $\mathrm{d}L_{ij}/\mathrm{d}t \neq 0$) with this convention regarding the meaning of W_m.

Commutation: In certain motors and generators, additional complications enter because electrical connections are constantly changed (by the brushes). A good approximation is that the net effect* is as if the inductances were constant in time but nevertheless had non-vanishing time derivatives (!):

$$\text{Effective} \quad \frac{\mathrm{d}L_{kl}}{\mathrm{d}t} = \frac{\mathrm{d}\theta}{\mathrm{d}t}\frac{\partial L_{kl}}{\partial \theta} \tag{3–119}$$

where $\partial L_{kl}/\partial\theta$ is evaluated for the circuits through (any) set of commutator bars as they momentarily engage the brushes.

EXAMPLE. If all I_k are constant and the rotor is mechanically driven at constant speed, $\mathrm{d}\theta/\mathrm{d}t$, then (3–107) and (3–119) show that a d.c.* voltage appears across the brushes. By (3–108) and (3–118), the mechanical power input, $T(\mathrm{d}\theta/\mathrm{d}t)$, is precisely accounted for by the electrical power output, $\sum V_i I_i$ (plus friction losses, in practice).

Quasi-Linear and Active Devices

Almost any device, provided it is to be subject to sufficiently small voltage and current *changes* can be approximated by a set of linear relations (Taylor's series) valid over small excursions. (Conversely, of course, almost any practical device becomes non-linear when excursions of voltage or current become very large.)

In many devices, it is also convenient to ignore (or separate out) "internal" processes which enter only as parameters into the overall relations between the "signal" voltages or currents at the terminals. In this way arises the concept of an "active" device, which can supply more power than is fed into it.

Important Examples of these Engineering Principles

1. **"Iron"-cored devices:** High inductances are most readily obtained with ferromagnetic flux paths. *If* this iron is not magnetically saturated, the non-linear, multi-valued relation between **B** and **H** may be approximated by an "average, effective" μ and an effective additional series resistance (in the winding) to simulate the power lost, $\frac{1}{8\pi}\oint(\oint\!\!\oint\!\!\oint \mathbf{H}\cdot\mathbf{B}\,\mathrm{d}V)\,\mathrm{d}t$ per cycle, by "hysteresis" (internal solid-state friction). This "resistor" is proportional to the frequency for sinusoidal currents. In addition, since ferromagnetic materials are usually good conductors, $\mathrm{d}\mathbf{B}/\mathrm{d}t$ generates conduction currents (geometry-dependent; hence laminated or powdered cores) whose power dissipation must also be represented by additional series resistance (which is proportional to the square of the frequency for sinusoidal currents).

2. **Transformers:** Neglecting internal losses, magnetic flux leakage and winding capacitance, it follows from (3–100) and $\oint \mathbf{H}\cdot\mathrm{d}\mathbf{l} = \oint\!\!\oint \nabla \times \mathbf{H}\cdot\mathrm{d}\mathbf{S} = \frac{4\pi}{c}\sum n_i I_i$ that

$$L_0 \frac{\mathrm{d}}{\mathrm{d}t}\sum_1^N n_i I_i = \frac{V_1 - R_1 I_1}{n_1} = \frac{V_2 - R_2 I_2}{n_2} = \cdots = \frac{V_N - R_N I_N}{n_N} \tag{3–120}$$

Winding capacitance may be adjoined to these relations by imagining equivalent lumped capacitors connected across (and perhaps between) the windings.‡ Power

---

* Strictly: as the number of commutator bars becomes infinite.

‡ These various capacitors determine the high-frequency cut-off of a transformer, while L_0 determines its low-frequency cut-off. As may be seen from (3–120), when only one current is non-zero, $n_i^2 L_0$ is the "open circuit inductance" of the ith winding and is thus easily estimated by (3–112) or (3–113).

losses due to hysteresis and eddy-currents are here proportional to $(\sum n_i I_i)^2$ (that is, $|\mathbf{B}|^2$); equivalent resistors may be placed in any winding (whose current is non-zero) but depend on the loads on all other windings. Alternatively, one may write in place of (3–120),

$$R_0 \sum_1^N n_i I_i + L_0 \frac{d}{dt} \sum_1^N n_i I_i = \frac{V_1 - R_1 I_1}{n_1} = \cdots = \frac{V_N - R_N I_N}{n_N} \tag{3–121}$$

where R_0 depends on frequency (for sinusoidal currents) as $a\omega + b\omega^2$. (Note that $n_i^2 R_0 + R_i$ is the total resistance of winding i with all others open-circuited.)

An *"ideal" transformer* is an approximation wherein all $R_i = 0$ and $L_0 \to \infty$ so that

$$\sum_1^N n_i I_i = 0; \qquad \frac{V_1}{n_1} = \frac{V_2}{n_2} = \cdots = \frac{V_N}{n_N} \tag{3–122}$$

The quantity $\sum n_i I_i$ (for a real transformer) is often called the "magnetizing current" and is usually referred to the input, or driven winding.

3. **Batteries:** The current-voltage relation can usually be approximated by

$$I = \frac{1}{R_i}(V_0 - V) - C_b \frac{dV}{dt} \tag{3–123}$$

That is, an ideal battery with voltage V_0 in series with the "internal" resistance R_i, the whole shunted by a capacitance C_b.

4. **Vacuum tubes; transistors, magnetic amplifiers, etc:** In all these devices there are fundamental requirements (bias, power supply, etc.) which, however, can be ignored when considering only the "signal" voltages and currents. The latter are connected by relations which are approximately linear and contain the biassing conditions only as implicit parameters, determining the coefficients in the linear "signal" equations. Some specific equations are given later.

Systematics of Stationary Circuit Analysis

Harmonic time dependence is a basic special case. If all currents and voltages vary as e^{pt} $(p = i\omega)$, the fundamental relations (for constant-parameter circuits) were shown to be:

$$\left.\begin{array}{ll} V = I/Cp, & \text{for a capacitor} \\ V = RI_0 + \sum_i L_{0i} p I_i, & \text{for a resistor or inductor} \end{array}\right\} (p = i\omega) \tag{3–124}$$

$$\sum I_k = 0, \quad \text{at a junction (node)} \tag{3–125}$$

$$\sum V_k = 0, \quad \text{around any closed path} \tag{3–126}$$

And the *average* power flow is given by ("Re" means "real part of"):

$$P_{\text{avg}} = \tfrac{1}{2}\text{Re}\,(VI^*) = \tfrac{1}{4}(VI^* + V^*I) \tag{3–127}$$

since $|V|$ and $|I|$ are the peak values and $\langle \sin^2 \omega t \rangle_{\text{avg}} = \frac{1}{2}$.

More generally, if all currents and charges vanish* at $t = 0$, (3–124) *is the Laplace transform* of the relations (3–99) and (3–107) (for constant parameters) and therefore (3–124) determines the transient and general-time-dependence behaviors as well

* If not, of course, terms such as CpV should be replaced by $CpV - CV_{t=0}$, etc.

(linearity and hence superposition was assumed at the outset). (Note that (3–127), being non-linear, is not so readily regarded as a transform.)

This observation involves a tacit idealization, for (3–124) is thereby assumed to be valid at arbitrarily high frequencies; although the latter is physically false, circuit theory is nevertheless a self-consistent idealization and experimentally correct results are obtained—to within the limitations of the original assumptions of moderate frequency-components and finite time resolution.

Circuit Concepts

Although (3–124)–(3–127) completely determine the behavior of any stationary circuit, much labor can be avoided and much insight gained by using some techniques and concepts developed for such problems:

Impedance between two terminals is defined as

$$Z(p) = R(p) + iX(p) \equiv \frac{V}{I} \tag{3–128}$$

with the sign convention that Re (VI^*) represents power fed *to* the circuit. Thus $R \geqslant 0$ for a passive circuit.

Admittance

$$Y(p) = G(p) + iB(p) \equiv \frac{I}{V} = \frac{1}{Z(p)} \tag{3–129}$$

(same sign convention, $G \geqslant 0$ for passive circuits).

External terminal. A "circuit," in a more general sense, is described not merely by its elements and their interconnections but also by the "context" in which it is to be used. Thus internal currents and voltages usually are of no interest. This distinction is conventionally described by denoting (as part of the definition of the circuit) certain nodes as "external terminals," at which a voltage may be applied or a current introduced from outside the network. The context may also specify that voltages may be applied *only* across certain *pairs* of external terminals.

Analysis

To analyze a complex circuit, it is first represented as an assemblage of interconnected impedances or admittances.* The conditions (3–125) and (3–126) can be satisfied automatically by either of the following systematic techniques. (A third technique is described under "signal flow graphs").

A. Mesh Analysis

(*Impedance Matrix;* always directly applicable but sometimes inefficient)

1. Envisage external voltage sources connected across all external terminals (as allowed by context or intended use). These (ideal) generators are regarded as parts of the circuits in the following steps.

2. Choose a set of ("independent mesh") currents, I_i, which circulate in closed

* Mutual inductive coupling must be represented by (arrows or other) notations on the diagram. The signs of such M_{ik} are arbitrary (*a priori*) but must be consistent:

$$M_{ik} = M_{ki}$$

loops through the circuit in such a manner that (a) every link is traversed by at least one current and (b) every current is the *only* one flowing in *some* link.*

2′. In addition it is usually expedient to require, if possible, that: (c) every generator, V_i, is traversed by only one current with such sign that $\mathrm{Re}\,(V_iI_i^*)$ represents power supplied by V_i.

3. One may always write out equations (3–126) for each of the loops [mutual coupling, M_{ik}, produces an extra voltage drop, $pM_{ik}I_k$, in coil L_i and $pM_{ik}I_i$ in coil L_k; the net current through any link is the algebraic sum of the mesh currents through it]. Better if applicable:

3′. If (c) above is satisfied, then, by (3–126), generator voltage in loop i is $V_i = \sum_k Z_{ik}I_k$ where:

$$\left.\begin{aligned} Z_{ii} &= \text{sum of } Z\text{'s in loop } i \\ Z_{ik} &= Z_{ki} = \text{sum of } Z\text{'s common to loops } i,\ k \end{aligned}\right\} \tag{3–130}$$

In the second line, a common impedance is taken negative if I_i and I_k flow through it in opposite directions; the second sum also includes (p times) any mutual inductance (sign ambiguous) which couples the loops.

If ideal transformers occur, (3–122) must be adjoined to the matrix relations (3–130) as separate restrictions. An *ideal* transformer has neither an impedance matrix nor an admittance matrix.

B. Node Pair Analysis

(*Admittance Matrix;* impractical if mutual inductances occur but otherwise very convenient—especially for interconnection of networks with more than two external terminals.)

Assume no mutual inductance (or at least none not already absorbed into link-admittances).

1. Choose one node of the network as reference (ground).

2. Choose as independent voltages, V_i, the voltage differences between each remaining node and ground. ("Internal" nodes must be included; the number of V_i = number of nodes — 1.)

3. By (3–125):

$$\text{current into node } i = I_i = \sum_k Y_{ik}V_k$$

where

$$\left.\begin{aligned} Y_{ii} &= \text{sum of } Y\text{'s connected to node } i \\ Y_{ik} &= Y_{ki} = \text{minus the sum of } Y\text{'s connected } \textit{directly} \\ &\qquad\qquad \text{between nodes } i,\ k \text{ (usually only one)} \end{aligned}\right\} \tag{3–131}$$

C. INTERRELATIONS OF A AND B

If the V_i and I_i involved in (3–130) and (3–131) are identical, then

$$Y_{ik} = (Z^{-1})_{ik} \tag{3–132}$$

and if the network contains mutual inductances, this may be the simplest way to evaluate Y_{ik}.

* The number of independent meshes is $m = z - n + p$, where the circuit has z links, n nodes, and p disconnected parts (which may be inductively coupled but are not connected metallically or by condensers).

Elimination of Floating (Open) Nodes or "Generatorless" (Shorted) Meshes

Usually A. or B. above give too much information and one desires to obtain results for some V's $= 0$ (with Z_{ik}) or some I's $= 0$ (with Y_{ik}). The method of sub-matrices (following (11–22)) is useful for eliminating uninteresting currents or voltages. Thus (all letters are matrices):

$$\text{If} \quad \begin{pmatrix} I \\ 0 \end{pmatrix} = \left(\begin{array}{c|c} Y & U \\ \hline H & y \end{array}\right) \begin{pmatrix} V \\ v \end{pmatrix} \quad \text{then}$$

$$I = (Y - Uy^{-1}H)V \tag{3–133}$$

Thus it is *always most convenient to assign to external nodes or meshes the lowest index numbers.*

Change of Reference (Ground) Node—"Floating" Admittance Matrix

First "border" Y_{ik} with an additional row and column, both labeled to correspond to the old reference (ground) node. Fill these $(2n + 1)$ extra boxes $Y_{i,n+1} = Y_{n+1,i}$ in such a manner that *all rows and columns sum to zero* in the new matrix.*

To choose any other node as ground, simply cross out the corresponding row and column from the new ("floating") matrix.

Shorting Two Nodes Together

Since the two node voltages are thus forced to be equal while their currents add to a new current, the proper manipulation on the Y matrix is to (a) replace the corresponding rows by their sum and (b) *then* replace the corresponding columns by *their* sum.

Interconnection of Networks

First, arrange each $Y^{(i)}$ matrix to contain rows and columns corresponding to all nodes which will appear in the final network (and which are composed of external nodes of the originals). [Those which are not part of, say, network #1 have zeros in the corresponding rows and columns of $Y^{(1)}$.]
Then

$$Y = Y^{(1)} + Y^{(2)}$$

(With practice, the explicit enlargement of $Y^{(i)}$ can be omitted and Y written down directly.)

Unless the two reference nodes are to be joined into one final reference node, this operation must be done with the "floating" matrices.

Active Circuits

Active circuits do not in general have symmetric Y or Z matrices:

---

* This matrix may also be obtained by "adding to" the circuit an extra node *not connected* to anything and using it as the reference node in B. That is the whole circuit is regarded as "floating above ground."

Vacuum tube: Floating Y matrix at low frequencies,

	g	p	c
g	0	0	0
p	g_m	g_p	$-g_m-g_p$
c	$-g_m$	$-g_p$	g_m+g_p

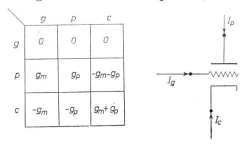

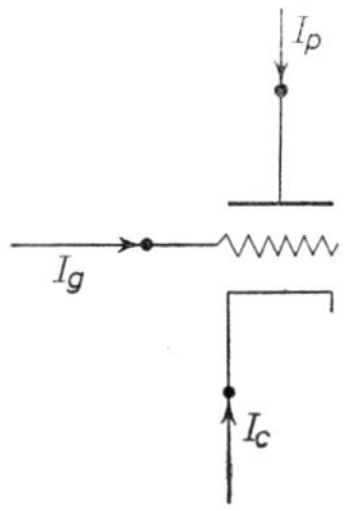

$$g_m = \text{“mutual conductance”} = (\partial I_p/\partial V_g)_{V_p}$$

$$g_p = 1/r_p = \text{“plate conductance”} = (\partial I_p/\partial V_p)_{V_g}$$

At high frequencies, add to this the capacity matrix:

$+p(C_{gp}+C_{gc})$	$-pC_{gp}$	$-pC_{gc}$
$-pC_{gp}$	$+p(C_{gp}+C_{pc})$	$-pC_{pc}$
$-pC_{gc}$	$-pC_{pc}$	$+p(C_{gc}+C_{pc})$

At still higher frequencies, "transit time" delay factors, $e^{-p\tau}$ should multiply the conductance elements (but not the capacities). Note that, in all connections, a tube has no $Z = Y^{-1}$ matrix at low frequencies. (This is not true of transistors, none of whose Y_{ik} vanish at low frequencies.)

Feedback

This is primarily a qualitative concept (important only for active circuits). The general principle is that the input and output of a circuit are compared (output is "fed back") and the resulting error signal is amplified in such a manner as to correct the output.

In quasi-linear analysis, feedback is mainly an heuristic guide, suggesting circuits worth analyzing. However, in practice, feedback has the great practical advantage of *reducing effects due to non-linearities and parameter variations* (e.g. tube aging) in the circuits across which it operates. This is the main effect of its "self-correcting" nature, but it can be brought out only by non-linear analysis or by studying parameter variations.

[*Stability of feedback*: If too much self-correcting (negative) feedback is applied across any amplifier, the circuit will oscillate. This arises from the inherent phase-shifts of the amplifier near its high-frequency cut-off (see (3–140)); in essence the phase-shift causes the feedback to become positive at high frequencies and if this occurs where the amplifier gain is larger than the feedback ratio, oscillation will occur.]

Other Matrix Techniques

Communication and transmission circuits frequently involve cascaded "two-terminal pair" networks,* and the matrix relating (V_{out}, I_{out}) to (V_{in}, I_{in}) is then

* Distinguished from "four terminal" networks by their *incomplete* specification; the description, (V_{in}, I_{in}) (V_{out}, I_{out}), for example, does not specify the effect of connecting a voltage between one input and one output terminal. Compare a transformer.

useful since the corresponding matrix for a cascade is simply the (matrix) product of the matrices for the individual "black boxes."

In particular *continuous transmission lines* may be approached from the circuit point of view as the limiting case of a cascade of very many short "filter sections," each containing a series impedance Z_s and a shunt admittance Y_s proportional to its physical length. The result is identical (except near joints) with analysis based on Maxwell's equations:

$$\begin{pmatrix} V_1 \\ I_1 \end{pmatrix} = \left(\begin{array}{c|c} \cosh \Gamma l & Z_0 \sinh \Gamma l \\ \hline Z_0^{-1} \sinh \Gamma l & \cosh \Gamma l \end{array} \right) \times \begin{pmatrix} V_2 \\ I_2 \end{pmatrix}$$

where

$$Z_0 = \sqrt{Z_s/Y_s} \quad \text{and} \quad \Gamma = \sqrt{Z_s Y_s}$$

Many simple circuits with "distributed constants" can profitably be approximated by lengths of such lines in combination with other elements. Eventually, however, circuit theory must give way to Maxwell's equations at very high frequencies.

Thévenin's Theorem

Any network "with two external terminals" is equivalent (externally) to an ideal (voltage) generator in series with an impedance. The voltage of the generator equals the open-circuit voltage at the terminals, and the impedance (= that seen looking in) is the ratio: (open-circuit voltage)/(short-circuit current).

The network is also equivalent to a current generator* in shunt with an admittance = (short-circuit current)/(open-circuit voltage) = admittance looking in at the terminals. The current of the generator = short-circuit current.

The theorem is an immediate consequence of the linearity of (3–124)–(3–126).

Maximum Power Transfer ("Matching") Theorem

A generator (with a series internal impedance, Z_g) delivers the greatest power to a load whose impedance is

$$Z = (Z_g)^* \qquad \text{or} \qquad Y = (Y_g)^* \tag{3–134}$$

Under this "matched" condition, half the total power is dissipated in the load.

This theorem is a consequence of (3–127). Even as an approximation, (3–134) can be satisfied only over a limited range of frequencies.

Complex Frequencies, Analycity

In (3–124)–(3–126) and all subsequent manipulations, p can perfectly well assume arbitrary complex values. The time dependance Re (e^{pt}) then represents an impractical but not impossible way of driving any network. In this way, all elements of all impedance and admittance matrices may be (*physically*) regarded as functions of a complex variable, p.

Moreover, since any Z_{ik} or Y_{ik} can be regarded as the ratio of the Laplace transforms of two functions, $I_i(t)$ and $V_k(t)$, these "immittance" elements are *analytic* functions

* An ideal device through which a given current always flows, independently of all other conditions; a current generator is always associated with a shunt admittance. In practice, it is approximated by a ("voltage") generator in series with a very high impedance.

of the complex variable, p, (at least for sufficiently large Re (p) and thus, by analytic continuation, elsewhere).

Stability

A zero of Det (Y_{ik}) at $p = p_0$ indicates that the network can support an oscillation, $V_j(t) = A_j e^{p_0 t}$, even if all external node-currents vanish identically. A circuit is said to be (open-circuit*) *stable* if all such natural oscillations do not grow† (that is, if Re $(p_0) \leqslant 0$ for each). The circuit need not be passive.

More general concepts of stability are often useful and are usually defined by the context. [EXAMPLES: Stability under a class of parameter-changes (such as tube-aging), stability with arbitrary passive loads across certain terminals. (No circuit capable of power gain is stable under *all* passive external connections; it can always be connected as an oscillator.)]

Raisbeck's Passivity Theorem

The total power delivered to a circuit is non-negative under all possible excitations if and only if the matrix $(Y + Y^{\dagger})$ is positive semi-definite: that is, if and only if all the roots of

are non-negative:

$$\left.\begin{aligned} \text{Det}\,\|Y_{ik} + Y_{ki}^* - y\,\delta_{ik}\| &= 0 \\ y_j &\geqslant 0 \end{aligned}\right\} \tag{3–135}$$

For a 2×2 admittance matrix $Y_{ik} = G_{ik} + iB_{ik}$, these conditions are

$$\left.\begin{aligned} G_{11} + G_{22} &\geqslant 0 \\ 4(G_{11}G_{22} - G_{12}G_{21}) &\geqslant (G_{12} - G_{21})^2 + (B_{12} - B_{21})^2 \end{aligned}\right\} \tag{3–136}$$

Violation of these conditions (at any complex frequency) implies that power gain can be obtained from the circuit (at that frequency).

The theorem (3–135) is an immediate consequence of (3–127):

$$2P = \text{Re}\,(\sum V_i Y_{ik}^* V_k^*) = \tfrac{1}{2}\text{Re}\,[\sum V_i(Y_{ik} + Y_{ki}^*)V_k^*] \geqslant 0,$$

for all V_i.

The theorem applies equally well to the impedance matrix, Z_{ik}.

Nyquist's Stability Criterion

This is essentially the observation that (see theorem preceding (12–11)) if $Y(p)$ is analytic in Re $(p) > 0$ and if its values are plotted (in a complex Y plane) as p traverses the imaginary axis plus a large $(|p| \to \infty)$ semi-circle in Re $(p) > 0$, then $Y(p)$ will encircle its origin, $Y = 0$, if and only if Y has zeros in Re $(p) > 0$.

Such a criterion is easy to apply to complicated circuits since it involves only straightforward evaluation of Y rather than solution of high-order algebraic equations.

---

* If all zeros of Det (Z_{ik}) lie in Re $(p) \leqslant 0$, then the circuit cannot oscillate with all $V_k = 0$ and is said to be short-circuit stable.

† In a practical circuit, a growing oscillation can continue its growth only so long as the approximation of linearity remains valid. The level of any practical oscillator is always set by some form of nonlinearity.

CIRCUIT SYNTHESIS

Brune's Theorem

A rational function $Z(p)$ is the impedance of a passive (lumped-constant) two-terminal circuit if and only if

$$\left.\begin{aligned} &1.\ Z(p) \text{ is real whenever } p \text{ is real} \\ &2.\ Z(p) \text{ is analytic in } \operatorname{Re}(p) > 0 \\ &\qquad (\text{except possibly at } p = \infty) \\ &3.\ \operatorname{Re}(Z(p)) \geqslant 0 \text{ whenever } \operatorname{Re}(p) \geqslant 0 \end{aligned}\right\} \tag{3–137}$$

The necessity of these conditions follows from the form of (3–124)-(3–126), from (short-circuit) stability and from (3–135). Sufficiency is proven by exhibiting a (lumped-constant) circuit with impedance $Z(p)$—thereby showing how any such impedance function can be *synthesized.*

In essence the Brune synthesis procedure consists of (a) "removing" from $Z(p)$ poles (and/or zeros) on $p = i\omega$, which are represented by series anti-resonant arms (and/or shunt series-resonant arms, respectively); (b) subtracting constant series resistors when this does not violate #3 in (3–137); (c) when none of these is possible, subtracting a series inductor ($L \gtrless 0$!) to produce a zero on $p = i\omega$ and proceeding with step (a) again. [The result after two further steps will then be a "T" of inductors equivalent $\{L_1L_2 + L_1L_3 + L_2L_3 = 0\}$ to a pair of perfectly coupled coils, or to an ideal transformer with one winding shunted by a (positive) inductance.]

The ideal transformers or perfectly coupled coils can be avoided by replacing (c) by other procedures, in which, however, the "reduced function," $Z_1(p)$, appears twice. See below (3–138).

Refs:

Bott and Duffin, *J. Appl. Phys.*, **20**, 816 (1949); R. H. Pantell, *Proc. Inst. Radio Engrs.*, **42**, 861 (1954).

Corollary Results

If $Z(p)$ and $f(p)$ satisfy (3–137) then so does $Z(f(p))$. (Frequency transformations.) In particular, $1/Z(p) = Y(p)$ is again an impedance function.

If k is real and positive

$$Z_1(p) = \frac{kZ(p) - pZ(k)}{kZ(k) - pZ(p)} \tag{3–138}$$

also satisfies* (3–137) and is of no greater complexity than $Z(p)$ (compare $p = k$).

The alternatives to step (c) of Brune's synthesis are based on (3–138). When (c) must be used, we have for some ω_0, $Z(i\omega_0) = i\omega_0 L$ where L may be taken positive (otherwise, work with $1/Z$). Define k (real and positive) as a root of $Z(k)/k = L$. Bott and Duffin's circuit is obtained by noting that, from (3–138),

$$Z(p) = (1/Z_2 + pC)^{-1} + (1/pL + 1/Z_3)^{-1}$$

where

$$C = 1/k^2L; \qquad Z_2(p) = kLZ_1; \qquad Z_3(p) = kL/Z_1.$$

$Z(p + \delta)$ where δ is real and positive also satisfies (3–137) if $Z(p)$ does. It represents a "uniformly dissipative" version of the impedance $Z(p)$. Namely, $Z(p + \delta)$ can be constructed from $Z(p)$ by paralleling each capacitor, C, by a conductance $= C\delta$ and inserting in series with each inductance, L, a series resistor $= L\delta$; finally each mutual inductance, M, is given an associated lossy coupling consisting of a *single* resistor $= M\delta$ connected in series with *both* of the coils coupled by M.

* P. I. Richards, *Duke Math. J.*, **14**, 777 (1947). Essentially a transformation of Schwarz's lemma; see (12–17).

Transfer Impedances

Several schemes for realizing transfer-impedances, Z_{ik}, are available and more are being discovered. The simplest practical one seems to be the following and its corollaries.

Bode's Theorem

Given a voltage generator V_g with purely resistive internal impedance R_g and a purely resistive load, R_l, these may be interconnected by a passive (lumped-constant) circuit so that $I_l = V_g Y_T(p)$ if and only if the (rational) function Y_T satisfies:

$$\left.\begin{array}{l} 1.\ Y_T(p) \text{ is real whenever } p \text{ is real} \\ 2.\ Y_T(p) \text{ is analytic in } \mathrm{Re}\,(p) \geqslant 0 \\ 3.\ |Y_T| \leqslant (4R_lR_g)^{-\frac{1}{2}} \text{ when } p = i\omega \\ \qquad \text{(and hence when } \mathrm{Re}\,(p) \geqslant 0) \end{array}\right\} \qquad (3\text{–}139)$$

COROLLARY: If #3 is false but $|Y_T|$ is bounded on $p = i\omega$, then a passive circuit cascaded with an (ideal, flat) amplifier will synthesize Y_T.

Necessity of (3–139) follows from the form of (3–124)–(3–126), from stability, and from power conservation. Sufficiency is exhibited by:

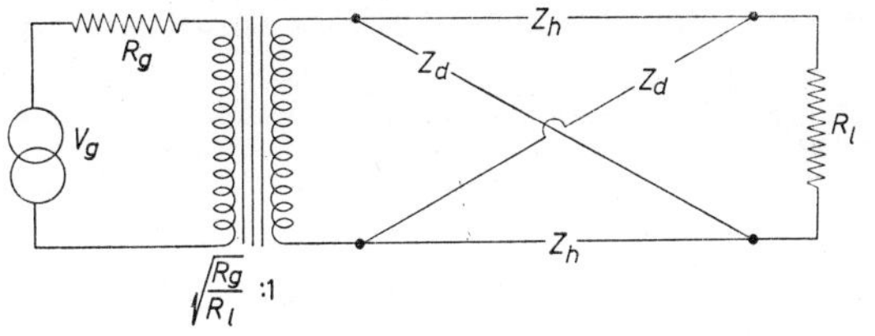

or:

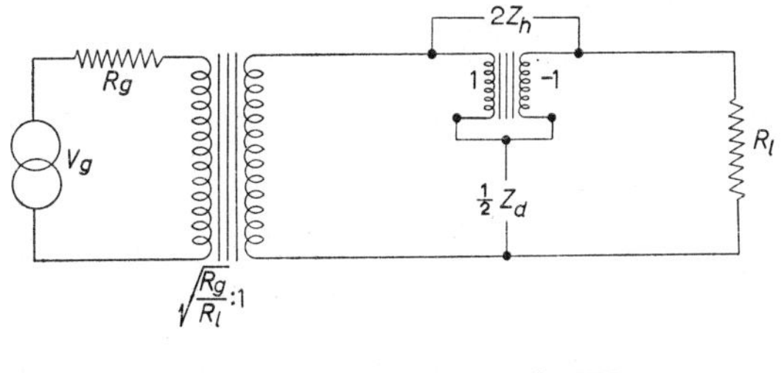

where:

$$\frac{Z_h}{R_l} = \frac{R_l}{Z_d} = \frac{1 - 2Y_T\sqrt{R_gR_l}}{1 + 2Y_T\sqrt{R_gR_l}}$$

Here, because of (3–139), Z_h and Z_d can be realized by Brune's theorem. Note that the impedance seen by the transformer is R_l.

The practicality of this theorem is that Y_T can be broken into factors each of which can be realized as above and the resulting circuits cascaded. [Provided, in general, that $|Y_T|$ is first so reduced that all factors simultaneously satisfy #3 in (3–139)].

Minimum-Phase Transfer Admittances

In (3–139) Y_T may have zeros in $\mathrm{Re}\,(p) > 0$. If so, Y_t, which is constructed from Y_T by reflecting *such* zeros in the imaginary axis, has the same magnitude as

Y_T everywhere on $p = i\omega$ but a smaller phase angle. Functions Y_t with no zeros in Re $(p) > 0$ are therefore called "minimum phase" functions. Such functions necessarily have one-signed real parts in Re $(p) \geqslant 0$.

Hence if Y_t is of minimum phase, the function $\pm\theta Y_t$ where $\theta < 1$ can be realized by a series connection of generator, load and an impedance $Z_t = (\pm\theta Y_t)^{-1} - R_g - R_l$ where the constant $\pm\theta$ is chosen so that Z_t satisfies (3–137). In general, however, it is more practical to factor Y_t and realize typical factors by "bridged-T" sections which may then be cascaded (input impedance of each $\equiv R_l$):

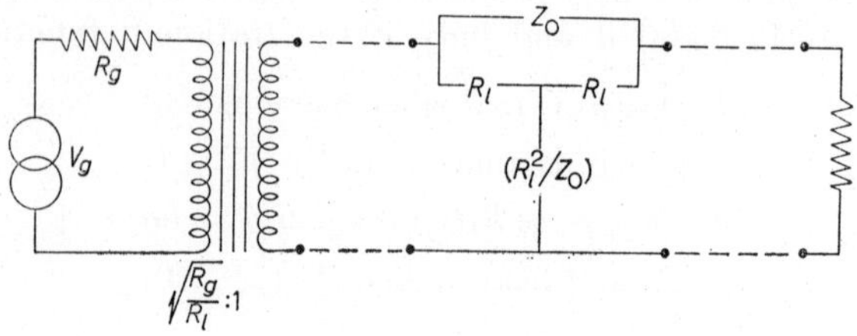

(R_l on the right of the mid-tap may in principle be opened or shorted—it is the "detector arm" in a balanced bridge—but the full bridged-T is less sensitive to slight parameter variations. Here $Z_0 = 1/\theta Y_t - R_l$.)

Connections Between Attenuation and Phase (or Resistance and Reactance)

Because network functions are analytic functions of p, and hence are largely unique when relatively few pieces of information are specified, many relations can be derived relating real and imaginary parts or magnitude and phase. Examples (due to Bode) are:

$$\begin{aligned} B(\omega) &= \frac{2\omega}{\pi} \int_0^\infty \frac{A(\Omega) - A(\omega)}{\Omega^2 - \omega^2}\, d\Omega \\ &= \frac{1}{\pi} \int_0^\infty \left[\frac{d}{d\Omega} A(\Omega)\right] \log_e \left|\frac{\Omega + \omega}{\Omega - \omega}\right| d\Omega \end{aligned} \qquad (3\text{–}140)$$

and

$$\begin{aligned} A(\omega) - A(0) &= -\frac{2\omega^2}{\pi} \int_0^\infty \frac{\Omega^{-1}B(\Omega) - \omega^{-1}B(\omega)}{\Omega^2 - \omega^2}\, d\Omega \\ &= -\frac{\omega}{\pi} \int_0^\infty \left[\frac{d}{d\Omega} \frac{B(\Omega)}{\Omega}\right] \ln \left|\frac{\Omega + \omega}{\Omega - \omega}\right| d\Omega \end{aligned} \qquad (3\text{–}141)$$

In these relations, the network function, $F(p) = A(\omega) + iB(\omega)$ on $p = i\omega$, may be an impedance or admittance (with no lossless resonances) or a *minimum-phase*, complex "gain" such as $\ln [2\sqrt{R_l R_g} Y_t]$—or, indeed, any function which is real for real p, analytic in Re $(p) \geqslant 0$ and bounded as $p \to \infty$. [Compare (13–38)-(13–40).]

Relations such as these are useful for such general considerations as limitations on the sharpness of gain cut off, $dA/d\Omega$, for a feedback loop to avoid instability ($B > \pi$ when $A > 0$).

The derivation of (3–140) and (3–141) is a straight-forward application of Cauchy's complex integration theorem.

With rational functions, the computations represented in (3–140) and (3–141) can be performed algebraically:

1. Given $G(\omega)$, real $\geqslant 0$, to find $Y = G + iB$: Set $\omega = p/i$ and expand in partial fractions,

$$G(p) = C + \sum_k \left[\frac{C_k}{p - a_k} - \frac{C_k^*}{p + a_k^*}\right]; \qquad \text{Re}\,(a_k) < 0 \tag{3–142}$$

(If G does not have this form, there is no physically realizable Y.) Then (note: $2G = Y + Y^*$ and $p^* = -p$ when $p = i\omega$)

$$Y(p) = C + \sum_k \frac{2C_k}{p - a_k} + \begin{pmatrix}\text{any pure} \\ \text{reactance}\end{pmatrix} \tag{3–143}$$

(A pure reactance has the form of the first two terms in (3–145) below.)

2. Given $B(\omega)$, to find $Y = G + iB$: Set $\omega = p/i$ and expand in partial fractions

$$B(p) = Cp + \sum_k \frac{pD_k}{p^2 + \alpha_k^2} + \sum_m \left(\frac{C_m}{p - a_m} + \frac{C_m^*}{p + a_m^*}\right) \tag{3–144}$$

$$(\alpha_k \text{ real}; \qquad \text{Re}\,(a_m) < 0)$$

(B must have this form if a physical Y exists.) Then

$$Y(p) = Cp + \sum_k \frac{pD_k}{p^2 + \alpha_k^2} + \sum_m \frac{2C_m}{p - a_m} + G_\infty \tag{3–145}$$

where G_∞ is real and positive but otherwise arbitrary.

3. Given $|Y_t(p)|^2 = F(\omega)$ when $p = i\omega$, to find $Y_t(p)$: Set $\omega = p/i$ and factor F into the form,

$$|Y_t(p)|^2 = k^2 \frac{\prod_1^n (p - a_k) \prod_1^n (p + a_k^*)}{\prod_1^m (p - b_k) \prod_1^m (p + b_k^*)} (-1)^{n-m} \tag{3–146}$$

$$\text{Re}\,(a_k) \leqslant 0; \qquad \text{Re}\,(b_k) < 0; \qquad m \geqslant n$$

then

$$Y_t(p) = k \frac{\prod_1^n (p - a_k)}{\prod_1^m (p - b_k)} \tag{3–147}$$

is the minimum-phase function with $|Y_t|^2 = F(\omega)$. A non-minimum-phase function with the same "gain" can be constructed by multiplying (3–147) by any number of factors of the form $(p - c)/(p + c)$ with c real > 0, or of the form $(p - \beta)(p - \beta^*)/(p + \beta)(p + \beta^*)$ with $\text{Re}\,(\beta) > 0$. Both types of factor correspond to cascaded "all pass" phase-shifting networks.

4. Given a phase shift factor $e^{i\phi} = f(\omega)$, to find $Y_t(p) = |Y_t(p)|\, e^{i\phi}$: Set $\omega = p/i$ and write $f^2(\omega)$ in the form:

$$e^{2i\phi} = \frac{\prod_1^n (p - a_k) \prod_1^m (p + b_k^*)}{\prod_1^m (p - b_k) \prod_1^n (p + a_k^*)} (-1)^{n-m} \tag{3–148}$$

$$\text{Re}\,(a_k) \leqslant 0; \qquad \text{Re}\,(b_k) < 0; \qquad m \geqslant n$$

Then (with k real)

$$Y_t(p) = k\frac{\prod_1^n (p - a_k)}{\prod_1^m (p - b_k)} \tag{3–149}$$

which is of minimum-phase type.

A non-minimum-phase Y_T (with equal phase shift but different gain!) can be obtained if $m \geqslant n + 4$, by multiplying (3–149) by $(p^2 - b_k{}^2)(p^2 - (b_k{}^*)^2)$ where b_k is one of the quantities in (3–148).

Nonlinear Circuit-Elements

Manley-Rowe Power Relations

1. Given a nonlinear capacitor whose charge is a known, single-valued function of the instantaneous voltage: $Q = F(V)$. Any periodic voltage will be a superposition of sinusoids, $V(t) = \Sigma\, C_\alpha \sin(\omega_\alpha t + \phi_\alpha) = \Sigma\, V_\alpha(t)$, and the power absorbed at angular frequency ω_α is

$$P_\alpha = \lim_{T\to\infty} \frac{1}{T}\int_0^T V_\alpha \frac{dQ}{dt}\,dt = \lim_{T\to\infty} \frac{-1}{T}\int_0^T F(V)\frac{dV_\alpha}{dt}\,dt$$

(integrating by parts). Let all ω_α be expressible as harmonics and combinations of the form

$$\omega_\alpha = n_1\omega_1 + n_2\omega_2 + \cdots + n_N\omega_N$$

where the ω_i are some set of "base" angular frequencies (and all $\omega_\alpha > 0$, although some of the n_i may be negative). Then, in particular, $dV_\alpha/dt = (\omega_\alpha/n_1 t)\,\partial V_\alpha/\partial\omega_1$ (if $n_1 \neq 0$) and

$$\sum_{\omega_\alpha>0} \frac{n_1 P_\alpha}{\omega_\alpha} = \lim \frac{-1}{T}\int_0^T F(V)\frac{\partial V}{\partial\omega_1}\frac{dt}{t} = \frac{\partial}{\partial\omega_1}\lim\frac{-1}{T}\int_0^T G(V)\frac{dt}{t}$$

where

$$G(V) = \int_{V(0)}^{V} F(V)\,dV$$

which is well-defined since F is single-valued. Since $V(t)$ and $F(V)$ are bounded, we conclude:

$$\boxed{\sum_{\omega_\alpha>0} n_i P_\alpha/\omega_\alpha = 0 \qquad \text{(for each } i\text{)}}$$

From these relations, it is easily shown that many modulators can exhibit power gain and/or negative effective input impedance ($P_\alpha < 0$).

2. Given a nonlinear inductor whose flux is a single-valued function of current, so that $V = (d/dt)F(I)$, it is only necessary to interchange V and I in the above arguments to derive the same results.

3. If some of the variation of charge on the capacitor (or flux in the inductor) is caused by mechanical motion, then it can be shown that the above results remain valid provided only that mechanical power is included throughout.

4. *Hysteresis:* If F is not single-valued but if (say) ω_1 is excited much more than any other ω_α, then it is easily seen that $F(V)$ cycles about its hysteresis loop (on an F-V graph) at an average rate of $\omega_1/2\pi$ cycles per unit time and that $G(V)$ above is asymptotic to $A\omega_1 t/2\pi$ where A is the area of the (average) V-F hysteresis loop.

It then follows from the formulas above that the power relations remain valid under these conditions provided P_1 includes the mean power, $\omega_1 A/2\pi$, dissipated in hysteresis.

5. Similarly, it may be shown that, for a nonlinear resistor, $V = F(I)$, the following relations hold between the *reactive* powers at the various frequencies.

$$\sum_{\omega_\alpha > 0} n_i X_\alpha = 0$$

Rowe's Small-Signal Theory

Consider a nonlinear reactor driven by a large-amplitude "local oscillator" voltage V_1 at frequency f_1 and connected to a circuit which can also support two signals at frequencies f_0 and either $f_+ = f_1 + f_0$ or $f_- = f_1 - f_0$ (where $f_0 < f_1$). By expanding $F(V_1 + \delta V)$ in a Taylor's series and noting that a function of a periodic variable is itself periodic so that further expansion in Fourier series is expedient, one finds that the (small) signal-frequency components satisfy in both cases a matrix equation of the form,

$$\begin{pmatrix} I_0/i\omega_0 \\ \pm I_\pm/i\omega_\pm \end{pmatrix} = \begin{array}{c|c} C_0 & C_1 \\ \hline C_1 & C_0 \end{array} \begin{pmatrix} V_0 \\ V_\pm \end{pmatrix}$$

(strictly, I_- and V_- here are the complex conjugates of the signal current and voltage). From the Manley–Rowe power relations and from these equations, one may then arrive at the following tabulation of the properties for a nonlinear reactor used in any of three different manners. (The term "inverter" arises from the fact that as f_0 is increased $f_1 - f_0$ decreases. Negative-resistance operation of the inverter consists in merely connecting a passive load, resonant at either signal frequency, and considering the in-going and out-going waves at the other signal frequency. For the inverter, A below is a constant, arbitrary to within the assumptions of high-gain, narrow-bandwidth operation.)

	Non-Inverter	*Inverter*	*Negative-Impedance Inverter*
Optimum signal-frequency load conductances, $g_0 = g_\pm$:	$2\pi C_1(f_0 f_+)^{1/2}$	$2\pi C_1(f_0 f_-/A)^{1/2}$	$2\pi C_1(f_0 f_-/A)^{1/2}$
Power gain, $G = P_{\text{out}}/P_{\text{in}}$:	$f_{\text{out}}/f_{\text{in}}$	$\dfrac{4A}{1 - A^2}(f_{\text{out}}/f_{\text{in}})$	$\left(\dfrac{1 + A}{1 - A}\right)^2$
Half-power bandwidth (assumed small compared to f_0):	$\dfrac{C_1}{C_0}(2f_0 f_+)^{1/2}$	$\dfrac{C_1}{C_0}\dfrac{1 - A}{2}(f_0 f_-)^{1/2}$	$\dfrac{C_1}{C_0}\dfrac{1 - A}{2}(f_0 f_-)^{1/2}$
Sensitivity to loading, $\partial(\ln G)/\partial(\ln g)$:	0	$\dfrac{A + 1}{A - 1}$	$\dfrac{4A}{A^2 - 1}$
Sensitivity to parameter changes, $\partial(\ln G)/\partial(\ln C_1)$	0	$2\dfrac{(1 + A)}{(1 - A)}$	$\dfrac{8A}{1 - A^2}$

Amplifiers of these types include vibrating-reed electrometers, various mechanical and electrical modulators, and certain types of microwave diodes. A truly reactive nonlinear element can in principle act as a noiseless amplifier.

COMMUNICATION THEORY

Communication theory is based on the observation that a communication channel need not be perfect in order to be useful. The essence of the approach lies in replacing the subjective, human concepts of "usefulness" or "meaning of a message" by an objective quantity: some measure of *statistical correlation* between the actual output of a system and a *specified*, desired output (often, of course, the "transmitter" input).

North's Theorem

Let the input of a linear, time-invariant system* be the sum of "white" noise (i.e. with a uniform frequency spectrum) and a pulse-signal of *known* shape, $P(t)$, and finite duration. It is desired to minimize the squared ratio of the output noise to the output *signal*, namely

$$\mathscr{S}(t) = \int_{-\infty}^{t} P(\tau)h(t-\tau)\,d\tau = \int_{-\infty}^{\infty} \mathscr{P}(\omega)H(\omega)e^{-i\omega t}\,d\omega$$

where $\mathscr{P}$ and H are the Fourier transforms of $P(t)$ and $h(t)$ which is the transfer function, or impulse response, of the filter (note $h(x) = 0$ for $x < 0$). Since the noise is "white," the average output noise is

$$\langle \mathscr{N}^2 \rangle = \text{constant} \times \int_{-\infty}^{\infty} |H(\omega)|^2\,d\omega$$

Thus

$$\frac{\mathscr{S}^2(t_0)}{\langle \mathscr{N}^2 \rangle} = \left\{\begin{matrix}\text{constant}\\ \text{independent}\\ \text{of } H\end{matrix}\right\} \times \frac{\left|\int \mathscr{P}(\omega)H(\omega)e^{-i\omega t_0}\,d\omega\right|^2}{\int |\mathscr{P}(\omega)|^2\,d\omega \times \int |H(\omega)|^2\,d\omega}$$

and by Schwarz's inequality, (8–17), this is a maximum (for any t_0) if and only if

$$H(\omega) = A\mathscr{P}^*(\omega)e^{i\omega t_0} = A\mathscr{P}(-\omega)e^{i\omega t_0} \tag{3–150}$$

Thus, the *impulse response*, $h(t)$, *of the system must be the signal pulse reversed in time*, $P(t_0 - t)$. [This is physically possible only if the signal pulse has finite duration; note that $\mathscr{S}(t)$ will usually be a distorted version of $P(t)$.]

---

* *Linear:* The output from a sum of inputs equals the sum of the individual outputs from each input when applied separately. By considering any input as a superposition of short impulses, it follows that

$$\mathscr{O}(t) = \int_{-\infty}^{t} h(t, \tau)\mathscr{I}(\tau)\,d\tau$$

where $h(t, \tau)$ is the response to an impulse, $\delta(t - \tau)$, applied at time τ. For any physical system, $h = 0$ for $t < \tau$. If the system is also *time-invariant*: $h(t, \tau) = h(t - \tau)$, and shifting the input in time merely shifts the output correspondingly.

Wiener–Kolmogoroff Linear Filtering Theorem

The problem is: To find, among all linear systems, that which minimizes the mean* square error, $\langle \mathscr{E}^2(t) \rangle$ with $\mathscr{E}(t) = \mathscr{O}(t) - \mathscr{D}(t)$ where

$$\mathscr{O}(t) = \int_0^T h(t, \tau)\mathscr{I}(\tau)\,\mathrm{d}\tau$$

is the output of the system in response to a finite sample, $(0, T)$, of an input $\mathscr{I}(t)$ and where $\mathscr{D}(t)$ is some specified (ensemble of) desired outputs for each given input. [Often, $\mathscr{D}(t) = \mathscr{S}(t \pm \alpha)$ when $\mathscr{I}(t) = \mathscr{S}(t) + \mathscr{N}(t)$ with $\mathscr{N}(t)$, a random noise voltage.]

We have

$$\langle \mathscr{E}^2(t) \rangle = \int_0^T\int_0^T h(t, x)h(t, y)\Gamma_{\mathscr{I}\mathscr{I}}(x, y)\,\mathrm{d}x\,\mathrm{d}y - 2\int_0^T h(t, x)\Gamma_{\mathscr{I}\mathscr{D}}(x, t)\,\mathrm{d}x + \langle \mathscr{D}^2(t) \rangle \tag{3–151}$$

where

$$\Gamma_{\mathscr{I}\mathscr{I}}(x, y) = \langle \mathscr{I}(x)\mathscr{I}(y) \rangle; \qquad \Gamma_{\mathscr{I}\mathscr{D}}(x, t) = \langle \mathscr{I}(x)\mathscr{D}(t) \rangle \tag{3–152}$$

(correlation functions; if the signal and noise ensembles are "stationary," that is invariant under time-shifts, then $\Gamma_{\mathscr{I}\mathscr{D}}(x, t) = \gamma_{\mathscr{I}\mathscr{D}}(t - x)$, etc.). Letting $h(t, x) = h_0(t, x) + \epsilon g(t, x)$ in (3–151) where h_0 is the optimum function, g an arbitrary function and ϵ an arbitrary constant, it is easily shown that

$$\Gamma_{\mathscr{I}\mathscr{D}}(x, t) = \int_0^T h_0(t, y)\Gamma_{\mathscr{I}\mathscr{I}}(x, y)\,\mathrm{d}y \tag{3–153}$$

This is a Wiener–Hopf equation to determine $h_0(t, y)$ and hence the filter itself. The irreducible minimum mean square error (with linear systems) is

$$\langle \mathscr{E}^2(t) \rangle_{\mathrm{Min}} = \langle \mathscr{D}^2(t) \rangle - \int_0^T h_0(t, x)\Gamma_{\mathscr{I}\mathscr{D}}(x, t)\,\mathrm{d}x \tag{3–154}$$

Note that minimizing $\langle \mathscr{E}^2 \rangle$ is not always the most desirable procedure (compare North's Theorem). Moreover, *non*linear operations may offer considerable improvement over (3–153) and (3–154). However, Bode and Shannon [*Proc. I.R.E.*, **38**, 417 (1950)] have pointed out that if the ensemble of signals has a Gaussian distribution of expected values (given those at $t' < t$)—that is, a flat power spectrum —then the linear filter (3–153) selects the center of the distribution and is therefore as good as any nonlinear filter with respect to almost any performance criterion.

Shannon's Theory of "Information"

This is based on a technical concept of "information." To forestall misconceptions, the term "unexpectedness" has been suggested as a better name. It is essentially a measure of the irreducible arbitrariness of members of a set of messages. We shall use the symbol $\mathscr{U}$ for "information."

* Averaged over the ensemble of expected inputs; angular brackets indicate such averages plus any further averaging required by the presence of random noise voltages.

"Information" (Discrete Signals)

$\mathscr{U}$ has meaning only *with respect to the statistical properties* of a preassigned set of possible messages*. For messages consisting of strings of discrete symbols ("letters," space marks, dots, dashes, etc.), the definition is

$$\mathscr{U} \text{ (per symbol)} = \begin{cases} \textit{The least possible average digits-per-symbol} \\ \text{required to code† the given statistical} \\ \text{ensemble of messages onto numbers.} \end{cases} \tag{3–155}$$

The type of numerical notation (decimal, binary, etc.) envisaged determines the units of $\mathscr{U}$ ("binary digits" is commonly abbreviated "bits"). Since $\mathscr{U}$ is an average, its value is seldom an integer and "numbers to the base e" (that is, natural logarithms in the formulas below) are also useful in formal manipulations.

The definition (3–155) may be written mathematically when it is recognized that average coding efficiency per symbol increases (a) when the shortest code-numbers are assigned to the most frequently occurring messages and (b) when longer and longer sequences of symbols (or messages) are used as code-units and assigned single code-numbers. (This not only makes greater use of any correlations between symbols or messages but also allows the assignment, (a), to be made on a more refined basis.) Such considerations lead to

$$\mathscr{U} = \lim_{L\to\infty} \left\{ \frac{-1}{L} \sum_{\mathscr{L}} \mathscr{P}(\mathscr{L}) \log \mathscr{P}(\mathscr{L}) \right\} \quad \text{(per symbol)} \tag{3–156}$$

where the sum is over all sequences, $\mathscr{L}$, containing L symbols and $\mathscr{P}(\mathscr{L})$ is the probability that the sequence $\mathscr{L}$ will actually occur; the base of the logarithm sets the units for $\mathscr{U}$. If the message-ensemble is equivalent to a Markov chain with transition matrix $p_{i\to k}$ then (3–156) can be further reduced‡ to

$$\mathscr{U} = -\sum_{i,k} P_i p_{ik} \log p_{ik} \tag{3–156}$$

where P_i are the mean recurrence probabilities, the (unique) solutions of,

$$P_i = \sum_k P_k p_{ki} \qquad (\sum_i P_i = 1) \tag{3–157}$$

Redundancy

Redundancy is a name for the quantity, $\mathscr{R} = (\log N_s - \mathscr{U})$ where N_s is the number of different symbols available. In all cases, $\mathscr{R} \geqslant 0$. A finite redundancy is often the most practical way of combating interference in "noisy" channels.

Discrete Communication Channels

(a) A noiseless § channel is characterized merely by a set of allowed symbols and a (maximum) rate of transmitting these symbols. (Note that the frequencies of occurrence of individual symbols are *not* specified; the user is free to choose them as desired.) By coding the symbols onto numbers, the maximum transmission rate is

* Assumed invariant in time.

† Meaning a one-to-one mapping such that any specific string of messages is recoverable from the corresponding numbers. It is assumed that certain strings of *messages* may be assigned single code numbers if this helps to reduce the average digits per symbol.

‡ Provided the chain is irreducible and aperiodic and contains no transient nor null states.

§ *Terminology:* "Distortion" is a predictable (and hence correctable) alteration of a signal; "noise" causes unpredictable (statistical) changes in the signals.

expressed in units similar to those of $\mathscr{U}$. The noiseless channel is then characterized merely by a "capacity":

$$C = \lim_{T \to \infty} \left[\frac{1}{T} \log M(T) \right] \quad \text{(per unit time)} \tag{3–159}$$

where $M(T)$ is the number of different *possible* channel-messages each of which could be sent during time, T.

It may be seen that a statistical message source which generates messages with an average symbol duration, $\bar{l}$, may be coded and sent over the channel (with all messages recoverable) if and only if $\mathscr{U}/\bar{l} \leqslant C$ (provided arbitrarily long coding and decoding delays are allowed if necessary).

(b) A noisy channel, on the other hand, has in addition a specified probability $p(a \to b)$ of converting an input symbol, a, to an output symbol, b. If Λ denotes an output sequence and $\mathscr{L}$ an input sequence, both having L symbols, the amount of "information" per symbol required to specify which $\mathscr{L}$ was actually sent when a particular Λ was received is

$$\frac{-1}{L} \sum_{\mathscr{L}} \mathscr{P}_\Lambda(\mathscr{L}) \log \mathscr{P}_\Lambda(\mathscr{L})$$

where $\mathscr{P}_\Lambda(\mathscr{L})$ is the probability that $\mathscr{L}$ was the actual cause of Λ. The average correction-information required (often called the "conditional entropy per symbol") is

$$\begin{aligned} \mathscr{U}_\Lambda(\mathscr{L}) &= \lim_{L \to \infty} \left\{ \frac{-1}{L} \sum_{\mathscr{L},\Lambda} \mathscr{P}(\Lambda) \mathscr{P}_\Lambda(\mathscr{L}) \log \mathscr{P}_\Lambda(\mathscr{L}) \right\} \\ &= \lim_{L \to \infty} \left\{ \frac{-1}{L} \sum_{\mathscr{L},\Lambda} \mathscr{P}(\mathscr{L}) \mathscr{P}(\mathscr{L} \to \Lambda) \log \left[\frac{\mathscr{P}(\mathscr{L}) \mathscr{P}(\mathscr{L} \to \Lambda)}{\sum_{\mathscr{L}'} \mathscr{P}(\mathscr{L}') \mathscr{P}(\mathscr{L}' \to \Lambda)} \right] \right\} \end{aligned} \tag{3–160}$$

(In practice, this correction information is often supplied by "redundancy" of the message source.)

A general definition of the channel capacity is then

$$C = \operatorname*{Max}_{\mathscr{U}(\mathscr{L})} \left\{ \frac{1}{\bar{l}} [\mathscr{U}(\mathscr{L}) - \mathscr{U}_\Lambda(\mathscr{L})] \right\} \tag{3–161}$$

where the maximum is taken over all conceivable statistical message generators, $\mathscr{U}(\mathscr{L})$, with average symbol duration, $\bar{l}$. (Usually, this formula is not the most convenient way to evaluate C. Compare the derivation of (3–164) below.)

It is surprising that in general the quantity (3–161) does not vanish, for it is the rate for *errorless* transmission. The essential point is that *average* properties of any "noise" are predictable with increasing accuracy over long periods of time.

Continuous Signals

Continuous signals, for most practical purposes, can be considered to have limited bandwidth, W, and limited duration, T. By "Fourier" expansion of such $f(t)$ in the (complete, orthogonal) set of functions, $[\sin \pi(2Wt - n)/\pi(2Wt - n)]$, it follows that $2WT$ numbers, namely $x_n = f(n/2W)$, suffice to specify completely such duration- and bandwidth-limited functions. Such functions can therefore be represented by points $(x_1, x_2, x_3, \cdots, x_{2WT})$ in a "space" of $2WT$ dimensions. The "radius," $\rho^2 = (\sum x_i^2)$ is equal to $2WTP$ where P is the mean "power" level, $\langle f^2 \rangle$, of the function $f(t)$ represented by the point $(x_1, \cdots, x_{2WT})$. Thus signals with at most a specified mean power, P_0, lie in a "sphere" $\rho^2 \leqslant P_0 2WT$.

*White thermal noise** which is merely added to the signal will shift each "coordinate" $x_n = f(n/2W)$ to a distribution, $x_n = f(n/2W) + N(n/2W)$ where the noise component $N(t)$ has a Gaussian distribution with mean "power" level, N. Thus the transmitted "point" $(x_1, \cdots, x_{2WT})$ is converted to a received "blur" with a distribution:

$$\mathscr{P}(x_1 + \Delta x_1, \cdots, x_{2WT} + \Delta x_{2WT})$$
$$= (4\pi WTN)^{-WT} \exp\left[-\sum_1^{2WT} \frac{(\Delta x_n)^2}{2WT}\right] \tag{3–162}$$

But $\sum (\Delta x_n)^2 = \sum N^2(n/2W)$ is essentially the mean "power" in a large sample of the noise and is therefore overwhelmingly likely to have the value, $2WTN$ if T is sufficiently long. Thus, received signals will eventually lie on small spheres of radius $2WTN$ about the transmitted points $(x_1, \cdots, x_n)$ and the maximum number of *distinguishable* signals, $f(t)$, with mean power $\sum x_i^2 < P_0 2WT$ will be given by the ratio of the ($2WT$-dimensional) volumes:

$$M(T) \sim \frac{(P_0 + N)^{WT}}{N^{WT}} \tag{3–163}$$

and by (3–159) [which can be used here because the effects of the noise have been laboriously inserted into $M(T)$], we have,

$$C = W \log \frac{P_0 + N}{N} \tag{3–164}$$

as the capacity of a channel of bandwidth W with additive white thermal noise of mean power N when used with a mean transmitter power P_0.

Note that power can be traded for bandwidth or vice versa. (As $N \to 0$, then $C \to \infty$, but this is because the signals were taken to be continuous whereas in practice they can be received (measured) only to finite accuracy; this effect was omitted above. The complication is typical of continuous-signal theories.)

Gaussian noise is any disturbance equivalent to white thermal noise which has passed through a *linear* filter. A channel of bandwidth W with (additive) Gaussian noise is equivalent to a "sum" of adjacent white-noise channels:

$$C_{(\text{trial})} \sim \int_A^{A+W} \log\left(1 + \frac{P(\omega)}{N(\omega)}\right) d\omega \tag{3–165}$$

where $P(\omega)$ and $N(\omega)$ are the transmitter and noise power spectra. Maximizing (3–165) subject to the constraint,

$$\int_A^{A+W} P(\omega)\, d\omega = P_0 \tag{3–166}$$

gives the prescription,

$$P(\omega) = \begin{cases} \lambda - N(\omega), & \text{when } N(\omega) < \lambda \\ 0, & \text{when } N(\omega) \geqslant \lambda \end{cases} \tag{3–167}$$

* A disturbance $N(t)$ with no correlation between $N(t_1)$ and $N(t_2)$ if $t_1 \neq t_2$ and with a Gaussian distribution for each $N(t_0)$. The term "white" refers to the flatness of the power spectrum, which is the Fourier transform of the autocorrelation function, $\gamma_{NN}(t) = \delta(t)$.

where λ is a constant which must be adjusted to satisfy (3–166). Then the capacity is

$$C_{P_0} = \int_{A}^{A+W} \log [\lambda/N(\omega)]\, d\omega \tag{3–168}$$

More general types of noise are treated by the concept of "entropy power," N_1, which is related to the "information," $\mathscr{U}_{Ne}$, contained in (a bandwidth W of) the *noise** by

$$N_1 = \frac{1}{2\pi e} \exp 2\mathscr{U}_{Ne} \tag{3–169}$$

where $\mathscr{U}_{Ne}$ is computed using natural logarithms. Then Shannon has shown that

$$W \log \frac{P_0 + N_1}{N_1} \leqslant C \leqslant W \log \frac{P_0 + N}{N_1} \tag{3–170}$$

Discussion

The main results of the theory are a fruitful set of concepts, such as the interchangeability of bandwidth and transmitter power, and a set of specific, numerical limitations. Thus it is now known that for (arbitrary, equally probable) continuous signals on a white-noise channel, pulse-code-modulation and pulse-position-modulation are about equivalent and lie within 8 *db* in transmitter power (at a level of one error in 10^5 symbols) from the unsurpassable ideal, (3–164). Thus, further appreciable progress must involve using the redundancy of, for example, speech-sounds themselves.

---

* The aptness of the term "unexpectedness" is especially obvious here. In (3–169) and (3–170), although C/W has dimensions of "bits," N_1 depends on physical units in a complex manner and must be consistent with those used for P_0 and N.

CHAPTER 4

RELATIVITY

The theory of "*Special* Relativity" is firmly and unequivocally required by experiment. Although further generalizations and extensions will manifestly be required (to treat accelerating or rotating coordinate systems, if for no other reason), the precise form of these extensions is still open to debate. No experiment capable of uniquely selecting one of the alternative "General Relativity Theories" has been discovered to date.

Despite some popular accounts, Special Relativity is not a purely philosophical or an esthetic theory. Rather, its adoption is *forced* by certain experiments which make untenable the classical intuitive ideas (which are, after all, also logically consistent). The latter just do not fit the *facts*. Since its discovery, special relativity has been further vindicated by the operation of high-energy accelerators and similar machines.

The central *fact of nature* which forces us to adopt special relativity is that a number of experiments together have shown that:

$$\left.\begin{array}{l}\textit{The speed of light in vacuum, c, is independent of}\\ \textit{the speed of the observer making the measurement.}\end{array}\right\} \quad (F)$$

An observer obtains the same value, $c = 3 \times 10^{10}$ cm/sec, whatever his own speed may be. Even two observers with different speeds, measuring the *same* light-pulse, *each* find that it travels 3×10^{10} cm/sec relative to *him*!

This fact is completely foreign to intuition and cannot be reconciled to one's natural experience. The only course is to abandon intuition and investigate what this strange but inescapable *fact* implies.

SPECIAL RELATIVITY

The theory of Special Relativity is concerned with the implications of fact (F) as regards systems moving relative to each other *with constant velocity*. It has nothing whatever to say concerning systems in relative acceleration (including rotation, of course).

Fundamental Relations

Consider two observers one of whom appears to move with constant velocity, $\mathbf{v}$, relative to the other. Fact (F) first implies that these two systems must be completely equivalent (except that the second sees the first move with oppositely directed velocity, $-\mathbf{v}$). Moreover, it is soon seen that (F) cannot be true unless the *time*-variables for the two observers are different.

The fact that the "clocks" in the two systems *cannot* run in synchronism is again contrary to our very idea of "time," but it is an inescapable consequence of (F) and is thus forced upon us by Nature herself.

In this simple situation of constant relative velocity, we expect that the relationship between the "coordinates," (x, y, z, t), of one observer and those of the other $(x', y', z', t',)$ would at least be linear. It turns out that this is indeed possible. The only connection between the systems* $(\mathbf{r}, t)$ and $(\mathbf{r}', t')$ which is both linear and at the same time satisfies: "$|d\mathbf{r}|^2 = c^2(dt)^2$ if and only if $|d\mathbf{r}'|^2 = c^2(dt')^2$" is given by

$$\left.\begin{aligned} \mathbf{r}' &= \mathbf{r} - \mathbf{v}\left\{\frac{(\mathbf{r}\cdot\mathbf{v})}{v^2}\left(1 - \frac{1}{\sqrt{1-\beta^2}}\right) + \frac{t}{\sqrt{1-\beta^2}}\right\} \\ t' &= \frac{t - \dfrac{(\mathbf{r}\cdot\mathbf{v})}{c^2}}{\sqrt{1-\beta^2}}; \qquad \text{where } \beta = v/c \end{aligned}\right\} \tag{4–1}$$

(Lorentz transformation)

In (4–1), if $\mathbf{r} = 0$, then $\mathbf{r}' = -\mathbf{v}t'$ so that the unprimed system is traveling with velocity $-\mathbf{v}$ relative to the primed system and conversely $(\mathbf{r}', t')$ has velocity $+\mathbf{v}$ as seen from $(\mathbf{r}, t)$. It is easily checked that the inverse of (4–1) is obtained merely by changing the sign of $\mathbf{v}$.

The famous effects of "time dilation" and "space contraction" may be most readily derived from (4–1) by writing $d\mathbf{r}$ for $\mathbf{r}$ and dt for t and then considering various special cases $d\mathbf{r} = 0$, $d\mathbf{r}' = 0$, $dt = 0$, $dt' = 0$. (Note that the "time dilations" seen from the two systems are for *different* physical conditions, $d\mathbf{r} = 0$ and $d\mathbf{r}' = 0$. Naturally, there is no "simultaneous time dilation in both directions.")

Velocities

If a body (or a third coordinate system, etc.) has velocity $\mathbf{u} = d\mathbf{r}/dt$ as seen from the system $(\mathbf{r}, t)$ then as seen from $(\mathbf{r}', t')$ its velocity is $\mathbf{u}' = d\mathbf{r}'/dt' = (d\mathbf{r}'/dt)(dt/dt')$, whence:

$$\mathbf{u}' = \left[1 - \frac{\mathbf{u}\cdot\mathbf{v}}{c^2}\right]^{-1}\left\{\mathbf{u}\sqrt{1-\beta^2} - \mathbf{v}\left[\frac{\mathbf{u}\cdot\mathbf{v}}{v^2}(\sqrt{1-\beta^2} - 1) + 1\right]\right\} \tag{4–2}$$

(where $\mathbf{v}$ has the same meaning as in (4–1).)

Accelerations

Similarly if a body has acceleration $\mathbf{a} = d^2\mathbf{r}/dt^2$ as seen from $(\mathbf{r}, t)$ then as seen from $(\mathbf{r}', t')$

$$\mathbf{a}' = \frac{d^2\mathbf{r}'}{(dt')^2} = \frac{1-\beta^2}{\left(1 - \dfrac{\mathbf{u}\cdot\mathbf{v}}{c^2}\right)^3}\left\{\mathbf{a}\left(1 - \frac{\mathbf{u}\cdot\mathbf{v}}{c^2}\right) + \mathbf{u}\frac{\mathbf{a}\cdot\mathbf{v}}{c^2} - \mathbf{v}\frac{(\mathbf{a}\cdot\mathbf{v})}{v^2}(1 - \sqrt{1-\beta^2})\right\} \tag{4–3}$$

Notation

To investigate further the implications of (F), it is expedient to utilize the concepts and notation of Riemannian geometry. The reason behind this is that, since neither of two systems with constant relative velocity is to be "preferred" over the other,† we must formulate our "laws" of physics so that they *read the same* (are "invariant")

---

* Aside from a *fixed* rotation before or after the transformation.

† Indeed, this much is true in all of classical physics (despite our natural feeling for "absolute space"), which is to say that it is supported by many experiments.

in any pair of systems with constant relative velocity. (This principle extended to *any* pair of systems is the basis for the theories of General Relativity.)

Writing relations in such a form is particularly easy and transparent with Riemannian geometry notation—"tensor analysis" notation.*

Tensor notation is introduced by regarding (x, y, z, t) and/or (x', y', z', t') as coordinates in an (abstract) "four dimensional space." "Distance" in this "space" is to be defined so that it is invariant under the coordinate transformations, (4–1). Fact (F) says immediately that this invariant "distance" must be

$$(ds)^2 = (dx)^2 + (dy)^2 + (dz)^2 - c^2(dt)^2 \tag{4–4}$$

It is convenient to use new variables x^i in place of (x, y, z, t), namely,

$$x^1 = x, \qquad x^2 = y, \qquad x^3 = z, \qquad x^4 = ict \tag{4–5}$$

Briefly, $x^i = (\mathbf{r}, ict)$. With this choice, the abstract space is "Euclidean" or "Cartesian" in the sense that,

$$(ds)^2 = \sum_{i=1}^{4} (dx^i)^2; \qquad g_{ij} = g^{ij} = \delta_{ij} \tag{4–6}$$

We also introduce the *summation convention*—that repetition of an index in any term implies summation over all four values of the index. (Thus in (4–6): $(ds)^2 = dx^i\,dx^i = g_{ij}\,dx^i\,dx^j$.)

Equation (4–6) *defines* the "geometry" and ensures that with the *interpretation* (4–5) this "geometry" will never violate (F). Equation (4–1) still indicates the type of transformations of coordinates which correspond to *physical* systems moving with constant velocity relative to the (x, y, z, t) system.

Our task as regards exploring the implications of (F) for any branch of physics will now be completed as soon as we have expressed the corresponding laws in tensor form, with the basic definitions (4–5), (4–6). The laws will then "read the same" in all coordinate systems which are related by transformations† of the type (4–1).

However, it is found that some physical laws have to be changed slightly to obtain a tensor form in the geometry (4–5), (4–6). In other words, their classic form is inconsistent with the "new" fact of Nature, (F). The classic form must therefore be abandoned, but this abandonment must be slight in the sense that all new expressions must agree not only with fact (F) but also, of course, with all the old experimental facts.

The new forms can then be subject to new experiments designed to test their new features. All the results below have withstood all such tests to date.

Electromagnetic Equations

No modification of the classical Maxwell's equations, (which, after all, deal with the propagation of light waves) is required to achieve a form consistent‡ with (F).

---

* This remark, logically, applies equally well to classical physics, and, indeed, ordinary "vector analysis" serves precisely this purpose (of obtaining equations independent of coordinate transformations) for the *Galilean* transformations of classical physics. However, since (F) forces us to use "geometry" (coordinate transformations) with *four* dimensions, the more formal and less intuitive full machinery of Riemannian geometry is more convenient than the notation used in (4–1)–(4–3).

† Actually, the most general transformation which leaves g_{ij} invariant (namely, $X^i = a_k{}^i x^k$ where $a_k{}^i a_k{}^j = \delta_{ij}$) is also physically useful; it corresponds to the transformation (4–1) plus an ordinary (fixed) rotation.

‡ Thus classical electrodynamics foreshadows relativity but nevertheless does *not* require or imply relativity. No transformation laws can be implied by any set of equations referred to a single system, and (4–7) through (4–10) are therefore *postulates*, however reasonable.

Namely, if we *define* tensors F^{ik} and H^{ik} (both antisymmetric) by

$$F^{ik} = \begin{array}{c|cccc} i \backslash k & 1 & 2 & 3 & 4 \\ \hline 1 & 0 & B_z & -B_y & -iE_x \\ 2 & -B_z & 0 & B_x & -iE_y \\ 3 & B_y & -B_x & 0 & -iE_z \\ 4 & iE_x & iE_y & iE_z & 0 \end{array}; \quad H^{ik} = \begin{array}{c|cccc} i \backslash k & 1 & 2 & 3 & 4 \\ \hline 1 & 0 & H_z & -H_y & -iD_x \\ 2 & -H_z & 0 & H_x & -iD_y \\ 3 & H_y & -H_x & 0 & -iD_z \\ 4 & iD_x & iD_y & iD_z & 0 \end{array} \quad (4\text{–}7)$$

and a (four-) vector by

$$s^i = (J_x, J_y, J_z, ic\rho) \quad (4\text{–}8)$$

Then Maxwell's equations (Gaussian units) can be written* as

$$\frac{\partial F_{kl}}{\partial x^i} + \frac{\partial F_{li}}{\partial x^k} + \frac{\partial F_{ik}}{\partial x^l} = 0$$

$$\left(\nabla \times \mathbf{E} = -\frac{1}{c}\frac{\partial \mathbf{B}}{\partial t} \quad \textit{and} \quad \nabla \cdot \mathbf{B} = 0\right) \quad (4\text{–}9)$$

(The other 60 equations in (4–9) merely state that $F_{ik} = -F_{ki}$.) and:

$$\frac{\partial H^{ik}}{\partial x^k} = \frac{4\pi}{c} s^i$$

$$\left(\nabla \times \mathbf{H} = \frac{4\pi}{c}\mathbf{J} + \frac{1}{c}\frac{\partial \mathbf{D}}{\partial t} \quad \textit{and} \quad \nabla \cdot \mathbf{D} = 4\pi\rho.\right) \quad (4\text{–}10)$$

(Note that, with the metric (4–6), for any tensor $T^{ik} = T^i{}_k = T_{ik}$ while for any vector $V^i = V_i$; these simple relations—an obvious asset in interpreting (4–10) for example—are the main reason for using $x^4 = ict$.)

The continuity equation reads (summation convention):

$$\frac{\partial s^i}{\partial x^i} = 0 \qquad \left(\frac{\partial \rho}{\partial t} + \nabla \cdot \mathbf{J} = 0)\right) \quad (4\text{–}11)$$

This, of course, is an immediate consequence of (4–10) and the anti-symmetry of H_{ik}.

The transformation rules for vectors like s^i and tensors like F^{ik} can be most readily re-written in ordinary vector notation by observing, for example, that s^i must transform like the vector $x^i = (\mathbf{r}, ict)$. Thus the transformation laws for $\mathbf{J}$ and ρ may be obtained directly from (4–1) by simply replacing $\mathbf{r}$ by $\mathbf{J}$ and t by ρ. Similarly F^{ik} must transform like $x^i x^k$, etc.

The assumption (!) that (4–7) are indeed tensors implies the transformation properties of $\mathbf{E}$, etc. One finds that, in ordinary notation, these are ($\beta = v/c$ as in (4–1)):

$$\mathbf{E}' = \frac{1}{\sqrt{1-\beta^2}}\left(\mathbf{E} + \frac{\mathbf{v}}{c} \times \mathbf{B}\right) - \frac{\mathbf{v}(\mathbf{E}\cdot\mathbf{v})}{v^2}\left(\frac{1}{\sqrt{1-\beta^2}} - 1\right) \quad (4\text{–}12)$$

$$\mathbf{B}' = \frac{1}{\sqrt{1-\beta^2}}\left(\mathbf{B} - \frac{\mathbf{v}}{c} \times \mathbf{E}\right) - \frac{\mathbf{v}(\mathbf{B}\cdot\mathbf{v})}{v^2}\left(\frac{1}{\sqrt{1-\beta^2}} - 1\right) \quad (4\text{–}13)$$

* Since by (4–6), $g_{ij} = \delta_{ij}$ for the coordinates of interest in special relativity, there is no distinction between the ordinary and covariant derivatives.

where, as before, $\mathbf{v}$ is the velocity of the primed coordinate system as seen from the unprimed system.

Except when the velocity v lies close to c these are nearly the same as (3–11) already implied by the classical force law (3–3).

The assumption that (4–8) is a vector implies that $s^i s_i$ is an invariant—a simple physical quantity independent of coordinate reference. From a microscopic point of view, $s_i s^i = \rho^2(c^2 - |\mathbf{u}|^2)$ where $\mathbf{u}$ is the local charge velocity; in co-moving coordinates ($\mathbf{u} = 0$), this is simply $\rho_o{}^2 c^2$ where the subscript, o, denotes the so-called "proper" (co-moving) value of a quantity. Thus in general

$$\rho = \frac{\rho_o}{\sqrt{1 - \beta^2}} \qquad (\beta = u/c) \tag{4–14}$$

which is indeed consistent with the Lorentz volume-contraction. From a microscopic view, then, in general

$$s^i = \rho_o \left(\frac{\mathbf{u}}{\sqrt{1-\beta^2}}, \frac{ic}{\sqrt{1-\beta^2}} \right) \qquad (\beta = u/c) \tag{4–15}$$

(which implies that the parenthesis is a four-vector and this is indeed consistent with (4–2)).

Potentials

Equation (4–9) may be satisfied identically by setting

$$F_{ik} = \frac{\partial \phi_k}{\partial x^i} - \frac{\partial \phi_i}{\partial x^k} \tag{4–16}$$

which may be interpreted as

$$\left(\mathbf{B} = \nabla \times \mathbf{A} \quad \text{and} \quad \mathbf{E} = -\nabla\phi - \frac{1}{c}\frac{\partial \mathbf{A}}{\partial t} \right)$$

where $\phi^i = (\mathbf{A}, i\phi)$. We are also free to require

$$\frac{\partial \phi^i}{\partial x^i} = 0 \qquad \left(\nabla \cdot \mathbf{A} + \frac{1}{c}\frac{\partial \phi}{\partial t} = 0) \right) \tag{4–17}$$

However, these quantities cannot in general be substituted into (4–10) without first examining the "constitutive" equations, the relations between F_{ik} and H_{ik}.

In vacuum, however, $F_{ik} = H_{ik}$ and from (4–10), (4–16) and (4–17):

$$\frac{\partial^2 \phi^i}{\partial x^k \, \partial x^k} = -\frac{4\pi}{c} s^i \tag{4–18}*$$

If $s^i \equiv 0$, solutions are $\exp(a_i x^i)$ with $a_i a^i = 0$. Thus if $a_j = (-i\mathbf{k}, \omega/c)$ then the solution reads $e^{i\omega t} e^{-i\mathbf{k}\cdot\mathbf{r}}$ with $|\mathbf{k}| = \omega/c$. The vector $a^j = (-i\mathbf{k}, \omega/c)$ must have the transformation law (4–1) with $-i\mathbf{k}$ for $\mathbf{r}$ and $+\omega/c$ for ict. This gives, where θ is the angle between $\mathbf{v}$ and $\mathbf{k}$,

$$\omega' = \omega \frac{1 - (v/c)\cos\theta}{\sqrt{1-\beta^2}} \tag{4–19}$$

* This equation, (4–18) is not covariant as it stands; the generally correct form is ($g = \text{Det}\,[g_{ij}]$)

$$\frac{1}{\sqrt{g}}\frac{\partial}{\partial x^l}\left(\sqrt{g}\, g^{lk} \frac{\partial \phi^i}{\partial x^k} \right) = -\frac{4\pi}{c} s^i$$

which reduces to (4–18) in view of (4–6).

(Doppler effect) and

$$\mathbf{k}' \cdot \mathbf{v} = \frac{\mathbf{k} \cdot \mathbf{v} - \beta^2 \omega}{\sqrt{1 - \beta^2}} \tag{4–20}$$

(*aberration of light*).

The general solution of (4–18) in an infinite vacuum region is

$$\phi^i(x^j) = \frac{1}{\pi c} \oint\oint\oint\oint \frac{s^i(\bar{x}^k)}{R^2} \, d\bar{x}^1 \, d\bar{x}^2 \, d\bar{x}^3 \, d\bar{x}^4 \tag{4–21}$$

where

$$R^2 = g_{ij}(x^i - \bar{x}^i)(x^j - \bar{x}^j)$$

whence

$$F^{kj} = \frac{2}{\pi c} \oint\oint\oint\oint \frac{R^j s^k - R^k s^j}{R^4} \, d\bar{x}^1 \, d\bar{x}^2 \, d\bar{x}^3 \, d\bar{x}^4 \tag{4–22}$$

Moving Media

The simple constitutive equations, $\mathbf{D} = \epsilon \mathbf{E}$, etc. cannot be immediately written in terms of (4–7) and hence (as foreshadowed in (3–11)) cannot remain valid in moving systems. Tensor forms, correct for motionless media and hence in general, are

$$H_{ik} u^k = \epsilon F_{ik} u^k \tag{4–23}$$

$$F^{ik} u^l + F^{kl} u^i + F^{li} u^k = \mu[H^{ik} u^l + H^{kl} u^i + H^{li} u^k] \tag{4–24}$$

where

$$u^l = (1 - \beta^2)^{-\frac{1}{2}}(\mathbf{v}/c, i)$$

and $\mathbf{v}$ is the velocity of the material medium in question. In ordinary notation, these read

$$\left.\begin{aligned} \mathbf{D} + \frac{\mathbf{v}}{c} \times \mathbf{H} &= \epsilon\left(\mathbf{E} + \frac{\mathbf{v}}{c} \times \mathbf{B}\right) \\ \mathbf{B} - \frac{\mathbf{v}}{c} \times \mathbf{E} &= \mu\left(\mathbf{H} - \frac{\mathbf{v}}{c} \times \mathbf{D}\right) \end{aligned}\right\} \tag{4–25}$$

These are equivalent to (3–21) and (3–22).

It might appear that $\mathbf{J} = \sigma \mathbf{E}$ could be transcribed as $s^i = \sigma F^{ik} u_k$ but the component $i = 4$ then would give $\rho \equiv 0$ in stationary media. The form which avoids this is

$$s^i - u^i(s^k u_k) = \sigma F^{ik} u_k \tag{4–26}$$

In ordinary notation, this reads

$$\mathbf{J} + \left(\frac{\mathbf{v}}{c}\right) \frac{\left(\frac{\mathbf{v}}{c} \cdot \mathbf{J}\right) - \rho c}{1 - \beta^2} = \sigma \frac{\mathbf{E} + \frac{\mathbf{v}}{c} \times \mathbf{B}}{\sqrt{1 - \beta^2}} \tag{4–27}$$

(and another equation which is a consequence of this). An equivalent form is given in (3–20).

Field Energy and Power Flow

The Poynting vector and Maxwell stress tensor are included in the four-dimensional tensor,

$$S^{ki} = S^{ik} = \frac{g^{ik}}{16\pi} F^{lm} F_{lm} - \frac{1}{4\pi} F^{ir} F^{kl} g_{rl} \tag{4–28}$$

wherein the components with $i \neq 4 \neq j$ are the Maxwell stress tensor, (3–7), while $S^{i4} = \left(\frac{-i}{c}\,\mathbf{S},\, U\right)$ where $\mathbf{S}$ and U are, in vacuum, the Poynting vector and field-energy density respectively.

If $\epsilon = 1 = \mu$ (vacuum; or else "microscopic point of view"), then $H^{ik} = F^{ik}$ and, by (4–9) and (4–10),

$$\frac{\partial S^{ik}}{\partial x^k} = \frac{1}{c}\, F^{il} s_l \tag{4–29}$$

which in turn is $\left(\rho\mathbf{E} + \frac{\mathbf{J}}{c} \times \mathbf{B},\, i\mathbf{J}\cdot\mathbf{E}\right)$.

Mechanics

Unlike electromagnetics, the laws of mechanics must be fundamentally altered to fit (F). For example (4–29) shows that the classical Lorentz electromagnetic-force is part of a four-vector, but (4–3) shows that accelerations are *not*; proportionality of the two would thus violate (F).

The closest four-vector analogs of velocity and acceleration are (where it is understood that $x^i = x^i(s)$ specifies the path of some body):

$$U^i = ic\,\frac{\mathrm{d}x^i}{\mathrm{d}s} = \frac{\mathrm{d}x^i}{\mathrm{d}t}\frac{\mathrm{d}x^4}{\mathrm{d}s} = \frac{(\mathbf{v},\, ic)}{\sqrt{1-\beta^2}} \tag{4–30}$$

$$ic\,\frac{\mathrm{d}U^i}{\mathrm{d}s} = \frac{\mathrm{d}U^i}{\mathrm{d}t}\frac{\mathrm{d}x^4}{\mathrm{d}s} = \left(\frac{\mathbf{a}}{1-\beta^2} + \frac{\mathbf{v}(\mathbf{v}\cdot\mathbf{a})}{c^2(1-\beta^2)^2},\, \frac{i(\mathbf{v}\cdot\mathbf{a})}{c(1-\beta^2)^2}\right) \tag{4–31}$$

[The last equalities in each equation follow from $U^iU_i = -c^2 = (\mathrm{d}x^4/\mathrm{d}s)^2(|\mathbf{v}|^2 - c^2)$ that is, $\frac{\mathrm{d}x^4}{\mathrm{d}s} = \frac{1}{\sqrt{1-\beta^2}}$.]

The definition of force (classical $\mathbf{f} = m\mathbf{a}$) thus can be approximated by a tensor form as

$$f^j = m_0(ic)\,\frac{\mathrm{d}U^j}{\mathrm{d}s} = \left(\mathbf{f},\, \frac{i}{c}\frac{\mathrm{d}E}{\mathrm{d}t}\right) \tag{4–32}$$

where m_0 ("rest mass") is a characteristic constant for any given body. The last expression in this equation comes from $ic(\mathrm{d}U^i/\mathrm{d}s)f_i = (\tfrac{1}{2}m_0c^2)\,\frac{\mathrm{d}}{\mathrm{d}s}\,U^iU_i = 0$ so that $\mathbf{f}\cdot\mathbf{v} + icf^4 = 0$.

The question of whether Newton's third law ("action = reaction") holds generally is fraught with the difficulty that "simultaneity" ($\mathrm{d}t = 0$) is not invariant under the Lorentz transformation (4–1). A *collision*, however, does not involve action at a distance and for such phenomena equality of action and reaction are found to hold. That is, "momentum" is conserved:

$$\sum_\alpha m_{0\alpha}U_\alpha{}^j = \sum_\alpha \frac{m_{0\alpha}(\mathbf{v}_\alpha,\, ic)}{\sqrt{1-\beta_\alpha{}^2}} = P^j = \text{constants}, \tag{4–33}$$

where the index α denotes the various particles. The fourth component of this relation involves the total energy (compare (4–32))

$$E_{\text{tot}} = \sum_\alpha \frac{m_{0\alpha}c^2}{\sqrt{1-\beta_\alpha{}^2}} \tag{4–34}$$

Conservation of this component of (4–33) is possible in an *inelastic* collision only if the lost kinetic energy appears as an additional *rest* mass of the system, according to $\Delta E = c^2 \, \Delta M_0$. This relation and its converse are indeed observed and it is basic to understanding the physical principles behind many relativistic effects.

The concept of "external" forces is also rather unsatisfactory (in general) because "simultaneity" is not an invariant concept. Thus gravitational forces are seldom treated by (4–32) but rather by the more elegant concepts of the General Relativity* of Einstein.

Cases which can be handled by Special Relativity are:

1. **Electromagnetic forces,**

$$f^j = \frac{1}{c} F^{jk} s_k = \frac{\partial S^{jl}}{\partial x^l} \tag{4–35}$$

When this is substituted into (4–32), the result (for a particle carrying charge q) may be written, in view of (4–15) and (4–30) (note the *time* derivative):

$$m_0 \frac{\mathrm{d}}{\mathrm{d}t}\left(\frac{\mathbf{v}}{\sqrt{1 - v^2/c^2}}\right) = q\mathbf{E} + \frac{q}{c}\,\mathbf{v} \times \mathbf{B} \tag{4–36}$$

(plus the energy equation which follows from this).

If we set

$$\mathrm{d}\tau = \mathrm{d}s/ic \quad \left(U^i = \frac{\mathrm{d}x^i}{\mathrm{d}\tau}\right) \tag{4–37}$$

(the so-called "proper time") then (4–35) and (4–36) can be written as a Lagrangian variational principle (with fixed end points τ_1, τ_2):

$$\delta \int_{\tau_1}^{\tau_2} L \, \mathrm{d}\tau = \delta \int_{\tau_1}^{\tau_2} \left[-\tfrac{1}{2} m_0 c^2 g_{ik} U^i U^k + \frac{q}{c} U^i \phi_i \right] \mathrm{d}\tau = 0 \tag{4–38}$$

Of course, as in classical mechanics, this form is not unique. (Any term of the form $(\mathrm{d}/\mathrm{d}\tau)F(x^i)$ can be added to L.) Similarly, the Hamiltonian form below is not unique:

Momenta:

$$p_k = \frac{\partial L}{\partial U^k} = -m_0 c^2 U_k + \frac{q}{c}\,\phi_k \tag{4–39}$$

Hamiltonian:

$$H = U^k \frac{\partial L}{\partial U^k} - L = \frac{-1}{2m_0 c^2}\left(p^k - \frac{q}{c}\,\phi^k\right)\left(p_k - \frac{q}{c}\,\phi_k\right) \tag{4–40}$$

Hamiltonian form of the equations of motion:

$$g_{kl} \frac{\mathrm{d}x^l}{\mathrm{d}\tau} = U_k = \frac{\partial H}{\partial p^k}; \qquad \frac{\mathrm{d}p_k}{\mathrm{d}\tau} = -\frac{\partial H}{\partial x^k} \tag{4–41}$$

2. **Continuous Matter** (local "elastic" forces plus electromagnetic forces; no gravitation).

The *local* elastic forces are uniquely defined simply by stipulating that, in *co-moving*

---

* Though it must be admitted that experimental evidence is not yet sufficient to single out this treatment as being necessary as well as elegant.

coordinates, they have their classical values given by* a three-by-three stress tensor $\mathfrak{P}_0$. Then define P^{ij} as a four-by-four tensor whose *co-moving* components are:

$$P_{(0)}{}^{ij} = \left[\begin{array}{ccc|c} & & & 0 \\ & \mathfrak{P}_0 & & 0 \\ & & & 0 \\ \hline 0 & 0 & 0 & 0 \end{array}\right] \tag{4–42}$$

The equations of motion and continuity are then taken to be the closest four-vector analogues of the classical equations:†

$$\frac{\partial}{\partial x^k}(\rho_0 U^i U^k - P^{ik} - S^{ik}) = 0 \tag{4–43}$$

It is sometimes more convenient to regard the sum of the first two tensors in (4–43) as a single (stress-energy) tensor:

$$T^{ik} = \rho_0 U^i U^k - P^{ik} \tag{4–44}$$

which may also be defined by its component values in co-moving coordinates:

$$T_{(0)}{}^{ik} = \left[\begin{array}{ccc|c} & & & 0 \\ & -\mathfrak{P}_0 & & 0 \\ & & & 0 \\ \hline 0 & 0 & 0 & -c^2\rho_0 \end{array}\right] \tag{4–45}$$

The general equations of motion are then

$$\frac{\partial}{\partial x^k}(T^{ik} - S^{ik}) = 0. \tag{4–46}$$

Note that a large "rigid" body should be described by these relations since it cannot be "rigid" in all coordinate systems (another facet of Lorentz contractions and destruction of simultaneity).

For a perfect fluid ($-\mathfrak{P}_0 = p_0 \mathbf{1}$), one finds from (4–45) that in general coordinates

$$T^{ik} = \left(\frac{p_0}{c^2} + \rho_0\right) U^i U^k + g^{ik} p_0 \tag{4–47}$$

Equation (4–46) is equivalent to

$$\frac{\partial}{\partial x^k}[x^i(T^{jk} - S^{jk})] = T^{ji} - S^{ji} \tag{4–48}$$

---

* See (1–62)–(1–66).

† The scalar, ρ_0, is the mass-density measured in co-moving coordinates. The U^i in (4–43) are the local mean (macroscopic) values of $dx^i/d\tau = ic\, dx^i/ds$ for the particles of the fluid.

It must be remembered that ρ_0 includes any internal ("invisible", thermodynamic) *energy*. Compare the remark following (4–34). To emphasize this, it is sometimes expedient to write

$$\rho_0 = \rho_{00}(1 + e_{00}/c^2)$$

where ρ_{00} and e_{00} are the non-relativistic density and internal energy per unit mass (in co-moving coordinates).

If the individual fluid particles can be neither created nor destroyed, there should be adjoined the conservation equation, $\partial(U^k \rho_{00})/\partial x^k = 0$.

of which, the antisymmetric part is an "angular momentum" equation of motion:

$$\frac{\partial}{\partial x^k}[x^i(T^{jk} - S^{jk}) - x^j(T^{ik} - S^{ik})] = 0 \tag{4–49}$$

and the trace (diagonal sum) of (4–48) is a "differential virial theorem"

$$\frac{\partial}{\partial x^k}[x^i(T_i^{\ k} - S_i^{\ k})] = T_i^{\ i} - S_i^{\ i} = 3p_0 - \rho_0 c^2 \tag{4–50}$$

both of which can be put into more usual forms by integrating over the space variables and converting to vector notation.

Thermodynamics

Thermodynamic concepts also require some alteration. Note that a mole of a substance must be defined as N_0 molecules (*not* as so many grams, since mass is not an invariant quantity).

Because of the Lorentz space contraction

$$V = V_0\sqrt{1 - \beta^2} \quad \text{(volume per mole)} \tag{4–51}$$

(β refers to the local fluid velocity of the medium).

Either from the transformation laws of force and area or from "pressure $= (-1/3)$ $P_i^{\ i}$", the pressure is invariant:

$$p = p_0 \tag{4–52}$$

Since macroscopic accelerations are "reversible", entropy per mole is also invariant

$$s = s_0 \tag{4–53}$$

(which also agrees with the statistical definition of entropy).

By (4–29), heat changes must transform like the fourth component of a four-vector,

$$\Delta Q = (\Delta Q)_0\sqrt{1 - \beta^2} \tag{4–54}$$

By the thermodynamic law,* $\Delta s \geqslant \int dQ/T$ (which is here *assumed* to hold in all coordinates; no experimental check is yet available), it follows from (4–53) and (4–54),

$$T = T_0\sqrt{1 - \beta^2} \tag{4–55}$$

Thus a fluid with very widely varying local fluid velocities can have a uniform proper temperature but a non-uniform temperature as seen from any one coordinate system.

Internal energy: It was noted, after (4-34), that the concept of "internal energy content" becomes inseparable from that of *rest* mass (rest density) in relativity. One can only take the two together. In co-moving coordinates, the total energy per unit volume is $c^2\rho_0 = -T_{(0)}^{\ 44}$ and, to agree with (4–28), (4–29) and (4–46), in general,

$$e = -VT^{44} = c^2\rho V \qquad \text{(per mole)} \tag{4–56}$$

For a fluid ($\mathfrak{P}_0 = -p\mathbf{1}$) the transformation of e can be written

$$e = \frac{e_0 + p_0 V_0 \beta^2}{\sqrt{1 - \beta^2}} \qquad \text{(per mole)} \tag{4–57}$$

---

* An inequality is used to avoid questions of the reversibility of the changes-of-state involved.

(There might seem to be a contradiction between (4–54) and (4–57), but the difficulty lies in $\delta W = \mathrm{d}e - \delta Q$, which is not a perfect differential and is difficult to evaluate in general. For example, even if $\mathrm{d}V = 0$, δW will be finite due to the change in mass associated with $\mathrm{d}e$ or δQ.)

GENERAL RELATIVITY

Special Relativity does not concern coordinate systems ("observers") with relative acceleration. Einstein's General Relativity simultaneously introduces such possibilities and presents a possible description of gravitational forces. Indeed its basic point of departure is that neither mechanical nor optical* experiments can *completely* separate gravitational fields from accelerations of the frame of reference.

Einstein therefore postulated that no physical experiment could distinguish gravitation completely† from acceleration. (*Principle of Equivalence.*) In particular, the general equations of physics must then "read the same" in any coordinates and under any physical circumstances whatever. (*Principle of Covariance.*)

By the Principle of Equivalence, the path of a particle or light ray must always be a "shortest path" (geodesic)‡

$$\frac{\mathrm{d}x^k}{\mathrm{d}s}\left(\frac{\mathrm{d}x^j}{\mathrm{d}s}\right)_{;k} = 0 \quad \text{or} \quad \frac{\mathrm{d}^2x^j}{\mathrm{d}s^2} = -\Gamma_{kl}{}^{j}\frac{\mathrm{d}x^k}{\mathrm{d}s}\frac{\mathrm{d}x^l}{\mathrm{d}s} \tag{4–58}$$

(with the additional restriction $g_{ij}\,\mathrm{d}x^i\,\mathrm{d}x^j = 0$ for a light ray). Thus (compare (4–32)) the derivatives of the "metric tensor", g_{ij}, determine gravitational as well as inertial forces. The actual physical presence of gravitational effects can show up only as the impossibility of transforming the coordinates so that the $\Gamma_{kl}{}^{j}$ vanish. That is, in contrast to Special Relativity, General Relativity asserts that *space time is not "flat" when (and only when) gravitational fields are present.* §

For continuous media, the corresponding equations of motion (again by the Principle of Equivalence) must be the covariant form of (4–46):

$$\mathcal{T}^{ik}{}_{;k} = 0, \quad \text{where} \quad \mathcal{T}^{ik} = T^{ik} - S^{ik} \tag{4–59}$$

where T^{ik} and S^{ik} are defined as before.

The field equations determining g_{ik} are more or less uniquely specified by (a) covariance, (b) validity of (4–59) and (c) reduction to Newtonian theory when gravitational effects and particle velocities are both small. Namely, the gravitational field must be primarily determined by the mass density, $(-1/c^2)T^{44}$, while the only

---

* Light rays transport energy (which can be converted to rest mass) and should therefore be slightly deflected by gravitational fields.

† Nevertheless, *some* types of acceleration can be measured. Thus, a frame of reference may be said to have "no rotation" if a free gyroscope (in gimbals) does not precess. Compare also the Foucault pendulum or the Sagnac optical experiments. Likewise any convergence of lines of "gravity" force would indicate the presence of a "truly gravitational" component, but its proportion of the total could not be determined by localized experiments. Such observations *remain valid* in general relativity (for it is completely covariant and also contains classical mechanics as a special case).

‡ For the remainder of this chapter, we use the full machinery of general Riemannian geometry. The latter is discussed in Chapter 21.

§ The geometric analogy becomes a little strained—though still useful—at this point since the metric tensor is *not given* a priori but is rather a *physical field*, determined, via (4–60) below, by the physical situation.

tensor which can be formed from g_{ik} and its first and second derivatives and whose divergence vanishes is the right side of: (Einstein's field equation)

$$-\kappa\mathscr{T}_{jk} = R_{jk} - \tfrac{1}{2}Rg_{jk} - \lambda g_{jk} \tag{4–60}$$

where:

$$\kappa = 8\pi G/c^4 = 2.073 \times 10^{-48}\ \mathrm{sec}^2/\mathrm{g\ cm} \tag{4–61}$$

where G is Newton's gravitational constant, λ must be a very small universal constant ("cosmological constant", less than 10^{-53} cm^{-2}) and R_{ik} and R are contractions of the curvature tensor—see (21–40)–(21–48).

Equation (4–60) is a set of second-order partial differential equations for g_{ik} in terms of the tensor $\mathscr{T}_{jk}$. Since all these tensors are symmetric, (4–60) represents ten equations and, by (4–59), only six of these are actually independent. Since there are ten different components of $g_{ik} = g_{ki}$, equations (4–60) leave precisely sufficient freedom to change the four coordinates x^i in any arbitrary manner. (This freedom is necessary since the g_{ik} play the dual role of gravitational field on the one hand and "geometric" metric tensor on the other; they are not determined by (4–60) until the coordinate system has been specified—another aspect of the Principle of Equivalence.)

By contraction of (4–60),

$$R + 4\lambda = \kappa\mathscr{T}_k^{\ k} \equiv \kappa\mathscr{T} \quad \text{(say)} \tag{4–62}$$

and (4–60) may therefore also be written

$$R_{jk} + \lambda g_{jk} = -\kappa(\mathscr{T}_{jk} - \tfrac{1}{2}\mathscr{T} g_{jk}) \tag{4–63}$$

which is more useful when $\mathscr{T}_{jk}$ vanishes. (Note from (4–62) that λ acts like a universal pressure.)

Electromagnetic Theory

There is no change beyond the *use of covariant derivatives everywhere* to replace the ordinary derivatives used previously (again by the Principle of Equivalence). Thus (with $x^1 = x$, $x^2 = y$, $x^3 = z$, $x^4 = ict$) F^{ik}, H^{ik}, s^i have the meanings given in (4–7) and (4–8) and the electromagnetic field equations, for example, are

$$F_{kl;i} + F_{li;k} + F_{ik;l} = 0 \tag{4–64}$$

$$\frac{4\pi}{c}s^j = H^{jk}{}_{;k} = \frac{1}{\sqrt{|g|}}\frac{\partial}{\partial x^k}(H^{jk}\sqrt{|g|}) \tag{4–65}$$

(where $g = \mathrm{Det}\,(g_{ik})$, and the last equality follows from $H^{jk} = -H^{kj}$).

Newtonian Approximation

For a body with $|\mathbf{v}| \ll c$, we have $dx^i/ds \doteqdot (0, 0, 0, 1)$—see (4–30)—and (4–58) reduces to

$$\frac{d^2x^j}{ds^2} \doteqdot -\Gamma_{44}{}^{j} = -\tfrac{1}{2}g^{jk}\left(\frac{\partial g_{4k}}{\partial x^4} + \frac{\partial g_{4k}}{\partial x^4} - \frac{\partial g_{44}}{\partial x^k}\right) \tag{4–66}$$

If $g_{jk} = (\delta_{jk}$ plus small terms) and if the field is static, this further reduces to

$$\frac{d^2\mathbf{r}}{dt^2} \doteqdot -\tfrac{1}{2}c^2\nabla g_{44} \tag{4–67}$$

Moreover, for matter nearly at rest ($v \ll c$), $T^{44} = -\rho c^2$ with all other components negligible, so that (4–63) becomes merely (neglecting λ)

$$\tfrac{1}{2}\kappa\rho c^2 = R_{44} \doteq -\frac{\partial}{\partial x^k}\Gamma_{44}{}^k = \tfrac{1}{2}\nabla^2 g_{44} \tag{4–68}$$

where products of Γ's have been neglected and time derivatives set equal to zero. Equations (4–67) and (4–68) are the Newtonian equations of motion and the Poisson equation for the gravitational field, if the classical gravitational potential, ϕ, is set equal to $\frac{1}{2}c^2 g_{44}$ plus a constant.

Rigorous Solutions

(In the following, g_{ik} is conveniently displayed by writing out the expression $(\mathrm{d}s)^2 = g_{ik}\,\mathrm{d}x^i\,\mathrm{d}x^k$.)

1. **Schwarzschild solution:** If $\mathscr{T}^{ik} = 0$ outside some sphere then the only spherically symmetric solution of (4–63) is (to within coordinate transformations)

$$(\mathrm{d}s)^2 = \frac{(\mathrm{d}r)^2}{1 - \dfrac{a}{r} - \dfrac{\lambda}{3}r^2} + r^2(\mathrm{d}\theta)^2 + r^2\sin^2\theta(\mathrm{d}\phi)^2 - \left(1 - \frac{a}{r} - \frac{\lambda}{3}r^2\right)c^2(\mathrm{d}t)^2 \tag{4–69}$$

Comparison with (4–68) shows that, if M is the mass inside the sphere,

$$a = (2G/c^2)M \tag{4–70}$$

The "metric" (4–69) is the analogue of the classical "$\phi = -1/r$" for a spherical mass in empty space. Substitution into (4–58) then predicts a precession of planetary orbits and a deflection of light rays passing near the central mass. Finally, the last term in (4–69) indicates a red-shift of spectral lines. All three effects are found experimentally but only the first has been quantitatively confirmed beyond doubt. The formulas are:

Orbit Precession $= \dfrac{3\pi a}{2}\left(\dfrac{1}{r_{\max}} + \dfrac{1}{r_{\min}}\right)$ radians/revolution

Light Deflection $= (2a/r_{\min})$ radians

Spectral Shift: From (4–69) (with $\lambda = 0$) the *proper* times at locations r, r' have the ratio $t/t' = \sqrt{\left(1 - \dfrac{a}{r}\right)\Big/\left(1 - \dfrac{a}{r'}\right)}$. Thus for $r' \to \infty$, the spectral shift is

$$\frac{\Delta\lambda}{\lambda} \doteq \frac{a}{2r}$$

2. **Cosmological models:** It may be shown* that homogeneity and isotropy of the universe ("anti-anthropomorphic hypothesis") require, to within coordinate transformations,

$$(\mathrm{d}s)^2 = \frac{e^{g(t)}}{[1 + r^2/4A^2]^2}[(\mathrm{d}r)^2 + r^2(\mathrm{d}\theta)^2 + r^2\sin^2\theta(\mathrm{d}\phi)^2] - c^2(\mathrm{d}t)^2 \tag{4–71}$$

where A is a real or imaginary *constant*. This form may even be obtained for co-moving coordinates.* From (4–71), it follows that light suffers a spectral shift,

$$\frac{\Delta\lambda}{\lambda} = \exp\left[\tfrac{1}{2}g(t_1) - \tfrac{1}{2}g(t_2)\right] - 1 \tag{4–72}$$

* See, for example, R. C. Tolman "*Relativity Thermodynamics and Cosmology*", section 148.

where t_1 is the time of emission and t_2 the time of reception; these times are related to the corresponding positions r_1, r_2 by setting $ds = 0$ in (4–71).

The experimentally observed red-shift (Hubble) requires

$$\left(\frac{dg}{dt}\right)_{\text{present}} = (4 \times 10^{-10}\, c) \text{ per light year}$$
$$= 13 \times 10^{-16}/\text{sec.} \qquad (4\text{–}73)$$

(The present value of g itself merely defines the length-scales of the coordinates. The remaining parameters, A^2, λ, and the higher derivatives of g can only be bounded with present data; all are very small and could have either sign or be zero.)

Note that, with the coordinates (4–71), t is a "cosmic" time, the same for all observers. It is thus proper, with (4–71), to speak of "present time" without specifying a spatial location.

Substitution of (4–71) into (4–60) gives $\mathscr{T}^{ik}$; the results are

$$\kappa\mathscr{T}_1^{\ 1} = \kappa\mathscr{T}_2^{\ 2} = \kappa\mathscr{T}_3^{\ 3} = -\frac{e^{-g(t)}}{A^2} - \frac{1}{c^2}\frac{d^2g}{dt^2} - \frac{3}{4}\left(\frac{1}{c}\frac{dg}{dt}\right)^2 - \lambda \qquad (4\text{–}74)$$

$$\kappa\mathscr{T}_4^{\ 4} = -\frac{3e^{-g(t)}}{A^2} - \frac{3}{4}\left(\frac{1}{c}\frac{dg}{dt}\right)^2 - \lambda \qquad (4\text{–}75)$$

with all other components zero. These represent the only distribution of matter and radiation which could generate the form (4–71) and hence lead to an isotropic, homogeneous universe.*

If the matter and radiation are approximated as a perfect fluid and if the coordinates are co-moving, (4–74) and (4–75) become

$$\kappa p_T = -\frac{e^{-g(t)}}{A^2} - \frac{1}{c^2}\frac{d^2g}{dt^2} - \frac{3}{4}\left(\frac{1}{c}\frac{dg}{dt}\right)^2 - \lambda \qquad (4\text{–}76)$$

$$\kappa\rho_T c^2 = \frac{3}{A^2}e^{-g(t)} + \frac{3}{4}\left(\frac{1}{c}\frac{dg}{dt}\right)^2 + \lambda \qquad (4\text{–}77)$$

where the total pressure, p_T, and the total energy density, $\rho_T c^2$, include both matter and radiation.

Equations (4–76) and (4–77) along with an equation of state for the "matter-radiation fluid" such as $p_T = F(E, \rho_T) = F(c^2\rho_T, \rho_T)$ become differential equations for $g(t)$, p_T, ρ_T (as is to be expected since (4–60) is the field equation).

Various specific models of this type have been studied and lead to $g(t)$ which are either oscillatory (passing through singular states) or monotonic, depending on the value of λ, etc. (The only models which—in contradiction to (4–73)—are static are also either unstable or empty.)

In the real universe, p_T is almost entirely due to radiation pressure. The radiation (energy) density is therefore essentially $3p_T/c^2$ and the average density of matter, ρ_m, is

$$\kappa\rho_m c^2 = \kappa\rho_T c^2 - 3\kappa p_T \qquad (4\text{–}78)$$
$$= \frac{6e^{-g}}{A^2} + 3\frac{1}{c^2}\frac{d^2g}{dt^2} + 3\left(\frac{1}{c}\frac{dg}{dt}\right)^2 + 4\lambda$$

* Averaged over very large distances, of course, as an approximation to the actual universe.

CHAPTER 5

QUANTUM MECHANICS

CLASSICAL Newtonian mechanics fails on the molecular and atomic levels. As a result of many hints from experiment, the proper modification, quantum mechanics, was discovered and is now as firmly established (at least in the extra-nuclear domain) as classical mechanics was (and still is) in the macroscopic domain. In principle, though hardly in practice, chemistry is merely applied quantum mechanics. We outline this atomistic, low-energy theory on its own postulational basis.

The basic point of philosophy which emerges from quantum mechanics is that "measurement" involves the paradox that the system measured must be an isolated whole but at the same time must interact with the measuring instruments; for very small systems, this contradiction has no practical resolution, and quantum mechanics presumably expresses the complicated consequences of this situation.

A. POSTULATES AND FORMALISM

(I) Planck's Hypothesis

While Maxwell's equations remain valid, a radiation beam nevertheless also acts as a stream of indivisible "quanta" or "photons" (packets or pulses) each of which carries an *irreducible minimum* of energy, given by

$$E = h\nu = \hbar\omega = hc/\lambda \tag{5-1}$$

where $\hbar = h/2\pi = 1.05 \times 10^{-27}$ erg sec (Planck's constant) and ν, λ are the (macroscopic) frequency and wavelength of the radiation. When molecules emit or absorb quanta, the frequency of the radiation is therefore determined by their energy change.

(II) Discrete-valued Variables

Any particle may have, besides its classical position variables, **r**, non-classical variables ("spin"), s, which can assume only a *finite* set of discrete values. [Such "quantum variables" are more like indices than ordinary variables, but indices are usually needed for other purposes.]

Notation

If ψ and ϕ are any (complex) functions of particle positions and spins, we abbreviate the "integral" over all values of all variables as,

$$\boxed{(\psi, \phi) \equiv \sum_{s_1} \cdots \sum_{s_n} \int_{-\infty}^{\infty} \cdots \int \psi^* \phi \, dV_1 \cdots dV_n = (\phi, \psi)^*} \tag{5-2}$$

where * denotes complex conjugate.

[Although we will generally use the function-concept to denote dependence on spin variables, it should be noted that such a function can be split into (relatively few) component functions, each with different, constant values of the s_i. These may then be arranged in a column and treated as a *vector* or column-matrix. When this is done, (5–2) is written,

$$(\psi, \phi) = \int_{-\infty}^{\infty} \cdots \int \psi^\dagger \cdot \phi \, dV_1 \cdots dV_n \tag{5–3}$$

where $\psi^\dagger$ is the Hermitian conjugate (row) vector and the product, $\psi^\dagger\phi$, is a matrix ("dot") product. In this notation, the spin operators introduced later become matrices which multiply such vectors. This notation is rather common in formal work.]

(III) **Description of State**

The "state" of a system of particles is described (as completely as is possible) by a single complex-valued function, $\Psi(\mathbf{r}_1, s_1, \mathbf{r}_2, s_2, \cdots, \mathbf{r}_n, s_n, t)$, called the **"wave function"** of the system.

(IV) **Interpretation**

The **probability** that, at time t, particle No. 1 will be found to have "spin" s_1 and to be in a volume dV_1 centered at $\mathbf{r}_1$; that particle No. 2 will have spin s_2 and be in dV_2 at $\mathbf{r}_2$; $\cdots$; and that particle No. n will have spin s_n and be in dV_n at $\mathbf{r}_n$, is

$$\frac{|\Psi|^2 \, dV_1 \, dV_2 \cdots dV_n}{(\Psi, \Psi)} \tag{5–4}$$

It is customary to adjust Ψ to make the denominator unity.

Quantum mechanics can predict only average ("mean", "expected") values of system-parameters. Whether this is "really" inherent in Nature can be debated indefinitely.

(V) **Mean Values**

The expected mean value, $\langle F \rangle$, of a function of the form, $F(\mathbf{r}_j, \mathbf{v}_k, t)$ is obtained from Ψ by constructing a **differential operator,** F, and setting

$$\langle F \rangle = \frac{(\Psi, \mathsf{F}\Psi)}{(\Psi, \Psi)} \tag{5–5}$$

To construct F, merely replace each particle-velocity, $\mathbf{v}_j$, by the operator,*

$$(\mathbf{v}_j)_{\text{op}} = \frac{-1}{m_j} \left[i\hbar \nabla_j + \frac{e_j}{c} \mathbf{A}(\mathbf{r}_j) \right] \tag{5–6}$$

where e_j and m_j are the charge and mass of particle j, and $\mathbf{A}$ is the vector potential of any external electromagnetic field acting on the system.

---

* *Conventions:* Unless otherwise stated, operators act on all factors following them in any product, but may be interchanged freely in any sum. A power (n) of an operator is interpreted as an n-fold application of the operator.

Example:

$$\begin{aligned}(\nabla + \mathbf{g})^2\psi &= (\nabla + \mathbf{g}) \cdot (\nabla + \mathbf{g})\psi = \nabla^2\psi + \nabla \cdot (\mathbf{g}\psi) + \mathbf{g} \cdot \nabla\psi + g^2\psi \\ &= \nabla^2\psi + g^2\psi + 2\mathbf{g} \cdot \nabla\psi + \psi(\nabla \cdot \mathbf{g})\end{aligned}$$

By deleting ψ everywhere, these become "pure" operator relations. In much of the literature, the gradient with respect to $\mathbf{r}_j$ is denoted by $(i/\hbar)\mathbf{p}_j$, that is

$$\mathbf{p}_j = -i\hbar\nabla_j$$

which is the operator analogue of the Hamiltonian momentum conjugate to $\mathbf{r}_j$. (Note that $\mathbf{p}_j \neq m_j\mathbf{v}_j$ in general.)

When forming such operators, ambiguities in the ordering of factors in a product are resolved by symmetrizing: BC is replaced by $\frac{1}{2}(BC + CB)$.

All such operators are linear [that is $F(a\psi + b\phi) = aF\psi + bF\phi$] and Hermitian [that is, $(\Psi, F\Phi) = (F\Psi, \Phi)$, so that (5–5) is always real].

Remark: The prescription (5–6) is the one used in practice, but an older form, frequently alluded to, is: "derive (classical) Hamiltonian variables, p_α, q_α, for the system and then replace p_α by $-i\hbar\partial/\partial q_\alpha$ everywhere". However, this prescription can lead to inconsistent results in different coordinate systems, while (5–6) has been found to give correct results in all cases.

Note that when new coordinates are introduced, their time derivatives (the new velocities) must be defined by (5–7) or (5–10) below—*not* by analogy to (5–6).

(VI) Time Derivatives

A time derivative, $\mathrm{d}F/\mathrm{d}t$, has the mean value,

$$\left\langle \frac{\mathrm{d}F}{\mathrm{d}t} \right\rangle = \frac{\mathrm{d}}{\mathrm{d}t} \langle F \rangle \tag{5–7}$$

[If F is independent of all $\mathbf{v}_j$ (5–7) must be consistent with (5–5) and (5–6); this will be shown below.] It will appear in (5–10) that an operator may also be assigned to $\mathrm{d}F/\mathrm{d}t$ so that (5–5) holds in all cases. Equation (5–7) is the ultimate root of the "correspondence principle" which asserts that classical, Newtonian mechanics must always emerge as a good approximation whenever excitation energies are large.

(VII) Schroedinger's Wave Equation

The wave function, Ψ, is to be calculated from Schroedinger's wave equation,

$$\boxed{i\hbar \frac{\partial \Psi}{\partial t} = H\Psi} \tag{5–8}$$

where H is the **Hamiltonian operator,** constructed as in (V) from the classical *energy*, $T + U$, plus any non-classical modifications discussed later. Thus,

$$\boxed{H = \sum_{j=1}^{n} \frac{1}{2m_j}\left[i\hbar\boldsymbol{\nabla}_j + \frac{e_j}{c}\mathbf{A}(\mathbf{r}_j)\right]^2 + U(\mathbf{r}_1, \cdots, \mathbf{r}_n, t) + \text{Spin terms}} \tag{5–9}$$

(where magnetic interactions of moving charged particles have been neglected as is customary).

Since H is Hermitian, it follows from (5–7) and (5–8) that (5–5) is generally valid if we set,

$$\left(\frac{\mathrm{d}F}{\mathrm{d}t}\right)_{\mathrm{op}} = \frac{1}{i\hbar}\left[FH - HF\right] + \frac{\partial F}{\partial t} \tag{5–10}$$

(where $\partial/\partial t$ acts only on F; without this convention, subtract $F\partial/\partial t$ from the right-hand side). If $F = F(\mathbf{r}_j, t)$, (5–9) and (5–10) are easily seen to be consistent with (5–5) and (5–6).

Boundary and Admissibility Conditions on Ψ in (5–8), besides those implied by the physical problem at hand, are:

(B_1) The function, $|\Psi|^2$, must be continuous and single-valued and have a finite integral over any region of space*—so that (5–4) and (5–5) always have meaning.

(B_2) If certain particles of the system are physically indistinguishable, an interchange of (all the coordinates of) two such particles can change Ψ only to the extent of multiplying all its values by e^{ia} where a is a constant (so that the physical results, (5–4) and (5–5) are unaffected). Since two successive interchanges of the same pair of particles is no change at all, $a = 0$ or π.

(VIII) Symmetry Conditions ("Statistics")

It is found empirically that, for all particles so far investigated, only *one* of the alternatives developed in (B_2) actually occurs in nature; that is,

(B_2') Fermi–Dirac particles (electrons, neutrons, protons, and probably all particles with half-integral spin):

Interchange of two Fermi–Dirac particles *must always* change the sign of Ψ.

(B_2'') Bose–Einstein particles (photons, pi-mesons, and probably all particles with integral spin):

Interchange of two Bose–Einstein particles must have no effect whatever on Ψ.

(IX) Spin

If is found empirically (Goudsmit and Uhlenbeck) that all particles investigated have an intrinsic, quantum mechanical "angular momentum" and an associated magnetic moment (even when the charge is zero). Unlike a classical spin, this "variable" can assume only a finite number of values.† The details are presented below (following (5–33)) but roughly, the "spin" of a particle also has expected mean values and is associated with an operator, **S**, which acts (only) on the spin-variables, s, in Ψ.

Spin effects frequently act primarily through (VIII), but there are also small direct effects on the energy, due to the magnetic moments. Typical terms in (5–9) are

$$(\text{Spin-Orbit}\ddagger)\ \Delta H = \sum_j \frac{g_j}{4c^2 m_j^2}\left\{\frac{1}{r_j}\frac{\partial U}{\partial r_j}\right\}\mathbf{L}_j \cdot \mathbf{S}_j \tag{5–11}$$

where $\mathbf{L}_j$ is the "orbital angular momentum" operator, $(-i\hbar\mathbf{r}_j \times \nabla_j)$ and g_j is an empirical factor, the gyromagnetic ratio, giving the strength of the spin magnetic moment of particle j. For electrons, $g = 2$ (except for very small correction terms).

---

* This may lead to (at least) formal difficulties if the system is not confined. These difficulties are often evaded by confining the system in a very large "box", the volume of which can become infinite *after* all physical results have been worked out. By (5–4), the appropriate boundary conditions for a confining box are $\Psi = 0$ outside of and at the faces of the box. Differential operators are then in general Hermitian *only* with respect to functions which satisfy this condition. For example,

$$\iiint (\phi\nabla^2\psi - \psi\nabla^2\phi)\,dV = \iint (\psi\nabla\phi - \phi\nabla\psi)\cdot d\mathbf{S}.$$

An alternative is to drop the requirement $(\Psi, \Psi) \neq \infty$ and base physical interpretations on (5–19) and (5–20) below.

† In fact, the word "spin" is in some ways misleading since no model of a "spinning sphere" really reproduces the characteristics which are experimentally required. The origin of the term is now purely historical, but it still has some degree of suggestiveness.

‡ The factor, 4, is a result of a relativistic effect (Thomas precession) acting in addition to classical effects; the field "seen" by the moving spin is not that which would be measured by a stationary observer. The result (5–11) also follows from the Dirac relativistic wave equation, (5–166)—(5–177).

In principle, there is also a spin-spin interaction, but this is so small as to be generally ignored in atomic theory.

General Remark

Corresponding to the ambiguity of the classical Hamiltonian function, there is an equivalence (or "contact") transformation of quantum mechanics. Namely, if $f = f(\mathbf{r}_1, \mathbf{r}_2, \cdots, \mathbf{r}_n, t)$ is any *real*-valued function and if (all) wave functions Ψ are replaced by

$$\Phi = \Psi \exp [(i/\hbar)f] \tag{5–12}$$

then (5–4) and (5–5) and all physical results will be unaffected if (5–6) and (5–8) are replaced by

$$-m_j\mathbf{v}_j = i\hbar\nabla_j + \frac{e_j}{c}\mathbf{A}(\mathbf{r}_j) + (\nabla_j f) \tag{5–13}$$

(where in the last term ∇_j acts only on f) and

$$i\hbar\frac{\partial\Phi}{\partial t} = H''\Phi = H'\Phi - \Phi\frac{\partial f}{\partial t} \tag{5–14}$$

where H' is constructed by the new rule, (5–13), from the classical energy, $T + U$.

Particular examples of this transformation are:

(i) $f = Ct$ which merely shifts all energies by the constant amount, C.

(ii) $f = \sum_j \mathbf{r}_j \cdot \mathbf{A}(\mathbf{r}_j)$ which removes the terms $\mathbf{A}(\mathbf{r}_j)$ from (5–6) and (5–9), replacing them by $(\nabla\mathbf{A}) \cdot \mathbf{r}_j$ [a vector whose z_j component, for example, is $\mathbf{r}_j \cdot \partial\mathbf{A}/\partial z_j$ etc.] and adds in explicitly the "electric dipole" term, $e_j\mathbf{r}_j \cdot \partial\mathbf{A}/\partial ct$.

(iii) A "gauge transformation", $(\mathbf{A}; \phi) \rightarrow (\mathbf{A} + \nabla F;\ \phi - \partial F/\partial ct)$ can be compensated by using $f = \sum_j (e_j/c)F(\mathbf{r}_j, t)$ in (5–12).

B. GENERAL CONSEQUENCES AND METHODS

Conservation Laws

From (5–7) and (5–10) it follows that $\langle F \rangle$ is constant in time if $\partial F/\partial t = 0$ and if $HF = FH$. In particular, the following are *strictly* true in quantum mechanics.

(i) *Conservation of Energy* holds if $\partial H/\partial t = 0$ $\left(\text{where } \partial/\partial t \text{ applies to } H \text{ only; without this convention, the condition would read } \frac{\partial}{\partial t}H = H\frac{\partial}{\partial t}\right)$.

(ii) *Conservation of Linear Momentum* holds if space-translation of the whole system has no effect (and similarly for any one component):

$$\sum_j \nabla_j H = H \sum \nabla_j$$

(iii) *Conservation of Angular Momentum** holds if rotation of the whole system has no effect (and similarly for any one component):

$$\sum \mathbf{r}_j \times \nabla_j H = H \sum_j \mathbf{r}_j \times \nabla_j$$

Other conservation laws will be mentioned later.

* That is, the quantity, $\sum \mathbf{r}_j \times \nabla_j = (i/\hbar) \sum \mathbf{r}_j \times [m_j\mathbf{v}_j + (e_j/c)\mathbf{A}(\mathbf{r}_j)]$ which is commonly called "angular momentum" but one component of which is conserved even in an external uniform magnetic field.

When a changing electromagnetic field is present, none of these laws need be valid for the mechanical system alone, but they are (empirically) valid if the radiant energy and momentum are included:

Photon Momenta

Either from special relativity (specifically: ($\mathbf{p}$, iE/c) and ($\mathbf{r}$, ict) are four-vectors) or from momentum considerations applied to Maxwell's stress-tensor form of pondermotive forces, it follows from postulate (I) that each photon has an associated mechanical momentum,

$$p = E/c = h/\lambda \tag{5–15}$$

Some simple consequences are:

Radiation pressure: If n quanta per second per unit area strike a surface at an angle, θ, and if Rn of these are specularly reflected, the pressure on the surface is

$$P = \frac{dp}{dt} = \frac{h}{\lambda} n(1 + R) \cos^2 \theta = \frac{1 + R}{c} \langle|\mathbf{S}|\rangle \cos^2 \theta \tag{5–16}$$

Compton relations: If a photon scatters from a particle, its frequency must change (!) according to postulate (I), and (relativistic) conservation of momentum and energy show,

$$\Delta\lambda = \frac{h}{mc}(1 - \cos \theta) \tag{5–17}$$

where θ is the scattering angle of the photon. The struck particle carries away an energy $h(\Delta\nu)$ and travels at angle ϕ to the incoming photon, where

$$\cot \phi = \left(1 + \frac{h\nu_0}{mc^2}\right) \tan \tfrac{1}{2}\theta \tag{5–18}$$

Further details require the relativistic Dirac wave equation. [See (5–213)–(5–215).]

Probability Currents

From (5–8),

$$\frac{\partial}{\partial t} |\Psi|^2 = \frac{1}{i\hbar}(\Psi^* H\Psi - \Psi H\Psi^*) = -\sum_j \nabla_j \cdot \mathbf{J}_j \tag{5–19}$$

where

$$\mathbf{J}_j = \frac{i\hbar}{2m_j}(\Psi\nabla_j\Psi^* - \Psi^*\nabla_j\Psi) - \frac{e_j}{m_j c}|\Psi|^2\mathbf{A}(\mathbf{r}_j) \tag{5–20}$$

which may be interpreted, through (5–4), as the average current or flux of matter produced by particle j.

This concept is one basis for quantum mechanical treatment of collision problems.

De Broglie Matter-Waves

These are important for semi-quantitative arguments. (Historically, they suggested (5–8) itself.) If (5–8) is solved for a single particle with $U = 0$ everywhere,* Ψ

* Strictly, (Ψ, Ψ) then does not exist, but the picture is not materially modified by using a large "box." Compare (5-96)–(5–98) below.

is found to take the form of plane waves with frequency and wavelength given by

$$\nu = E/h; \quad \lambda = h/p = h/mv \tag{5–21}$$

where $E = \langle H \rangle$ is the energy of the particle and $p = \langle mv \rangle$ is its momentum. (Note $\lambda\nu \neq c$.)

A common notation is

$$\mathbf{k} = \mathbf{p}/\hbar; \qquad k = |\mathbf{k}| = 2\pi/\lambda \tag{5–22}$$

EXAMPLES:

(i) To confine an electron inside a nucleus requires $\lambda \doteqdot 10^{-13}$ cm, whence $E = \sqrt{(m_0c^2)^2 + (pc)^2} \doteqdot 2 \times 10^{-3}$ erg $\doteqdot 1$ Bev, which is more than the known binding energies; thus electrons cannot exist as such inside a nucleus in spite of their emergence in beta decay.

(ii) *Chemical binding*: If two atoms can "cooperate" in such a manner that some of their electrons can *share* the same region of space (thus increasing their wavelengths), the total energy will be lowered and the atoms therefore held together. This, together with the Pauli principle qualitatively explains covalent bonding (a purely quantum phenomenon).

(iii) Diffraction and interference effects with beams of matter are readily predicted and are indeed observed (Davisson and Germer).

Uncertainty Principles (Heisenberg)

For any two functions, F and G, consider the deviations from their mean values; these are also operators,

$$f = F - \langle F \rangle; \qquad g = G - \langle G \rangle$$

Let*

$$C = i[FG - GF] = i[fg - gf]$$

Then

$$\tfrac{1}{2}(C\Psi, \Psi) = \tfrac{1}{2}(\Psi, C\Psi) = \tfrac{i}{2}[(f\Psi, g\Psi) - (f\Psi, g\Psi)^*] \leqslant |(f\Psi, g\Psi)|$$

Therefore,

$$\tfrac{1}{4}(\Psi, C\Psi)^2 \leqslant |(f\Psi, g\Psi)|^2 \leqslant (f\Psi, f\Psi)(g\Psi, g\Psi) = (\Psi, f^2\Psi)(\Psi, g^2\Psi)$$

(by the Schwarz inequality). Thus, writing ΔF, ΔG for f, g respectively, we have

$$\sqrt{\langle(\Delta F)^2\rangle\langle(\Delta G)^2\rangle} \geqslant \tfrac{1}{2}|\langle FG - GF \rangle| \tag{5–23}$$

In particular, for any particle position and velocity,

$$\sqrt{\langle(\Delta x)^2\rangle\langle(\Delta mv_x)^2\rangle} \geqslant \frac{\hbar}{2} \tag{5–24}$$

Also since (see (5–8)) the energy operator is $i\hbar\partial/\partial t$ (as well as H),

$$\sqrt{\langle(\Delta t)^2\rangle\langle(\Delta E)^2\rangle} \geqslant \frac{\hbar}{2} \tag{5–25}$$

* The operator $(1/i)C$ is usually called the "commutator" of F and G and is often written $[F, G]$. Some authors use this name and notation for other multiples of C.

Constants of the Motion

If the dispersion of F is zero, that is

$$0 = \langle (F - \langle F \rangle)^2 \rangle = \langle F^2 \rangle - \langle F \rangle^2$$

$$= \frac{(\Psi, \mathsf{F}^2 \Psi)}{(\Psi, \Psi)} - \left[\frac{(\Psi, \mathsf{F}\Psi)}{(\Psi, \Psi)} \right]^2$$

or

$$(\Psi, \mathsf{F}\Psi)^2 = (\mathsf{F}\Psi, \mathsf{F}\Psi)(\Psi, \Psi)$$

but by the Schwarz inequality, this is possible only if $\mathsf{F}\Psi$ is a multiple of Ψ. Thus,

$$\mathsf{F}\Psi = \langle F \rangle \Psi, \qquad \text{if} \qquad \langle (\Delta F)^2 \rangle = 0 \tag{5-26}$$

That is, any state Ψ in which F has zero dispersion must be an *eigenfunction* of the operator, F, and the stationary value, $\langle F \rangle$, must be an *eigenvalue* of F.

By (5–23) two functions F, G cannot simultaneously be dispersionless constants unless their operators commute. [Note the connection with the conservation laws preceding (5–15).] In particular, F cannot be dispersionless in a stable (constant-energy) state unless $\mathsf{FH} = \mathsf{HF}$.

Independent Systems

If U has the form (and similarly for spin-energy terms),

$$U = U_{\mathrm{I}}(\mathbf{r}_1, \mathbf{r}_2, \cdots, \mathbf{r}_k, t) + U_{\mathrm{II}}(\mathbf{r}_{k+1}, \cdots, \mathbf{r}_n, t) \tag{5-27}$$

then

$$\mathsf{H} = \mathsf{H}_{\mathrm{I}} + \mathsf{H}_{\mathrm{II}} \tag{5-28}$$

and solutions of (5–8) are

$$\left.\begin{aligned} \Psi &= \Psi_{\mathrm{I}}(\mathbf{r}_1, \cdots, \mathbf{r}_k, t) \cdot \Psi_{\mathrm{II}}(\mathbf{r}_{k+1}, \cdots, \mathbf{r}_n, t) \\ &\text{where} \\ i\hbar \frac{\partial \Psi_{\mathrm{I}}}{\partial t} &= \mathsf{H}_{\mathrm{I}}\Psi_{\mathrm{I}}; \qquad i\hbar \frac{\partial \Psi_{\mathrm{II}}}{\partial t} = \mathsf{H}_{\mathrm{II}}\Psi_{\mathrm{II}} \end{aligned}\right\} \tag{5-29}$$

The problem thus breaks into two separate problems, with the total Ψ given merely by the product of the individual Ψ_i. Similarly for many independent systems. If the latter are indistinguishable only those Ψ with the proper symmetry are valid solutions.

The property (5–29) is frequently useful for obtaining "zeroth" approximations, which may then be improved by regarding a neglected interaction energy as a perturbation.

Angular Momenta

Define:

$$\mathsf{L} = \sum_j \frac{\hbar}{i} \mathbf{r}_j \times \nabla_j \tag{5-30}$$

It is easily shown that

$$\left.\begin{aligned} \mathsf{L}_x\mathsf{L}_y - \mathsf{L}_y\mathsf{L}_x &= i\hbar\mathsf{L}_z \\ \mathsf{L}_y\mathsf{L}_z - \mathsf{L}_z\mathsf{L}_y &= i\hbar\mathsf{L}_x \\ \mathsf{L}_z\mathsf{L}_x - \mathsf{L}_x\mathsf{L}_z &= i\hbar\mathsf{L}_y \\ \text{or, symbolically,} \qquad \mathsf{L} \times \mathsf{L} &= i\hbar\mathsf{L} \end{aligned}\right\} \tag{5-31}$$

If we let $L^2 = L_x^2 + L_y^2 + L_z^2$, it follows from these relations that

$$L^2 L_z = L_z L^2 \qquad (L^2\mathbf{L} = \mathbf{L}L^2) \tag{5–32}$$

If L^2 and L_z both commute with H, then (5–32) shows that L^2 and L_z can simultaneously have constant mean values in a stable state, and in fact such values are almost completely determined* by (5–31) and (5–32):

$$\left.\begin{aligned} \langle L^2\rangle &= l(l+1)\hbar^2 \\ \langle L_z\rangle &= -l\hbar, -(l-1)\hbar, \cdots, (l-1)\hbar, l\hbar \\ &= m\hbar \quad \text{in common notation} \end{aligned}\right\} \tag{5–33}$$

where $2l$ is an integer. It can be shown from group theory (applied to the three-dimensional rotation group, of which L is the infinitesimal operator; compare the remark after (5–40) below) that, with L defined by (5–30), l itself must be an integer in (5–33). However:

Spin Operators

These are postulated to satisfy (5–31) and hence (5–32) and (5–33), but half-integer values of "l" in (5–33) are experimentally required. [Thus (5–30) does *not* hold for spin operators.] Each "fundamental particle" is found to have a *single*, unvarying value of l, called its "spin" and usually written, s.

Electrons, protons and neutrons all have spin, $s = \frac{1}{2}$.

By the second half of (5–33), there are $2s + 1$ independent spin states, and these eigenfunctions are usually labelled by the corresponding value of m_s. Here and below, m_s is the discrete spin *variable* introduced in (II) and (5–2) above.

---

* PROOF: By (5–26),

$$L^2\Psi = \alpha^2\Psi; \qquad L_z\Psi = \beta\Psi$$

From (5–31) it follows then that $(L_x \pm iL_y)\Psi$ is itself another such eigenfunction with $(\alpha')^2 = \alpha^2$ and $\beta' = \beta \pm \hbar$. Continuing in this way, Ψ generates a series of eigenfunctions with the same α and with values of β spaced at intervals of $\hbar$. But all such eigenfunctions must satisfy $\alpha^2 \geqslant \beta^2$ because

$$(L_x^2 + L_y^2)\Psi = (L^2 - L_z^2)\Psi = (\alpha^2 - \beta^2)\Psi$$

and hence

$$\alpha^2 - \beta^2 = (\Psi, L_x^2\Psi) + (\Psi, L_y^2\Psi) = (L_x\Psi, L_x\Psi) + (L_y\Psi, L_y\Psi) \geqslant 0.$$

Thus the above series of eigenfunctions must terminate in both directions and termination can only occur if

$$(L_x + iL_y)\Psi_{\text{max}} = 0 = (L_x - iL_y)\Psi_{\text{min}}$$

From these and (5–31),

$$(L_x - iL_y)(L_x + iL_y)\Psi_{\text{max}} = (\alpha^2 - \beta^2_{\text{max}} - \hbar\beta_{\text{max}})\Psi_{\text{max}} = 0$$

$$\alpha^2 = \beta^2_{\text{max}} + \hbar\beta_{\text{max}}$$

and similarly

$$\alpha^2 = \beta^2_{\text{min}} - \hbar\beta_{\text{min}}$$

Thus

$$\beta_{\text{min}} = -\beta_{\text{max}}$$

and hence (recall the spacing of the β values)

$$\beta_{\text{max}} = -\beta_{\text{min}} = \tfrac{1}{2}n\hbar; \qquad \alpha^2 = \tfrac{1}{2}n(\tfrac{1}{2}n + 1)\hbar$$

where n is an integer. Setting $l = \frac{1}{2}n$ gives (5–33).

It is often convenient, especially when H does not contain $\mathbf{S}$, to represent the wave functions by expressions of the type,

$$\left.\begin{aligned} \psi_k(\mathbf{r}, m_s) &= \phi(\mathbf{r})\delta_k(m_s); \qquad k = -s, -s+1, \cdots, s-1, s \\ \delta_k(m_s) &= \begin{cases} 1, & \text{if } m_s = k \\ 0, & \text{otherwise} \end{cases} \end{aligned}\right\} \tag{5–34}$$

which are orthonormal: $\sum_{m_s} \delta_k(m_s)\delta_p(m_s) = \delta_{kp}$. (Note the close connection of (5–34) with the vector notation mentioned preceding (5–3).) Any function, $\Phi(\mathbf{r}, m_s)$ can be written in the form,

$$\Phi(\mathbf{r}, m_s) = \sum_k \Phi(\mathbf{r}, k)\delta_k(m_s) \tag{5–35}$$

In terms of *this* representation, the spin (angular momentum) *operators*, $\mathbf{S}$, are defined by the fact that δ_k is, by supposition, an eigenfunction of both S^2 and S_z with eigenvalues $s(s+1)\hbar^2$ and $k\hbar$ respectively:

$$S_z\delta_k = k\hbar\delta_k; \qquad (S_x^2 + S_y^2 + S_z^2)\delta_k = s(s+1)\hbar^2\delta_k \tag{5–36}$$

and then (5–31) requires (see footnote to (5–33) and use the normalization and reality of the δ_k):

$$(S_x \pm iS_y)\delta_k = \begin{cases} 0, & \text{if } |k \pm 1| > s \\ \hbar\sqrt{(s \mp k)(s \pm k + 1)}\, \delta_{k\pm 1} \end{cases} \tag{5–37}$$

These relations (and the observation (5–35)) completely define all components of the operator, $\mathbf{S}$.

Spin and rotation of coordinates: In (5–34) the spin functions were chosen real, but complex values must be considered when transforming to rotated coordinates. Considering a rotation by an arbitrarily small angle, ϵ, about the z-axis, one finds, since (as for any vector) $S_x' \pm iS_y' = (1 \pm i\epsilon)(S_x \pm iS_y)$, that (5–36) and (5–37), which must hold in any coordinates, require (to order ϵ),

$$\delta_k' \doteq (1 + i\epsilon k)\delta_k = \delta_k + (i\epsilon/\hbar)S_z\delta_k \tag{5–38}$$

Through (5–35), this defines the infinitesimal operator of the group of coordinate rotations insofar as it affects the spin variables. By (22–4), the operator for a *finite* rotation, ϕ, about the z-axis is therefore given by the power series of

$$\delta'_k = e^{(i/\hbar)\boldsymbol{\phi}\cdot\mathbf{S}}\delta_k \tag{5–39}$$

(where $\boldsymbol{\phi} = \phi\hat{z}$). By the isotropy of space, (5–39) must be true for any rotation of coordinates (where $\boldsymbol{\phi}$ lies along the axis of rotation and $|\boldsymbol{\phi}|$ is the angle of rotation measured clockwise looking out along $\boldsymbol{\phi}$). By (22–10), the operator which rotates the space variables in ψ is $\exp[(i/\hbar)\boldsymbol{\phi}\cdot\mathbf{L}]$ and (since $\mathbf{L}$ and $\mathbf{S}$ commute, for they act on different variables) the operator which accomplishes the full change of all variables into the rotated coordinate system is given by

$$\psi' = \exp\left[\frac{i}{\hbar}\boldsymbol{\phi}\cdot(\mathbf{L} + \mathbf{S})\right]\psi \tag{5–40}$$

Similarly, for many particles, the total angular momentum of the system appears in (5–40). Note that for spin $\frac{1}{2}$ particles $\boldsymbol{\phi} = 2\pi\hat{z}$ gives $\psi' = \psi e^{\pm i\pi} = -\psi$, and thus the wave functions "belong to" *double valued* representations—or better, they belong to representations of an extended group which includes the rotation group and can be (homomorphically) mapped onto it in an obvious way.

10

Total Angular Momentum

(i) When the spin-orbit coupling, (5–11), is added to the Hamiltonian, (5–9), neither $\mathbf{L}$ nor $\mathbf{S}$ commutes with H but their sum,

$$\mathbf{J} = \mathbf{L} + \mathbf{S} \tag{5–41}$$

may commute with H in problems of appropriate symmetry.

(ii) Similarly, when several particles are present, the individual $\mathbf{J}_j = \mathbf{L}_j + \mathbf{S}_j$ do not commute with H [unless the particles do not interact, $U = \sum_j U_j(\mathbf{r}_j)$] but their sum does.

All these quantities satisfy (5–31) and (5–32) in any case so that *when* they have definite, fixed average values, these are given by (5–33). Using some combinatoric arguments based on (5–33), it can be shown that, in the simple case (5–41), the possible compound values constructable (using (5–29) and linear combinations of the results) from (approximate) states with given l, s are

$$\left.\begin{aligned} j &= l + s,\ l + s - 1, \cdots, |l - s| \\ m_j &= -j, \cdots, j \text{ (for each such } j) \end{aligned}\right\} \tag{5–42}$$

This "vector model" holds similarly for any sum of two angular momenta.

In particular, the four spin eigenfunctions, $\delta_{\pm\frac{1}{2}}(m_{s1})\delta_{\pm\frac{1}{2}}(m_{s2})$, for two spin $\frac{1}{2}$ particles may be replaced by the orthonormal linear combinations:

$$\left.\begin{aligned} &\delta_{\frac{1}{2}}(m_{s1})\delta_{\frac{1}{2}}(m_{s2}) &&, m_{s\,\text{tot}} = +1 \\ &\frac{1}{\sqrt{2}}[\delta_{\frac{1}{2}}(m_{s1})\delta_{-\frac{1}{2}}(m_{s2}) + \delta_{-\frac{1}{2}}(m_{s1})\delta_{\frac{1}{2}}(m_{s2})], && m_{s\,\text{tot}} = 0 \\ &\delta_{-\frac{1}{2}}(m_{s1})\delta_{-\frac{1}{2}}(m_{s2}) &&, m_{s\,\text{tot}} = -1 \end{aligned}\right\} s_{\text{tot}} = 1 \tag{5–43}$$

$$\frac{1}{\sqrt{2}}[\delta_{\frac{1}{2}}(m_{s1})\delta_{-\frac{1}{2}}(m_{s2}) - \delta_{-\frac{1}{2}}(m_{s1})\delta_{\frac{1}{2}}(m_{s2})],\ m_{s\,\text{tot}} = 0 = s_{\text{tot}} \tag{5–44}$$

and these remain spin eigenfunctions (of $\mathbf{S}_{\text{tot}} = \mathbf{S}_1 + \mathbf{S}_2$) even when the two spins interact.

Similarly, for two particles of spin s (spin angular momentum $s\hbar$), it is not difficult to show that,

$$\left.\begin{aligned} \text{fraction of even spin states} &= \frac{s+1}{2s+1} \\ \text{fraction of odd spin states} &= \frac{s}{2s+1} \end{aligned}\right\} \tag{5–45}$$

where "odd and even" refer to sign-change or lack of sign-change when the particle (spin) coordinates are interchanged.

Parity

If H is invariant under the reflection of *all* coordinates,* then the operator which performs this reflection,

$$P\Psi(\mathbf{r}_1, s_{1z}, \cdots) = \Psi(-\mathbf{r}_1, -s_{1z}, \cdots) \tag{5–46}$$

commutes with H and the mean values of P are therefore constant in a stable state. Because P^2 is just the identity operator,

$$\langle P \rangle = \pm 1 \tag{5–47}$$

* Until recently, this was thought to be universally true of all Hamiltonian operators.

Thus P has physical meaning in that $\langle P\rangle$ exists and can be measured* for any state; the value (or sign) of $\langle P\rangle$ is called the "parity" of the state.

Stationary States

If H does not contain t, the latter can be eliminated from (5–8) by setting,

$$\Psi = \psi \exp [Et/i\hbar]; \qquad H\psi = E\psi \tag{5–48}$$

(in agreement with (5–26)) where the constant, E, according to (5–5), is the average value of H and therefore is the total energy of the system.

Thus when $\partial H/\partial t = 0$, the problem (5–8) reduces to an eigenvalue problem. The eigenvalues represent the only possible energy states of the system. *If the system is confined* in a large box, the general theory of eigenvalue problems for finite space regions shows (compare Chapter 19):

(i) Stable energy levels are discrete, $E = E_i$, and the E_i have no finite limit point.

(ii) The corresponding wavefunctions, ψ_i, can be chosen orthonormal: $(\psi_i, \psi_j) = \delta_{ij}$.

(iii) Any state (any wavefunction ψ defined in the "box" and satisfying all the boundary conditions) can be expanded in a series of eigenfunctions:

$$\psi = \sum_i c_i(t)\psi_i; \qquad [\sum_i |c_i|^2 = 1] \tag{5–49}$$

(iv) According to (5–5) and (5–26), $|c_i|^2$ here can be interpreted as the *probability* that the system described by ψ will be "found in" (have parameters characteristic of) the stable state, ψ_i.

As the volume of the confining box is allowed to increase indefinitely, the low-energy parts of the energy spectrum, E_i, usually change very little, but other parts (at large values of E_i) become denser and denser, approaching a continuous spectrum, corresponding physically to states so energetic that the system is no longer bound together but consists of several independent subsystems. (Compare also Collision Theory below.)

The solution of the eigenvalue problems (5–48) *forms the main content of practical applications of quantum mechanics.* Some specific results are listed later in section C.

Virial Theorem

Write

$$H = -\sum \frac{\hbar^2}{2m_i} \nabla_i^2 + W = T + W$$

If $V = \sum \mathbf{r}_i \cdot \nabla_i$ then by (8–6), $VT - TV = -2T$ and for a stable† state, $(\psi, [VH - HV]\psi) = E(\psi, V\psi) - (H\psi, V\psi) = 0$. Thus

$$2\langle T\rangle = \langle VW - WV\rangle = \langle \sum_i \mathbf{r}_i \cdot (\nabla_i W)\rangle$$

where, in the last form, ∇_i acts only on W.

If W contains only Coulomb potentials, then Euler's theorem shows that $2\langle T\rangle = -\langle W\rangle$. Similarly, if ΔW is the spin-orbit interaction, the corresponding term is $-3\langle \Delta W\rangle$, etc.

---

* By interactions with electromagnetic radiation. For atoms, the parity is determined by the orbital angular momenta of the electrons: $\langle P\rangle = (-1)^{\Sigma l_i}$

† In particular, $(\psi, V\psi)$ must exist; note also that $(\psi, HV\psi)$ need not equal $(H\psi, V\psi)$ for a system confined in a box because the function, $V\psi$, will not necessarily satisfy the boundary conditions.

Complete Sets of Observables

The majority of stable energies, E_i, are degenerate, that is, have more than one eigenfunction ϕ_i; call them ϕ_i^α. Eigenfunctions with the same i remain eigenfunctions when freely intercombined. Not only can they be orthonormalized but also:

If $FH = HF$, then $F\phi_i^\alpha$ is also an eigenfunction of H and belongs to E_i; hence $(\phi_j^\alpha, F\phi_i^\alpha) = 0$ unless $i = j$ and moreover, for fixed I, $(\phi_I^\alpha, F\phi_I^\beta)$ is a (finite) Hermitian matrix and thus can be diagonalized by a unitary transformation of the ϕ_I^α. In this way, *all* eigenfunctions can be *chosen* to be not only orthonormal but eigenfunctions of F as well as H. If there is still some remaining degeneracy (several ϕ with equal values of $\langle F\rangle$ and E_j) then a third operator G such that both $GH = HG$ and $GF = FG$ can be treated in the same way. When this is no longer possible, the set $(H, F, G, \cdots)$ is said to be a *complete set of mutually commuting observables*. The set of numbers $(E_i, \langle F\rangle, \langle G\rangle, \cdots)$ then completely specifies a unique wave function. All stable wavefunctions may then be labelled by such sets of numbers.

The most important case is the triplet (H, J^2, J_z) which selects out wavefunctions with definite (constant, dispersionless) energy, total angular momentum, and z-component of total angular momentum. In molecules, further symmetries introduce still further specifications (such as evenness or oddness with respect to interchange of like nucleii, etc.).

Perturbation Theory

Since few problems can be solved exactly, approximate methods are the mainstay of applications and many an involved theory is in essence a search for an adequate and tractable approximation.

Standard perturbation formalism is presented in Chapter 19. Usually, since energy levels are of primary interest, (19–66), (19–67) and (19–71) are the formulas most often used.* Compare also (5–80) and (5–81).

An important simplification is introduced by postulate (VIII) above, which implies that only "zero order" functions ϕ_i which themselves satisfy (VIII) need be considered to contribute to ψ in (19–64)–(19–73). For Fermi–Dirac particles, a common choice is the form,

$$\phi(\mathbf{r}_1, s_1, \cdots, \mathbf{r}_n, s_n) = \frac{1}{n!}\,\mathrm{Det}\,\|f_k(\mathbf{r}_j, s_j)\| \tag{5–50}$$

where f_k may be chosen for convenience.†

The **variational principle** (see (19–38)) and its ramifications are also powerful calculational tools for obtaining ground state energies (and energies of the lowest state of each symmetry type).

The technique of handling such perturbation calculations in complex cases relies heavily on what, in the last analysis, is group theory. Thus, when two or more states with given angular momenta are combined according to (5–29), the new angular momenta will appear "mixed up" unless linear combinations of the various products,

---

* For quantum mechanics, $\mathbf{r}$ in Chapter 19 is to be interpreted as an abbreviation for the set $(\mathbf{r}_1, s_1, \mathbf{r}_2, s_2, \cdots, \mathbf{r}_n, s_n)$; the function $\rho(\mathbf{r}) \equiv 1$, and thus $V^{ij} = V_{ij} = (\psi_i, V\psi_j)$ in our present notation.

† The form (5–50) is most useful when the particles are independent before the perturbation is introduced $\left[H_0 = \sum_j H_j(\mathbf{r}_j, s_j)\right]$; then the functions f_k may be eigenfunctions of the one-particle Hamiltonians, H_j; compare (5–29) or the discussion of (5–134) below.

$\psi_{J_1,m_1} \cdot \psi_{J_2,m_2}$, are taken to select out* functions of the type $\psi_{J,m}$ schematically enumerated in (5–42). This should be done *before* the perturbation calculation is set up since it will then cause many of the V_{ij} to vanish. [This example refers to the three-dimensional rotation group of symmetry; other symmetries introduce further possibilities of simplifying results by finding the "right linear combinations." Compare (5–158) ff.]

Pauli Exclusion Principle

Perturbation theory naturally introduces the picture that states of complex systems can be "built up" by placing the constituent particles one by one into (sub)states —compare (5–27)–(5–29). With this picture, postulate (VIII) states:

Not more than one Fermi–Dirac particle can occupy any given (sub)state.

(There is no limitation for Bose–Einstein particles.) Since electron spins provide an extra degree of choice in states, spin allows two electrons in each of the substates found by neglecting spin; this "combinatorial" effect of spin is generally more important than the direct energy effect, (5–11), except in the heaviest atoms (where $\partial U/\partial r$ is large except near the outer edge).

Matrix Mechanics

This form is now used mainly as a scheme of notation.† (It lacks the detail provided by (5–4), (5–19) and (5–20) and similar concepts.)

If ϕ_i are *any* "complete" set of orthonormal functions independent of t, define (for any operator, H),

$$H_{ij} = (\phi_i, H\phi_j) \tag{5–51}$$

In (5–8) expand $\psi = \sum_i c_i\phi_i$ where the c_i are regarded as unknown variables. The wave equation (5–8) becomes,

$$\sum_i H_{ij}c_j = i\hbar(\mathrm{d}c_i/\mathrm{d}t) \tag{5–52}$$

while (5–6) is replaced by [recall $\mathbf{r}_{jk} = (\phi_j, \mathbf{r}\phi_k)$]

$$\sum_k [x_{jk}(mv_x)_{kl} - (mv_x)_{jk}x_{kl}] = i\hbar\delta_{jl} \tag{5–53}$$

When the arrays and types of indices become complicated, a common alternative notation (Dirac) is

$$\begin{aligned} H_{ij} &= (\phi_i, H\phi_j) = \langle i|H|j\rangle \\ c_j &= \langle\psi|j\rangle \qquad \text{or simply} \qquad |j\rangle \\ c_j^* &= \langle j| \qquad \text{or} \qquad \langle j|\psi\rangle \end{aligned} \tag{5–54}$$

From the general properties (5–31) of angular momentum, it may be shown (compare footnote to (5–33)) that whenever $\mathbf{J}$ and J_z are part of a "complete set of observables",

* The formulas for doing this define the "Clebsch–Gordon coefficients." *Warning*: their numerical values depend on the particular sets of spherical harmonics being used (the particular "representation" of the rotation group generated by the $\psi_{J,m}$).

† Historically, this form was independently postulated (Heisenberg) and only later proved to be equivalent to "wave mechanics" (Schroedinger).

the only non-vanishing matrix elements of **J** are (to within phase factors, e^{ia}, for the last two),

$$\langle j, m|J^2|j, m\rangle = j(j+1)\hbar^2$$
$$\langle j, m|J_z|j, m\rangle = m\hbar$$
$$\langle j, m+1|J_x + iJ_y|j, m\rangle = \hbar\sqrt{(j-m)(j+m+1)}$$
$$\langle j, m-1|J_x - iJ_y|j, m\rangle = \hbar\sqrt{(j+m)(j-m+1)}$$

"Heisenberg representation": Sometimes, the "full" wavefunctions, $\Psi_j = \phi_j \exp(-itE_j/\hbar)$ are used in place of ϕ_j in (5–51) and (5–54). Then H_{ij} varies with t and the matrix elements are said to be written in the Heisenberg representation.

Another common notation is

$$\text{Trace}\,(H) = \sum_i H_{ii} = \sum_i (\phi_i, H\phi_i) \tag{5–55}$$

which is a quantity independent of the "basis" functions, ϕ_i.

"Transformation theory" is the set of formulas for changing to a different set of "basis" functions, Φ_α, replacing the ϕ_i. Essentially, everything transforms in the obvious manner by the (unitary) matrix, $U_{\alpha j} = (\Phi_\alpha, \phi_j)$, often written $\langle\alpha\,|\,j\rangle$ in Dirac notation. See Chapters 18 and 19.

In particular, the wave equation (5–52) can be regarded as specifying a transformation in time,

$$c_i(t) = \sum_k \Omega_{ik}(H/i\hbar)\cdot c_k(0) \tag{5–56}$$

where Ω is the "matrizant" defined in (14–46). Since $H/i\hbar$ is anti-Hermitian, Ω is unitary. If H is independent of t, $\Omega = \exp(tH/i\hbar)$, as defined by its power series, and if, further, the basis functions, ϕ_i, are all eigenfunctions of H, then $H_{ij} = E_j\delta_{ij}$ (diagonal) and $\Omega_{ij} = \exp(tE_j/i\hbar)\delta_{ij}$ in agreement with earlier results.

In quantum field theory, Ω (or the integral form of the corresponding operator) is often called a "*propagator*". Often in formal work Ω is written as $\exp[Ht/i\hbar]$ (even when its power series $\neq\Omega$) but this solecism is untangled by "time ordering" the terms of all expansions so as to yield precisely the series (14–46) defining Ω.

Interactions with Radiation

For radiation of moderate intensity and photon energy ($h\nu$), time-dependent perturbation theory may be used. Neglecting terms* in $|\mathbf{A}|^2$, noting that for a radiation field $\nabla\cdot\mathbf{A} = 0$, and finally assuming† that $\mathbf{A}$ does not vary appreciably over the dimensions of the system ($\lambda \gg 1$ Angstrom), one finds from (5–9) that the perturbation-energy operator is,

$$\Delta H = \mathbf{A}\cdot\sum_j \frac{i\hbar e_j}{m_j c}\nabla_j = -\mathbf{A}_0\cos(\omega t + \phi)\cdot\sum \frac{e_j}{c}\dot{\mathbf{r}}_j \tag{5–57}$$

where $\dot{\mathbf{r}}_j$ denotes the velocity operators for the unperturbed system.

Let ϕ_i be the stable states of the unperturbed system, with corresponding energies, E_i (that is, solutions and eigenvalues of (5–48) with $\mathbf{A} = 0$). From (19–86), the solution of the perturbed wave equation (5–8), with the condition, $\psi = \phi_I$ when $t = 0$, is

$$\psi = \sum_k c_k(t)\phi_k \tag{5–58}$$

* These produce effects comparable to relativistic corrections.

† Compare remarks preceding (5–64) below.

wherein terms with $E_k - E_I \doteq \pm\hbar\omega$ dominate, and for these (when t is not too large),

$$|c_k(t)|^2 = \left\{\frac{\sin\,[(E_k - E_I \pm \omega\hbar)t/2\hbar]}{c(E_k - E_I \pm \omega\hbar)}\right\}^2 |\mathbf{A}_0 \cdot \langle I|\sum e_j\dot{\mathbf{r}}_j|k\rangle|^2 \tag{5–59}$$

(using the notation (5–54)). This is the probability that during time t the system makes the transition $I \rightarrow k$ (photon absorption or emission according to the $\pm$ sign).

In general, the radiation is unpolarized and the atomic systems are unoriented, so that the second factor in (5–59) should be replaced by its average over all polarizations and orientations,

$$\tfrac{1}{3}|\mathbf{A}_0|^2\{|\langle I|\sum e_j\dot{x}_j|k\rangle|^2 + |\langle I|\sum e_j\dot{y}_j|k\rangle|^2 + |\langle I|\sum e_j\dot{z}_j|k\rangle|^2\} \tag{5–60}$$

Since, according to (5–10)

$$\langle k|\dot{x}_j|I\rangle = \frac{E_I - E_k}{i\hbar}\langle k|x_j|I\rangle \tag{5–61}$$

(5–60) essentially involves the square of the electric dipole moment, written symbolically,

$$|\langle I|\sum_j e_j\mathbf{r}_j|k\rangle|^2 = |\mathbf{P}_{Ik}|^2 \tag{5–62}$$

(where the absolute-value signs denote both a complex-number magnitude and the length of a vector—in all a Hermitian scalar product).

Finally, the radiation is seldom monochromatic and $|\mathbf{A}_0|^2 = (2c^2/\omega^2)\langle\mathbf{E}\cdot\mathbf{E}\rangle$ should be replaced by a frequency *distribution* and (5–59) should be integrated over that distribution. Since the first factor in (5–59) has a very sharp peak, the final result is very nearly

$$\begin{aligned}\underset{I\rightarrow k}{\text{Prob}} &= \int |c_k(t)|^2\,d\nu = \tfrac{1}{3}|\mathbf{A}_0|^2\cdot|\langle I|\sum e_j\mathbf{r}_j|k\rangle|^2\,\frac{\pi^2\nu^2}{c^2\hbar^2}\,t \\ &= \frac{2\pi}{3\hbar^2}|\langle I|\sum_j e_j\mathbf{r}_j|k\rangle|^2\,\rho(\nu)t\end{aligned} \tag{5–63}$$

where $\rho(\nu)\,d\nu$ is the energy of the radiation per unit volume and with frequency in $(\nu \pm \tfrac{1}{2}\,d\nu)$.

Taking account of the space-variation of $\mathbf{A}$ by expanding in a Taylor's series and including the postulated spin magnetic-moments, $g\mathbf{S}(e/2mc)$ for each particle, gives the more refined result,

$$\left.\begin{aligned}B_{I\rightarrow k}\,\rho(\nu) &= \text{Rate of transition, } I \rightarrow k \\ &= \frac{2\pi}{3\hbar^2}\rho(\nu)\left\{|\langle I|\sum e_j\,\mathbf{r}_j|k\rangle|^2 + \left|\langle I\left|\tfrac{1}{2}\sum\frac{e_j}{m_jc}\mathbf{L}_j + g_j\mathbf{S}_j\right|k\rangle\right|^2\right. \\ &\quad\left. + \frac{3\pi^2\nu^2}{10c^2}|\langle I|\sum e_j\mathbf{r}_j\mathbf{r}_j|k\rangle|^2 + \cdots\right\}\end{aligned}\right\} \tag{5–64}$$

wherein the second term is called magnetic-dipole radiation and the third (dyadic) term, electric-quadrupole radiation.* Their relative orders of magnitude are, respectively, 1, v^2/c^2, $(r/\lambda)^2$.

Note that the result (5–64) applies both to absorption and to (stimulated) emission.

---

* To the approximations of the derivation, $\nu \doteq (E_I - E_k)/h$ and no significance should be attached to the ν^2 term in (5–64) for other values of ν.

The only reason for one process to dominate over the other in a macroscopic experiment is the relative *populations* of different levels; the individual transition probabilities are symmetric (time reversal). Absorption and stimulated emission together produce a (resonant) *scattering* of radiation.

[Stimulated emission is the basis of "masers" or "quantum-mechanical amplifiers;" the power-supply of such a device prepares a system so that a higher-energy state has a greater population than a lower state. (For example, by selecting out certain states with molecular-beam focussing or by "saturating"—equalizing—the populations of the lower and a third, still higher state with very high power radiation.) The input signal then stimulates—"triggers"—emission to the lower level and the output power can be greater than the signal input power.]

Spontaneous emission: This rate cannot be derived from first principles without a quantum theory of the radiation field itself. But assuming microscopic reversibility, $N_I B_{I\to k}\rho(\nu) = N_k[B_{k\to I}\rho(\nu) + A_{k\to I}]$ where $E_k > E_I$ and assuming the Boltzmann distribution law, $N_k/N_I = \exp{(E_I - E_k)}/kT$, it would follow that $\rho(\nu) = (A_{k\to I}/B_{I\to k})$ $[\exp{(h\nu)/kT}) - 1]^{-1}$ which agrees with the Planck radiation law only if

$$A_{k\to I} = \text{Rate of spontaneous transitions } k \to I = \frac{8\pi h\nu^3}{c^3} B_{I\to k} \tag{5–65}$$

$$(A_{k\to I} = 0 \quad \text{if} \quad E_k < E_I)$$

Quantum field theory gives the same result (see (5–202)–(5–207)).

Second-order effects: If (5–64) vanishes identically between the states k, I the transition $I \to k$ will be very weak but can still occur by such processes as given in (19–87) and (19–88). Especially useful for molecular structure determination is:

Raman scattering: consists in the absorption of an incident photon, $h\nu$, and emission of a photon of different frequency, $\nu' = \nu + (E_k - E_I)/h$. This occurs, according to (19–88) and arguments similar to the above, if for some state, ϕ_l, we have $E_l - E_I = h\nu$ and if also at least one of the (dyadic) elements of

$$|\langle I|\sum e_j\mathbf{r}_j|l\rangle\langle l|\sum e_j\mathbf{r}_j|k\rangle|^2 \tag{5–66}$$

is sufficiently large.

Some common notational conventions: A common abbreviation is

$$\nu_{nm} = (E_n - E_m)/h = \omega_{nm}/2\pi \tag{5–67}$$

which may serve to distinguish resonant frequencies, $|\nu_{nm}|$, (which we are using throughout) from a general value of ν when both must be considered. Note also that (5–10) then reads,

$$\frac{\mathrm{d}}{\mathrm{d}t} F_{nm} = 2\pi i\nu_{nm}F_{nm} \tag{5–68}$$

"Oscillator strengths" are often used (mainly for historical reasons) when discussing electronic transitions. They are dimensionless numbers defined by

$$f_{nm} = \frac{2\mu\hbar\nu_{mn}}{e^2} B_{n\to m} = \frac{4\pi\mu\nu_{mn}}{3\hbar e^2} |\langle m|\sum e_j\mathbf{r}_j|n\rangle|^2 \tag{5–69}$$

(e = electron charge; μ = reduced mass = $mM/(m + M)$ where m = electron mass; M = nuclear mass). Note the sign change: $f_{nm} = -f_{mn}$.

Sum rules are useful for checking calculations and estimating effects of omitted terms. The Thomas–Kuhn sum rule applies to a system of similar particles: ($\mathbf{R}$ denotes $\sum_j \mathbf{r}_j$)

$$\sum_n f_{nm} = \frac{\mu}{3\hbar}\, 2 \sum_n 2\pi\nu_{nm}\, \mathbf{R}_{nm} \cdot \mathbf{R}_{nm}{}^*$$

$$= \frac{\mu}{3i\hbar} \sum_n (\mathbf{R}_{mn} \cdot \dot{\mathbf{R}}_{nm} - \dot{\mathbf{R}}_{mn} \cdot \mathbf{R}_{nm}) = \frac{\mu}{3i\hbar}\, (\mathbf{R} \cdot \dot{\mathbf{R}} - \dot{\mathbf{R}} \cdot \mathbf{R})_{mm}$$

$$= \frac{\mu}{3i\hbar} [\textstyle\sum \mathbf{r}_j \cdot \sum \mathbf{v}_j - \sum \mathbf{v}_j \cdot \sum \mathbf{r}_j]_{mm} = \frac{N}{i\hbar}\, (xp_x - p_x x)_{mm}$$

(where N = number of particles and the last term is a typical example of the $3N$ equal, non-vanishing terms). Finally, by (5–53),

$$\sum_n f_{nm} = N = \text{number of electrons in the system} \qquad (5\text{–}70)$$

The sum is over *all* states (including any continuum) and due regard must be paid to the signs of the f_{nm}.

Note on the calculation of matrix elements: Often, only approximate wavefunctions are available for calculating such quantities as $\langle I|\mathbf{r}|k\rangle$. An estimate of the final accuracy may be obtained by also computing,

$$im\omega_{Ik}\langle I|\mathbf{r}|k\rangle = \langle I|m\dot{\mathbf{r}}|k\rangle = -i\hbar(\phi_I, \nabla\phi_k)$$

$$-m\omega_{Ik}{}^2\, \langle I|\mathbf{r}|k\rangle = \langle I|m\ddot{\mathbf{r}}|k\rangle = -(\phi_I, \phi_k\, \nabla U)$$

etc. One of such a set may be obviously more accurate than others if the main contribution to the integral comes from regions of space where the ϕ's are known to be most accurate.

Selection Rules

Selection rules are *necessary* conditions for non-vanishing of transition probabilities. By symmetry (or group-theoretic) arguments, rather stringent conditions for non-vanishing of the matrix elements in (5–64) and (5–66) can be quite generally established. In terms of the changes which a transition from ϕ_I to ϕ_k entails, some important examples are:

For electric dipole transitions [$\langle I|\sum e_j \mathbf{r}_j|k\rangle \neq 0$] all of the following are necessary in all cases*

Parity: must change $(\pm \rightarrow \mp)$

Angular momentum: $\Delta J = 0, \pm 1$ except $0 \rightarrow 0$ forbidden

z-component: $\Delta M = 0, \pm 1$

and for atoms in which spin-orbit coupling (5–11) is negligible so that L and S have meaning:

$\Delta S = 0$ and $\Delta L = 0, \pm 1$ $(0 \rightarrow 0$ forbidden$)$

---

* Typical proofs: $\langle I\,|\mathbf{r}|\,k\rangle = \int \phi_I{}^* \mathbf{r} \phi_k\, dV$. Changing variables in the integral by reflecting all coordinates will change its sign (so it must = 0) unless ϕ_I and ϕ_k have opposite parity.

Since $\mathbf{r} = (x,\ y,\ z) = r(\sin\theta\cos\phi,\ \sin\theta\sin\phi,\ \cos\phi)$ behaves under rotation of coordinates like a set of wavefunctions with angular momentum, $J = 1$, it follows from (5–42) that, if ϕ_k has angular momentum J, then the set $\mathbf{r}\phi_k$ will have rotational properties characteristic of $J + 1$, J and/or $J - 1$; thus ϕ_I will be orthogonal to the set $\mathbf{r}\phi_k$ unless ϕ_I also has one of these angular momenta. Hence $\Delta J = 0, \pm 1$. Compare also (22–50) and (5–115) and (5–116) below.

For Raman scattering:

Parity: must not change ($\pm \rightarrow \pm$)

Angular momentum: $\Delta J = 0, \pm 1, \pm 2$

z-component: $\Delta M = 0, \pm 1, \pm 2$

In molecules, a number of additional selection rules are available, but they are most readily expressed in group theoretic language (because of the many different types of symmetries which can occur). See preceding (5–158) below.

Line Widths, Line Shapes, Cross Sections

(a) **Natural width:** From (5–65), the number of systems, N_k, which are in state k decreases at least as rapidly as $dN_k/dt = -N_k/T_k$, where

$$T_k = \left[\sum_l A_{k\to l}\right]^{-1} \tag{5–71}$$

is called the mean (natural) lifetime of state k. According to (5–25) this finite lifetime implies a corresponding (root mean square) energy spread of the order of

$$\Delta E_k \doteqdot \hbar/T_k = \hbar \sum_l A_{k\to l} \tag{5–72}$$

A spectral line between two excited states therefore has an irreducible width,

$$\Delta\nu_{kl} \doteqdot \frac{1}{2\pi}\left(\frac{1}{T_k} + \frac{1}{T_l}\right) \tag{5–73}$$

It is seldom that this width is detectable behind the various other causes of broadening. Typical orders of magnitude of T_k are, for optical (electronic) transitions:

electric dipole decay: 10^{-8} sec

magnetic dipole decay: 10^{-3} sec

electric quadrupole decay: 10^{0} sec

Superradiant States of Compound Systems

If the dimensions of a system (of many independent particles) are small compared to the wavelength of the radiation, certain very special states of the system-as-a-whole have exceedingly high *spontaneous* emission rates (and others have equally low spontaneous rates). Normally, these states are of no importance but they may be preferentially excited in specially-designed experiments.

An example is a system of spin-$\frac{1}{2}$ particles in a fixed magnetic field, $H_0\hat{z}$; because of the magnetic dipole associated with each spin, the energy of any state of the system is proportional to the population difference, $N_{\text{down}} - N_{\text{up}} = -2m$ where m is the z-component of the total spin, $\mathbf{S} = \Sigma\, \mathbf{S}_i$. If a resonantly vibrating small magnetic field, $\mathbf{H}$, is present at right angles to $\mathbf{H}_0$, transition rates are all determined by the perturbation energy, $\mathbf{H}\cdot\mathbf{S}$. According to (5–37),

$$(1/\hbar H)^2|\langle s, m|\mathbf{S}\cdot\mathbf{H}|s, m \pm 1\rangle|^2 = (s \mp m)(s \pm m + 1) = M(\pm), \text{ say}$$

Now the net rate of stimulated emission and absorption of photons varies as $B_{m\to m-1} - B_{m\to m+1}$ which is proportional to $M(-) - M(+) = 2m$ and therefore depends only on the energy of the overall state. But the spontaneous emission rate, $A_{m\to m-1} = (8\pi h\nu^3/c^3)B_{m\to m-1}$ depends only on $M(-) = (s + m)(s - m + 1)$ which is not completely determined by the energy (m). In particular, if m is small compared to N (the number of particles), as would usually be true, while, if $s \doteqdot Ns_i = \frac{1}{2}N$, the rate is proportional to $M(-) \doteqdot \frac{1}{4}N^2$—inordinately larger than $2m$ for a macroscopic system.

Note that these superradiant states will have line widths far narrower than the width which might be expected if (5–73) were merely evaluated for a single spin.

(b) **Unresolved levels:** A group of energy states is often "bunched" at a spacing smaller than (5–72)—or smaller than other applicable limits (5–75), (5–76). Individual lines are then unobservable; only a superposition of several overlapping distributions of the type (5–73) can be seen. The unresolved groups of states are called "levels" or "terms" and their total widths may be determined as much by their *spacing* as by (5–72). A spectral line will have a width proportional to the sum of the widths of the levels between which the transition occurs.

(c) **Doppler broadening** is the classical frequency shift due to random thermal velocities of molecules. For non-relativistic velocities, $(\nu - \nu_0)/\nu_0 = v_x/c$ where v_x is the velocity component along the direction of observation. This relation between ν and v_x combined with Maxwell's velocity distribution yields the frequency distribution (line shape):

$$\frac{c}{\nu_0} \exp\left[-\frac{\frac{1}{2}c^2 M}{kT}\left(\frac{\nu - \nu_0}{\nu_0}\right)^2\right] \tag{5–74}$$

The full width at half-maximum is therefore,

$$(\Delta\nu)_{1/2} = 7.16 \times 10^{-7}\, \nu_0 \sqrt{T/M} \tag{5–75}$$

where T is the temperature (°K) and M the molecular weight (gr/mole). Constancy of $\Delta\nu/\nu_0$ is characteristic of Doppler broadening.

(d) **Collision broadening.** Since collisions are effective in de-exciting a molecule, the lifetime is shortened:

$$dN_k/dt = -N_k(1/T_k + 1/T_C)$$

where T_C is the mean time between collisions. Thus by (5–25)

$$\left.\begin{aligned} \Delta E &\doteq \hbar\left(\frac{1}{T_k} + \frac{1}{T_C}\right) \doteq \frac{\hbar}{T_C} \\ \Delta\nu &\doteq 1/2\pi T_C \end{aligned}\right\} \tag{5–76}$$

(e) **Power broadening** occurs only when the radiation field is so intense that induced transitions decrease the mean lifetimes. In the notation of (5–64), a term $\sum B_{ik}\rho(\nu)N_k$ is added to the expression for $-dN_k/dt$. (The sum is over all states to which the radiation induces transitions.) Thus if I is the radiant flux

$$\frac{1}{T_p} = \bar{\rho} \sum B_{ik} = \frac{I}{c} \sum B_{ik}$$

and the effective lifetime becomes

$$\frac{1}{T_{\text{eff}}} = \frac{1}{T_k} + \frac{1}{T_C} + \frac{1}{T_p}$$

(f) **Pressure shifts:** At very high pressures, events *during* collisions must be considered; the collision causes perturbations leading to actual shifts of the energy levels. In the limit, of course, such perturbations dominate entirely and the molecules can no longer be considered independent (approach to liquid or solid state).

(g) **Line shapes** (due to natural, collision or power broadening): These depend in no way on the detailed physics of the molecules. Correct *average* results are obtained if the excited molecules are considered to emit monochromatic radiation during their lifetimes (even though the actual emission is quantized). The power spectrum of a pulse, $\sin(\omega_0 t + \phi)$, lasting for a time, τ, is the complex magnitude of its Fourier transform, and averaging over the random, uncorrelated phases, ϕ, then gives the average power spectrum (compare (5–59)),

$$\left\{\frac{\sin\left[(\omega_0 + \omega)\tau/2\right]}{\omega_0 + \omega}\right\}^2 + \left\{\frac{\sin\left[(\omega_0 - \omega)\tau/2\right]}{\omega_0 - \omega}\right\}^2 \tag{5–77}$$

Averaging this again over the excitation-duration, τ, which has an exponential distribution,* then gives the line shape (Lorentz factor):

$$\frac{1/2\pi^2 T_{\text{eff}}}{(\nu_0 - \nu)^2 + (1/2\pi T_{\text{eff}})^2} + \frac{1/2\pi^2 T_{\text{eff}}}{(\nu_0 + \nu)^2 + (1/2\pi T_{\text{eff}})^2} \tag{5–78}$$

where T_{eff} is the mean lifetime. The second term is usually negligible and the numerator factors make the integral of the first term unity.

(h) **Absorption cross section:**† The amount of energy removed from an incident beam by a spectral line depends on the frequency width, $\Delta\nu_{\text{inc}}$, of the incident beam. Then if I is the incident flux (energy per unit area per unit time),

$$\rho = I/c\Delta\nu_{\text{inc}}$$

and the diminution of I in a distance, dx, due to a specific transition is according to (5–64),

$$-dI = (N_m\, dx)\left(B_{mn}\frac{I}{c\Delta\nu_{\text{inc}}}\right)h\nu$$

where N_m is the number of systems per unit volume in state m. Accordingly, the cross section for a specific transition is

$$\sigma_{m\to n} = \frac{h\nu B_{m\to n}}{c\Delta\nu_{\text{inc}}} = \frac{4\pi^2\nu}{3\hbar c(\Delta\nu)_{\text{inc}}}\left|\langle m|\sum e_j\mathbf{r}_j|n\rangle\right|^2 \tag{5–79}$$

[or: $\pi e^2|f_{nm}|/\mu c(\Delta\nu)_{\text{inc}}$]. The total cross section is the sum of (5–79) over all lines falling in the spectral range of the beam (provided $(\Delta\nu)_{\text{inc}} > \Delta\nu$ for each). In more general cases, σ must be replaced by the concept of a cross section (or absorption coefficient) *per* $d\nu$.

Free-Particle Problems (Collision Theory)

Analysis is simplified if the free particle is assigned a *precise momentum* (vector); by (5–24), the system is then infinite in extent‡ and $(\Psi, \Psi) = \infty$. Physical interpretation is then based on the concept of a probability current or mass flux, (5–20).

---

* $P(\tau)\, d\tau = \exp(-\tau/T)\, d\tau/T$; true for any process where the rate of de-excitation is independent of past history.

† The area which would intercept the same energy from an incoming beam as does the actual molecule. This total cross section can be further divided, conceptually, into parts representing different processes (scattering, absorption, etc.). The concept is then isomorphic to that of probability.

‡ Occasionally, a very large confining box is momentarily introduced to establish relative numbers and energy-spacings of various types of states; the consequent broadening of the momentum vector is seldom introduced explicitly. (It returns to zero as the box is made infinitely large.) Note also that it is sometimes convenient to consider a lattice of such boxes in each of which the same phenomena are occurring. The appropriate boundary conditions are then *periodicity* of the wavefunctions. This has the advantage that monodirectional beams can be represented (by traveling waves) instead of the standing waves generated by impenetrable walls.

(a) **Perturbation method:** According to (19–83) and (19–84), the probability that a time-independent perturbation, V, causes a transition during t from state ϕ_I to state ϕ_f is small unless $E_I \doteqdot E_f$ and then (using the notation (5–67)),

$$P_{I\to f} = \frac{4\sin^2(\frac{1}{2}\omega_{If}t)}{\hbar^2\omega_{If}^{\;2}}\,|V_{If}^{\text{eff}}|^2 \tag{5–80}$$

where

$$V_{If}^{\text{eff}} = \begin{cases} (\phi_I, V\phi_f), & \text{if this} \neq 0 \\ \sum\limits_{l\neq I} \dfrac{(\phi_f, V\phi_l)(\phi_l, V\phi_I)}{E_I - E_l}, & \text{otherwise} \end{cases} \tag{5–81}$$

In the latter case, the states ϕ_l are called "*virtual states.*" These formulas are also extensively used in radiation and field-theory problems. They are sometimes referred to as "golden rules."

The total probability of transition to any group, G, of states with* $E_f \doteqdot E_I$ is the sum of (5–80) over the states in G, or approximately, since the first factor of (5–80) has, as a function of ω, a very narrow peak for moderate t,

$$\begin{aligned} P_{I\to G} &= \sum_G P_{I\to f} \doteqdot \int P_{I\to f}\,\rho_G(E)\,\mathrm{d}E \\ &\doteqdot \frac{2\pi}{\hbar}\langle|V_{If}^{\text{eff}}|^2\rangle_{\text{avg}}\,\rho_G(E)t \end{aligned} \tag{5–82}$$

where

$$\rho_G(E)\,\mathrm{d}E = \begin{cases} \text{number of states in the} \\ \text{group } G \text{ with energy in} \\ \text{the range } E \pm \frac{1}{2}\,\mathrm{d}E \end{cases} \tag{5–83}$$

$$\langle\ \ \rangle_{\text{avg}} = \text{average over the group } G \tag{5–84}$$

(Often V_{If}^{eff} varies negligibly over groups of interest.)

Equation (5–82) gives the rate of transitions (scatterings, decays, etc.). For scattering problems, *cross sections* are more useful. If a large "box" with sides L is introduced the initial and final states involve (at least for large separations, $\mathbf{r}$, of the particles; compare (5–29) and (5–96)) the approximate wavefunctions (factors),

$$L^{-3/2}\exp(i\mathbf{k}_0\cdot\mathbf{r}) \quad \text{and} \quad L^{-3/2}\exp(i\mathbf{k}\cdot\mathbf{r}),$$

where $\hbar\mathbf{k}_0$ and $\hbar\mathbf{k}$ are the initial and final momenta of the scattered particle. The group of states of interest requires $\mathbf{k}$ to lie in the solid angle, $\sin\theta\,\mathrm{d}\theta\,\mathrm{d}\phi$, and to have magnitude $k \pm \frac{1}{2}\,\mathrm{d}k$. The number of such states in the box (see (5–96), (5–97) below) is $(L/2\pi)^3\,k^2\sin\theta\,\mathrm{d}\theta\,\mathrm{d}\phi\,\mathrm{d}k$ and since $\mathrm{d}E = \hbar^2k\,\mathrm{d}k/m$, we have,

$$\rho = [mL^3/2\pi\hbar^2]k\sin\theta\,\mathrm{d}\theta\,\mathrm{d}\phi \tag{5–85}$$

The incident flux, according to (5–20), contains $\hbar k_0/mL^3$ particles per unit area per unit time. The "differential cross section," $\sigma(\theta, \phi)$, is thus

$$\sigma\begin{pmatrix}\text{for scattering}\\ \text{into } \mathrm{d}\theta,\,\mathrm{d}\phi\end{pmatrix} = \sigma(\theta,\phi)\sin\theta\,\mathrm{d}\theta\,\mathrm{d}\phi$$

where

$$\sigma(\theta,\phi) = \frac{k}{k_0}\left(\frac{m}{2\pi\hbar^2}\right)^2\langle|V_{If}^{\text{eff}}|^2\rangle\,L^6 \tag{5–86}$$

---

* Approximate equality is indicated because the E_k are unperturbed (approximate) energies. Overall energy conservation for entire processes always holds strictly.

where V^{eff}_{If} is evaluated for the system in a large box of side L (which will then cancel in (5–86)), and V^{eff} must be summed over available spin-states (which were neglected in evaluating $\rho(E)$ above).

If the wavefunctions of the system can be taken* as $L^{-3/2}\exp(i\mathbf{k}_0\cdot\mathbf{r})\phi_I$, etc., where ϕ_I and ϕ_f are the initial and final states of the scattering center, then setting $\Delta\mathbf{p}=\hbar(\mathbf{k}-\mathbf{k}_0)$ and representing the coordinates of the scattering center by dV_c,

$$\sigma(\theta,\phi)\doteq\left|\left(\frac{m}{2\pi\hbar^2}\right)\int dV_r\int e^{i\Delta\mathbf{p}\cdot\mathbf{r}}\,\phi_I{}^*\,V\,\phi_f\,dV_c\right|^2(k/k_0) \tag{5–87}$$

This is often called the Born approximation since it may also be derived from (19–75). The term has also come to designate the use of plane-wavefunctions, not the formalism in which they may be used.

(b) **Method of partial waves:** (For elastic scattering and/or pure absorption by spherically symmetric interactions.) The scattering is here regarded as the continuous splitting of a steady incoming beam into steady outgoing beams. The wavefunction is independent of time and solutions are sought with the asymptotic form (in center-of-mass coordinates),

$$\text{as } r\to\infty:\qquad \psi(r,\theta,\phi)\sim A\left[e^{ikz}+\frac{1}{r}f(\theta,\phi)e^{ikr}\right]$$

$$\left[k=\mu v/\hbar=\frac{v}{\hbar}\frac{m_1m_2}{m_1+m_2}\cdot\right] \tag{5–88}$$

Here v is the initial relative velocity between the incoming particle and the scattering center (in any coordinate system). By (5–20), the first term in (5–88) represents the incoming beam (along $\theta=0$) and the second, the scattered beams. If interference between these is ignored,† the differential scattering cross section in the center-of-mass system‡ is found to be, in terms of (5–88),

$$\sigma_{\text{com}}(\theta,\phi)=|f(\theta,\phi)|^2 \tag{5–89}$$

---

* This assumes, see (5–29), that the scattered particle and scattering center are "nearly independent"; this will be a poor approximation if the energy of the whole system is near to a bound (or merely metastable) state. It is also assumed in (5–87) that no particle-exchange takes place (for such wavefunctions must satisfy postulate (VIII)).

† Actual beams have finite transverse area, and measurements are made in regions where the incident and scattered beams do not overlap.

‡ General relations between center-of-mass and laboratory (L) coordinates, in which m_2 is initially at rest:

$$\tan\theta_L=\frac{\sin\theta}{\gamma+\cos\theta};\quad \phi_L=\phi$$

$$\sigma(\theta_L,\phi_L)=\frac{(1+2\gamma\cos\theta+\gamma^2)^{3/2}}{|1+\gamma\cos\theta|}\,\sigma_{\text{com}}(\theta,\phi)$$

where $\gamma=m_1/m_2$ for elastic collisions. If particles m_3, m_4 emerge (replacing m_1, m_2) with kinetic energy $Q+E_{\text{inc}}$, then if θ,ϕ refer to the path of m_3

$$\gamma=\sqrt{\frac{m_1m_3}{m_2m_4}\frac{E_c}{E_c+Q}};\quad E_c=\frac{m_1m_2v^2}{2(m_1+m_2)}=E_{\text{inc},L}\frac{m_2}{m_1+m_2}$$

Here E_c is the initial kinetic energy as seen in the center-of-mass coordinates. The distribution of any outgoing particle in $\cos\theta\pm\frac{1}{2}d(\cos\theta)$ is related to its distribution in final laboratory energy, $E_L'\pm\frac{1}{2}dE_L'$ (even relativistically) by

$$P(E_L')=(1/p_2'v_c)\sqrt{1-v_c{}^2/c^2}\,P(\cos\theta)$$

where v_c is the velocity of the center-of-mass (in the laboratory) and p_2' is the final momentum of the outgoing particle in the center-of-mass system.

$f(\theta, \phi)$ is usually independent of ϕ. It is often termed the "scattering amplitude" (complex). In (5–89) a sum over spin states (Hermitian product) is also implied, where applicable, in $|f|^2$.

In (5–88), ψ is a solution of the wave equation:

$$\frac{-\hbar^2}{2\mu}\nabla^2\psi + U\psi = E_{\text{com}}\,\psi \tag{5–90}$$

If U is spherically symmetric, the method of partial waves consists in setting,

$$\psi = \sum_{l=0}^{\infty} R_l(r)P_l(\cos\theta) \tag{5–91}$$

When this is substituted into (5–90), an equation in $R_l(r)$ alone results (independence of the Legendre polynomials, P_l). Solutions with the property $|R_l| \sim 1/r$ as $r \to \infty$ are demanded (by $\oint\!\!\oint \mathbf{J}\cdot d\mathbf{S}$ finite). Let their asymptotic form be*

$$\text{as } r\to\infty: \qquad R_l \sim \frac{A_l}{kr}\sin\left(kr - \tfrac{1}{2}l\pi + \delta_l\right) \tag{5–92}$$

The constant, δ_l, is called the *phase shift* of the lth partial wave. If there is absorption, δ_l will be complex. Comparing (5–92) with (5–88), using the Legendre expansion of $\exp(ikz) = \exp(ikr\cos\theta)$ given in (9–22), one finds that $A_l = A(2l+1)i^l \exp(i\delta_l)$ and

$$\sigma_{\text{com}}(\theta) = |f(\theta,\phi)|^2 = \frac{1}{k^2}\left|\sum_l (2l+1)e^{i\delta_l}(\sin\delta_l)P_l(\cos\theta)\right|^2 \tag{5–93}$$

so that the phase shifts, δ_l, alone determine the cross section and angular distribution. The total cross section is the integral of (5–93) over all angles:

$$\sigma_{\text{com}} = \sigma_L = \frac{4\pi}{k^2}\sum_l (2l+1)\sin^2\delta_l \tag{5–94}$$

The quantity, $\pm\sqrt{\sigma/4\pi}$, is often called the "scattering length." For short range forces (and especially for very large k) it is approximately equal to the range of the interaction forces.

Physical interpretations: The terms P_l in (5–93) represent scattering when the distance of closest approach and incident velocity correspond (roughly) to angular momentum $l\hbar$. Thus, with short range forces and low incident velocities, only the $l = 0$ term is important and (generally speaking) successive terms "come in" one by one as the bombarding energy is raised. Moreover, by (5–92), δ_l measures the extent to which the interaction energies "pull in" or "push out" the wavefunction. Thus

$\delta_l > 0$ implies attractive forces
$\delta_l < 0$ implies repulsive forces

Indistinguishable particles: If the incident particle and the scattering center are identical, the wavefunction must satisfy the symmetry requirements of postulate (VIII). For spinless particles, the net effect in (5–93) and (5–94) is that the sum

* For very long range (Coulomb) interactions, additional terms such as ln (kr) appear in the argument of the sine in (5–92); these complicate the discussion and are best handled by separate treatment. The method above, however, can be usefully employed to correct for short-range modifications of Coulomb forces.

includes only odd-l terms for Fermi–Dirac particles and only even-l terms for Bose–Einstein particles. (The values of δ_l are unaffected and may be computed ignoring statistics.)

Similarly, for two identical particles of spin s, from (5–45),

$$\sigma_{B.E.} = \frac{s+1}{2s+1}\sigma_{\text{even}} + \frac{s}{2s+1}\sigma_{\text{odd}}$$

$$\sigma_{F.D.} = \frac{s+1}{2s+1}\sigma_{\text{odd}} + \frac{s}{2s+1}\sigma_{\text{even}}$$

Using the connection between spin and statistics mentioned under (VIII), these results can be combined in the form,

$$\sigma_{\text{com}}(\theta) = |f(\theta)|^2 + |f(\pi-\theta)|^2 + [(-1)^{2s}/(s+\tfrac{1}{2})]\,\text{Re}\,\{f(\theta)f^*(\pi-\theta)\}$$

"Coherent" and "incoherent" scattering: This distinction is of importance only when waves from different scattering centers can interfere (as in scattering from crystals or from molecules at long wavelengths). An important case in nuclear physics occurs when $U(r)$ is spin-dependent (as in (5–127) below). For spin $\frac{1}{2}$ incident particles, when the spin-sum implied in (5–89) is carried out (after summing the waves, $f_j(\theta)$, from *different* centers), the "spin-flip" and "no flip" waves do not interfere. Scattering even from a monoisotopic crystal would thus act as if there were two independent (randomly) mixed types of scattering center with respective concentrations,

$$c_+ = \frac{I+1}{2I+1}; \quad c_- = \frac{I}{2I+1}$$

where I is the spin of the scattering centers (compare (5–45)).

As for any random mixture, the extent of the remaining interference can be expressed in terms of effective average cross sections, per scattering center. For spherically symmetric scattering,

$$\sigma_{\text{coh}} = [\sum_i c_i \sqrt{\sigma_i}]^2$$

$$\sigma_{\text{inc}} = \sigma_{\text{tot}} - \sigma_{\text{coh}} = \sum_i c_i\sigma_i - [\sum_i c_i\sqrt{\sigma_i}]^2$$

where the signs of the $\sqrt{\sigma_i}$ must be chosen consistently with the respective phase-shifts for the different scattering processes. ($\sigma_{\text{inc}}/\sigma_{\text{tot}}$ represents the fraction of scattered intensity which is unaffected by interference effects.)

Inverse processes: When (5–82) refers to a scattering or absorption process, the corresponding cross section is given by

$$v_{\text{inc}\,I}\,\sigma_{I\to G} = P_{I\to G}/t$$

Hence *provided* that the effective perturbation *matrix elements are equal* in the direct and inverse processes

$$\sigma_{G\to I} = \frac{v_I\rho_I(E)}{v_G\rho_G(E)}\sigma_{I\to G}$$

Since all "physical" matrices in quantum mechanics are Hermitian, the two $|V^{\text{eff}}|^2$ will be equal if I and G truly refer to the same sets of individual quantum states for each process. (In the second line of (5–81) recall that $E_G = E_I$ by energy conservation.) However, since cross sections are often evaluated by summing over many outcomes, considerable care must be used in applying this result.

EXAMPLE: The cross sections (a) for recombination of an ion and an electron (of momentum p_e) with emission of a photon, $h\nu$, and (b) for photo-ionization of an atom by a photon $h\nu$ with emission of an electron with momentum p_e are related by

$$\frac{\sigma_{\text{ph}}}{\sigma_{\text{rec}}} = \left(\frac{cp_e}{h\nu}\right)^2 \frac{g_{\text{ion}}}{g_{\text{atom}}}$$

where the g's refer to the number of quantum states of the ion and atom involved in *both* processes.

C. SPECIFIC RESULTS

One-Particle Problems

(a) **Particle in a box:** ($U = 0$ inside, $\psi = 0$ outside). Here, (5–48) becomes $(\hbar^2/2m)\nabla^2\psi + E\psi = 0$ and solutions are known for boxes of many shapes. For any shape, by (15–56), the number of states with energy less than E is, asymptotically,

$$N(E) = \int_0^E \rho(E)\,\mathrm{d}E \sim \frac{V}{6\pi^2}\left(\frac{2mE}{\hbar^2}\right)^{3/2}(2s+1) \tag{5–95}$$

where V is the volume of the box and s is the spin of the particle.

For a rectangular box, ψ is a product of sines (standing waves).

Note that the density of states increases indefinitely as $V \to \infty$ so that essentially all positive values of E are eventually allowed in very large boxes.

(b) **Particles in boxes:** ($U \equiv 0$, ψ periodic in space). If a cubic box is imagined repeated throughout space with identical events occurring in each box, the allowed states become traveling waves. If L is the length of each side of a box,

$$\psi = L^{-3/2}\, e^{i\mathbf{k}\cdot\mathbf{r}} = L^{-3/2} \exp\left(\frac{i}{\hbar}\,\mathbf{p}\cdot\mathbf{r}\right) \tag{5–96}$$

where the allowed values of $\mathbf{k}$ are

$$\begin{pmatrix} k_x \\ k_y \\ k_z \end{pmatrix} = \frac{2\pi}{L}\begin{pmatrix} n_x \\ n_y \\ n_z \end{pmatrix}; \quad n_i = 0, \pm 1, \pm 2, \cdots \tag{5–97}$$

Here (as frequently) ψ does not depend on the spin variables but their alternative values must be considered in counting the number of available states.

The corresponding allowed energies are

$$E = (\hbar^2/2m)|\mathbf{k}|^2 = (h^2/2mL^2)(n_x^2 + n_y^2 + n_z^2) \tag{5–98}$$

and (5–95) is valid in this case also. As $L \to \infty$, all values of $\mathbf{k}$ are allowed eventually and (5–96), without the normalizing factor, $L^{-3/2}$, is said to be the wavefunction of a free particle (with prescribed momentum, $\hbar\mathbf{k}$).

(c) **"Tunnel effect":** One-dimensional problem with

$$U = \begin{cases} U_0, \text{ for } 0 \leqslant x \leqslant a \\ 0, \text{ elsewhere} \end{cases}$$

Solving $(\hbar^2/2m)\,\mathrm{d}^2\psi/\mathrm{d}x^2 + (E - U)\psi = 0$ with $\psi = Ce^{ikx}$ when $x > a$ [that is, only emergent particles on the right; compare (5–20)] shows that the probability of a particle penetrating the potential barrier is

$$\text{Transmission Coefficient} = \left\{1 + \frac{U_0^2}{4E}\left|\frac{\sinh\sqrt{(2ma^2/\hbar^2)(U_0 - E)}}{\sqrt{U_0 - E}}\right|^2\right\}^{-1} \tag{5–99}$$

The fact that this is finite for $E < U_0$ explains why many reactions and decays (chemical, nuclear) proceed despite an energy barrier which is insurmountable in classical physics.

For any $U(x)$, an approximate treatment (*WKB* method) gives the result,

$$\text{Transmission Coefficient} \doteq \exp\left[\frac{-2}{\hbar}\int_{U>E}\sqrt{2m[U(x)-E]}\,dx\right] \tag{5–100}$$

(With a spherical-shell barrier, $U = U(r)$, these same formulas may be used with no change if the angular momentum vanishes; compare (5–116).)

(d) **Particle in a sinusoidal potential** (3-dim.): This exactly solvable case is an important "yardstick" for evaluating various computational approaches to the band theory of solids outlined in (e) below. Let

$$U(x, y, z) = 2mv_0^2a^2\left[\sin^2\frac{\pi x}{a} + \sin^2\frac{\pi y}{a} + \sin^2\frac{\pi z}{a}\right] \tag{5–101}$$

Here a is the lattice spacing and m the mass of the particle; the constant, $2mv_0^2a^2$, is chosen so that the low-lying ("bound atomic") states maintain approximately the same energies as the lattice spacing, a, is varied. With (5–101), the wave equation (5–48) can be solved by separation of variables, $\psi = u_x(x)u_y(y)u_z(z)$, which gives Mathieu's equation (repeated three times):

$$\frac{\hbar^2}{2m}\frac{d^2u_x}{dx^2} + mv_0^2a^2\left(1 - \cos\frac{2\pi x}{a}\right)u_x - E_xu_x = 0$$

where E_x etc., are separation constants with $E = E_x + E_y + E_z$. From known results on Mathieu's equation, only certain values of E allow the wavefunction, ψ, to remain bounded over all space. As the lattice spacing, a, is decreased from very large values, allowed values of E remain narrowly restricted (at approximately $hv_0(n + \frac{1}{2})$) until the "barrier height," $2mv_0^2a^2$ in (5–101), between potential minima becomes comparable to E. As a decreases further, these highly degenerate states first drop in energy ("resonance") and then broaden into *bands* of allowed values of E which eventually overlap into an unbroken continuum.

For a detailed treatment, see J. C. Slater, *Phys. Rev.*, **87**, 807 (1952).

(e) **Particle in a periodic potential (band theory of crystalline solids):** An electron in a crystal will experience a potential, U, which has the same periodicity as the crystal. Any crystal is characterized by a "unit cell" (which may contain one or many atoms) and three independent translation vectors, $\mathbf{a}_1$, $\mathbf{a}_2$, $\mathbf{a}_3$, such that the entire crystal may be generated from a single unit cell by translations of the form, $\mathbf{r}' = \mathbf{r} + (n_1\mathbf{a}_1 + n_2\mathbf{a}_2 + n_3\mathbf{a}_3)$, where n_i are positive or negative integers.

The potential, U, and hence the Hamiltonian, H, will be invariant under the group whose elements are such translations. This group is Abelian (translations commute) and hence, by the note following (22–38), all its unitary, irreducible representations are of the form wherein a translation, $\sum_1^3 n_i\mathbf{a}_i$, corresponds to the number, $\exp(i\sum_j \lambda_j n_j)$; here the λ_j can have any real values. Thus, by (22–24), any stable wavefunction has the property that, for some λ_j,

$$\psi(\mathbf{r} + \sum n_j\mathbf{a}_j) = e^{i\Sigma\lambda_j n_j}\,\psi(\mathbf{r})$$

It follows* that there is a vector **k** such that

$$\psi(\mathbf{r}) = e^{i\mathbf{k}\cdot\mathbf{r}}\, u(\mathbf{r}) \tag{5–102}$$

where u has the periodicity of the lattice:

$$u(\mathbf{r} + \sum n_i \cdot \mathbf{a}_i) = u(\mathbf{r}) \tag{5–103}$$

(Bloch wavefunctions).

It will be convenient to label the states by the (continuous†) vector variable, **k**. Note, however, that **k** is not unique; (5–102) remains valid if **k** is replaced by any vector of the form, $\mathbf{k} + \sum n_i\mathbf{b}_i$, where $\mathbf{b}_i$ are the reciprocal lattice vectors, defined by

$$\mathbf{b}_j \cdot \mathbf{a}_i = \delta_{ji}$$

This ambiguity in **k** is usually resolved by choosing from these the vector with the shortest length (first "Brillouin zone").

By (5–103), both $u(\mathbf{r})$ and $U(\mathbf{r})$ can be expanded in a Fourier series,‡

$$U(\mathbf{r}) = \sum_{l,m,n} C_{\mathbf{g}} e^{i\mathbf{g}\cdot\mathbf{r}}\,; \qquad u(\mathbf{r}) = \sum_{l,m,n} c_{\mathbf{g}} e^{i\mathbf{g}\cdot\mathbf{r}}$$

where

$$\mathbf{g} = 2\pi(l\mathbf{b}_1 + m\mathbf{b}_2 + n\mathbf{b}_3); \qquad \left.\begin{matrix} l \\ m \\ n \end{matrix}\right\} = 0, \pm 1, \pm 2, \cdots$$

The wave equation (5–48) then becomes a set of linear equations:

$$\{E - C_0 + (\hbar^2/2m)|\mathbf{k} + \mathbf{g}|^2\}c_{\mathbf{g}} = \sum_{\mathbf{h}} c_{\mathbf{g}-\mathbf{h}}\, C_{\mathbf{h}} \tag{5–104}$$

Qualitative features of the solutions may be exhibited as follows.

For weakly bound electrons, C_0 is the dominant term in U and one expects $u \doteqdot c_0$. Approximate solutions of this type are readily derived from (5–104) *except* when **k** is near the edge of a Brillouin zone: $|\mathbf{k} + \mathbf{g}| \doteqdot |\mathbf{k}|$ for one of the $\mathbf{g}$; call it **G**. Then c_0 and $c_{\mathbf{G}}$ will have comparable magnitudes. This gives two simultaneous dominant equations in the set (5–104) and their determinantal equation is

$$\begin{aligned} E &= C_0 + \frac{\hbar^2}{4m}\{|\mathbf{k}|^2 + |\mathbf{k} + \mathbf{G}|^2\} \pm \left\{|C_{\mathbf{G}}|^2 + \frac{\hbar^4}{16m^2}[|\mathbf{G}|^2 + 2\mathbf{k}\cdot\mathbf{G}]^2\right\}^{1/2} \\ &\doteqdot C_0 + \frac{\hbar^2}{2m}|\mathbf{k}|^2 \pm |C_{\mathbf{G}}| \end{aligned} \tag{5–105}$$

(the last step in view of $|\mathbf{k} + \mathbf{G}|^2 \doteqdot |\mathbf{k}|^2$). Thus E has a discontinuity as a function of **k** at the edges of the Brillouin zones. The energy spectrum therefore breaks up into bands which are continuous (for an infinite crystal) with forbidden gaps between

---

* Define **k** by $\mathbf{k}\cdot\mathbf{a}_j = \lambda_j$. Consider a given unit cell and define u by (5–102) in that cell and by periodicity elsewhere.

† If the crystal is not infinite, only discrete values of **k** are allowed; see below.

‡ For accurate numerical computations, other series (whose terms more closely approximate the expected $u(\mathbf{r})$) are more appropriate. Compare J. C. Slater, *Phys. Rev.*, **87,** 807 (1952) and **92,** 603 (1953).

(usually; occasionally bands overlap). Since $\mathbf{k}$ is not unique, E may be regarded either as a multiple valued function of $\mathbf{k}$ in one zone or as a discontinuous function of a continuously varying $\mathbf{k}$. Schematically, in one dimension,

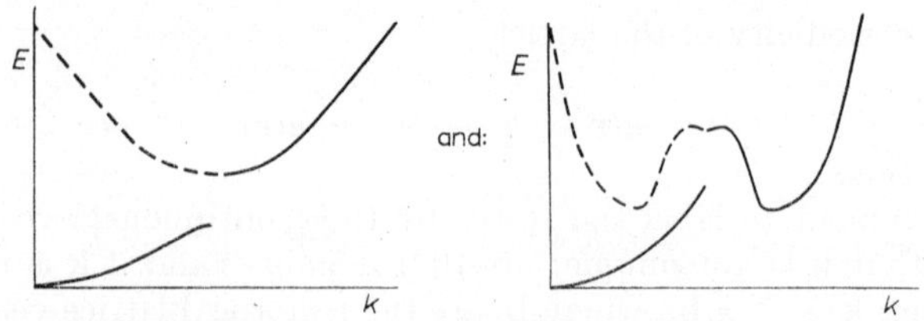

In a finite crystal, the "bands" are actually sets of very closely spaced, discrete energy levels. The number of levels in a band is equal to the number of cells in the crystal, multiplied by the degeneracy, $2(2l + 1)$, of the corresponding electron levels (orbital angular momentum l) in the isolated atoms.* (To show this, choose periodic boundary conditions in the infinite crystal—as in (b) above.) Thus a complete band may be regarded as approximately representing a state with $2(2l + 1)$ electrons in each unit cell.

By the Pauli principle, each way of occupying the available energy levels corresponds to only *one* (electronic) state for the crystal as a whole (that is, permutation of individual electrons is a meaningless concept).

Simple consequences: By the Pauli principle for electrons, the bands may be regarded as filled from the bottom to a certain level. If this final level occurs at the middle of a band, electrons are easily excited (wave packets can be formed with little expenditure of energy) and the material will be a *conductor*. (Non-zero resistivity originates from thermal motions of the nuclei, from impurities or from other irregularities which can scatter the wave packets; see Chapter 6.) Thus an element with an odd number of electrons and an odd number of atoms in its unit cell must be a conductor. If the filled states end at the top of a band, just below a wide gap, the material will be an *insulator*. (The solid as a whole then has a single ground state, well separated from the first excited electronic state.) If, however, the gap is not too large, thermal excitations to the subsequent unfilled band ("conduction band") can occur; the material will then be a *semi-conductor* and its conductivity (proportional to available charge carriers) will vary rapidly with temperature. (The remaining electrons in the last filled band—the "valence band"—are then also free to move and, in effect, the "holes" act as positive charge carriers; see following (5–110).)

Velocity and effective mass: A spatially *localized* electron with wave number $\mathbf{k}$ must be represented by a superposition ("wave packet") of wave functions (5–102) including time-factors [see (5–48)]:

$$\Psi_e(\mathbf{r}, t) = \int w(\boldsymbol{\varkappa}) u_{\boldsymbol{\varkappa}}(\mathbf{r}) \exp i[\boldsymbol{\varkappa} \cdot \mathbf{r} - tE(\boldsymbol{\varkappa})/\hbar]\, d\boldsymbol{\varkappa} \tag{5–106}$$

where $w(\boldsymbol{\varkappa})$ is a weight-function† with appreciable magnitude only when $\boldsymbol{\varkappa} \doteqdot \mathbf{k}$. By expanding $E(\boldsymbol{\varkappa})$ in a series about $\mathbf{k}$ and noting that $u(\mathbf{r})$ changes only slowly with $\boldsymbol{\varkappa}$, it is seen that (5–106) consists of a factor with Bloch form (5–102) (with time

* At very small lattice spacings, bands may not only overlap but may split into differently arranged "new" bands. This effect is important in relatively few cases under ordinary conditions.

† In fact, $w(\boldsymbol{\varkappa})$ is the Fourier transform of $\Psi_e(\mathbf{r}, 0) = \sqrt{\rho_0(\mathbf{r})}$ where ρ_0 is the charge-density at $t = 0$ associated with the localized "electron."

factor) modulated by a factor, $f[\mathbf{r} - (t/\hbar)\nabla_{\mathbf{k}}E]$. Thus the velocity to be associated with spatially localized electrons with wave number $\mathbf{k}$ is (the "group velocity")

$$\mathbf{v} = \frac{1}{\hbar}\nabla_{\mathbf{k}}E(\mathbf{k}) \tag{5–107}$$

If an external force, $\mathbf{F}$, is also present, then, since the classical relation $\mathrm{d}E/\mathrm{d}t = \mathbf{F}\cdot\mathbf{v}$ must hold for quantum mechanical averages (see (5–7)), it follows that

$$\frac{\mathrm{d}\mathbf{v}}{\mathrm{d}t} = \frac{1}{\hbar^2}\mathbf{F}\cdot[\nabla_k\nabla_k E(\mathbf{k})] \equiv \mathbf{F}\cdot\left(\frac{1}{\mathfrak{m}_e}\right) \tag{5–108}$$

where the dyadic, $\mathfrak{m}_e$, is known as the "effective mass" (for spatially localized charge). When the energy surfaces are nearly spherical, $\mathfrak{m}_e$ becomes a simple number,

$$m_e \doteqdot \frac{\hbar^2}{\mathrm{d}^2E/\mathrm{d}k^2} \tag{5–109}$$

which is a common approximation; m_e is usually within a factor of ten of the free electron mass. The relation,

$$\mathbf{F} = \hbar\frac{\mathrm{d}\mathbf{k}}{\mathrm{d}t} \tag{5–110}$$

also follows from (5–107) and the requirement, $\mathbf{F}\cdot\mathbf{v} = \mathrm{d}E/\mathrm{d}t$ for arbitrary $\mathbf{v}$.

Holes: Note that m_e in (5–109) will usually be negative near the top of an energy band. If the solid possesses a nearly filled band, then, in an electromagnetic field, any spatially localized features of the electron density will move as if positively charged (leading, for example, to an "anomalous" Hall effect), and it is therefore convenient to ascribe such electrical phenomena to "holes" in the band with an effective mass of $|m_e|$. (Electro*mechanical* experiments, however, will still correctly indicate that the actual charge-carriers are negative.)

Two-Particle Problems

(a) **Center of mass coordinates:** If we set,

$$\mathbf{R} = \frac{m_1\mathbf{r}_1 + m_2\mathbf{r}_2}{m_1 + m_2}; \qquad \mathbf{r} = \mathbf{r}_2 - \mathbf{r}_1 \tag{5–111}$$

then, if there are no external fields and if U depends only on $\mathbf{r}_2 - \mathbf{r}_1$ (and spin variables), the Hamiltonian operator (5–9) is readily computed to be

$$\left.\begin{aligned} H &= \frac{-\hbar^2}{2M}\nabla_R{}^2 + \left[\frac{-\hbar^2}{2\mu}\nabla_r{}^2 + U(\mathbf{r}, s_1, s_2)\right] \\ M &= m_1 + m_2; \quad \mu = m_1m_2/(m_1 + m_2) \end{aligned}\right\} \tag{5–112}$$

Thus the kinetic energy of motion of the center of mass separates out and, by (5–27)–(5–29), the total wave function (which is seldom explicitly written out) will be the product of a "free particle" wave function and a solution of

$$\frac{-\hbar^2}{2m}\nabla_r{}^2\psi + U(\mathbf{r}, s_1, s_2)\psi = E\psi \tag{5–113}$$

(b) **Central forces:** If

$$U = U(|\mathbf{r}|, s_1, s_2) \tag{5–114}$$

then (5–113) is separable in spherical coordinates:

$$\psi = \psi_{l,m} = Y_l^m(\theta, \phi)u(r, s_1, s_2) \tag{5–115}$$

where $Y_l^m(\theta, \phi)$ is a spherical harmonic,* such as $\exp(im\phi)P_l^m(\cos\theta)$, and u satisfies,

$$\frac{1}{r}\frac{d^2}{dr^2}(ru) - \frac{l(l+1)}{r^2}u + \frac{2\mu}{\hbar^2}[E - U]u = 0 \tag{5–116}$$

From (5–30)–(5–33) it may be verified that $\psi_{l,m}$ has (orbital) angular momentum, $\hbar\sqrt{l(l+1)}$, with z-component, $m\hbar$. In (5–116), E will be independent of m; this $(2l+1)$-fold degeneracy is "normal" in the sense that it is a consequence of the symmetry of H.

Spin: Solutions of (5–116) are often independent of spin variables, but if the two particles are *identical*, postulate (VIII) must be satisfied. The consequence is that for identical particles only certain spin functions can multiply a given Y_l^m. If the spin of each is $\frac{1}{2}$ and they are Fermi–Dirac particles, the three spin factors, (5–43), must be used with odd l and the single function, (5–44), with even l. (Important example: the Hydrogen molecule, resulting in ortho- and para-hydrogen.)

(c) **Harmonic oscillator:**

$$U = \tfrac{1}{2}k(r - r_0)^2$$

When this is a good approximation, ψ is small except when $|r - r_0| \ll r_0$ and the $1/r^2$ term in (5–116) can be expanded in series about r_0. If the first three terms of that series are retained, the result is the equation for the *ideal harmonic oscillator*:

$$\frac{d^2f}{dx^2} + \frac{2\mu}{\hbar^2}(W - \tfrac{1}{2}\beta x^2)f = 0 \tag{5–117}$$

where:

$$\left.\begin{aligned} f(x) &= ru(r) \\ x &= r - r_0 - \frac{l(l+1)\hbar^2 r_0}{3l(l+1)\hbar^2 + k\mu r_0^4} \\ E &= W + l(l+1)(\hbar^2/2\mu r_0^2) - \frac{l^2(l+1)^2\hbar^4/2\mu r_0^2}{3l(l+1)\hbar^2 + k\mu r_0^4} \\ \beta &= k + 6l(l+1)\hbar^2/2\mu r_0^4 \end{aligned}\right\} \tag{5–118}$$

If x is allowed to take all real values (another approximation as regards (5–116) itself), equation (5–117) has the allowed "energy" values,

$$W = (n + \tfrac{1}{2})\hbar\omega_0; \qquad \text{with } \omega_0 = \sqrt{\beta/\mu} \tag{5–119}$$

The corresponding (normalized) eigenfunctions are†

$$ru_n(r) = f_n(x) = \left(\frac{\sqrt{\gamma/\pi}}{2^n n!}\right)^{\frac{1}{2}} H_n(x\sqrt{\gamma})e^{-\gamma x^2/2} \qquad \text{with} \quad \gamma = \sqrt{\mu\beta}/\hbar \tag{5–120}$$

As an approximate solution to (5–116), the energy levels, E, given by (5–118) and

* Different authors use many different Y_l^m, often with different definitions of the associated Legendre polynomials P_l^m. That l and m are integers with $0 \leqslant |m| \leqslant l$ follows from the requirement that $\psi\psi^*$ be integrable.

† $H_n(z) = (-1)^n e^{z^2}(d^n/dz^n)\, e^{-z^2}$, Hermite polynomials.

(5–119) represent rotation-vibration levels for diatomic molecules.* A better approximation is:

(d) **Morse potential:**

$$U(r) = D\{1 - e^{-a(r-r_0)}\}^2 \tag{5–121}$$

When this is used in (5–116), approximations are again required; if $y = \exp[-a(r - r_0)]$ is taken as a new variable and $1/r^2$ is expanded in a series about $y = 1$ to three terms, the confluent hypergeometric equation is obtained. The resulting eigenvalues are usually written in the approximate form (which is more easily fitted to empirical data):

$$\left.\begin{aligned} \frac{1}{hc} E_{n,l} &= \frac{\nu_0}{c}(n + \tfrac{1}{2}) - x\left(\frac{\nu_0}{c}\right)(n + \tfrac{1}{2})^2 \\ &+ l(l+1)B_0 + D_0 l^2(l+1)^2 \\ &- \alpha(n + \tfrac{1}{2})l(l+1) \end{aligned}\right\} \tag{5–122}$$

where:

$$\nu_0 = \frac{a}{2\pi}\sqrt{2D/\mu}$$

$$x = h\nu_0/4D$$

$$B_0 = \hbar/(4\pi\mu r_0^2 c)$$

$$D_0 = -\frac{(\hbar/2\pi\mu r_0^2)^3}{2\nu_0^2 c}$$

$$\alpha = \frac{3\hbar^2\nu_0}{4c\mu r_0^2 D}\left(\frac{1}{ar_0} - \frac{1}{a^2 r_0^2}\right)$$

The gross features of the spectrum implied by (5–122) are due to transitions of the type† $n_1 \rightarrow n_2$. These main transitions are spread out into very broad bands by the last three terms in (5–122). The selection rule on total angular momentum, $\Delta l = 0, \pm 1$, implies three sets of "satellites":

P—Branch	$\Delta l = -1$	
R—Branch	$\Delta l = +1$	(for $n_1 \rightarrow n_2 > n_1$)
Q—Branch	$\Delta l = 0$	

The lines of the R—Branch at first move toward smaller wavelengths, but, as l increases the α-term in (5–122) eventually reverses this trend, producing a "band *head*" below which no lines appear. (Unless sufficiently large l values are present—high temperature—for the D_0 term to appear.)

(e) **Coulomb potential:** (Hydrogen atom, He^+, Li^{++}). When $U(r) = -Ze^2/r$, equation (5–116) is the confluent hypergeometric equation. For $E < 0$, the states are "bound" and the allowed energies are

$$E_n = -\left(\frac{\mu Z^2 e^4}{2\hbar^2}\right)\frac{1}{n^2}; \qquad n = l+1, l+2, \cdots. \tag{5–123}$$

* The reduction of this many-body problem to an approximate two-body problem is discussed in (5–140)–(5–144) below.

† For a molecule with identical atoms, there must simultaneously be a change of electronic state (see (5–140)–(5–144)); otherwise, electric dipole transitions are "forbidden" by symmetry.

The normalized eigenfunctions are usually taken as

$$\left.\begin{aligned}
\psi_{n,l,m} &= u_{n,l}(r)\sqrt{\frac{2l+1}{4\pi}\frac{(l-|m|)!}{(l+|m|)!}}\,P_l^{|m|}(\cos\theta)\,e^{\pm im\phi} \\
&\text{with} \\
u_{n,l}(r) &= \left(\frac{2Z}{na_0}\right)^{3/2}\sqrt{\frac{(n-l-1)!}{2n[(n+l)!]^3}}\left(\frac{2Zr}{na_0}\right)^{l} \\
&\qquad\times e^{-Zr/na_0}L_{n+l}^{2l+1}\left(\frac{2Zr}{na_0}\right) \\
a_0 &= \hbar^2/\mu e^2 \\
l = 0, 1, 2, \cdots ;&\qquad |m| \leqslant l; \qquad n = l+1, l+2, \cdots .
\end{aligned}\right\} \qquad (5\text{–}124)$$

The associated Laguerre polynomials are here defined by

$$L_k^{\,s}(z) = \frac{d^s}{dz^s}\left[e^z\frac{d^k}{dz^k}(z^k e^{-z})\right]$$

There is "accidental degeneracy" since E is (partially) independent of l, a result that depends on the special analytic form of U and is not a consequence of symmetry.

When $E > 0$, all values of E are allowed (for an unconfined system). Because of the long range of Coulomb forces, the wave functions do not become plane waves ("free particle functions") even at infinite separation, r. This problem is best treated directly from (5–113) using parabolic coordinates ($\xi = r - z$, $\eta = r + z$, ϕ) and setting $\psi = e^{ikz}f(\xi)$. The result (normalized to unit flux) is*

$$\psi = v^{-1/2}\Gamma(1+iq)e^{-q\pi/2}e^{ikz}{}_1F_1(-iq;\ 1;\ 2ikr\sin^2\tfrac{1}{2}\theta) \qquad (5\text{–}125)$$

where

$$q = Ze^2/\hbar v$$

$$v = \text{relative velocity} = \hbar k/\mu = \sqrt{2E/\mu}$$

Scattering cross sections following from (5–125) are (in center of mass coordinates and per unit solid angle):

(1) Distinguishable particles,

$$\sigma_{\text{com}}(\theta) = \left(\frac{Ze^2}{2\mu v^2}\right)^2\frac{1}{\sin^4(\frac{1}{2}\theta)} \qquad (5\text{–}126)$$

Note that the total cross section, $\oint\!\!\oint \sigma\, d\Omega$, is infinite; *every* particle in the beam suffers some deflection.

(2) Indistinguishable particles: (postulate (VIII) must be satisfied by symmetrizing (5–125))

$$\sigma_{\text{com}}(\theta) = \left(\frac{Ze^2}{2\mu v^2}\right)^2\left\{\frac{1}{\sin^4(\frac{1}{2}\theta)} + \frac{1}{\cos^4(\frac{1}{2}\theta)} + \frac{2(-1)^{2s}}{2s+1}\cdot\frac{\cos[(2e^2/\hbar v)\ln\tan(\frac{1}{2}\theta)]}{\sin^2(\frac{1}{2}\theta)\cos^2(\frac{1}{2}\theta)}\right\}$$

where s is the spin of each particle and it is assumed that no experimental distinction is made between different spin states.

---

* $_1F_1(a; b; z) = 1 + \dfrac{az}{1!b} + \dfrac{a(a+1)z^2}{2!b(b+1)} + \cdots$.

(f) **Spin-spin coupling:** This is of importance primarily for nuclear forces where the effects are large.

$$U = f(r) + g(r)\mathbf{S}_1 \cdot \mathbf{S}_2 = F(r) + \left[\frac{1}{\hbar^2}\mathbf{S}_1 \cdot \mathbf{S}_2 - \frac{1}{4}\right] G(r) \tag{5–127}$$

The formalism (5–114)–(5–116) remains valid, but (for spin $\frac{1}{2}$ particles) U is effectively equal to $F(r)$ when the (triplet) spin-state factors (5–43) are used and $F - G$ when the (singlet) state (5–44) is used. (Compare (5–128) for evaluation of $\mathbf{S}_1 \cdot \mathbf{S}_2$.)

(g) **Spin-orbit coupling (non-central):** Addition of the interaction (5–11) to U destroys the property (5–114) and solutions of the form (5–115) no longer exist; that is l and s are no longer "constants of the motion." However, if the spin-orbit effects are small, the dominant term in ψ will still have the form (5–115) (and (5–43) or (5–44)) and in such cases ψ may still be labelled by the l, s values of this dominant term (Russell–Saunders coupling). The effect of (5–11) on the energy may then be computed by assuming $L^2 = l(l+1)\hbar^2$, etc. (first order perturbation theory). Then since

$$J^2 = |\mathbf{L} + \mathbf{S}|^2 = L^2 + S^2 + 2\mathbf{L} \cdot \mathbf{S}$$

the energy changes are approximately,

$$\Delta E_{l,s} = \frac{\hbar^2}{2}\Big[j(j+1) - l(l+1) - s(s+1)\Big] \times \begin{Bmatrix}\text{Mean value of coef.}\\ \text{of } \mathbf{L}\cdot\mathbf{S} \text{ in (5–11)}\end{Bmatrix} \tag{5–128}$$

A similar formula holds for *hyperfine splitting*, due to the interaction ($\mu \mathbf{S}_{nuc} \cdot \mathbf{H}$) of nuclear magnetic moments with the magnetic field ($\mathbf{H}$ = constant $\times \langle \mathbf{J} \rangle$) generated by the electrons of an atom.

(h) **Zeeman effect:** A uniform external magnetic field, $\mathbf{B}$, along the z-axis may be represented by $\mathbf{A} = \frac{1}{2}\mathbf{B} \times \mathbf{r}$ in (5–9). The energy operators linear in $\mathbf{B}$ are found to be $(-e/2\mu c)\mathbf{B} \cdot \mathbf{L}$, while the postulated intrinsic spin-magnetic-moment gives a term $(-eg/2\mu c)\mathbf{B} \cdot \mathbf{S}$ for each particle. If, as in atoms, only one of the latter is important,

$$\Delta H = \frac{-e}{2\mu c} B(J_z + (g-1)S_z) \tag{5–129}$$

If this is much larger than the spin-orbit coupling (5–128), its values are simply $(-e\hbar B/2\mu c)(m_l + g m_s)$. Otherwise, $\langle L_z \rangle = \hbar m_l$ has no meaning and (5–129) must be evaluated in terms of J_z, l, j, s. An involved calculation, ultimately based on (5–31), shows that the first-order perturbation result is

$$\Delta E_{j,m_j,l,s} = \frac{-eB}{2\mu c}(\hbar m_j)\left[1 + \frac{g-1}{2}\,\frac{j(j+1) - l(l+1) + s(s+1)}{j(j+1)}\right] \tag{5–130}$$

(For electrons, $g = 2$.) The last factor is known as the "Landé g-factor." Historically, the Zeeman effect played a central role in determining the spin of the electron, its magnetic moment, and in determining the structure and origin of atomic energy levels generally.

(i) **Stark effect:** A uniform external electric field, E_z, along the z-axis is represented by a potential, $\phi = -zE_z$, and the added energy is $\Delta U = -E_z \sum e_j z_j$. Since this expression reverses sign when the coordinate system is inverted, all its diagonal matrix elements, $\langle \alpha | \Delta U | \alpha \rangle$, must vanish and the first order perturbation energy vanishes. Accordingly, the level shifts are always (at least) quadratic in E_z.

For two particles, in center-of-mass coordinates, $\Delta U = -E_z(e_2/m_2 - e_1/m_1)\mu z$, if $e_1 + e_2 = 0$. For diatomic molecules, $z \doteq r_0 \cos\theta$ where r_0 is the equilibrium separation and $\Delta U \doteq -E_z\mu_e \cos\theta$ with μ_e constant. One finds (from (5–115) and the orthogonality of the vibrational factors, such as (5–120)) that the only non-zero matrix elements of ΔU are

$$|\langle l, m, n\,|\Delta U|\, l-1, m, n\rangle|^2 = |\langle l-1, m, n\,|\Delta U|\, l, m, n\rangle|^2$$
$$= \frac{\mu_e{}^2 E_z{}^2 (l^2 - m^2)}{4l^2 - 1}$$

and the second order perturbation energy (19–67) is a sum of only two terms. Using as an approximation to the energy levels (5–118) or (5–122), $E_{l,m,n} = B_0 l(l+1) + h\nu_0(n + \frac{1}{2})$, the results are

$$\left.\begin{aligned} \Delta E_{l,m,n} &= \frac{-\mu_e{}^2 E_z{}^2}{2B_0} \frac{3m^2 - l(l+1)}{l(l+1)(2l-1)(2l+3)} \qquad (l \neq 0) \\ \Delta E_{0,0,n} &= -\mu_e{}^2 E_z{}^2 / 6B_0 \end{aligned}\right\} \tag{5–131}$$

An interesting consequence is

$$\sum_m \Delta E_{l,m,n} = 0 \qquad \text{if} \qquad l \neq 0 \tag{5–132}$$

so that, to first order, only the last line of (5–131) contributes to the overall energy change of a macroscopic gas sample.

(j) **Tensor forces (non-central):** These are characterized by potential terms of the form,

$$\Delta U = [(3/r^2)(\mathbf{S}_1 \cdot \mathbf{r})(\mathbf{S}_2 \cdot \mathbf{r}) - \mathbf{S}_1 \cdot \mathbf{S}_2] f(r) \tag{5–133}$$

Since (5–114) is violated, the form (5–115)–(5–116) could not be used for ψ in general. However, $\mathbf{J}$ and $|\mathbf{S}_1 + \mathbf{S}_2|^2$ still commute with H and parity can also be used as a label (since H is invariant under coordinate inversion in this case). One finds that (5–133) applied to the spin state (5–44) yields zero, so that (5–115) and (5–116) can be used for singlet ($S_{\text{tot}} = 0$) states and indeed (5–133) has no effect on them. Likewise, of the triplet states, (5–43), the ones with $l = j$ have different parity from those with $l = j \pm 1$. Thus (5–115)–(5–116) can again be used for $l = j$ triplet states. All remaining states become mixtures of at most two states, $l = j \pm 1$ of the type (5–115), requiring simultaneous solution of only two coupled equations of the general type of (5–116).

In this way, the non-symmetric (average) electric charge distribution of the deuteron has been explained ($s = 1$; $j = 1$; $l = 0, 2$ mixed).

Many-Particle Problems

(a) **Center of mass coordinates** can always be introduced and the kinetic energy of translation will always separate out; this is most readily seen by induction on (5–111) and (5–112). [That is, apply (5–111) and (5–112) to any two particles and then, considering these as a compound particle, $\bar{m}_1$, reapply between m_3 and $\bar{m}_1$, etc.] The actual transformations are complicated, but the classical-Hamiltonian rule (see remark under postulate (V)) will usually give the correct result.

(b) **Atoms:** Only the hydrogen atom (and one-electron ions) has been rigorously solved,* though quite accurate numerical results have been obtained for the simpler atoms. An approximate, qualitative picture, useful in spectroscopy and chemical theory, is readily obtained, however: Neglecting motion of the nucleus, one may write for the electrons,

$$\left.\begin{aligned} H = \sum_1^N \left[\frac{-\hbar^2}{2m}\nabla_i^2 - \frac{Ze^2}{r_i} + u_i(r_i)\right] \\ + \left[\tfrac{1}{2}\sum_{i\neq j}^N\sum^N \frac{e^2}{|\mathbf{r}_i - \mathbf{r}_j|} - \sum_1^N u_i(r_i)\right] \\ + \text{Spin-Orbit terms} \end{aligned}\right\} \quad (5\text{–}134)$$

By appropriate choice of the functions, u_i, it should be possible to make the second bracketed term a small perturbation (at least for a given state of the atom).

Initially neglecting the last two terms in (5–134), the problem separates, as in (5–28)-(5–29), into N problems of the two-body type, (5–113)-(5–116). Since $u_i - Ze^2/r_i$ is not in general a Coulomb potential, the "partial" energies, E_i, will depend on both l and n_r. When (5–28) and (5–29) are used to assemble approximate wavefunctions for the complete atom from these one-electron problems, the antisymmetry postulate (VIII) requires† the use of the determinant form, (5–50). Thus:

The energy of an atomic state is **primarily** *determined by the electron* **"configuration"** that is, by a list of occupied (approximate) one-electron levels. (The energies of the latter do not depend on m_l or m_s, and thus only the various n and l need be explicitly listed, but the list will often be generic for many zero-order states.) For historic reasons, the common notation is esoteric:

$$\text{"}n\text{"} \quad \text{denotes} \quad n + l$$

(notation: (5–123)) and n is given numerically while the value of l is given in "code":

$$\left.\begin{aligned} l = 0, 1, 2, 3, 4, 5, 6, \cdots \\ \text{denoted by: } s, p, d, f, g, h, i, \cdots \end{aligned}\right\} \quad (5\text{–}135)$$

EXAMPLE: $(1s)^2(4d)^3$ would be a configuration containing two occupied levels with $l = 0$, $n = 1$ and three with $l = 2$, $n = 4$. By convention,

$$n \geqslant l + 1$$

Furthermore, the "exponent" on a "factor" in the configuration list is at most $2(2l + 1)$ (the number of combinations (m_l, m_s) possible for given n and l) and when it has this value, the corresponding "shell" is filled and contributes only one state to the level.

Madelung's rule: *Configuration shells build up in energy in the order of increasing $n + l$ and, within such groups, by increasing n.*

---

* Even for these, there are relativistic effects and others still smaller (Lamb shift) which can only be calculated on the basis of somewhat incomplete theories; see "high-energy quantum mechanics" below.

† Compare the definition, (11–3) of a determinant.

Thus, with few exceptions,* the ground state of an isolated atom† can be inferred from its atomic number.

[EXAMPLE: *Rb* ($Z = 37$): $(1s)^2(2s)^2(2p)^6(3s)^2(3p)^6(4s)^2(3d)^{10}(4p)^6(5s)$.]

Coupling schemes: Configuration energies are split into neighboring energy "terms" by the last two interactions in (5–134).

j–j Coupling obtains when the spin-orbit interaction, (5–11), dominates the electrostatic, $e^2/|\mathbf{r}_i - \mathbf{r}_j|$, interaction. The total angular momenta of the individual electron levels, $j = |l \pm \frac{1}{2}|$, are then approximate constants of the motion. This case occurs mainly in heavy atoms with nearly complete shells (or with very strong external magnetic fields, when a sum of terms (5–129) is added to (5–134) and dominates the others).

L–S Coupling (Russell–Saunders): The electrostatic energy dominates spin-orbit effects. Although L_z and S_z do not commute with H, the (total) magnitudes, L^2 and S^2, do so approximately and appropriate quantum labels are L, S, J, M $\left[\text{where } \mathbf{J} = \mathbf{L} + \mathbf{S} = \sum_i \mathbf{L}_i + \sum_i \mathbf{S}_i\right]$.

"Terms" and "Levels": Electrostatic interactions, $e^2/|\mathbf{r}_i - \mathbf{r}_j|$, have split the configuration-energies into "terms" (or "multiplets") with different energies, labelled by L, S. Finally, the very small spin-orbit effects split these "terms" into closely-spaced energy "levels," labelled by L, S, J. Each "level" contains $2J + 1$ states‡ whose natural (symmetry-induced) degeneracy is lifted only by an asymmetric environment, such as a magnetic field. Notation for levels follows the form,

$$^{2S+1}L_J \tag{5–136}$$

where the value of L is given by a capital letter in the code, (5–135). Examples: $^2S_{1/2}$ (ground level of Cu, Ag, Au and alkali metals); $^2P_{3/2}$ (halogen ground levels).

Thomas–Fermi atom: Since even numerical calculations are forbiddingly complex for the majority of atoms, a very useful approximation is a simple statistical approach which regards an atom as an electron gas (at "zero temperature") in an electrostatic potential field and includes only the gross quantum effects in such a gas. (For later refinements, see *Phys. Rev.* 1957; compare also Chapter 6 for some of the concepts used.)

If $\phi(r)$ is the electrostatic potential with $\phi_\infty = \phi(\infty)$ (zero for a neutral atom) then at each point in space, $p^2/2m \leqslant p_0{}^2/2m \equiv e(\phi - \phi_\infty)$ if electrons are not to escape. A small space-volume, dV, can therefore contain about $(p_0{}^3\, dV/3\pi^2\hbar^3)$ such electrons (Pauli exclusion principle and (5–95)) and thus the electric charge density, ρ, satisfies

$$\frac{-1}{4\pi}\nabla^2\phi = \rho = \frac{e}{3\pi^2\hbar^3}[2me(\phi - \phi_\infty)]^{3/2} \tag{5–137}$$

---

* These exceptions are:

One electron "promoted" from the (last) s shell to the (last) d shell:

Cr, Cu, Nb, Mo, Ru, Rh, Ag, Pt, Au

Two electrons "promoted" from s to d: Pd

One promotion from f to d: La, Ce, Gd, Tb, Ac, U

Two f to d promotions: Th; Three: Pa.

Still uncertain: Dy, Ho, Er and the transuranium elements.

† "Promotion" of electrons may be induced by molecular environment if the energy change involved is not large. Example: Carbon is $(1s)^2(2s)^2(2p)^2$ when isolated but becomes $(1s)^2(2s)(2p)^3$ in most molecules.

‡ Ignoring hyperfine splitting which arises from magnetic interactions between $\mathbf{J}$ and the nuclear spin, $\mathbf{I}$. The total angular momentum, $\mathbf{F} = \mathbf{J} + \mathbf{I}$, then plays the role of $\mathbf{J}$ above in the obvious fashion.

with the boundary conditions $\phi \rightarrow \phi_\infty$ as $r \rightarrow \infty$ and $\phi \sim Ze/r$ as $r \rightarrow 0$. Setting

$$y = r(\phi - \phi_\infty)/Ze; \qquad x = rZ^{1/3}(me^2/\hbar^2)2(4/3\pi)^{2/3}$$

(5–137) becomes

$$\sqrt{x}\,\frac{d^2y}{dx^2} = y^{3/2}; \qquad y(0) = 1; \qquad y(\infty) = 0 \tag{5–138}$$

A good approximation to the solution is,

$$y = \left[1 + \frac{x}{1.860}\right]^{-2} \tag{5–139}$$

from which the electron density, etc., can be evaluated. Examination of the number of electrons in the "gas" with a given angular momentum provides an approximate justification for Madelung's rule.

(c) **Molecules:** Chemical binding was first successfully explained by quantum mechanics. In essence, proximity of two atoms allows the unpaired* electrons of each to share common orbits, thereby decreasing their wavelengths and energies. A similarly qualitative concept is:

Resonance (exchange energy): According to the variational principle, (19–38), the lowest energy level of a system always lies *below* the value, $(\phi, H\phi)/(\phi, \phi)$, computed from any inexact wavefunction, ϕ. As a general rule of thumb, the decrease is greatest when the system has two or more approximate ground states of equal energy and can jump from one to the other by surmounting at most a potential barrier not large compared to its mean (kinetic) energy. (Likewise, a low barrier implies larger values of the approximate "one state" wavefunctions near the barrier and thus large values of any integral, $(\phi_1, H\phi_2)$ which depends on the region of overlap—"exchange integral".)

The consequent reduction of the true ground-state energy below the approximate values is often referred to as "resonance energy", "resonance binding" or "exchange energy".

The ground state wavefunction in such cases is almost always† the one with *greatest symmetry in the various space coordinates.* (Symmetry implies smaller derivatives, longer wavelengths, and hence smaller curvature or kinetic energy, $\nabla^2\psi$.)

Valence: For electrons, such completely symmetric wavefunctions must (by postulate (VIII)) be associated with antisymmetric spin functions, such as (5–44), implying oppositely directed spins. If this pairing of spins is unavailable, the spatially symmetric (low energy) state is also not available. The valence of an atom is thus equal to the *number of unpaired electrons.* (This effect is so strong that the H^- ion is quite stable—binding energy about 0.7 ev.)

In some cases (notably Be, C), electron configurations must be presumed to change in molecular environments in order to explain the observed valences, but the energies entailed are always small in such cases.

Additional applications of the resonance concept arise in explaining, for example, the unusually high binding energy of benzene, the stability of the "CO(O)–" termination

---

* Paired "electrons" are filled orbits which differ only in spin orientation.

† An important exception is the O_2 molecule which has a net electronic spin of 1 in the ground state.

in organic acids, and in explaining "hydrogen bonding*" in complex organic molecules. In all of these cases, the system has two (or more) essentially identical

structures $\left[\bigcirc\right.$ and $\bigcirc$ for benzene; $-C\begin{smallmatrix}O\\\\O\end{smallmatrix}H$ and $-C\begin{smallmatrix}O\\\\O\end{smallmatrix}H$ for organic

acids$\Big]$ and the true ground state is presumably† a mixture, or "resonance", of both,

with correspondingly lower energy than either one alone.

Formal methodology: Denoting the nuclei of a molecule by N or α and the electrons by e or i, the complete Hamiltonian has the schematic form,

$$H = -\sum_\alpha \frac{\hbar^2}{2M_\alpha} \mathbf{\nabla}_\alpha^2 + \left[-\sum_i \frac{\hbar^2}{2m} \mathbf{\nabla}_i^2 + U(e, N) \right]$$

$$= -\sum_\alpha \frac{\hbar^2}{2M_\alpha} \mathbf{\nabla}_\alpha^2 + H_e \tag{5-140}$$

Let ψ_e ("electronic wavefunction") be an eigenfunction of H_e (with the nuclear coordinates regarded as parameters). If ψ_N involves *only* nuclear coordinates, then

$$\psi = \psi_e(e, N)\psi_N(N) \tag{5-141}$$

is an approximate eigenfunction of H provided that terms involving $\mathbf{\nabla}_\alpha\psi_e$ can be neglected‡ and provided that ψ_N satisfies

$$\left[-\sum_\alpha \frac{\hbar^2}{2M_\alpha} \mathbf{\nabla}_\alpha^2 + E_e(N) \right] \psi_N = E\psi_N \tag{5-142}$$

where $E_e(N)$ is the electronic energy (with fixed but arbitrary nuclear separations, "N"):

$$H_e\psi_e = E_e(N)\psi_e \tag{5-143}$$

In practice, the function, $E_e(N)$, can seldom be evaluated from (5-143); usually

---

* Namely, the tendency for valence-saturated molecules with loosely-bound hydrogen atoms to associate in various ways, apparently in such relative orientations that the hydrogens can easily jump from one molecule to another. A simple example is dimerization of alcohols:

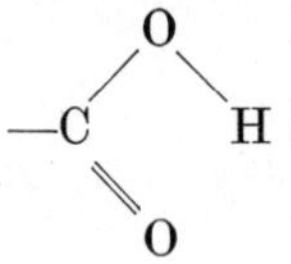

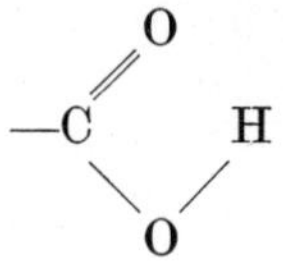

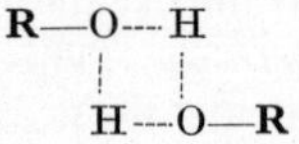

R—O‐‐‐H
: :   or even:
H‐‐‐O—R

‐‐‐O‐‐‐H‐‐‐O‐‐‐H‐‐‐O‐‐‐H‐‐‐
| | |
R   R   R

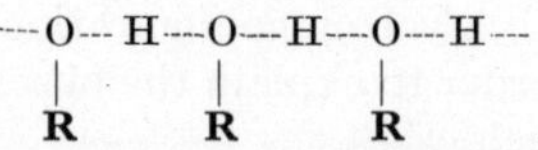

These phenomena probably account for many of the peculiar properties of water ($\mathbf{R} = \mathbf{H}$). The characteristic shapes of protein molecules are probably due to hydrogen-bonding between the amino acid groups within the giant molecule.

† An important piece of evidence for benzene is that the molecule is planar, in contrast to cyclohexane, C_6H_{12}.

‡ Justified by Born and Oppenheimer, *Ann. d. Phys.* **84**, 457 (1927) on the basis of the smallness of m/M_α.

the *form* (5–142) is used with some assumed potential function, $E_e(N)$. For each electronic state there is in general a different nuclear potential, E_e.

Hellmann–Feynman theorem: The average force on nucleus α (for a specific electronic state, $\psi_e(e, N)$) is the gradient of the nuclear potential, $E_e(N)$, which may be written,

$$\begin{aligned}\mathbf{F}_\alpha &= \nabla_\alpha(\psi_e, H_e\psi_e) = (\psi_e, (\nabla_\alpha U)\psi_e) + E_e(N)\nabla_\alpha(\psi_e, \psi_e)\\ &= (\psi_e, (\nabla_\alpha U)\psi_e) = \mathbf{F}_{\text{nucl}} + e\sum_i (\psi_e, \mathbf{E}_{i\alpha}\psi_e)\end{aligned}$$

where $\mathbf{F}_{\text{nucl}}$ is the Coulomb force due to the other nuclei and $\mathbf{E}_{i\alpha}$ is the electric field at $\mathbf{r}_\alpha$ due to a point charge, e, at $\mathbf{r}_i$. But,

$$e\int \psi_e^*\psi_e \, d\mathbf{r}_2 \cdots d\mathbf{r}_n = \rho_1$$

(the charge density due to electron #1) and the electrons are indistinguishable so that $n\rho_1 = \rho$, the total charge density due to all electrons. Thus

$$\mathbf{F}_\alpha = \mathbf{F}_{\text{nucl}} + e\int \rho(\mathbf{r})\, \mathbf{E}_{\alpha,\mathbf{r}}\, dV_r \tag{5–144}$$

which is just the classical force due to all the charges in the molecule. This simplifies visualization of the bonding (or anti-bonding) tendencies of a given electronic state. Note, however, that the quantum exclusion principle etc., may still play a central role by determining $\rho(\mathbf{r})$.

The Franck–Condon principle states that, during a transition between different *electronic* states, the internuclear separations cannot change greatly and that therefore *only certain vibrational states* (those with large but not too strongly oscillating wave-functions at that internuclear separation) will appear with the final electronic state. This principle is another consequence of the smallness of m/M_α—or the large velocity ratios, $\langle v_i\rangle/\langle v_\alpha\rangle$.

The order of magnitude of various contributions to the total energy of a molecule is roughly,

Electron levels $\sim$1–10 ev (visible frequencies, $\sim10^{15}$/sec)
Molecular vibration $\sim$0.1 ev (infrared, $\sim10^{13}$/sec)
Molecular rotation $\sim10^{-4}$ ev (microwave, $\sim10^{10}$/sec)
Nuclear quadrupole $\sim10^{-7}$ ev (radio, $\sim10^{7}$/sec)
Nuclear magnetic dipole $\sim10^{-10}$ ev (audio, $\sim10^{4}$/sec)

Relatively few electronic levels are of importance since large electronic excitations will usually disrupt the chemical bonds. (1 ev/molecule = 23 kilocalories/mole.)

Diatomic molecules: Equation (5–142) for diatomic molecules represents a two-body problem. The main results for a single electronic state, ψ_e, have been given above in (5–117)–(5–122).

Important properties of each electronic state, ψ_e, are its symmetry with respect to the molecular axis: The component of electronic angular momentum along the axis is denoted by λ and the electronic state-label gives its value in the "code", Σ, Π, Δ, Φ, $\cdots$ in analogy with the code (5–135); a superscript $\pm$ on the Σ states indicates parity under reflection in (any) plane containing the nuclear axis; for "X_2" molecules, a subscript, g or u (German: "gerade" or "ungerade" = even or odd) denotes parity under inversion in the center (point) of the axis.

The selection rule, $\Delta\lambda = 0, \pm 1$, applies to (electric dipole) radiation and other symmetry arguments establish selection rules (in addition to the electronic spin rule, $\Delta S = 0$ as for atoms) which lead to the following list of allowed transitions:

$$\Sigma^+ \leftrightarrow \Sigma^+; \qquad \Sigma^- \leftrightarrow \Sigma^-;$$

$$\Pi \leftrightarrow (\Sigma^\pm, \Pi, \Delta); \qquad \Delta \leftrightarrow (\Pi, \Delta, \Phi); \cdots$$

For "X–X" molecules: $g \leftrightarrow u$ (Thus $\Pi_g \leftrightarrow \Sigma_u^\pm$ etc.) Thus "X_2" molecules (and linear, symmetric molecules but no others) require a change of electronic state in all allowed (electric dipole) transitions and hence have no true infrared spectra.

Finally, *nuclear spins* interact very weakly with the rest of the molecule, but in "X_2" molecules,* they exert a strong influence because of the symmetry requirements, postulate (VIII). In particular for Σ states, even and odd values of the molecular angular momentum (l in (5–122), J in (5–145)) have alternating populations (statistical weights, intensities) in the ratio, $(I + 1)/I$, where I is the nuclear spin. [EXAMPLE: ortho- and para-hydrogen, the former having total nuclear spin one and only odd values of J, parahydrogen having the nuclear spin function (5–44) and only even values of J. Because of the weakness of nuclear spin interactions, appreciable amounts of ortho-H_2 persist for long times even at the lowest temperatures.]

Rotational Energies

Unlike the translational motion, rotation of the entire molecule cannot be exactly separated from the other motions (compare the α-term in (5–122)), but fortunately the internuclear forces actually turn out to be so "stiff" that interaction between rotation and vibration ("centrifugal stretching") is usually very small and is commonly neglected to first order.

Linear Top: A linear molecule has the same rotational properties as a diatomic molecule (neglecting interaction with vibrations) and its rotational energy levels are given by the first order terms in (5–118) or (5–122):

$$E_r = J(J + 1)\,\hbar^2/2I \tag{5–145}$$

where I is the classical moment of inertia (about an axis perpendicular to the molecular axis and passing through the center of mass).

The wavefunctions (rotational factors) are simply $Y_l^m(\theta, \phi)$ as in (5–115) or (5–124), where θ and ϕ specify the direction of the molecular axis.

Symmetric Top: If C is the moment of inertia about the figure axis and A, A are the other two (equal) principal moments of inertia, the wave equation can be shown to be [θ, ϕ = spherical polar angles of the figure axis in space; χ = angle of rotation of the top about its figure axis]:

$$\left.\begin{aligned} &\frac{1}{\sin\theta}\frac{\partial}{\partial\theta}\left(\sin\theta\frac{\partial\psi}{\partial\theta}\right) + \frac{1}{\sin^2\theta}\frac{\partial^2\psi}{\partial\phi^2} + \left(\cot^2\theta + \frac{A}{C}\right)\frac{\partial^2\psi}{\partial\chi^2} \\ &\qquad - \frac{2\cos\theta}{\sin^2\theta}\frac{\partial^2\psi}{\partial\chi\partial\phi} + \frac{2A}{\hbar^2}E_r\psi = 0 \end{aligned}\right\} \tag{5–146}$$

* Here, the two atoms must be the same *isotopes*.

The energy levels are:

$$E_r = \frac{\hbar^2}{2}\left(\frac{J(J+1)-\Lambda^2}{A} + \frac{\Lambda^2}{C}\right) \tag{5-147}$$

wherein $\Lambda = -J, -J+1, \cdots, J-1, J$. The eigenfunctions (rotational factors, not normalized) are,*

$$\left.\begin{aligned} \psi &= \mathrm{X}^{|\Lambda - M|/2}(1-\mathrm{X})^{|\Lambda+M|/2}\,{}_2F_1(\tfrac{1}{2}\gamma - J, \tfrac{1}{2}\gamma + J + 1; \\ &\qquad 1 + |\Lambda - M|; \mathrm{X})e^{i(M\phi+\Lambda\chi)} \\ \text{where} \quad \mathrm{X} &= \tfrac{1}{2}(1-\cos\theta) = \sin^2\tfrac{1}{2}\theta \\ \gamma &= |\Lambda + M| + |\Lambda - M| \end{aligned}\right\} \tag{5-148}$$

$\Lambda\hbar$ is the projection of the molecular angular momentum along the figure axis and $M\hbar$ is the component along the z coordinate axis.

Asymmetric Top: There are no known explicit general formulas for the energy levels. By expanding the rotational (factor of the) wavefunction as a series of functions of the type (5–148) for each J, the problem can be reduced to solution of a finite set of algebraic equations. If the principal moments of inertia are $A < B < C$ and if $\alpha = \hbar^2/2A$, $\beta = \hbar^2/2B$, $\gamma = \hbar^2/2C$, then

$$E_r = \tfrac{1}{2}(\beta+\gamma)J(J+1) + [\alpha - \tfrac{1}{2}(\beta+\gamma)]\omega_i \tag{5-149}$$

where, if $b = (\gamma - \beta)/(2\alpha - \beta - \gamma)$:

$$\begin{aligned} &\text{for } J = 0, \quad \omega_i = 0 \\ &\text{for } J = 1, \quad \omega_i = 0,\ 1 \pm b \\ &\text{for } J = 2, \quad \omega_i = 1 \pm 3b,\ 4,\ 2 \pm 2\sqrt{1+3b^2} \end{aligned} \tag{5-150}$$

For higher J, the determination of ω_i rapidly becomes more laborious; for details, see Randall *et al.*, *Phys. Rev.*, **52**, 160, (1937) and references therein, especially Wang, *Phys. Rev.*, **34**, 243 (1929).

Vibrational Energies

A rough approximation to the potential function, $E_e(N)$, in (5–142) is a positive-definite quadratic form,

$$E_e(N) = \sum_{i,j} A_{ij}\,(\xi_i - \xi_{i0})(\xi_j - \xi_{j0}) \tag{5-151}$$

where the ξ_i stand for the various Cartesian coordinates of the various nuclei and ξ_{i0} is the equilibrium (minimum-energy) value of ξ_i. Taking

$$q_i = (\xi_i - \xi_{i0})\sqrt{M_i} \tag{5-152}$$

as new variables, equations (5–142) and (5–151) combine into the form,

$$\frac{-\hbar^2}{2}\sum_i \frac{\partial^2\psi_N}{\partial q_i^2} + \sum_{i,j} a_{ij}q_iq_j\psi_N = E\psi_N \tag{5-153}$$

$* \; {}_2F_1(a, b;\ c;\ x) = 1 + \frac{ab}{1!c}x + \frac{a(a+1)b(b+1)}{2!c(c+1)}x^2 + \cdots$

12

Since a_{ij} is positive definite, it can be diagonalized by an *orthogonal* (real and unitary) transformation to new variables, Q_i, called "normal coordinates". The form of the "Laplacian operator" in (5–153) is unaltered by an orthogonal transformation and the result is

$$\sum_i \left[-\frac{\hbar^2}{2} \frac{\partial^2}{\partial Q_i^2} + \frac{\lambda_i}{2} Q_i^2 \right] \psi_N = E \psi_N \tag{5–154}$$

(Symmetries of the molecule may force sets of λ_i to be equal. Six of them must vanish since translation or rotation of the molecule as a whole cannot change $E_e(N)$.)

According to (5–28), (5–29), (5–117) and (5–120), the solutions (of the true vibrational parts, those with $\lambda_i \neq 0$) are

$$\psi_{n_1, n_2, \ldots, n_{3N-6}} = B \exp \left(-\tfrac{1}{2} \sum \alpha_i Q_i^2\right) \prod_{i=1}^{3N-6} H_{n_i}(\sqrt{\alpha_i}\, Q_i) \tag{5–155}$$

where B is a normalizing factor and $\alpha_i = \sqrt{\lambda_i}/\hbar$. The energy levels are,

$$E_v = \sum_{i=1}^{3N-6} (n_i + \tfrac{1}{2}) h\nu_i\,; \qquad \nu_i = \sqrt{\lambda_i}/2\pi \tag{5–156}$$

With more realistic potential functions, $E_e(N)$, there would also appear correction terms quadratic in the n_i ("anharmonicity corrections" as in (5–122)).

Transitions of the type, $\psi_{0,\ldots,0,1,0,\ldots,0} \leftrightarrow \psi_{0,\ldots,0}$ that is,

$$n_k = \delta_{pk} \leftrightarrow n_k = 0 \text{ (ground state)} \tag{5–157}$$

are called "fundamental transitions" (of the pth vibrational mode or normal coordinate) and the corresponding spectral line is called the fundamental frequency.

(For the potential (5–151), a selection rule, $\Delta n_k = \pm 1$, can be derived, but this restriction seldom holds since (5–151) is not sufficiently accurate to serve as a basis for selection rules.)

Vibrational states are the most characteristic features of the molecule; before the theory was well developed, extensive empirical work had shown that in many cases each chemical bond in the molecule generates a characteristic (fundamental) frequency, nearly independent of its environment. (This somewhat surprising result is a consequence of disparity in atomic masses and/or in the force constants; the rule breaks down for the more "homogeneous" molecules.)

Group theory has proven nearly indispensable, not only in further theoretical analysis, but also for systematizing observations, selection rules, etc. The group involved is the *set of transformations* (rotations and reflections) *which interchange like atoms* and hence bring the molecule to a position indistinguishable from its initial position—the "*symmetry group*" of the molecule.

Symmetry Types (*Labelling* ψ): According to (22–22)–(22–25), each wave function, ψ, must "belong to" some irreducible* representation of the symmetry group. A name for that particular representation then serves as a convenient quantum label for ψ; this group-representation label is usually called the "*symmetry-type*" or "*species*" of the state, ψ. (For diatomic molecules, the special (older) notation given earlier is more common, but it serves exactly the same purpose.)

Note that these symmetry labels may be applied to the complete wavefunction or

---

* Except for "numerical coincidences" in the nuclear potential function (accidental degeneracy); these seem never to occur in practice.

to its electronic or nuclear factors separately. The symmetry type of the nuclear vibration factor determines* the pure vibration (infrared) properties.

Some Selection Rules: Dipole matrix elements (occurring in (5–63)) such as $(\psi_i, x_\alpha \psi_k)$ will vanish (see (22–50)) if ψ_i and $(x_\alpha \psi_k)$ have different symmetry types. The (vibrational) ground state is always invariant† under the transformations of the symmetry group, and hence (electric dipole) transitions between ψ_i and the ground state are forbidden unless ψ_i has the same symmetry type as one or more of the functions x, y or z. Similarly, Raman transitions between ψ_i and the ground state are forbidden unless ψ_i has the same symmetry type as one or more of the functions, x^2, y^2, z^2, xy, xz or yz.

Qualitative Calculations: *The number of distinct fundamental frequencies, their individual degeneracies, symmetry types and selection rules can be determined with relatively little calculation when only the spatial arrangement of the atoms in the molecule has been specified.* The method requires only a character-table for the symmetry group involved. (For a sketch of the reasoning behind the rules, compare the discussion of (5–159), (5–160) below.)

Evaluate the character system‡:

$$\left.\begin{aligned} \chi(C_p) &= (n-2)\,[1 + 2\cos(2\pi/p)] \\ \chi(iC_p) &= \quad -n\,[1 + 2\cos(2\pi/p)] \\ \chi(\sigma_h C_p) &= \quad -n\,[1 - 2\cos(2\pi/p)] \\ \text{where} \quad n &= \text{number of atoms whose centers do not move} \\ &\quad\ \text{under the operation in question.} \end{aligned}\right\} \qquad (5\text{–}158)$$

Using a standard character table, determine by inspection (or using (22–37) if necessary) the irreducible representations contained in (see (22–30)) this character system. Then:

Each irreducible representation (including repeated ones) corresponds to a different fundamental vibration frequency, and conversely.

The dimension $(=\chi(E))$ of the irreducible representation equals the degeneracy of its vibration levels and the symbol, Γ_l, for that representation is the "symmetry-type" or "species" of the fundamental level (only).

The selection rules above state that a (fundamental) frequency associated with the representation Γ_l is:

(a) Infrared inactive unless the "vector" (x, y, z) representation of the group contains Γ_l.

(b) Raman inactive unless the $(x^2, y^2, z^2, xy, xz, yz)$ representation contains Γ_l.

[The "infrared active" and "Raman active" symmetry types are usually noted in the character tables. If not, the vector representation (reducible) may be obtained from (5–158) by omitting the factors, $n-2, n, n$. The "Raman active" representation (also reducible) is given (see (22–39)) by the squares of the vector-representation characters, but only the part obtained by subtracting the axial-vector representation

---

* Except in "X – X" and in molecules with the same symmetry.

† By (5–155), $\psi_{\text{gnd}} = \exp(-\frac{1}{2}\sum \alpha_i Q_i^2)$, which has the same invariance properties as $E_e(N) = \frac{1}{2}\sum \lambda_i Q_i^2$, because $\alpha_i = \alpha_j$ if and only if $\lambda_i = \lambda_j$.

‡ C_p denotes a rotation through angle $2\pi/p$; (note that $C_1 = E$, the identity operation); i denotes an inversion in the center (point) of symmetry; σ_h denotes a reflection in a plane of symmetry (normal to the axis of C_p if $p \neq 1$; any pure plane-reflection has $\chi(\sigma) = n$); "S_p" is often used, but may denote either iC_p or $\sigma_h C_p$.

is of practical importance. The axial-vector representation (to obtain from (5–158), set $n = 1$ and reverse the signs) also determines the "activity" of a fundamental vibration state under magnetic dipole radiation.]

EXAMPLE. A plane XY_3 molecule

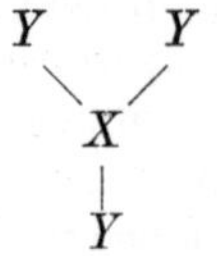

(symmetry group "D_{3h}"). Applying (5–158), the character system of the vibrations is:

Symmetry operators R (schematic):	$\chi(R) =$
Identity E	6
Reflection in plane of molecule σ_h	4
Rotations about axis normal to plane of molecule $2C_3$	0
$2\sigma_h C_3$	-2
Rotations about an X—Y bond $3C_2$	0
Reflections in a plane containing an X—Y bond $3\sigma_v$	2

By standard character tables, this representation contains the irreducible representations usually called A_1', A_2'' (each one-dimensional, occurring once) and E' (two-dimensional, occurs twice). Thus there are four fundamental vibrations:

Fundamental	Symmetry type of fundamental states	Infrared activity	Raman activity	Degeneracy (number of independent ψ)
ν_1	A_1'	no	yes	1
ν_2	A_2''	yes	no	1
ν_3	E'	yes	yes	2
ν_4	E'	yes	yes	2

By the same manipulations, a *pyramid*-shaped XY_3 molecule has four fundamentals with similar degeneracies but all four are both infrared and Raman active.

Detailed Calculations: The step from (5–153) to (5–154) is exceedingly laborious in practice and may be largely avoided as follows. In place of (5–152), set up *symmetry coordinates*, S_i (= linear combinations of the q_i in (5–152))—defined by the property that the group representation generated* by the S_i is (a) completely reduced (has "diagonal block" form), (b) is orthogonal (all matrices real and unitary) and (c) exhibits repeated (irreducible) representations in identical (not merely equivalent) form. [Compare (5–159) for a mathematical statement of these requirements.]

* Any symmetry operation, R, changes the S_i to $S_j' = \sum_i S_i D_{ij}(R)$. The set of matrices $D(R)$ is a "representation" of the symmetry group; it is "equivalent" to the representation generated by the q_i.

[It is also expedient to use only $3N$-6 coordinates, S_i, chosen such that the center-of-mass motion and angular momentum about the center of mass are zero for each S_i. Usually, motions along or normal to chemical bonds are most appropriate.]

Although the setting up of such coordinates,* establishing their relation to Cartesian coordinates, and establishing the corresponding transformations of H is all rather laborious, the saving of later work is quite considerable in view of the following theorem:

In an invariant quadratic form (such as $E_e(N) = U = \sum u_{ij}S_iS_j$ or $T = \sum t_{ij}\dot{S}_i\dot{S}_j$) the coefficients vanish except only when either $i = j$ or S_i and S_j are associated with the *same* row of (different occurrences of) the *same* irreducible representation; moreover, the (diagonal) coefficients within any one irreducible representation are equal as are also all those (off-diagonal) coefficients which connect any one pair of repeated irreducible representations. [Compare (5–160) for a mathematical statement.]

Thus the equations of motion simplify drastically, though not quite so completely as in (5–154).

Example. In the plane XY_3 molecule discussed above, if symmetry coordinates with no net translation of, or rotation about the center-of-mass are adopted, the T and U matrices will take the form,

	A_1'	A_2''	E'		E'	
A_1'	α					
A_2''		β				
E'			γ		ϵ	
				γ		ϵ
E'			ϵ		δ	
				ϵ		δ

Schematic equations of motion are then:

$$\alpha = 0; \qquad \beta = 0; \qquad \begin{vmatrix} \gamma & \epsilon \\ \epsilon & \delta \end{vmatrix} = 0 \qquad \text{(twice)}$$

Ordinary Cartesian coordinates, (5–152), would require diagonalization of a 12-by-12 matrix.

Sketch of Proof: Replace the index, i, on S_i by a compound index (Γ, o, r) where Γ labels the irreducible representation to which $S_{\Gamma or}$ belongs, o labels the occurrence of Γ with which $S_{\Gamma or}$ is associated, and r labels the row of Γ to which $S_{\Gamma or}$ belongs. By construction of the S's, for any group element (symmetry operation), R,

$$RS_{\Gamma or} = \sum_{\rho} S_{\Gamma o \rho} D_{\rho r}{}^{\Gamma}(R) \tag{5–159}$$

* Many cases have been worked out in the literature; see G. Herzberg "*Infrared and Raman Spectra*," D. Van Nostrand (1945) and references therein.

where $D_{\rho r}{}^{\Gamma}$ is some real, unitary form of the irreducible representation Γ (the form not depending on o). Represent U by

$$U = \sum S_{\Gamma or} \langle \Gamma or | u | \Gamma' o' r' \rangle S_{\Gamma' o' r'}$$

The value of U must remain unchanged under every group operation, which replaces $S_{\Gamma or}$ by $RS_{\Gamma or}$. Writing this out, substituting (5–159) and comparing coefficients,

$$\langle \Gamma or | u | \Gamma' o' r' \rangle = \sum_{\rho} \sum_{\rho'} D_{r\rho}{}^{\Gamma}(R) \langle \Gamma o\rho | u | \Gamma' o' \rho' \rangle D^{\Gamma'}_{r'\rho'}(R)$$

for any R. Summing this result over all group elements, R, applying (22–35) and the real, unitary nature (by hypothesis) of the D matrices, one finds

$$\langle \Gamma or | u | \Gamma' o' r' \rangle = \delta_{rr'} \, \delta_{\Gamma\Gamma'} f(\Gamma, o, o') \tag{5–160}$$

as asserted.

This property of both the kinetic energy, T, and the potential energy, U, plus the fact that the *fundamental*-state wavefunctions, according to (5–155), have the same transformation properties as $Q_j = \sum_o \sum_r S_{\Gamma or}$ suffices to establish the rules given under (5–158). [The group representation specified by (5–158) is that of the S's with the translation (vector) and rotation (axial-vector) parts subtracted out.]

Note the distinction: Normal coordinates, Q_i, are essentially unique but they depend on the force constants, u_{ij}; symmetry coordinates, S_i, are not completely unique but are independent of the u_{ij}.

(d) **van der Waals forces:** Given two molecules at a separation, R, large compared to their diameters, each molecule may be analyzed as under (c) above, but there remain, in the complete H operator for the entire system, interaction terms of the form, $\sum e_i e_j / R_{ij}$, between the various particles of the two systems. Since each molecule is electrically neutral and $R_{ij} \doteq R$ in all these terms, the sum is almost zero. Taking $\mathbf{R} = R\hat{z}$, a series expansion gives the form,

$$\Delta H = \frac{e^2}{R^3} \{x_1 x_2 + y_1 y_2 - 2z_1 z_2 + \cdots\} + O(R^{-4}) \tag{5–161}$$

(where only terms arising from two particular electrons are shown explicitly). If the molecules are in their ground (symmetric) states, this perturbation (anti-symmetric in the individual coordinates) will vanish to first order, but the second order change in the total energy will have the form,

$$U_{vdw} = -\frac{A}{R^6} + O\left(\frac{1}{R^8}\right) \tag{5–162}$$

For two hydrogen molecules, ($a_0 = \hbar^2/me^2 = 0.529$ Å)

$$U_{vdw} = -\frac{6e^2 a_0^5}{R^6} - \frac{135 e^2 a_0^7}{R^8} - \frac{1416 e^2 a_0^9}{R^{10}} + \cdots \tag{5–163}$$

while for two helium atoms, A in (5–162) is about $1.4e^2 a_0^5$. ("A" can also be estimated from molecular polarizabilities; see footnote under (6–96).)

In general, however, these coefficients cannot be calculated accurately and a *form* similar to (5–162) must be assumed, with parameters to be evaluated from experiment. Considerable success in fitting data has been attained with the "Lennard-Jones 6-12 potential,"

$$U_{vdw} = -\frac{A}{R^6} + \frac{B}{R^{12}} \tag{5–164}$$

which has the correct leading term and provides for repulsion in close encounters; the exponent "12" has been chosen to give the best agreement with experiment under the greatest variety of conditions. Compare Chapter 6.

D. HIGH-ENERGY QUANTUM MECHANICS

This section merely surveys briefly some highly successful but definitely incomplete and often ambiguous quantum theories of high-energy phenomena. These subjects lie on the boundary of present knowledge concerning fundamental processes, and the present theories must eventually be extended or replaced. Present difficulties lie primarily in the proper blending of quantum theory, electromagnetic theory and relativity. There is as yet no clear-cut evidence as to whether sweeping new concepts are required or merely more powerful mathematical tools which can avoid inappropriate use of perturbation theories.

(a) **Dirac's Relativistic Electron Theory** (*one particle*)

It might appear from the relativistic relation, $E^2 = m^2c^4 + c^2p^2$, that a relativistic wave equation could be obtained by setting $\mathbf{p} = -i\hbar\nabla$ and $E = i\hbar\partial/\partial t$ with the result,

$$-\hbar^2 \frac{\partial^2 \psi}{\partial t^2} = -\hbar^2 c^2 \nabla^2 \psi + m^2 c^4 \psi \tag{5-165}$$

This, however, disagrees* with experiment (hydrogen atom, Compton effect) and also in general requires (second degree in t) that the initial state *and* the "initial rate of transition," $(\partial\psi/\partial t)_0$, both be specified.

Dirac therefore postulated a relativistic wave equation of the first degree in t (and hence, by space-time symmetry, in x, y, z). If $\mathbf{A}$, ϕ are the potentials of any external electromagnetic field† acting on the particle (charge $+e$),

$$i\hbar \frac{\partial \psi}{\partial t} = H\psi = \boldsymbol{\alpha} \cdot [-i\hbar c\nabla - e\mathbf{A}]\boldsymbol{\psi} + (\beta mc^2 + e\phi)\psi \tag{5-166}$$

In order that the classical limit ($\hbar \to 0$) of (5–166) coincide with "classical relativity" ($E^2 = m^2c^4 + c^2p^2$), solutions of (5–166) when $\mathbf{A} = 0 = \phi$ must also be solutions of (5–165); this requires,

$$\alpha_i\alpha_j + \alpha_j\alpha_i = 2\delta_{ij} \qquad (\alpha_0 = \beta; \quad i, j = 0, 1, 2, 3) \tag{5-167}$$

where a unit matrix must be understood‡ to multiply δ_{ij}, for (5–167) cannot be true of simple numbers.

---

* When used to describe electrons; (5–165) is probably correct for charged spin-zero particles if $|\psi|^2$ is interpreted as the net charge density.

† Note that (5–166) is "gauge invariant": the transformation $(\mathbf{A};\ \phi) \to (\mathbf{A} + \nabla f;\ \phi - \partial f/\partial ct)$ which does not change the $(\mathbf{E}, \mathbf{B})$ fields, can be compensated by $\psi \to \psi \exp(ief/\hbar c)$.

‡ It is common to omit such factors throughout. While confusing, such notation is unambiguous and compact, but the reader must be careful not to infer the matrix nature of an equation from any one term.

Thus ψ in (5–166) must be a (column) "vector" and H a matrix of operators; ψ in fact contains four component functions,

$$\psi = \begin{Vmatrix} \psi_1(x, y, z, t) \\ \psi_2(x, y, z, t) \\ \psi_3(x, y, z, t) \\ \psi_4(x, y, z, t) \end{Vmatrix} \tag{5–168}$$

because matrices satisfying (5–167) are unique* to within transformations of the type, $M\alpha_i M^{-1}$. The "representation" commonly used is,

$$\left.\begin{aligned} \alpha_1 = \alpha_x &= \begin{Vmatrix} 0 & 0 & 0 & 1 \\ 0 & 0 & 1 & 0 \\ 0 & 1 & 0 & 0 \\ 1 & 0 & 0 & 0 \end{Vmatrix} \qquad \alpha_2 = \alpha_y = \begin{Vmatrix} 0 & 0 & 0 & -i \\ 0 & 0 & i & 0 \\ 0 & -i & 0 & 0 \\ i & 0 & 0 & 0 \end{Vmatrix} \\ \alpha_3 = \alpha_z &= \begin{Vmatrix} 0 & 0 & 1 & 0 \\ 0 & 0 & 0 & -1 \\ 1 & 0 & 0 & 0 \\ 0 & -1 & 0 & 0 \end{Vmatrix} \qquad \alpha_0 = \beta = \begin{Vmatrix} 1 & 0 & 0 & 0 \\ 0 & 1 & 0 & 0 \\ 0 & 0 & -1 & 0 \\ 0 & 0 & 0 & -1 \end{Vmatrix} \end{aligned}\right\} \tag{5–169}$$

Interpretation of ψ: From (5–166) and its Hermitian conjugate, it follows that

$$\frac{\partial}{\partial t}(\psi^\dagger \psi) + \boldsymbol{\nabla} \cdot (c\psi^\dagger \boldsymbol{\alpha} \psi) = 0 \tag{5–170}$$

[where $\psi^\dagger$ is the row-vector, $(\psi_1^*, \psi_2^*, \psi_3^*, \psi_4^*)$]. Thus $\psi^\dagger\psi = \|\psi\|^2 = |\psi_1|^2 + |\psi_2|^2 + |\psi_3|^2 + |\psi_4|^2$ may be regarded as a probability density and $c\psi^\dagger\boldsymbol{\alpha}\psi$ as a probability current density; these quantities multiplied by e are then the average electric charge and current density.

From the latter, $c\boldsymbol{\alpha}$ would appear to be a velocity operator and indeed, from (5–166) and (5–10),

$$\mathbf{v} = \frac{d\mathbf{r}}{dt} = \frac{1}{i\hbar}\left[\mathbf{r}H - H\mathbf{r}\right] = c\boldsymbol{\alpha} \tag{5–171}$$

[Since $\alpha_i^2 = I$ by (5–167), the only eigenvalues of any component of $\mathbf{v}$ are $\pm c$ (though $|\langle \mathbf{v} \rangle|$ is always less than c). This peculiar behavior is called "Zitterbewegung" and may be connected with the spin effects.]

Angular momentum: Even with $\mathbf{A} = 0$, $\phi = \phi(r)$, the operator $\mathbf{L} = \mathbf{r} \times (-i\hbar\boldsymbol{\nabla})$ does not commute with H in (5–166) but rather one finds

$$\frac{d}{dt}\mathbf{L} = \frac{1}{i\hbar}(\mathbf{L}H - H\mathbf{L}) = c\boldsymbol{\alpha} \times (-i\hbar\boldsymbol{\nabla}) \tag{5–172}$$

If we define,

$$\sigma_x = i\alpha_z\alpha_y; \qquad \sigma_y = i\alpha_x\alpha_z; \qquad \sigma_z = i\alpha_y\alpha_x \tag{5–173}$$

* The matrices, $\alpha_0 = \beta$, α_1, α_2, α_3, and all possible products of them form, in view of (5–167), a finite *group* of 32 elements, and this particular group has only one irreducible, true representation. (The group has 17 classes—namely, I, $-I$, $\pm\alpha_i$, $\pm\alpha_i\alpha_j$, $\pm\alpha_i\alpha_j\alpha_k$, $\pm\alpha_0\alpha_1\alpha_2\alpha_3$, where $i < j < k$—and by (22–34) there must be one four-dimensional and sixteen one-dimensional irreducible representations; only the former can be a "true" representation.)

then it is found that

$$\frac{\hbar}{2}\frac{d\boldsymbol{\sigma}}{dt} = -i\hbar c\boldsymbol{\nabla} \times \boldsymbol{\alpha} \tag{5–174}$$

and thus

$$\frac{d\mathbf{J}}{dt} = \frac{d}{dt}(\mathbf{L} + \tfrac{1}{2}\hbar\boldsymbol{\sigma}) = 0 \tag{5–175}$$

This indicates that the particle has a *spin* whose operators are the matrices, $\frac{1}{2}\hbar\boldsymbol{\sigma} = (-i\hbar/4)(\boldsymbol{\alpha} \times \boldsymbol{\alpha})$. Since by (5–167) and (5–173), $\sigma_z^2 = I$ so that σ_z has eigenvalues, ± 1, it follows that the spin is $\frac{1}{2}$.

Non-relativistic limit: Defining (Pauli spin matrices),

$$s_x = \begin{Vmatrix} 0 & 1 \\ 1 & 0 \end{Vmatrix}; \qquad s_y = \begin{Vmatrix} 0 & -i \\ i & 0 \end{Vmatrix}; \qquad s_z = \begin{Vmatrix} 1 & 0 \\ 0 & -1 \end{Vmatrix} \tag{5–176}$$

and letting,

$$\Phi_{\mathrm{I}} = \begin{Vmatrix} \psi_1 \\ \psi_2 \end{Vmatrix} e^{-imc^2t/\hbar}; \qquad \Phi_{\mathrm{II}} = \begin{Vmatrix} \psi_3 \\ \psi_4 \end{Vmatrix} e^{-imc^2t/\hbar}$$

$$\mathbf{P} = \frac{\hbar}{i}\boldsymbol{\nabla} - \frac{e}{c}\mathbf{A}; \qquad \epsilon = -\hbar\frac{\partial}{\partial t} - ie\phi$$

equation (5–166) can be written as a pair of two-dimensional matrix equations

$$c\mathbf{s}\cdot\mathbf{P}\Phi_{\mathrm{I}} = (2mc^2 - i\epsilon)\Phi_{\mathrm{II}}$$

$$c\mathbf{s}\cdot\mathbf{P}\Phi_{\mathrm{II}} = -i\epsilon\Phi_{\mathrm{I}}$$

Eliminating Φ_{II},

$$\frac{1}{2m}\mathbf{s}\cdot\mathbf{P}\left[1 - \frac{i\epsilon}{2mc^2}\right]^{-1}\mathbf{s}\cdot\mathbf{P}\Phi_{\mathrm{I}} = -i\epsilon\Phi_{\mathrm{I}}$$

Since $\epsilon\Phi$ will be of the order of magnitude of $(E_c + e\phi)\Phi$, where E_c is the classical energy, we may expand the operator, $[1 - i\epsilon/2mc^2]^{-1}$ in a power series. The result is Schroedinger's wave equation (in column-vector notation for spin states) with correction terms,

$$i\hbar\frac{\partial}{\partial t}\Phi_{\mathrm{I}} = \left\{\frac{1}{2m}P^2 + e\phi - \frac{e\hbar}{2mc}\mathbf{s}\cdot\left(\mathbf{B} + \frac{1}{2mc}\mathbf{E}\times\mathbf{P}\right) + i\frac{e\hbar}{4mc}\mathbf{E}\cdot\mathbf{P}\right\}\Phi_{\mathrm{I}} \tag{5–177}$$

(where $\mathbf{P}$ operates only on Φ_{I}). Here the term in $\mathbf{s}$ contains precisely the correct magnetic moment—magnetic field interaction for electrons (the spin operator, $\mathbf{S} = \frac{1}{2}\hbar\mathbf{s}$) and also the spin-orbit interaction, complete with the "Thomas precession" factor of $\frac{1}{2}$.

Rigorous solutions: The hydrogen atom ($\mathbf{A} = 0$, $\phi = e/r$) can be treated by a rather complex transition to polar coordinates in (5–166). The resulting energy levels are

$$E = mc^2\left\{1 + \frac{\alpha^2}{[n' + \sqrt{k^2 - \alpha^2}]^2}\right\}^{-1/2} \tag{5–178}$$

where

$\alpha = e^2/\hbar c = 1/137.036$ (the fine-structure constant)

$n' = 0, 1, 2, \cdots$

$k = \pm 1, \pm 2, \pm 3, \cdots$, except $k < 0$ when $n' = 0$.

The connection with standard atomic notation is

$$|k| + n' = n$$

$$k = l(l+1) - j(j+1) - \tfrac{1}{4} = \begin{cases} l, & \text{when } j = l - \tfrac{1}{2} \\ -l-1, & \text{when } j = l + \tfrac{1}{2} \end{cases}$$

These results check experiment except for a very small correction (Lamb shift) considered later.

The free particle ($\mathbf{A} = 0 = \phi$) is readily treated by (5–166); the solutions are plane waves and it is found that besides the two (spin) states which would be expected with $E = (m^2c^4 + c^2p^2)^{1/2}$, there are two other spin states with $E = -(m^2c^4 + c^2p^2)^{1/2}$. The latter cannot be simply ignored since radiative transitions between any formally available states are always allowed. "Sophisticated" attempts to remove these states from the formalism have all failed to give correct results and it is generally agreed that a qualitatively correct solution is:

Dirac's positron theory: This interpretation of (5–166) holds that, in the "vacuum" state, all the negative energy states are *filled but unobservable*; the Pauli principle then prevents a "normal electron" from dropping to a negative energy state. When sufficient energy ($2mc^2$) is available, one of the latent "electrons" in the negative-energy states can jump to a positive-energy state (becoming observable) while the "hole" acts as a *positron* ($E < 0$ equivalent to $|e| > 0$). This, of course, is indeed observed and, moreover, approximate forms of the theory give *quantitatively correct* results (see pair–creation, Compton scattering, etc.). The main formal reservation is that this theory intrinsically involves many particles and we do not yet know the correct wave equation for even two particles. (The main difficulty lies in the lack of a concept of simultaneity in relativity.)

Other particles: At present writing, the anti-proton and anti-neutron have been found, and it appears likely that the proton and probably the (unstable) neutron also satisfy the Dirac equation (spin $\frac{1}{2}$). Their magnetic moments are not correctly given by (5–166) as it stands, but Pauli has observed that a term,

$$-\Lambda\beta\boldsymbol{\sigma}\cdot\mathbf{B} + i\Lambda\beta\boldsymbol{\alpha}\cdot\mathbf{E} \tag{5–179}$$

may be added to H in (5–166) without changing any of its formal properties; (5–179) introduces an additional magnetic moment, $\Lambda\boldsymbol{\sigma}$, which can be adjusted to the experimental value by proper choice of Λ.

The neutrino also appears to be closely connected with (5–166); its mass may very well be exactly zero, in which case the term involving β disappears and only three idempotent, anti-commuting matrices (equation (5–167)) are required. These *need* be only two-dimensional and in fact we may take* for the free particle,

$$i\hbar\frac{\partial\psi}{\partial t} = -i\hbar c\mathbf{s}\cdot\nabla\psi \qquad \text{where} \qquad \psi = \begin{Vmatrix} \psi_1 \\ \psi_2 \end{Vmatrix} \tag{5–180}$$

This equation does not conserve parity (is not invariant under space-inversion; see remark following (5–40)), but it is now known that at least some reactions involving neutrinos do not conserve parity (first suggested by Yang and Lee).

---

* This choice is "essentially unique"; there is another set not expressible as $M\mathbf{s}M^{-1}$ but they merely involve changing the sign of i.

For a given momentum, $\mathbf{p}$, (plane waves), the energy and spin along $\mathbf{p}$ are given by

$$E = c(\mathbf{s}\cdot\mathbf{p}), \qquad 2s_p = (\mathbf{s}\cdot\mathbf{p})/p$$

hence (5–181)

$$E = cps_p = \pm\tfrac{1}{2}pc$$

A neutrino ($E > 0$) would thus have spin parallel to its momentum and an antineutrino ($E < 0$) would have spin opposite to its momentum.

Equations (5–180)–(5–181) are basic to the "two-component" theory of the neutrino. At present writing, it is not clear whether this simple theory is adequate.

Transformation (tensor) properties: For formal work, it is convenient to define a new set of matrices (*not* Hermitian),

$$\left.\begin{aligned} \gamma^\mu &= (-i\beta\boldsymbol{\alpha}, \beta) \qquad \text{with} \qquad \mu = 1, 2, 3, 4 \\ \gamma^5 &= \gamma^1\gamma^2\gamma^3\gamma^4 \end{aligned}\right\} \tag{5–182}$$

which are anticommuting and idempotent:

$$\gamma^\mu\gamma^\nu + \gamma^\nu\gamma^\mu = 2\delta_{\mu\nu} \tag{5–183}$$

Then, multiplying (5–166) on the left by β (and adding $\beta\cdot$(5–179)), the result, using the summation convention, is

$$\gamma^\mu\left[\hbar c\,\frac{\partial}{\partial x^\mu} - ie\phi_\mu\right]\psi + mc^2\psi + \frac{i\Lambda}{2}F_{\mu\nu}\gamma^\mu\gamma^\nu\psi = 0 \tag{5–184}$$

(where $x^4 = ict$; $\phi_\mu = (\mathbf{A}, i\phi)$; $F_{\mu\nu}$ is the electromagnetic field tensor defined in (4–7)).

To demonstrate the Lorentz invariance of (5–184), note that a linear transformation, $\bar{x}^\mu = C^\mu{}_\rho x^\rho$, changes ψ to $\Phi(\bar{x}) = \psi(x)$ and essentially replaces γ^μ by $\Gamma^\alpha = C^\alpha{}_\mu\gamma^\mu$ which satisfy (5–183) because $C^\mu{}_\alpha C^\nu{}_\alpha = \delta_{\mu\nu}$ (orthogonality of Lorentz transformations; $dx^\mu\,dx^\mu$ invariant). But matrices satisfying (5–183) are essentially unique [see footnote to (5–168)] in the sense that there is a (unique) matrix, S, such that

$$\Gamma^\alpha = \frac{\partial\bar{x}^\alpha}{\partial x^\rho}\gamma^\rho = S^{-1}\gamma^\alpha S \tag{5–185}$$

Thus, if we set

$$\bar{\psi}(\bar{x}) = S\Phi(\bar{x}) = S\psi(x) \tag{5–186}$$

then $\bar{\psi}(\bar{x})$ satisfies the *same* equation as $\psi(x)$ and the eigenvalues, etc. must be unchanged. Equations (5–185) and (5–186) specify how a given state function appears when viewed from several coordinate systems, *provided* the same representation, (5–169), is used for $\boldsymbol{\alpha}$, β, γ^μ in all systems (which is the common convention).

It may be verified that,

(5–187):

For space reflection ($\mathbf{r} \to -\mathbf{r}$):

$$S = \gamma^4$$

For $\bar{x}^\mu = x^\mu + \epsilon^\mu{}_\nu x^\nu + O(\epsilon^2)$ with $\epsilon^\mu{}_\nu = -\epsilon^\nu{}_\mu$:

$$S = I + \tfrac{1}{4}\epsilon^\mu{}_\nu\gamma^\mu\gamma^\nu + O(\epsilon^2)$$

In particular, it follows* that

For rotation about the z-axis by angle ϕ:

$$S = \cos\tfrac{1}{2}\phi + \gamma_1\gamma_2\sin\tfrac{1}{2}\phi$$

For moving axes ($\bar{x} = x\cosh\chi - ct\sinh\chi$; $\dfrac{v}{c} = \tanh\chi$):

$$S = \cosh\tfrac{1}{2}\chi - i\gamma_1\gamma_4\sinh\tfrac{1}{2}\chi$$

* From the theory of Lie groups, Chapter 22.

If we define,

$$\psi^{\ddagger} = i\psi^{\dagger}\gamma^4 = i\psi^{\dagger}\beta \tag{5–188}$$

which satisfies (5–184) with all matrices, γ^{μ}, written to the right of $\psi^{\ddagger}$, analogous arguments show,

$$\bar{\psi}^{\ddagger}(\bar{x}) = \psi^{\ddagger}(x)S^{-1} \tag{5–189}$$

From (5–185), (5–186), (5–189) it follows that (*provided* the representation (5–169) is used in all coordinates):

$$\psi^{\ddagger}\psi = i\psi^{\dagger}\beta\psi \text{ is an invariant (a scalar)}$$

$$\psi^{\ddagger}\gamma^{\mu}\psi = (\psi^{\dagger}\boldsymbol{\alpha}\psi;\ i\psi^{\dagger}\psi) \text{ is a four-vector}$$

$$(1 - \delta_{\mu\nu})\psi^{\ddagger}\gamma^{\mu}\gamma^{\nu}\psi \text{ is an antisymmetric tensor}$$

$$(1 - \delta_{\mu\nu})(1 - \delta_{\mu\rho})(1 - \delta_{\nu\rho})\psi^{\ddagger}\gamma^{\mu}\gamma^{\nu}\gamma^{\rho}\psi \text{ is a completely antisymmetric tensor (a pseudo-vector)}$$

$$\psi^{\ddagger}\gamma^5\psi \text{ is a pseudo-scalar}$$

(Note that $\psi^{\ddagger}\gamma^{\mu} = \psi^{\dagger}\alpha^{\mu}$ if $\alpha^4 = i$.)

These expressions are useful for setting up possible, relativistically correct coupling energies between two Dirac-type wave fields—for example in theories of beta decay.

(b) Electromagnetic Radiation

Consider the purely radiative fields ("transverse" field*; solutions with $\rho = 0 = \mathbf{J}$) in a large box with reflecting walls. Radiative fields can be completely represented by a vector potential (compare (3–39)).

$$\nabla^2\mathbf{A} - \frac{1}{c^2}\frac{\partial^2\mathbf{A}}{\partial t^2} = 0; \qquad \nabla \cdot \mathbf{A} = 0 \tag{5–190}$$

with the boundary conditions, $\mathbf{n} \cdot \mathbf{A} = 0$ at the reflecting walls. [Sometimes, as for the free particle, *periodic* boundary conditions in an array of cubic boxes are more convenient; the formal results are the same, and the functions $\mathbf{A}_{\lambda}$ below have the form,

$$\mathbf{A}_{\lambda} = \sqrt{4\pi c^2/L^3}\,\mathbf{e}_{\lambda} \exp(i\mathbf{k}_{\lambda} \cdot \mathbf{r}) \tag{5–191}$$

where $k_{\lambda} = \omega_{\lambda}/c$; $\mathbf{e}_{\lambda} \cdot \mathbf{k}_{\lambda} = 0$, $e_{\lambda} = 1$ and L is the side of a typical box.]

Solutions of the problem (5–190) are a series of normal modes (eigenfunctions), each with a characteristic frequency, $\nu_l = \omega_l/2\pi$ (eigenvalues):

$$\mathbf{A} = \sum_l \mathbf{A}_l(x, y, z)q_l(t); \qquad \nabla^2\mathbf{A}_l + (\omega_l/c)^2\mathbf{A}_l = 0 \tag{5–192}$$

$$\frac{d^2q_l}{dt^2} + \omega_l^2 q_l = 0 \tag{5–193}$$

The mode-patterns, $\mathbf{A}_l(\mathbf{r})$, are (or may be chosen) orthogonal and if we choose the normalization,

$$\iiint_V \mathbf{A}_l^*(\mathbf{r}) \cdot \mathbf{A}_m(\mathbf{r})\, dx\, dy\, dz = 4\pi c^2\, \delta_{lm} \tag{5–194}$$

* The remaining, "longitudinal" part can also be quantized by considerable extension and some alteration of the formalism. Photons, in the usual sense, can occur only in the radiative field.

then the total (radiant) field energy in the resonator is given by (integrate by parts):

$$\mathscr{H}_{\text{rad}} = \frac{1}{8\pi}\iiint\{|\mathbf{E}|^2 + |\mathbf{B}|^2\}\, dx\, dy\, dz = \sum_l \tfrac{1}{2}(\dot{q}_l^{\,2} + \omega_l^{\,2} q_l^{\,2}) \tag{5–195}$$

The mode patterns, $\mathbf{A}_l(\mathbf{r})$, depend only on the shape of the resonator box; with these given, the *field* itself is completely specified by the "coordinates," $q_l(t)$. Thus (Jeans' theorem), the radiant field is equivalent to a set of independent harmonic oscillators, (5–193).

The radiation field in a box is thus equivalent to the system treated quantum mechanically in (5–151)–(5–156). Since there are infinitely many "oscillators" (5–193) in the present case, the energy sum, (5–156), diverges even if all $n_i = 0$, but, as this "zero point energy" is necessarily unobservable, it is simply subtracted off* and the allowed energies become,

$$E = \sum_l n_l(\hbar\omega_l) \qquad (\text{each } n_l = 0, 1, 2, \cdots) \tag{5–196}$$

The quantum state of the field is specified by the number of photons, n_l, of each type, l. The photon concept is particularly striking if cubic boxes with periodic boundary conditions are used, for then the classical electromagnetic momentum [(3–6) and remarks thereafter] may be reduced to

$$\mathbf{P}_{\text{rad}} = \frac{1}{4\pi c}\iiint \mathbf{E} \times \mathbf{H}\, dV = \sum_l n_l \hbar \mathbf{k}_l \tag{5–197}$$

where $\mathbf{k}_l$ is the propagation ("wave") vector of the lth traveling wave mode ($k_l = \omega_l/c$). Note that for a single photon, $E_l^{\,2} - c^2 p_l^{\,2} = 0$, as is relativistically correct for a "particle" with zero mass. (The "longitudinal," non-radiative photons do not have this "particle" property.)

From (5–155), the matrix elements of q_l between two quantum states $(n_1, n_2, \cdots)$ and $(m_1, m_2, \cdots)$ vanish except when $m_l = n_l \pm 1$ and all other $m_i = n_i$:

$$\langle n_1, n_2, \cdots |q_l|\, m_1, m_2, \cdots \rangle = \sqrt{\frac{\hbar}{2\omega_l}}\,(\delta_{m_l, n_{l+1}}\sqrt{n_l + 1} + \delta_{m_l, n_{l-1}}\sqrt{n_l}) \prod_{i \neq l} \delta_{m_i n_i} \tag{5–198}$$

Applications of the theory are simplest in matrix-mechanics formalism. For such calculations, the following *non-Hermitian* operators are often used.

$$a_l = \frac{1}{2}\left(q_l + \frac{i}{\omega_l}\dot{q}_l\right); \quad a_l^{\dagger} = \frac{1}{2}\left(q_l - \frac{i}{\omega_l}\dot{q}_l\right) \tag{5–199}$$

By (5–198), they have as their only non-zero matrix elements,

$$\langle n_l - 1\, |a_l|\, n_l\rangle = \langle n_l\, |a_l^{\dagger}|\, n_l - 1\rangle = \sqrt{\hbar n_l/2\omega_l} \tag{5–200}$$

* This particular subtraction can be disguised by formally using (5–12) with $f = t\sum \hbar\omega_l$ so that $H'' = \sum \frac{1}{2}(\dot{q}_l^2 + \omega_l^2 q_l^2 - \hbar\omega_l)$ in (5–14). The classical limit ($\hbar \to 0$) is unaffected. This is only the first of the infinity-subtractions with which quantum field theory is currently plagued.

(schematically; $n_i = m_i$ for $i \neq l$ understood) and they satisfy,

$$\left.\begin{array}{r} a_l a_k^\dagger - a_k^\dagger a_l = (\hbar/2\omega_l)\,\delta_{lk} \\ a_l a_k - a_k a_l = 0; \qquad a_l^\dagger a_k^\dagger - a_k^\dagger a_l^\dagger = 0 \end{array}\right\} \tag{5–201}$$

[as follows from (5–200); conversely, (5–201) implies (5–200) as may be shown by algebraic arguments similar to those under (5–33)].

By (5–200), a_l converts a state with n_l photons into a state with $n_l - 1$ photons of type l, and a_l is therefore called an anihilation (or photon absorbing) operator; similarly, $a_l^\dagger$ is a creation (or photon emitting) operator for photons of the lth mode.

Low-energy (optical) interactions with matter: First regard the radiation field and "molecule" as independent systems; the quantum states are then given by (5–27)–(5–29): symbolically, $(N, n_1, n_2, n_3, \cdots, n_l, \cdots)$ where N denotes the molecular state. Then regard the (first order) interaction energy, (5–57), as a perturbation on the compound system:

$$\Delta H = \frac{-1}{c}\,\dot{\mathbf{P}} \cdot \mathbf{A} = \frac{-1}{c}\,\dot{\mathbf{P}} \sum_l \mathbf{A}_l q_l \tag{5–202}$$

where $\mathbf{P} = \sum_j e_j \mathbf{r}_j$ is the electric dipole moment operator for the molecule.

By (5–198), the matrix elements of (5–202) (with respect to the unperturbed states) vanish unless *precisely one* $n_l' = n_l \pm 1$ (all others being unchanged) and thus only one term in the sum (5–202) survives. Schematically,

$$\langle F, n_l - 1|\Delta H|I, n_l\rangle = \langle F, n_l|\,\Delta H|I, n_l - 1\rangle = \frac{-1}{c}\,\langle F|\dot{\mathbf{P}} \cdot \mathbf{A}_l|I\rangle \sqrt{\frac{\hbar n_l}{2\omega_l}} \tag{5–203}$$

Squaring, averaging over all orientations of $\dot{\mathbf{P}}$ (compare (5–60)) and replacing $|\mathbf{A}_l|^2$ by its average value* from (5–194), the result may be rewritten, using (5–198) again,

$$|\langle F, n_1, \cdots|\Delta H|I, m_1, \cdots\rangle|^2_{\text{Avg}} = \frac{4\pi}{3V}\,|\langle F|\dot{\mathbf{P}}|I\rangle|^2 \sum_l |\langle n_1, \cdots|q_l|\,m_1, \cdots\rangle|^2 \tag{5–204}$$

(where V is the volume of the resonator confining the electromagnetic field; the sum actually contains at most one non-zero term). By time-dependent perturbation theory, (compare (5–80), (5–81)), the probability of a transition, $\alpha \to \beta$, in time t is $\{2 \sin [t(E_\beta - E_\alpha)/2\hbar]/[E_\beta - E_\alpha]\}^2 \cdot |\langle\beta|\Delta H|\alpha\rangle|^2$. The total probability of a molecular transition, $I \to F$, is therefore, using (5–198),

$$\mathscr{P}(I \to F) = \frac{2|\langle F|\dot{\mathbf{P}}|I\rangle|^2}{3\pi\hbar V}\left\{\sum_l \frac{n_l}{\nu_l}\left[\frac{\sin \pi(\nu_{FI} + \nu_l)t}{\nu_{FI} + \nu_l}\right]^2 + \sum_l \frac{n_l + 1}{\nu_l}\left[\frac{\sin \pi(\nu_{FI} - \nu_l)t}{\nu_{FI} - \nu_l}\right]^2\right\} \tag{5–205}$$

[where ν_{FI} is defined by (5–67)]. The terms of the sums are large only in a narrow range where $\nu_l \doteqdot \nu_{FI}$; moreover, if the box, V, is large enough, the ν_l will be so closely spaced that the sums may be replaced by integrals. The radiation energy density function, $\rho(\nu)$, will then be given by

$$\rho(\nu)\,d\nu = (1/V)\sum_{d\nu} n_l(h\nu_l) \qquad (\text{sum over } \nu_l \text{ in } \nu \pm \tfrac{1}{2}\,d\nu)$$

* This step assumes that $\mathbf{A}_l$ is constant over the molecule and restricts the results to low-energy quanta (optical region).

Noting that,* by (19–5), as $V \to \infty$

$$(1/V)\sum_{d\nu} \nu_l = (8\pi\nu^3/c^3)\,d\nu$$

we find:

$$\mathscr{P}(I \to F) = \frac{2\omega_{FI}{}^2|\mathbf{P}_{FI}|^2}{3\pi\hbar^2}\left\{\int \frac{\rho(\nu)}{\nu^2}\left[\frac{\sin \pi(\nu_{FI} + \nu)t}{\nu_{FI} + \nu}\right]^2 d\nu + \int \frac{\rho(\nu) + (8\pi h\nu^3/c^3)}{\nu^2}\left[\frac{\sin \pi(\nu_{FI} - \nu)t}{\nu_{FI} - \nu}\right]^2 d\nu\right\} \tag{5–206}$$

whence for absorption ($\nu_{FI} = -\nu$; first integral dominant),

$$\text{Rate } (I \to F) = \frac{\mathscr{P}(I \to F)}{t} = \frac{8\pi^3}{3h^2}|\mathbf{P}_{FI}|^2\,\rho(\nu) \tag{5–207}$$

in agreement with (5–64). For emission ($\nu_{FI} = \nu$):

$$\text{Rate } (I \to F) = \frac{8\pi^3}{3h^2}|\mathbf{P}_{FI}|^2\left\{\rho(\nu) + \frac{8\pi h\nu^3}{c^3}\right\} \tag{5–208}$$

where the first term is the *stimulated* emission, and the second, the *spontaneous* emission. (In a steady state, emission must balance absorption and the argument preceding (5–65) may be used to derive Planck's radiation law from (5–207), (5–208) and the Boltzmann distribution for the molecules.)

(c) Some Results

High energy phenomena necessarily involve primarily scattering processes and usually relatively few particles. Virtually the only currently useful technique of calculation is based on perturbation theory, (5–80)–(5–81). The computations are often very lengthy and we either sketch the procedure or merely give the results. All results have checked experiment to date.

(1) **Photoelectric absorption** (of soft gamma-rays by bound electrons): Any sufficiently energetic photon can give all its energy to a *bound* electron since a continuum of free-electron states is available (the atom must carry off the excess momentum). The probability is greatest for the most tightly bound† electrons (K shell or $(1s)^2$ electrons). The perturbation matrix elements are given by (5–203) wherein we take $\mathbf{A}_l$ to be a traveling wave (see (5–191)), $n_l = 1$, and $\dot{\mathbf{P}}/e$ is the electron velocity. The initial electron state is given (non-relativistically) by (5–124) and the final state (approximately) by (5–96) and the density of such states by (5–82).

$$\psi_I(\mathbf{r}) = \sqrt{\frac{Z^3}{\pi a_0{}^3}}\,e^{-Zr/a_0}; \qquad \psi_F(\mathbf{r}) = \frac{e^{i\mathbf{p}\cdot\mathbf{r}/\hbar}}{L^{3/2}}; \qquad \rho = \frac{mL^3}{h^3}\,p\sin\theta\,d\theta\,d\phi \tag{5–209}$$

Inserting all these into (5–203) and (5–80), etc. the final result can be written as a cross section for ejection of the electron into a solid angle, $d\Omega$, centered at angle θ from the photon momentum, $\mathbf{k}$,

$$d\sigma = \left(\frac{e^2}{mc^2}\right)^2 \frac{Z^5}{(\hbar c/e^2)^4}\left(\frac{mc}{k}\right)^{7/2} \frac{4\sqrt{2}\sin^2\theta\cos^2\phi}{[1 - (v/c)\cos\theta]^4}\,d\Omega \tag{5–210}$$

where ϕ is the angle between the planes $(\mathbf{p}, \mathbf{k})$ and $(\mathbf{k}, \mathbf{A})$ [$\mathbf{A}$ has the direction of $\mathbf{E}$, the polarization of the photon]. Since $v/c \ll 1$, since there are two K-electrons per

* Recall that there are two polarizations of $\mathbf{A}$ for each eigenvalue, ν_l.

† Assuming the gamma-ray energy is sufficient.

atom, and since the other electrons (mainly L-shell) give about 25% additional absorption, the total cross section per atom (nuclear charge Z) is approximately,

$$\sigma_k \doteqdot \sigma_T \alpha^4 Z^5 5\sqrt{2}\left(\frac{mc^2}{h\nu}\right)^{7/2} = \sigma_T \frac{80}{\alpha^3 Z^2}\left(\frac{I}{h\nu}\right)^{7/2} \tag{5–211}$$

where,

$$\sigma_T = (8\pi/3)(e^2/mc^2)^2 = 0.6653 \times 10^{-24}\ \text{cm}^2$$
$$\text{(Thomson cross section)}$$
$$\alpha = e^2/\hbar c = 1/137.036$$
$$I = K\text{-shell ionization potential}$$
$$\doteqdot \tfrac{1}{2}\alpha^2 Z^2 mc^2 = Z^2(13{\cdot}6\ \text{ev})$$

Several further corrections to this result (relativistic Dirac wave functions; more accurate continuum functions, etc.) lead to the more accurate formula for the total cross section per atom,

$$\sigma_k = \sigma_T \frac{15}{8}\alpha^4 Z^5 f(\xi)\left(\frac{mc^2}{h\nu}\right)^5 G(\gamma)\exp\left[2(\alpha Z)^2(1 - \ln \alpha Z) - \pi\alpha Z\right] \tag{5–212}$$

where

$$G(\gamma) = (\gamma^2 - 1)^{3/2}\left[\frac{4}{3} + \frac{\gamma(\gamma-2)}{\gamma+1}\left(1 - \frac{1}{2\gamma\sqrt{\gamma^2-1}}\ln\frac{\gamma+\sqrt{\gamma^2-1}}{\gamma-\sqrt{\gamma^2-1}}\right)\right]$$
$$\gamma = 1 + (h\nu/mc^2) = 1/\sqrt{1 - v^2/c^2}$$
$$f(\xi) = 2\pi\sqrt{I/h\nu}\,\frac{\exp\left[-4\xi \operatorname{arccot} \xi\right]}{1 - \exp(-2\pi\xi)}$$
$$\xi = \sqrt{I/(h\nu - I)}$$

Photoelectric absorption is of dominant importance for low energy photons (below 80 kev in water, below 500 kev in lead). Equations (5–211) and (5–212), of course, are inapplicable below the K-absorption edge ($h\nu < I$).

Wheeler and Fireman, using the Thomas–Fermi atom model, have calculated that, in the region (13·6 ev) $\gamma < h\nu < I/\gamma$ where γ is of the order of 2 or 3, the photoelectric cross section per atom is given approximately by

$$\sigma_{\text{ph}} = \text{Min}\left[2, \frac{1}{20Z^2}\left(\frac{I}{h\nu}\right)^2\right] \times 10^{-16}\ \text{cm}^2$$

where "Min" denotes "the smaller of".

(2) **Compton scattering** (of gamma rays by free electrons): Using the Dirac equation for the electron, the interaction energy is given by (5–202) and (5–203) with $\dot{\mathbf{P}} = ec\boldsymbol{\alpha}$. Since $\mathbf{A}_l$ and the electron wavefunctions all have "free particle" form, $\exp(i\mathbf{p}\cdot\mathbf{r}/\hbar)$, the matrix elements (5–203) will vanish unless the total momentum is the same in the two states, but (compare (5–17) and (5–18)) energy cannot be conserved unless two photons of different frequencies are involved. Thus, by (5–203), the first-order perturbation vanishes and the second part of (5–81) must be used. Since *each* matrix element (5–203) conserves momentum, there are only two types of intermediate states, ϕ_l in (5–81) (eight values of l because the Dirac equation has four states with a given momentum). Namely, (I) absorption of the incoming photon

followed by emission of the outgoing photon; (II) emission of the outgoing photon followed by absorption of the incoming photon.

(The above description allows negative-energy intermediate states and gives the empirically correct result. Dirac positron theory forbids such states but gives exactly the same expression with a different picture of the intermediate states: (I) The incoming photon is absorbed and a pair created; then the positron annihilates with the original electron, emitting the outgoing photon; (II) the outgoing photon is first emitted and a pair created; the positron and original electron annihilate, absorbing the momentum of the initial photon.)

The final result is expressible as a cross section for photon scattering into the solid angle, $d\Omega$, with reduction of photon energy from $h\nu_0$ to $h\nu$ (Klein–Nishina formula):

$$d\sigma_c = \left(\frac{e^2}{2mc^2}\right)^2 \left(\frac{\nu}{\nu_0}\right)^2 \left[\frac{\nu_0}{\nu} + \frac{\nu}{\nu_0} - 2 + 4\cos^2\psi\right] d\Omega \tag{5–213}$$

where ψ is the angle between the polarizations of the two photons.* Note that ν depends on the scattering angle through (5–17) and the electron scattering angle is given by (5–18). If polarizations are ignored (averaged), replace $(-2 + 4\cos^2\psi)$ in (5–213) by $(-\sin^2\theta)$ where θ is the scattering angle of the photon and multiply by two.

Expressing ν in terms of θ,

$$d\sigma_c = \left(\frac{e^2}{mc^2}\right)^2 \frac{1+\cos^2\theta}{2(1+\xi)^2}\left\{1 + \frac{\xi^2}{(1+\xi)(1+\cos^2\theta)}\right\} d\Omega \tag{5–214}$$

where

$$\xi = (h\nu_0/mc^2)(1 - \cos\theta); \qquad [e^2/mc^2 = 2.82 \times 10^{-13}\ \text{cm}]$$

The total cross section per electron is the integral over all angles:

$$\sigma_c = \frac{3}{4}\sigma_T\left\{\frac{1+\gamma}{\gamma^3}\left[\frac{2\gamma(1+\gamma)}{1+2\gamma} - \ln(1+2\gamma)\right] + \frac{1}{2\gamma}\ln(1+2\gamma) - \frac{1+3\gamma}{(1+2\gamma)^2}\right\} \tag{5–215}$$

where

$$\sigma_T = 0.665 \times 10^{-24}\ \text{cm}^2; \qquad \gamma = h\nu_0/mc^2$$

These various results are often quoted in various alternative forms; for example, the scattered *intensity* distribution is (5–214) multiplied by $(1+\xi)^{-1}$.

Compton scattering dominates at intermediate gamma-ray energies (0.08 to 20 Mev in water; 0.5 to 5 Mev in lead).

(3) **Pair production** ($\gamma \rightarrow e^+ + e^-$; $h\nu > 2mc^2 = 1.02$ Mev): This process can occur only in the field of a charged particle, which carries off the excess momentum. For pair production near a nucleus, if plane wave functions are used throughout, then the "perturbation" energy is $\Delta H + V$ where $V = Ze^2/r$ is the electron-positron potential in the (fixed) nuclear Coulomb field and ΔH is the electron-radiation interaction, given by (5–203) with $\dot{\mathbf{P}} = ec\boldsymbol{\alpha}$. Since (as noted under (2)) the matrix elements of ΔH vanish unless momentum is conserved, whereas those of V vanish unless the radiation field remains unchanged, pair production is also a second-order effect, and the second part of (5–81) applies. (In fact, the numerators take the forms, $\langle F|V|l\rangle\langle l|\Delta H|I\rangle$ and $\langle F|\Delta H|l\rangle\langle l|V|I\rangle$.) As in (2), only eight intermediate states

* (5–213) has already been averaged over the initial electron spin and summed over the final spin states.

13

can occur. The process differs only slightly in formalism from Bremsstrahlung ((4) below) and the main results are usually taken over directly from that formalism. The results are subject to several corrections (better wave functions, screening by atomic electrons, etc.).

We quote only results valid in the important range where *all energies are large compared to* mc^2 ($= 0.511$ Mev).

$$\frac{d\sigma_{pp}}{4\bar{\sigma}(\zeta/h^3\nu^3)\, dE_+} = \begin{cases} \ln(2E_+E_-/h\nu mc^2) - \frac{1}{2} - \frac{1}{2}Q(Z), \\ \qquad \text{if } (2E_+E_-/h\nu mc^2) \ll 1/\alpha Z^{1/3} \\ \ln(183/Z^{1/3}) - \frac{1}{2}Q(Z) - E_+E_-/9\zeta \\ \qquad \text{if } (2E_+E_-/h\nu mc^2) \gg 1/\alpha Z^{1/3} \end{cases} \tag{5–216}$$

where

$$Q(Z) = \begin{cases} 2.414(\alpha Z)^2, & \text{if } \alpha Z \ll 1 \\ 0.67, & \text{for } Z = 82 \end{cases}$$

$$\zeta = E_+{}^2 + E_-{}^2 + \tfrac{2}{3}E_+E_-$$

$$\bar{\sigma} = \alpha Z(Z + 0.8)(e^2/mc^2)^2 = Z(Z + 0.8) \times 5.79 \times 10^{-28}\ \text{cm}^2$$

The positron and electron energies, E_+ and E_-, are relativistic (include rest energy); $E_+ + E_- = h\nu$. A correction (the "0.8") for pair production near the atomic electrons has been included in $\bar{\sigma}$.

The total cross sections per atom are

$$\sigma_{pp} = \begin{cases} \bar{\sigma}\left[\frac{28}{9}\ln\frac{2h\nu}{mc^2} - \frac{218}{27} - \frac{14}{9}Q(Z)\right], & \text{if } \frac{h\nu}{2mc^2} \ll \frac{1}{\alpha Z^{1/3}} \\ \bar{\sigma}\left[\frac{28}{9}\ln\frac{183}{Z^{1/3}} - \frac{2}{27} - \frac{14}{9}Q(Z)\right], & \text{if } \frac{h\nu}{2mc^2} \gg \frac{1}{\alpha Z^{1/3}} \end{cases} \tag{5–217}$$

Pair production is dominant for high energy gamma rays (above 20 Mev in water; above 5 Mev in lead).

(4) **Bremsstrahlung*:** This is the quantum theory of electromagnetic radiation from electrons accelerated (scattered) by charged particles.† The process is mathematically the inverse of pair production (except for a change in sign of the energy of the final electron state and a change in the density-of-states factors). Again, numerous corrections are needed to the simple theory which uses Dirac plane-wave functions. Some results are:

Differential cross section for electron scattering, $\mathbf{p}_0 \rightarrow \mathbf{p}$, accompanied by photon emission with momentum $\mathbf{k}$, at low electron energies,

$$d\sigma_B = \frac{2\alpha Z^2 e^4}{\pi c^2}\frac{d\nu}{\nu}\frac{p}{p_0}\frac{\sin\theta\, d\theta \sin\theta_0\, d\theta_0\, d\phi}{|\mathbf{p} - \mathbf{p}_0|^4}\frac{\xi}{\xi_0} \times \frac{1 - e^{-2\pi\xi_0}}{1 - e^{-2\pi\xi}}\{p^2\sin^2\theta + p_0{}^2\sin^2\theta_0 - 2pp_0\sin\theta\sin\theta_0\cos\phi\} \tag{5–218}$$

where

$\theta_0 = \text{angle}\ (\mathbf{k}, \mathbf{p}_0)$; $\qquad \theta = \text{angle}\ (\mathbf{k}, \mathbf{p})$

$\phi = \text{angle between the planes}\ (\mathbf{k}, \mathbf{p}_0)\ \text{and}\ (\mathbf{k}, \mathbf{p})$

$\xi_0 = Ze^2/\hbar v_0$; $\qquad \xi = Ze^2/\hbar v = Ze^2 m/\hbar p$

* German for "deceleration radiation" (Bremse: "brake").

† This electron scattering is often called a "free-free transition"—particularly when the resultant photon lies in the optical region.

This expression diverges as $\nu \to 0$ because of approximations; the energy radiated, however, is finite.

At extreme relativistic electron energies, the angular distribution takes the form (E_0 = initial total relativistic energy of the electron),

$$\{\ln [1 + (\theta_0 mc^2/E_0)^2] + A\} \frac{\theta_0 \, d\theta_0}{[\theta_0{}^2 + (mc^2/E_0)^2]^2} \tag{5–219}$$

The frequency distribution (per unit $d\nu$) of the radiation is very roughly uniform (to about a factor of two over the possible range) at both low and high incident electron energies.

The energy-loss cross section per atom (defined by $dE/dx = -N\sigma_{\text{rad}}E$, where N = atoms/cm³ and E is the *total* relativistic energy) is

$$\sigma_{\text{rad}} = \begin{cases} \frac{16}{3}\bar{\sigma}, \text{ at low energies } (10\% \text{ for } E - mc^2 < \frac{1}{2}\text{Mev}) \\ \bar{\sigma}\{4 \ln (183/Z^{1/3}) + \frac{2}{9} - 2Q(Z)\}, \\ \quad \text{at very high energies } (10\% \text{ for } E - mc^2 > 200 \text{ Mev}) \end{cases} \tag{5–220}$$

[For $\bar{\sigma}$ and $Q(Z)$, see (5–216).] The quantity $1/N\sigma_{\text{rad}}$ is called the "radiation length".

Bremsstrahlung accounts for almost all the energy lost by electrons with extremely high energies (above 10 Mev in lead; above 1000 Mev in water). At low energies, it constitutes "continuous" X-ray emission. From (5–220), a plasma at temperature T and with n_e electrons and n_i ions (of charge Ze), both per unit volume, will radiate energy at the following rate per unit volume.

$$\begin{aligned} P &= -n_e \, dE/dt = n_e n_i v \, mc^2(16\bar{\sigma}/3) \\ &= Z^2 n_e n_i \sqrt{kT} \, (0.54 \times 10^{-30} \text{ watt cm}^3/\text{kev}^{1/2}) \end{aligned}$$

Ionization Loss: For completeness, we quote here formulas for electron energy loss by ionizing collisions (the dominant process when radiation loss is small). For low energies,

$$-\left(\frac{dE}{dx}\right)_{\text{coll}} = NZ\sigma_T mc^2 \frac{3mc^2}{4T}\left[\ln \frac{T}{IZ\sqrt{2}} + \frac{1}{2}\right]$$

where $T \ll mc^2$ is the kinetic energy, $(E - mc^2)$; $I \doteq 10$ ev; $\sigma_T = 0.665 \times 10^{-24}$ cm².

At very high energies, ionization loss is nearly constant:

$$-\left(\frac{dE}{dx}\right)_{\text{coll}} \sim 20NZ\sigma_T mc^2$$

For a particle with charge ze and mass M, replace T by mT/M and σ_T by $z^2\sigma_T$.

(5) **Positron annihilation:** According to Dirac's "hole" theory, a positron is unstable in that it can annihilate with an ordinary free electron with release of (at least) $2mc^2$ of energy as gamma rays; and (to order $\alpha = e^2/\hbar c = 1/137$) two-photon annihilation is the dominant process. The calculations are very similar to those for Compton scattering and are conveniently carried out in the center-of-mass system. Averaging over spins, the differential cross section is

$$\begin{aligned} d\sigma_{A,\,\text{com}} = \frac{e^4}{8cpE} \Bigg[& \frac{E^2 - (E^2 - c^2p^2 \cos^2\theta)(\mathbf{e}_1 \cdot \mathbf{e}_2)^2 + 4c^2(\mathbf{p} \cdot \mathbf{e}_1)(\mathbf{p} \cdot \mathbf{e}_2)(\mathbf{e}_1 \cdot \mathbf{e}_2)}{E^2 - c^2p^2 \cos^2\theta} \\ & - \frac{4c^4(\mathbf{p} \cdot \mathbf{e}_1)^2(\mathbf{p} \cdot \mathbf{e}_2)^2}{(E^2 - c^2p^2\cos^2\theta)^2}\Bigg] d\Omega \end{aligned} \tag{5–221}$$

where E and $\mathbf{p}$ are the (relativistic) energy and momentum of the electron in center-of-mass coordinates while $\mathbf{e}_1$ and $\mathbf{e}_2$ are unit polarization vectors for the photons, and θ is the angle between $\mathbf{p}$ and (either) photon momentum. (An interesting consequence of (5–221) is that the photons are polarized at right angles when p is small. Experiment has verified this.)

The total annihilation cross section, transformed* to a system where the *electron is at rest*, is

$$\sigma_A = \frac{\pi(e^2/mc^2)^2}{\gamma+1}\left[\frac{\gamma^2+4\gamma+1}{\gamma^2-1}\ln\{\gamma+\sqrt{\gamma^2-1}\} - \frac{\gamma+3}{\sqrt{\gamma^2-1}}\right] \qquad (5\text{–}222)$$

$$\gamma = E_+/mc^2; \qquad [\pi(e^2/mc^2)^2 = 0.25\times 10^{-24}\ \mathrm{cm}^2]$$

This has a singularity at very low energies ($\gamma \to 1$) but the positron lifetime, $1/ZN\sigma_A v_+$, remains finite.

Positronium: A positron and electron can form a short-lived "hydrogen atom," $e^+ - e^-$. The main energy levels are those of hydrogen (with a factor of $\frac{1}{2}$ in the reduced mass), but the fine structure is quite different owing to the Pauli exclusion principle. The ground state is ^1S (zero spin) and the ^3S (unity spin) state lies 8.5×10^{-4} ev above it. The lifetime of ^1S, which can decay into two photons, is (setting $NZ \doteq |\psi(0)|^2$ above) about 10^{-10} seconds, but that of ^3S, which must decay into at least three photons (conservation of angular momentum), is about 10^{-7} seconds. These phenomena also have been found experimentally.

(d) **Second Quantization** (*of particle waves*):

This formalism is used for a *mathematical* form of Dirac's positron theory. In (b), the classical wave equation was converted to an equivalent set of "oscillators" by using normal-mode functions; see (5–190)–(5–201). A one-particle quantum wave equation can be subject to the same procedure and the result is a formalism describing many such particles, wherein the number of particles can *change spontaneously*—as cannot occur in the standard Schroedinger many-particle equations, (5–4)–(5–9).

Specifically, for a single particle, expand in (any) orthonormal set:

$$\psi = \sum_n b_n(t)\psi_n(\mathbf{r})$$

Then the single-particle wave equation, $i\hbar\,\partial\psi/\partial t = H\psi$, becomes,

$$i\hbar\frac{db_n}{dt} = \sum_m H_{nm}b_m; \qquad \text{or:} \qquad -i\hbar\frac{db_n^*}{dt} = \sum_m b_m^* H_{mn} \qquad (5\text{–}223)$$

If we let,

$$\left.\begin{aligned} q_n = i\hbar b_n; \qquad p_n = b_n^* \\ \mathscr{H}(q_n, p_n) = \langle H\rangle = \sum_{m,n} H_{mn}b_m^* b_n \end{aligned}\right\} \qquad (5\text{–}224)$$

then (5–223) are the classical Hamilton's equations with the Hamiltonian function, $\mathscr{H}$, and the reduction to a "set of classical oscillators" is complete. (The b_l, b_l^* correspond to a_l, a_l^* of (5–199).) If *this* formalism is then (second) quantized by allowing the b_n to be (non-Hermitian) *operators* and requiring that they satisfy the analogue of (5–201),

$$\left.\begin{aligned} b_n b_m^\dagger - b_m^\dagger b_n = \delta_{nm} \\ b_n b_m - b_m b_n = 0; \qquad b_n^\dagger b_m^\dagger - b_m^\dagger b_n^\dagger = 0 \end{aligned}\right\} \qquad (5\text{–}225)$$

* Cross sections are invariant under Lorentz transformations with velocity along that of the incoming particle; intuitively: the "cross" section is normal to the relative velocity vector and is thus not subject to the Lorentz contraction.

then the formalism becomes identical to (5–190)–(5–201). The result is then a theory capable of describing Bose–Einstein particles (because $n_l = 0, 1, 2, \cdots$) but with creation and annihilation of particles.

If (5–225) is replaced by "anticommutators:"

$$\left.\begin{aligned} b_n b_m^\dagger + b_m^\dagger b_n &= \delta_{nm} \\ b_n b_m + b_m b_n = 0; \qquad b_n^\dagger b_m^\dagger + b_m^\dagger b_n^\dagger &= 0 \end{aligned}\right\} \tag{5–226}$$

then the formalism can describe Fermi–Dirac particles, for $n_l = 0$ or 1 only [because $n_l^2 = (b_l^\dagger b_l)^2 = b_l^\dagger(1 - b_l^\dagger b_l)b_l = b_l^\dagger b_l = n_l$]. The matrix elements of these b_l have the form,

$$\left.\begin{aligned} \langle n_1, n_2, \cdots |b_l| m_1, m_2, \cdots\rangle &= \langle m_1, m_2, \cdots |b_l^\dagger| n_1, n_2, \cdots\rangle \\ &= \Big(\prod_{i\neq l}\delta_{m_i n_i}\Big)\delta_{on_l}\delta_{1m_l} \exp\Big(i\pi \sum_{j=1}^{l-1} n_j\Big) \end{aligned}\right\} \tag{5–227}$$

as can be shown from (5–226) by algebraic arguments.

The Hamiltonian, $\mathscr{H}$, in (5–224) does not include any interaction *between* the particles of the field (the numbers H_{mn} are characteristic of the single-particle operator, H). If any two particles of the type involved have a (classical) potential function, $V(|\mathbf{r}_1 - \mathbf{r}_2|)$, their (first) quantum interaction is $\iint \psi^*(\mathbf{r}_1)\psi(\mathbf{r}_1)V(|\mathbf{r}_1 - \mathbf{r}_2|)\Psi^*(\mathbf{r}_2)\Psi(\mathbf{r}_2)\, d\mathbf{r}_1\, d\mathbf{r}_2$ and substitution of $\psi = \sum b_n\psi_n$ then suggests the following Hamiltonian to include interactions.

$$\mathscr{H}_{\text{mat}} = \sum_{mn} H_{mn} b_m^\dagger b_n + \sum_{mnpl} V_{np;ml} b_n^\dagger b_p^\dagger b_l b_m \tag{5–228}$$

with

$$V_{np;ml} = \iint \psi_n^*(\mathbf{r}_1)\psi_p^*(\mathbf{r}_2)\psi_m(\mathbf{r}_1)\psi_l(\mathbf{r}_2)V(|\mathbf{r}_1 - \mathbf{r}_2|)\, d\mathbf{r}_1\, d\mathbf{r}_2 \tag{5–229}$$

The correct order of the factors, namely that shown in (5–228), (the same for both Bose–Einstein and Fermi–Dirac particles) may be fixed by the requirement that the second term must not cause transitions in single-particle states (without intermediate creations). It may be shown that replacing (5–224) by (5–228) indeed introduces the proper interactions into the theory.

(e) Second Order Effects; Renormalization:

Quantum field theory is currently in the frustrating position where the theory gives infinite interactions between fields (clearly indicating a basic imperfection) and yet every new result wrested from the theory (by physically-motivated subtraction of divergences) agrees with experiment, thus giving no clue as to where the trouble lies.

At present, quantized coupled fields can be treated only by perturbation theory (with the interaction energy as the perturbation), but all terms after the first (or the first non-vanishing) term in the perturbation-expansion always diverge. It has recently been realized that *all* these divergences correspond physically to two processes, which are induced by the perturbation, $\boldsymbol{\alpha} \cdot \mathbf{A}$, and hence may be regarded as "due to" the electron:

(*A*) Virtual emission (and reabsorption) of photons ("electron self-energy").
(*B*) Virtual creation (and re-annihilation) of pairs ("vacuum polarization").

If these processes were indeed to occur (and if their result were finite) then (*A*) would primarily change the effective *mass* of the electron and (*B*) would primarily change its effective *charge*. Such "corrections" are, by their very nature, unobservable;

that is, the experimental mass and charge would necessarily include all such effects. They should therefore be disregarded, but these same perturbation terms presumably contain other, probably observable effects which should not be discarded.

The key to this puzzle is relativistic invariance; it has been shown (Schwinger, Tomonaga) that this requirement uniquely identifies the (infinite!) expressions which correspond to extra mass and charge, and the subtraction of these is called "mass and charge renormalization." The residue of the perturbation series then gives finite* observable effects.

The mathematics of all this is exceedingly involved and we quote only the two experimentally verified results (others are too small to detect as yet).

(1) **"Anomalous" magnetic moment of the electron:** The magnetic moment differs slightly from $e\hbar/mc$, the value given by the Dirac theory without radiation; to fourth order† in $\alpha(\alpha = e^2/\hbar c = 1/137.036)$

$$\mu_e = (e\hbar/mc)\left\{1 + \frac{\alpha}{2\pi} + \frac{\alpha^2}{\pi^2}\left(\frac{197}{144} + \frac{\pi^2}{12} + \frac{3}{4}\zeta(3) - \tfrac{1}{2}\pi^2 \ln 2\right)\right\} \qquad (5\text{–}230)$$

$$= (e\hbar/mc)(1.0011596)$$

[experimental values: 1.001146 ± 0.000012
1.001165 ± 0.000011]

(2) **Shift of atomic levels (Lamb shift):** This correction arises partly from an effect similar to (5–230) but mainly (98.5%) from a change in the electron's interaction with Coulomb fields, due to radiative processes.

$$\Delta E_k = \frac{\alpha}{3\pi}\left(\frac{\hbar}{mc}\right)^2 \left\{\langle k\,|\nabla^2 U|\,k\rangle\left[\ln\left(\frac{mc^2}{2\epsilon_k}\right) + \frac{76}{120}\right] - \langle k\,|O|\,k\rangle\right\} \qquad (5\text{–}231)$$

(where the matrix elements are those of standard—Schroedinger or Dirac—atomic theory) and where

$$\alpha = e^2/\hbar c$$

$$O = (3/4\hbar)\nabla U \cdot [\boldsymbol{\sigma} \times \mathbf{p}]$$

ϵ_k is computed from

$$\langle k\,|\nabla^2 U|\,k\rangle \ln \frac{mc^2}{\epsilon_k} = -\frac{2}{\hbar^2}\sum_n |\langle k\,|\mathbf{p}|\,n\rangle|^2 (E_k - E_n) \ln \frac{mc^2}{|E_k - E_n|}$$

Equation (5–231) lifts the degeneracy given by the Dirac theory for the $^2S_{\frac{1}{2}}$ and and $^2P_{\frac{1}{2}}$ states of hydrogen (Lamb shift). Calculations to fourth order in α give the differences (in megacycles frequency shift):

	Theoretical:	Experimental:
Hydrogen	1057.99 ± 0.13	1057.77 ± 0.10
Deuterium	1059.23 ± 0.13	1059.00 ± 0.10
Ionized Helium	14055.9 ± 2.1	14043 ± 13

The uncertainties in the theoretical values are estimates of uncomputed theoretical effects; see C. M. Sommerfield, *Phys. Rev.*, **107**, 328 (1957).

* This is true only when field theory (second quantization) is used for the electron.

† C. M. Sommerfield, *Phys. Rev.*, **107**, 328 (1957).

CHAPTER 6

STATISTICAL PHYSICS

STATISTICAL physics attempts to derive the properties of macroscopic materials from the physics of their ultimate constituents, electrons and nuclei. Many of the basic concepts and techniques antedate quantum theory, and classical mechanics still provides adequate, simple explanations of many phenomena. There are, however, macroscopic effects (notably thermal-radiation spectra and temperature-variation of specific heats) which can be adequately derived only from quantum theory.

A. SIMPLE KINETIC THEORY

This is essentially a rapid estimate of the main consequences of regarding matter as an assemblage of molecules.

Ideal Gas Laws

If there are n molecules, each of mass, m, per unit volume moving in random directions, the mean pressure on a containing wall is, by (1–6),

$$p = \tfrac{1}{3}nm\langle v^2\rangle = \tfrac{1}{3}\rho\langle v^2\rangle \tag{6–1}$$

where ρ is the density. If several gases are present, the partial pressures, (6–1), due to each will simply add (Dalton's law). If N_0 is the number of molecules in a mole of gas, comparison with the ideal gas law, (2–45), gives,

$$\tfrac{1}{2}m\langle v^2\rangle = \frac{3}{2}\frac{RT}{N_0} = \frac{3}{2}kT \tag{6–2}$$

where k is Boltzmann's constant, the "gas constant per molecule."

If kinetic energy accounted for all internal energy of the gas, (6–2) would imply (per mole)

$$c_v = \frac{3}{2}R \qquad \text{(monatomic)} \tag{6–3}$$

The following simple rules for including rotational energy will emerge in (6–50) below.

$$c_v = \frac{5}{2}R \qquad \text{(diatomic or linear)} \tag{6–4}$$

$$c_v = 3\,R \qquad \text{(polyatomic)} \tag{6–5}$$

but quantum theory is needed to explain variations about these values.

Mean Free Path

If all molecules but one were stationary but randomly placed, the probability that the moving one would suffer a collision in traveling a distance, dx, is $n\sigma\, dx$

where σ is the effective cross-sectional area per molecule. Allowing all molecules to move at a common speed* alters this to $(4/3)n\sigma\,\mathrm{d}x$. If

$$\lambda \doteqdot \frac{3}{4n\sigma} \tag{6–6}$$

the probability, $P(x)$, of a flight of length x without collision is (since $\mathrm{d}P = -P\,\mathrm{d}x/\lambda$),

$$P(x) = e^{-x/\lambda} \tag{6–7}$$

and the *mean* free path is λ. (The most probable free path is zero.)

Viscosity

The drag force (per unit area) appearing with a gradient of macroscopic fluid velocity, (1–87), may be envisaged as arising from interchange of molecules between layers about λ deep. The average momentum transfer is about $m\lambda(\mathrm{d}u/\mathrm{d}x)$ per molecule and the final result is

$$\eta \doteqdot \frac{m\langle v\rangle}{4\sigma} = \frac{M\langle v\rangle}{4N_0\sigma} \tag{6–8}$$

(where M is the mass of one mole). Note that η is independent of density.

Thermal Conduction

With a temperature gradient, ∇T, interchange of molecules over an average distance, λ, entails an exchange of thermal energies of about $(c_v/N_0)(\lambda\nabla T)$ per molecule. The resulting coefficient of thermal conduction is

$$K \doteqdot \frac{c_v\langle v\rangle}{4N_0\sigma} = \frac{c_v\eta}{M} \tag{6–9}$$

The conductive heat current is thus $\mathbf{Q} = -K\nabla T$, while the heat (internal energy) density is $\rho C_v T$ per unit volume. If no other energy flows occur, a conservation equation must hold:

$$\frac{\partial}{\partial t}(\rho C_v T) = \nabla\cdot(K\nabla T) \tag{6–10}$$

Value of N_0

If in van der Waal's equation, (2–58), the constant, B, is regarded as the volume of the molecules themselves, this relation in combination with (6–8) and (6–9) determines N_0 and σ from empirical data. The results are $N_0 \doteqdot 6 \times 10^{23}$ per mole and $\sigma \doteqdot 10^{-16}\ \mathrm{cm}^2$, in agreement with later more sophisticated determinations.

Diffusion

If gas A (concentration, c_A) is non-uniformly distributed in gas B (where $c_\mathrm{B} \gg c_\mathrm{A}$) there will arise a mass flow current, $\mathbf{J}_\mathrm{A} = -\mathscr{D}_\mathrm{AB}\nabla c_\mathrm{A}$ of gas A where, by arguments similar to those for (6–8) and (6–9), the diffusion coefficient is

$$\mathscr{D}_\mathrm{AB} = \lambda_\mathrm{AB}\langle v\rangle/3 \tag{6–11}$$

where λ_AB is the mean free path of a molecule of A in an environment of gas B. Roughly, the "diameters" may be averaged:

$$2\sqrt{\sigma_\mathrm{AB}} \doteqdot \sqrt{\sigma_\mathrm{A}} + \sqrt{\sigma_\mathrm{B}} \tag{6–12}$$

* Further refinements of calculation are seldom justified with these very simple physical models.

The conservation equation for A-molecules reads (diffusion equation),

$$\frac{\partial \rho_A}{\partial t} = \mathscr{D}\nabla^2 \rho_A \tag{6–13}$$

If A molecules have a finite lifetime, T_A, a term, ρ_A/T_A, should be added on the left. (The substitution $\rho_A = e^{-t/T_A}\rho_{A_0}$ will then reduce this to the case $T_A = 0$ again.)

At very high temperatures and in bodies opaque to their own thermal radiation (e.g. the interior of stars), the transport of energy by radiation can exceed that due to thermal conduction. A useful approximation in this situation consists in writing for the energy flux, in analogy to (6–11) and (6–13), $\mathbf{Q} = (\lambda_R c/3)\nabla U_R$ where λ_R is an average mean free path for the thermal radiation and $U_R = (4\sigma/c)T^4$ is its energy density (see (2–56)). Then the conservation equation is

$$\frac{\partial U_R}{\partial t} = \nabla \cdot (\tfrac{1}{3}\lambda_R c \nabla U_R)$$

which, under the above conditions, replaces (6–10) in determining the temperature distribution.

Mobility

If $c_A \ll c_B$ and if an external force, **F**, (e.g., gravity, electric field) can act on molecules A, they will be repeatedly accelerated by **F** and decelerated by collisions with molecules *B*. The net result is an average drift velocity directed along **F** and superposed on the random thermal motion.

$$\langle \mathbf{v}_{\text{drift}} \rangle = \mu_{AB}\mathbf{F} \tag{6–14}$$

where the proportionality constant, μ_{AB}, is usually called the "mobility" and is given by

$$\mu_{AB} = \frac{1}{kT}\mathscr{D}_{AB} \tag{6–15}$$

This relation is actually rigorous* for particles which follow Boltzmann statistics. In theories of electrical conduction, it is often convenient to call $\mu' = e\mu$ the "mobility."

Steady Flow of Gases

If directions of molecular motion are random, the number of impacts per unit time on a unit area is $\frac{1}{4}n\langle v\rangle$. Thus the mass flow through an aperture of area A is

$$Q = \frac{d\mathscr{M}}{dt} = \left(\frac{p_2}{\sqrt{T_2}} - \frac{p_1}{\sqrt{T_1}}\right) A \sqrt{\frac{M}{2\pi R}} \tag{6–16}$$

(assuming $\lambda^2 > A$ so that no important pressure gradients are set up by the flow).

At thermal equilibrium in (6–16), $p_2/p_1 = \sqrt{T_2/T_1}$; this effect is called "thermal effusion."

Knudsen Flow

None of the foregoing, (6–1)–(6–16), is altered if specular reflection of molecules at walls is replaced by the following more reasonable and empirically verified assumption (Knudsen): *Gas molecules adsorb on walls and then revaporize as if coming through an*

---

* Consider thermal equilibrium in a potential field, $F = -\nabla\phi$. The forced current, $-\mu c\nabla\phi$, must be balanced by a diffusion current, $-\mathscr{D}\nabla c$, while Boltzmann's distribution law requires $c = c_0 \exp(-\phi/kT)$; the result is (6–15).

aperture in the wall (cosine distribution); their speeds are characteristic of the **wall** *temperature* while their numbers balance the impinging flow.*

This picture readily explains:

(a) Mechanical forces arising from thermal gradients.†

(b) Mass flow through a tube of length, L, and radius, a, (very low pressures: $\lambda > a$)

$$Q = \frac{d\mathscr{M}}{dt} = \frac{4}{3}\sqrt{\frac{2\pi M}{RT}}\frac{a^3}{L}(p_1 - p_2)$$

where M is the mass of one mole.

(c) Drag forces in very low density gases:

The normal pressure on a surface having temperature, T_W, and accommodation coefficient, α, and moving with velocity, $\mathbf{v}$, through a gas at temperature, T, and density, ρ, is

$$\frac{p}{\frac{1}{2}\rho v^2} = \sin^2\theta\left[\left(\frac{1}{\sqrt{\pi}} + \frac{1}{2S}\sqrt{\frac{T_r}{T}}\right)\frac{e^{-S^2}}{S} + \left(1 + \frac{1}{2S^2} + \frac{\sqrt{\pi}}{2S}\sqrt{\frac{T_r}{T}}\right)(1 + \operatorname{erf} S)\right]$$

where θ is the angle between $\mathbf{v}$ and its projection onto the surface and where

$$S = \frac{v \sin\theta}{\sqrt{2RT/M}}; \quad \frac{T_r}{T} = 1 - \alpha + \alpha\frac{T_W}{T}; \quad \operatorname{erf} x = \frac{2}{\sqrt{\pi}}\int_0^x e^{-u^2}\, du$$

(T_r is the temperature of the "reflected" molecules.) The drag "pressure" (tangential force per unit area) is

$$\frac{\tau}{\frac{1}{2}\rho v^2} = \sin\theta\cos\theta\left[\frac{e^{-S^2}}{S\sqrt{\pi}} + 1 + \operatorname{erf} S\right]$$

(T_W or T_r does not appear since emergent molecules exert no net tangential force.)

The surface temperature, T_W, is often determined by energy balance. The net energy carried away from the surface by impinging and emergent molecules (per unit area per unit time) is

$$E = N\left[2k(T_r - T) - \tfrac{1}{2}mv^2 - \frac{\frac{1}{2}kT}{\phi + 1}\right]$$

Where m is the mass of a molecule, k is Boltzmann's constant, R/N_0, and

$$\phi = \frac{e^{-S^2}}{\sqrt{\pi}\, S(1 + \operatorname{erf} S)}$$

$$N = \frac{\rho}{m}\sqrt{\frac{kT}{2\pi m}}\left[e^{-S^2} + S\sqrt{\pi}\,(1 + \operatorname{erf} S)\right]$$

(the number of impinging molecules per unit area and time).

Ionic Crystals

If the atoms of a crystal are ionized, the main binding comes from Coulomb forces (long range). These must be balanced by short range repulsions which can only be calculated from quantum mechanics. The latter suggests taking the potential between two ions as

$$\phi_{ij} = e_i e_j / r_{ij} + \beta \exp(-r_{ij}/\rho)$$

* Approximately, for common wall surfaces. The ratio of actual energy change per molecule to the maximum possible energy change is called the "accommodation coefficient."

† Hence the common "radiometer" runs in reverse to the direction expected from radiation pressure. The Knudsen vacuum gage works on a similar principle.

If a is the anion-cation spacing and N the total number of atoms, the binding energy ("lattice energy") is then of the form

$$U_0 = \sum_{i<j} \phi_{ij} = N(A/2)e^{-a/\rho} + Ne \sum_{i \neq 0} \frac{e_i}{r_{i0}} = \tfrac{1}{2}N\left(Ae^{-a/\rho} - \frac{\alpha e^2}{a}\right)$$

where α, known as "Madelung's constant", depends only on the structure of the crystal lattice. It is surprisingly difficult to calculate, but Ewald and others have shown, for example,

$$\alpha = \begin{cases} 1.747558, \text{ for cubic (NaCl)} \\ 1.762670, \text{ for b.c.c. (CsCl)} \\ 1.6381, \text{ for ``zincblende''} \\ 1.641, \text{ for ``wurzite''} \\ 5.0388, \text{ for ``fluorite''} \end{cases} \tag{6–17}$$

The constant, A, may be determined from the empirical lattice spacing, since $\partial U_0/\partial a = 0$ at equilibrium ($a = a_0$),

$$Ae^{-a/\rho} = \alpha e^2 \rho / a^2$$

and, finally, ρ is determined both by the empirical binding energy and by the compressibility. One finds

$$U_0 = -\frac{\alpha N e^2}{2a_0}\left(1 - \frac{\rho}{a_0}\right) \tag{6–18}$$

while (at 0° K, strictly),

$$\frac{1}{K_T} \doteq V \left.\frac{\partial^2 U_0}{\partial V^2}\right|_{a=a_0} = \frac{1}{9Na}\frac{\partial^2 U_0}{\partial a^2} = \frac{e^2\alpha}{18a_0{}^4}\left(\frac{a_0}{\rho} - 2\right) \tag{6–19}$$

(the latter for NaCl structures). A value, $a_0/\rho = 10 \pm 3$ checks the data for various ionic crystals fairly well. Note that $1/K_T \doteq U_0/V$ with these a_0/ρ.

Concepts of the Solid State

Except for glasses and plastics, ordinary solids prove to be agglomerations of many microscopic (10^{-4} to 10^{-6} cm) "grains" of nearly perfect crystals.* The electron band theory is thus appropriate (see (5–101)–(5–110) where the simpler consequences regarding electrical conductivity are also given).

It is convenient to picture these electron levels on a diagram of energy versus position. The positions are usually chosen on a line (or curve) passing through the centers of the atomic nuclei. On such a diagram, the effective electron potential may be graphed as a curve and the electronic allowed energy bands may be represented by shaded areas, whose lateral extents indicate regions where the corresponding wave functions, (5–102), have appreciable magnitude.† Further distinctions in shading may indicate whether a band is normally filled or empty. See Fig. 1, page 193.

Hall Effect

Although the detailed theory is rather subtle, the important empirical concepts are very simple. If the electric current density is $\mathbf{J} = \hat{x}J_x$ and if the magnetic field is $\mathbf{B} = \hat{z}B_z$, then (with uniform temperature; compare (2–139)–(2–147)) a transverse

* Glasses appear to be disordered, like liquids; plastics are briefly discussed below.

† The shaded segments represent *one*-dimensional sections of three-dimensional "globules" of high electron density.

electric field, $E_y = RJ_xB_z$ (definition of R, the Hall constant) must arise to balance, on the average, the force due to the magnetic field. If the current carriers have charge, q, and the material has conductivity, σ,

$$qE_y = qR\sigma E_xB_z = (q/c)\langle v_x\rangle B_z$$

but $\langle v_x\rangle = qE_x\mu = E_x\mu'$ by definition of μ (or μ' in much of the literature), the mobility. Then, also using $\sigma = nq^2\mu$, where n is the number of charge carriers per unit volume,

$$R\sigma = \frac{q\mu}{c} = \frac{\mu'}{c} \qquad \text{and} \qquad R = \frac{1}{nqc}$$

which serve to determine μ' and nq.

Defects

All real solids contain bulk impurities, adsorbed gases, vacancies,* interstitial atoms, etc. Such situations, which are spatially localized, may conveniently be incorporated into diagrams like Fig. 1. Such defects frequently carry (or otherwise imply) a localized electric charge, and the energy bands may then be considered to bend up or down at such locations. (This also accounts for scattering of conduction-electrons by defects.)

Examples

(a) "Donor levels" may be generated by: impurities with greater atomic charge than the host crystal (Fig. 2), by interstitial cations (A^+) in ionic crystals, and by *vacant* anion (A^-) *sites* in ionic crystals. The last are called "F-centers"; when an additional electron is trapped at the same site, they become "F'-centers".

(b) "Acceptor levels" may correspondingly be generated by mechanisms dual to those producing donor levels. A "V-center" in an ionic crystal is shown in Fig. 3.

(c) "Excitons" explain optical (ultraviolet) absorption without accompanying (photo-) conductivity. They may be envisaged as an electron bound to a hole (Fig. 4).

(d) "Surface states" arise in a normally forbidden energy region of some crystals, depending on the behavior of the electronic potential near the surface (Fig. 5).

(e) Interaction of defects: Many defects can interact when sufficiently close together, with a consequent splitting of their energy levels and (usually) a tendency to agglomerate (Fig. 6). When large numbers of defects agglomerate (nascent crystal), these states broaden into new electronic bands.

Defects of the above types are usually very rare compared to the normal atoms and they therefore have little effect on thermodynamic (equilibrium) properties of the solid. However, they provide the dominant, if not the sole mechanism for many dynamic and transport properties (photo absorption and emission, photoconduction, electrical and thermal conduction, solid diffusion, chemical catalysis, etc.).

Note that thermal lattice vibrations will modify the effective electron potentials, especially at the potential-peaks and especially at extreme temperatures.

Dislocations

Definitions: Choose any surface, S, whose boundary lies at least partly within the crystal; imagine the material on one side of S displaced uniformly by a lattice-translation vector, **d** (and let material be added or removed as necessary to restore the

---

* Vacant atomic sites are thermodynamically required when $T > 0°K$; see (6–140) below. The same is true of other defects when they are permitted by the physical circumstances.

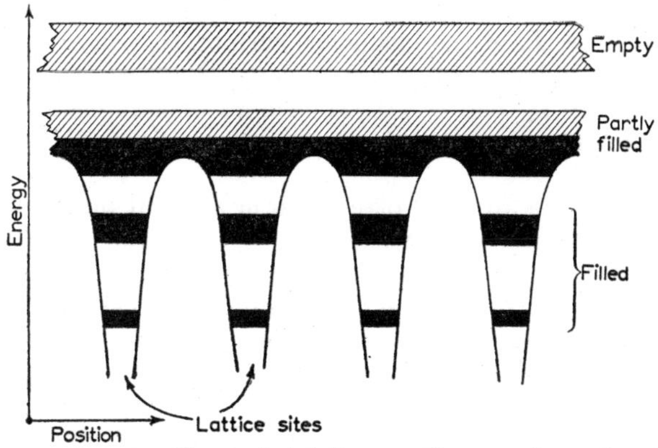

FIG. 1.—Energy-band diagram (for a conductor).

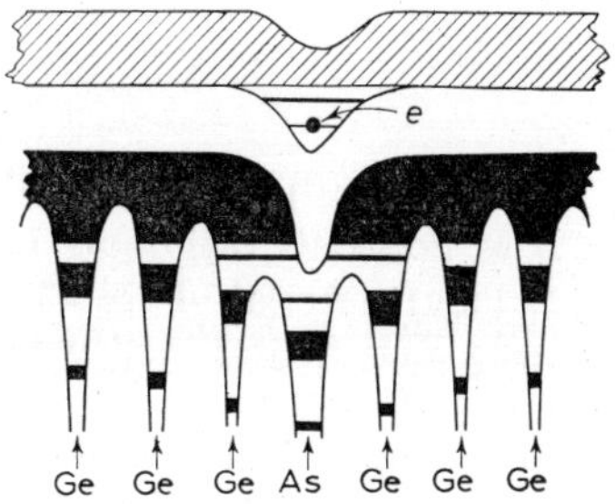

FIG. 2.—Donor level in Ge from As impurity (schematic).

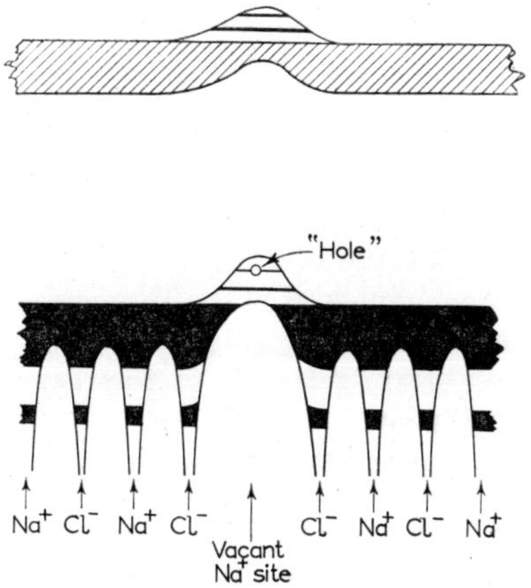

FIG. 3.—V-center in NaCl due to Na^+ vacancy (schematic).

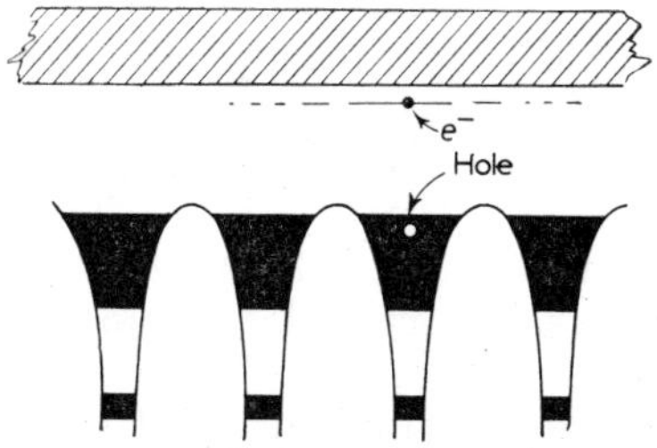

FIG. 4.—An "exciton".

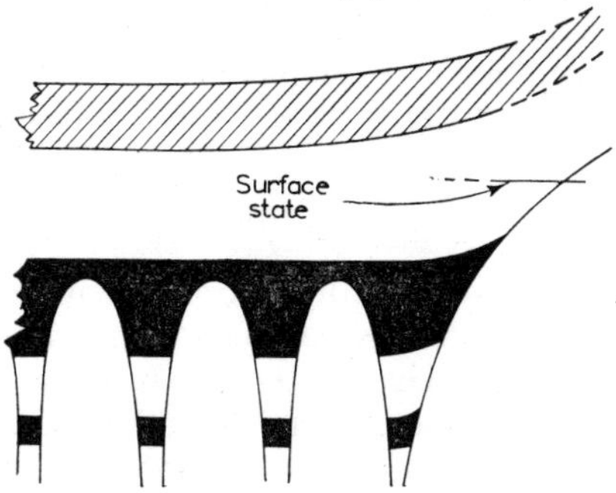

FIG. 5.—A surface state.

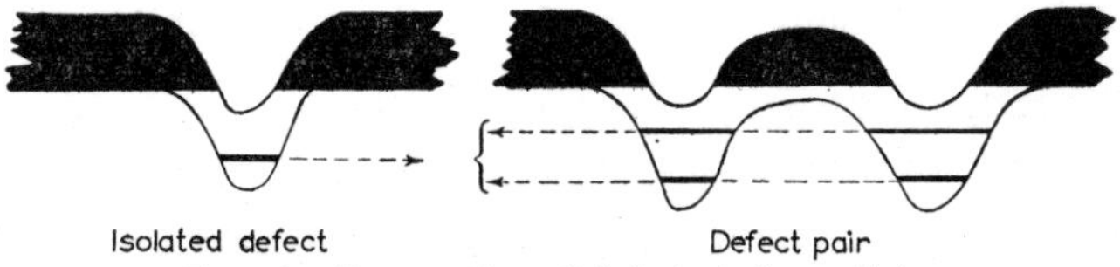

FIG. 6.—Interaction of defects (schematic).

lattice structure across S). The result is a crystal which is "perfect" except along and near the boundary curve, L, of the imaginary surface, S. Curve L is called a "dislocation line" and the displacement vector, **d**, is its "Burgers vector".

If **d** is perpendicular to L, then L is the edge of an "extra" plane of atoms and the imperfection is called an "edge dislocation". The plane of **d** and L is called the "slip plane".

If **d** is parallel to L, the atomic "planes" form a spiral ramp about L and the imperfection is called a "screw dislocation".

Quantitative theories are based primarily on ordinary (continuous medium) elastic theory. The stress field of a dislocation depends only on L and **d** (not on S). Such theories show that dislocations interact; those with antiparallel (respectively, parallel) vectors **d** tend to coalesce (resp., repel one another).

Qualitatively:

1. Dislocations may be moved* through a crystal by relatively small stresses (and the result is a displacement, **d**, of half the crystal relative to the remainder). This mechanism explains the low yield stress of most materials.†

The elastic theory of dislocation-forces gives relations of the form,

$$\sigma = \frac{G\sqrt{2\mathrm{d}/L_1}}{2\pi(1-\nu)}\sqrt{\gamma}$$

where σ is the shear stress ("force"), γ is the slip strain ("deformation"), G is the usual shear modulus, **d** is the Burgers vector of a dislocation, ν is Poisson's ratio and L_1 the width of a typical grain or crystallite in the (microcrystalline) material. Parabolic stress-strain relations of this type are typical of the theory and accord well with experiment.

2. Impurities in the lattice can tend to "anchor" dislocations and thus increase the hardness of a material (e.g. carbon in steel).

3. Cold-working will move dislocations until those with similar vectors, **d**, are brought together, whereupon their mutual repulsion prevents further motion and the material has become harder.

4. Boundaries between crystal grains are arrays of many dislocations and their motion under stress explains the growth of some grains at the expense of others during deformation of a sample.

5. Crystal growth and solid diffusion often take place more readily on or along dislocations.

Plastics (*Qualitative*)

Plastics are usually disordered masses of very large molecules. The softer plastics usually contain exceedingly long *chain*-like molecules, intertwined and randomly kinked; at elevated temperatures, the chains can be more readily "disentangled" by applied external forces and thus the material flows more readily ("thermoplastics"). In rubbers, the chains can slip easily past one another and the material is easily stretched, thus straightening the chains; but the entropy is higher (free energy lower) when the chains are randomly kinked, whence the strong restoring force. In the

* As a wave; there is little motion of the material.

† In a perfect crystal (since the shear force will vanish, by symmetry, when adjacent lattice planes have been displaced by one-half an atomic spacing), the critical shear stress, σ_e, should be of the order of $\frac{1}{4}G$ where G is the shear modulus. Empirically, G/σ_e lies in the range 100 to 10,000, rather than $\sim$4.

harder plastics, there are long chains of (sub-) molecules, but there are also "*cross bridging*" chemical bonds which connect nearby chains at various points throughout their lengths, thus forming giant molecules with three-dimensional structure and complex interlinking and interbonding.

B. THERMODYNAMIC EQUILIBRIUM

1. General Theory

Macroscopic specification of a physical system limits only very slightly its possible micro (quantum) states. Each macrostate is compatible with a literally astronomic number of quantum states. Neither the actual quantum state at any instant nor their succession over any interval of time is ever actually known. The experimentally observed macroscopic regularities must therefore represent some sort of average over the quantum states.

Indeed, since no system can be *completely* isolated from external influences (for example, a low-temperature radiation field, however much attenuated), it must unceasingly make transitions amongst its quantum states, omitting those forbidden by the macroscopic constraints. This succession of transitions is essentially a Markoff chain (see Chapter 20) with *symmetric* transition probabilities (at least to first order, namely in (5–80) we have $|V_{ik}|^2 = |V_{ki}|^2$).* By (20–52)–(20–53), it follows that:

The system (eventually) passes through each available† quantum state equally often. (A)

Thus the (available) quantum states can be regarded as equally probable ("microcanonical ensemble").

Consider next any *macroscopic* system at *fixed volume and temperature*; let the given temperature be maintained by a thermal reservoir consisting of a great many *duplicates* of the given system (all in thermal contact). Let the "grand total" energy, $\mathscr{E}$, of the (constant-volume) full assembly be held constant. Let each system have available quantum states, ψ_j, (with energy E_j) and denote by n_j the number of systems in the assembly which are in the state, ψ_j.

According to (5–27)–(5–29), the total number of quantum states, Ψ, for the full assembly, which are compatible with a given set, $n_1, n_2, n_3, \cdots$ is

$$\mathscr{W}(n_1, n_2, n_3, \cdots) = \frac{n!}{\prod_{\psi} (n_j!)} \tag{6–20}$$

where n is the total number of systems:

$$n = \sum_{\psi_i} n_j \tag{6–21}$$

* Admittedly, this argument is weak, and indeed, despite many more sophisticated efforts, this step has not yet been cleared up by any completely inescapable arguments. There is little doubt of the correctness of the results, but the point is that either (*A*) they must follow rigorously (for *every* sufficiently large system) from the mechanics of fundamental particles or (*B*) phenomenological thermodynamics contains some information about Nature which is not implied by the mechanics of fundamental particles.

† Transitions to certain sets of energetically possible states may be "forbidden" under the perturbations which are inducing the transitions; this presumably accounts for metastable thermodynamic systems (such as air or steel at ordinary temperatures).

If the system is confined and has a bounded total energy, the number of available states is always finite (compare remarks following (5–48)).

The choice of n_j is also restricted by

$$\mathscr{E} = \sum_{\psi_j} n_j E_j \tag{6–22}$$

According to (A), the probability (frequency) of the set $(n_1, n_2, \cdots)$ is proportional to $\mathscr{W}$. Thus the average value of n_k is

$$\langle n_k \rangle = [\mathscr{N}(\mathscr{E}, n)]^{-1} \sum\nolimits^{(\mathscr{E},n)} n_k \mathscr{W}(n_1, n_2, \cdots) \tag{6–23}$$

where $\sum^{(\mathscr{E},n)}$ denotes summation over all sets of n_j subject to (6–21) and (6–22) and where

$$\mathscr{N}(\mathscr{E}, n) = \sum\nolimits^{(\mathscr{E},n)} \mathscr{W}(n_1, n_2, \cdots) \tag{6–24}$$

which is the total number of quantum states available for the entire assembly.

Substitute (6–20) into (6–23) and set $n = n' + 1$ and $n_k = n_k' + 1$ in the summation. The result is*

$$\langle n_k \rangle = \frac{n\mathscr{N}(\mathscr{E} - E_k, n - 1)}{\mathscr{N}(\mathscr{E}, n)}$$

Taking logarithms and expanding $\ln \mathscr{N}$ in series, it follows that for $n \gg 1$ and $\mathscr{E} \gg E_k$,

$$\langle n_k \rangle = n \exp\left[-\frac{\partial \ln \mathscr{N}}{\partial n} - E_k \frac{\partial \ln \mathscr{N}}{\partial \mathscr{E}}\right]$$

or defining a new function, β, and using (6–21),

$$\boxed{\langle n_k \rangle = \frac{ne^{-\beta E_k}}{\sum_{\psi} e^{-\beta E_j}}} \tag{6–25}$$

(Boltzmann distribution law; "canonical ensemble"; valid for macroscopic systems.)

By (6–22) and (6–25), the mean internal energy of any one system in the assembly is

$$\frac{\mathscr{E}}{n} = U = -\frac{\partial}{\partial \beta}\left\{\ln\left[\sum_{\psi_j} e^{-\beta E_j}\right]\right\}_V \tag{6–26}$$

where the notation indicates that all external constraints are held constant in such a way that the sub quantum levels, E_j, do not change. To identify β, consider any such process ($\mathrm{d}E_j = 0$) in which there is also no external mechanical work, $\delta W = 0$; for example, warming at constant volume. Then

$$\mathrm{d}\left\{\ln\left[\sum_{\psi} e^{-\beta E_j}\right] + \beta U\right\} = \beta\, \mathrm{d}U = \beta \delta Q$$

so that β is an integrating factor for δQ. Hence by definition of thermodynamic temperature

$$\boxed{\beta = \frac{1}{kT}} \tag{6–27}$$

---

* Similarly,

$$\langle (n_k)^2 \rangle \mathscr{N}(\mathscr{E}, n) = n\mathscr{N}(\mathscr{E} - E_k, n - 1) + n(n-1)\mathscr{N}(\mathscr{E} - 2E_k, n - 2)$$

If $n \gg 1$ and $\mathscr{E} \gg E_k$, then $\langle(\Delta n_k)^2\rangle/\langle n_k\rangle^2 \doteqdot 1/\langle n_k \rangle$ so that the relative deviation of n_k from $\langle n_k \rangle$ is very small.

and also by definition of entropy

$$S - S_0 = k \ln \left[\sum_{\psi_j} e^{-\beta E_j} \right] + \frac{U}{T} = k \ln \mathcal{N}_{(1)} \tag{6–28}$$

where k is a universal constant and where $\mathcal{N}_{(1)} = \mathcal{N}^{1/n}$ is the number of quantum levels available to each system.* The last form shows that S_0 *can be consistently set equal to zero for any system whatever.* Note also the connection between entropy and "randomness". (In fact, S/k is the "information" needed to specify the quantum state, given the macrostate.)

The proportionality factor, k, is Boltzmann's constant and can be evaluated by considering an ideal gas (see later); it is found that $k = R/N_0$, the "gas constant per molecule".

Partition Function

From (6–26) and (6–28), if g_j = *number of states with energy* E_j ("statistical weights" or degeneracies), then,

$$\boxed{e^{-(U-TS)/kT} = e^{-F/kT} = Z = \sum_{\psi_j} e^{-E_j/kT} = \sum_{E_j} g_j e^{-E_j/kT}} \tag{6–29}$$

Z is called the "partition function" or "sum-over-states" for the system. *This relation completely determines all thermodynamic equilibrium properties of any system.* Namely (compare the relations following (2–31)),

$$\left.\begin{aligned} &U = kT^2 \left.\frac{\partial \ln Z}{\partial T}\right|_V; \quad S = k \ln Z + \frac{U}{T}; \quad F = -kT \ln Z \\ &p = kT \left.\frac{\partial \ln Z}{\partial V}\right|_T; \quad H = U + pV; \\ &G = -kT \ln Z + kTV \left.\frac{\partial \ln Z}{\partial V}\right|_T \end{aligned}\right\} \tag{6–30}$$

Macroscopic variables, V, etc., enter implicitly in (6–29) through the boundary conditions etc., on the ψ_j.

In principle, the partition function can be evaluated directly from spectroscopic measurements of the E_k; this method is most practical for gases.

By (19–56) and (19–57), not even the ψ_n and E_n need be known (at least in principle):

$$Z = \text{Trace}\,(e^{-\beta H}) = \sum_j \int \phi_j^* \, e^{-\beta H} \, \phi_j \, dV \tag{6–31}$$

---

* The last equality in (6–28) may be derived as follows. Comparing (6–25) with the relation preceding it and recalling our original definition of β we have

$$(S - S_0)/k = \frac{\partial}{\partial n} \ln \mathcal{N} + \frac{\mathcal{E}}{n} \frac{\partial}{\partial \mathcal{E}} \ln \mathcal{N}$$

but $\mathcal{N}(\mathcal{E}, n)$ is the total number of quantum states available to the assembly under the given macroscopic constraints. Hence $\mathcal{N}(a\mathcal{E}, an) = [\mathcal{N}(\mathcal{E}, n)]^a$ since, for example, doubling the number of systems and the total energy of the assembly merely corresponds to forming a new assembly from two identical smaller ones. Euler's theorem then states that $S - S_0 = (k/n) \ln \mathcal{N}$.

It then follows that k must be a *universal* constant since, when any set of systems (alike or not) is considered as a single system, the new $\mathcal{N}$ is the product of the individual $\mathcal{N}$ and (6–28) must hold for the compound system and also for each individual system.

where H is the Hamiltonian operator for the entire system and ϕ_j are *any* complete, orthonormal set of *admissible* functions. In this form, V, etc., enter Z through the range of integration and the boundary (admissibility) conditions on the ϕ_j.

From (6–26) and (6–29) follows the "third law" in its most acceptable form:

$$\lim_{T\to 0} S = k \ln g_0 \tag{6–32}$$

where g_0 is the degeneracy of the ground level. It is probable that when *all* interaction effects are taken into account, $g_0 = 1$ for chemically pure systems.

A Fine Point

The sum in (6–29) will obviously diverge if the system has an infinite number of states with energy less than some finite limit (example: the free hydrogen atom). The key to this paradox is that *confined* systems do not have this property (see (19–5)) and the effects of a finite container size cannot, strictly, be neglected. Usually, however, (6–29) is simply treated as an asymptotic relation, the series being broken off as soon as the terms become small.*

Extensions

(a) It was tacitly assumed above that the system possessed no linear or angular momentum. It is readily shown that addition of the six conditions, $\delta\mathbf{P} = \delta(\sum_j n_j\mathbf{p}_{jj}) = 0$ and $\delta\mathbf{J} = \delta(\sum_j n_j\mathbf{J}_{jj}) = 0$, to the problem $\delta\mathscr{W} = 0$ simply replaces the terms, $\exp(-\beta E_j)$ by $\exp[-\beta E_j - \boldsymbol{\alpha}\cdot\mathbf{P}_{jj} - \boldsymbol{\gamma}\cdot\mathbf{J}_{jj}]$ throughout, where $\boldsymbol{\alpha}$ and $\boldsymbol{\gamma}$ are related to the macroscopic momenta and the temperature. Similarly, for any other quantity which is additive over the full system.

(b) If the system can exchange mass with its environment, Z in (6–29) should then be computed as a function of N_α, the number of molecules of chemical "α"; the chemical potentials $\mu_\alpha \equiv (\partial G/\partial N_\alpha)_{T,p}$ can then be obtained† by differentiation.

However, it is often expedient to compute the function,

$$\boxed{Z_G(V, T, \mu_\alpha) = \sum_{\text{all } N_\alpha}\left\{Z(V, T, N_\alpha)e^{\sum_\alpha N_\alpha\mu_\alpha/kT}\right\}} \tag{6–33}$$

("grand partition function").

The meaning of Z_G is established as follows (also verifying the "zeroth law", equalization of temperature). Consider the system of interest, $\mathscr{S}_1$, imbedded in an environment, $\mathscr{S}_2$, such that $(\mathscr{S}_1 + \mathscr{S}_2)$ has constant energy, U_0, and constant numbers of molecules, M_α, of each substance "α". The probability that $\mathscr{S}_1$ have energy, U_1, and N_α molecules of "α" will be, as before, proportional to the number of quantum states for the whole system consistent with these given constraints, namely,

$$\mathscr{N}_1(U_1, N_\alpha)\mathscr{N}_2(U_0 - U_1, M_\alpha - N_\alpha) = e^{S_1(U_1,N_\alpha)/k}\, e^{S_2(U_0-U_1, M_\alpha - N_\alpha)/k} \tag{6–34}$$

* When ionization can occur (free electrons present) this approach loses meaning. An approximate correction for the perturbations is: Multiply each term, $e^{-E_i/kT}$, by p_i where

$$\ln p_i = -(5.1 \times 10^{-6}\ \text{cm})^3 N_e n_i^6/Z^4$$

where n_i is the principal quantum number of ψ_i, N_e is the density of free electrons and Z is the nuclear charge.

† These μ_α have units, "energy per molecule" whereas in Chapter 2 we used N_α to denote number of moles and μ_α had units "energy per mole."

(Maximizing this with respect to U_1 and N_α and using (2–24) and (2–86) gives $T_1 = T_2$ and $\mu_{1\alpha} = \mu_{2\alpha}$ as expected.) By taking $\mathscr{S}_2$ sufficiently large, we can make $\mathscr{N}_2$ or S_2 nearly constant:

$$\frac{1}{k} S_2(U_0 - U_1, M_\alpha - N_\alpha) = \frac{1}{k} S_2(U_0, M_\alpha) - \left.\frac{\partial S_2}{\partial U_0}\right|_{M,V} \frac{U_1}{k} - \sum_\alpha \left.\frac{\partial S_2}{\partial M_\alpha}\right|_{UV} \frac{N_\alpha}{k}$$

$$= \frac{1}{k} S_2 - \frac{U_1}{kT} + \sum_\alpha \frac{\mu_{\alpha 1} N_\alpha}{kT}$$

Thus the probability that $\mathscr{S}_1$ is characterized by U_1, N_α (when embedded in $\mathscr{S}_2$) is, finally,

$$\begin{aligned} \Pr(U_1, N_\alpha) &= \text{Const} \times e^{S_1/k} e^{-U_1/kT} \exp\left(\frac{1}{kT} \sum_\alpha \mu_\alpha N_\alpha\right) \\ &= \text{Const} \times Z_{(1)}(T, V, N_\alpha) \exp\left(\frac{1}{kT} \sum_\alpha \mu_\alpha N_\alpha\right) \end{aligned} \qquad (6\text{–}35)$$

This distribution is called a "grand canonical ensemble".

It may be verified that (where the averages are taken over the distribution, (6–35)):

$$\left.\begin{aligned} \left.\frac{\partial}{\partial T}(kT \ln Z_G)\right|_{V,\mu_\alpha} = \langle S_1 \rangle; \quad kT \left.\frac{\partial \ln Z_G}{\partial \mu_\alpha}\right|_{T,V} = \langle N_\alpha \rangle \\ kT \left.\frac{\partial \ln Z_G}{\partial V}\right|_{T,\mu_\alpha} = \langle p \rangle \end{aligned}\right\} \qquad (6\text{–}36)$$

Thus, according to (2–25), (2–84) and (2–86),

$$\boxed{Z_G = e^{-F/kT} \exp\left(\frac{1}{kT} \sum \mu_\alpha N_\alpha\right) = e^{pV/kT}} \qquad (6\text{–}37)$$

(If surface or interface energies are important, the Gibbs–Duhem relation, (2–84), cannot be used and the last equality should be ignored.)

Knowledge of the grand partition function, (6–33), as a function of V, T, μ_α again suffices (compare (6–36)) to establish all thermodynamic equilibrium properties of any system. Note that (6–37) itself is essentially an equation of state when the μ_α are replaced by the N_α through (6–36).

Mean Values

According to (6–25), if a system is in thermal contact with a reservoir at temperature, $T = 1/k\beta$, the probability that the system is in eigenstate ψ_j is $Z^{-1} e^{-\beta E_j}$, and the mean value of any (operator) quantity, L, is

$$\boxed{\langle L \rangle = \frac{1}{Z} \sum_{\psi_j} \langle j|\mathsf{L}|j \rangle e^{-\beta E_j} = \frac{\text{Trace } (\mathsf{L}e^{-\beta \mathsf{H}})}{\text{Trace } (e^{-\beta \mathsf{H}})}} \qquad (6\text{–}38)$$

in a system with specified V, T. (Note that (6–38) cannot be written in the form,

$\sum_{E_j}$.) Many such consequences (not derivable from phenomenological thermodynamics) are independent of (6–29). Thus not only is $\langle H \rangle = U = -(\partial \ln Z/\partial\beta)_V$ but also (6–38) verifies that $\langle U^2 - H^2 \rangle = -(\partial U/\partial\beta)_V = kT^2C_V$. Thus

$$\langle (\Delta U)^2 \rangle = kT^2C_V \tag{6–39}$$

(Of course, $\Delta U \equiv 0$ in a system with specified U.)

Statistical matrix: In view of (6–38), the operator,

$$e^{-\beta H} = \sum_{\psi_j} e^{-\beta E_j} P_{[\psi_j]}$$

(where the P are projection operators) or, more generally, the operator,

$$\rho = \sum_{\psi_j} w_j P_{[\psi_j]} \tag{6–40}$$

is often called the "statistical operator" or "density matrix". (w_j is the probability that ψ_j actually occurs.) In matrix form, if $\psi_j = \sum_\alpha c_j{}^\alpha(t)\phi_\alpha(\mathbf{r})$,

$$\langle\alpha|\rho|\beta\rangle = \sum_{\psi_j} [c_j{}^\alpha(t)]^* c_j{}^\beta(t) w_j \tag{6–41}$$

and in integral-kernel form,

$$\rho(\mathbf{r}, \mathbf{r}', t) = \sum_{\psi_j} w_j \psi_j{}^*(\mathbf{r}', t) \cdots \psi_j(\mathbf{r}, t) \tag{6–42}$$

(where the dots indicate the positions of any functions or operators to which ρ is applied). When $w_j = e^{-\beta E_j}$ so that $\rho = e^{-\beta H}$, then (6–42) or any multiple of it is known as a "Slater sum". From (6–41), the equation of motion is,

$$i\hbar \frac{\partial \rho}{\partial t} = \rho H - H\rho$$

of which a formal solution is $\rho(t) = \Omega\left(\frac{i}{\hbar} H\right)\rho(0)\Omega^{-1}\left(\frac{i}{\hbar} H\right)$; see (14–48).

Wigner's quantum-mechanical distribution function is a function which gives means of variables by a simple integration over phase space (in spite of not being positive everywhere). If

$$F(\mathbf{r}, \mathbf{p}, t) = \frac{1}{h^{3N}} \int e^{(i/\hbar)\mathbf{p}\cdot\mathbf{r}'} \rho(\mathbf{r} - \tfrac{1}{2}\mathbf{r}', \mathbf{r} + \tfrac{1}{2}\mathbf{r}', t)\, d\mathbf{r}'$$

then

$$\langle x \rangle = \iint Fx \, d\mathbf{r}\, d\mathbf{p}$$

2. The Classical Limit

For simplicity, consider an assembly of N identical particles (with arbitrarily strong interactions) confined to a rectangular volume. Functions, $e^{i\mathbf{k}\cdot\mathbf{r}}$, where $\mathbf{r}$ and $\mathbf{k}$ are $3N$-dimensional vectors, can be chosen complete and orthonormal in (the configuration-space for N particles in) this volume by selection of a suitable set of $\mathbf{k}$ [$3N$-dimensional Fourier series]. *Admissible* functions, however, must satisfy the symmetry requirements, postulate (VIII) of Chapter 5. Over *that* "function space", the following are complete and (for a subset of $\mathbf{k}$, at least) orthonormal:

$$\phi_{\mathbf{k}} = \frac{1}{V^N\sqrt{N!}} \sum_\pi \sigma^\pi e^{i\mathbf{k}\cdot\pi\mathbf{r}} \tag{6–43}$$

where the sum is over all the $N!$ permutations, π, of the particles and

$$\sigma^{\pi} = \begin{cases} 1, \text{ for Bose–Einstein particles} \\ \pm 1, \text{ for Fermi–Dirac particles and} \end{cases} \tag{6–44}$$

$$\pi \text{ an } \begin{Bmatrix} \text{even} \\ \text{odd} \end{Bmatrix} \text{ permutation}$$

Substituting in (6–31), the result reduces* to

$$Z = \frac{1}{V^N} \sum_{\mathbf{k}} \sum_{\pi} \sigma^{\pi} \int e^{-i\mathbf{k}\cdot\pi\mathbf{r}} e^{-\beta H} e^{i\mathbf{k}\cdot\mathbf{r}}\, d\mathbf{r} \tag{6–45}$$

It is readily verified by direct evaluation that

$$[-i\boldsymbol{\nabla}_j \pm \mathbf{A}(\mathbf{r}_j)]e^{i\mathbf{k}\cdot\mathbf{r}} = [\mathbf{k}_j \pm \mathbf{A}(\mathbf{r}_j)]e^{i\mathbf{k}\cdot\mathbf{r}}$$

where $\mathbf{r}_j$ is the three-dimensional position vector of the jth particle and $\mathbf{k}_j$ is the corresponding segment of $\mathbf{k}$. Hence if $\boldsymbol{\nabla} \cdot \mathbf{A}(\mathbf{r}) = 0$ (as may always be arranged; see (3–39)), then any operator of the form (5–9) has† the property that

$$H\left(\frac{\hbar}{i}\boldsymbol{\nabla}_j;\quad \mathbf{r}_j\right)e^{i\mathbf{k}\cdot\mathbf{r}} = e^{i\mathbf{k}\cdot\mathbf{r}} H(\hbar\mathbf{k}_j;\quad \mathbf{r}_j)$$

where H is the *function* obtained by substituting $\mathbf{k}_j$ for $-i\boldsymbol{\nabla}_j$ in the operator, H. Thus

$$Z = \frac{1}{V^N} \sum_{\mathbf{k}} \sum_{\pi} \sigma^{\pi} \int e^{i\mathbf{k}\cdot(\mathbf{r}-\pi\mathbf{r})} e^{-\beta H}\, d\mathbf{r} \tag{6–46}$$

If $\mathbf{p} = \hbar\mathbf{k} = (\mathbf{p}_1, \mathbf{p}_2, \mathbf{p}_3, \cdots)$ then $\mathbf{p}_j$ is essentially the mean momentum of the jth particle in the state $\phi_{\mathbf{k}}$ of (6–43) and H is the *classical Hamiltonian function.* For large $\mathbf{k}$, the first exponential factor in (6–46) will oscillate very rapidly unless π is the identity permutation; moreover if on the average, $|\mathbf{p}_j| \gg \hbar/L$ (where L is a side of the confining box), then primarily the larger $\mathbf{k}$ will contribute in (6–46) and the summation over $\mathbf{k}$ can be replaced by an integral:‡

$$Z = \frac{1}{N!h^{3N}} \int\int \exp\left[\frac{-1}{kT} H(\mathbf{p}, \mathbf{r})\right] d\mathbf{p}\, d\mathbf{r} \tag{6–47}$$

(Recall that $\mathbf{r}$ and $\mathbf{p}$ each have $3N$ components.) This classical limit for Z is valid when the particle wavelengths are very small compared to the dimensions of the ("smallest macroscopic portion of") the system.

---

* Note that: (1) $\Pi\int g(\mathbf{r})\, d\mathbf{r} = \int g(\mathbf{r})\, d\mathbf{r}$ since the order of integration is immaterial; (2) $\Pi f(H)h(\mathbf{r}) = f(H)h(\Pi\mathbf{r})$ since the operator, H, is invariant under permutations (indistinguishability); (3) $\sum_{\pi} \pi\Pi^{-1} = \sum_{\pi} \pi$ by the "rearrangement theorem" of elementary group theory; finally, $\sum_{\pi} 1 = N!$

† Ignoring spin terms for simplicity.

‡ Compare (5–95)–(5–97) for the distribution and spacing of the $\mathbf{k}$ values in an orthonormal set of functions $e^{i\mathbf{k}\cdot\mathbf{r}}$. A factor, $N!$, in (6–47) arises since $\mathbf{k}$ and $\pi\mathbf{k}$ generate the same function in (6–43); that is symmetrization reduces by $N!$ the number of independent wave functions for given $\mathbf{p}$ (approximately, for large N).

Similarly, the classical limit of (6–38) is

$$\langle L(\mathbf{p}, \mathbf{r})\rangle = \frac{1}{N!h^{3N}Z}\int\int L(\mathbf{p}, \mathbf{r})e^{-H(\mathbf{p},\mathbf{r})/kT}\,d\mathbf{r}\,d\mathbf{p} \tag{6–48}$$

In both (6–47) and (6–48), the integrals may, of course, be transformed to any convenient set of canonical coordinates and momenta.

The classical *equipartition theorem* follows upon taking $L = p_i\,\partial H/\partial p_i$ and integrating by parts (with respect to p_i); if $\partial H/\partial p_i \neq 0$, one obtains,

$$\left\langle p_i \frac{\partial H}{\partial p_i}\right\rangle = kT = \left\langle q_i \frac{\partial H}{\partial q_i}\right\rangle \tag{6–49}$$

In particular for an ideal gas of N non-interacting particles, H is quadratic in the linear and angular momenta of the particles and

$$U = \langle H\rangle = \tfrac{1}{2}NfkT \tag{6–50}$$

where f is the number of momenta (degrees of freedom) per particle, namely $f = 3, 5, 6$ for monatomic, diatomic and polyatomic classical molecules respectively.

The classical *Maxwell velocity-distribution* for an ideal gas also follows from (6–48) [by setting $L =$ constant for v in $v_0 \pm \frac{1}{2}dv$, and $L = 0$ otherwise and evaluating the constant by $\int n(v)\,dv = N$].

$$n(v)\,dv = \frac{4Ne^{-mv^2/2kT}\,v^2\,dv}{\sqrt{\pi}(2kT/m)^{3/2}} \tag{6–51}$$

whence if v_m denotes the most probable value of v,

$$v_m = \sqrt{2kT/m}; \quad \langle v\rangle = \frac{2}{\sqrt{\pi}}v_m; \quad \langle v^2\rangle = \tfrac{3}{2}\,v_m^{\,2} \tag{6–52}$$

Similarly, the distribution over individual velocity components, v_x, v_y, v_z is Gaussian.

3. Thermal Radiation

Consider, a fixed volume, V, of a radiation field at (equilibrium with matter at) a fixed temperature, T. The system is described quantum mechanically by (5–190)–(5–196). By (5–196), the partition function, (6–29), factors into the form,

$$e^{-F/kT} = Z = \prod_l \left\{\sum_{n_l=0}^{\infty} e^{-n_l h\nu_l/kT}\right\} = \left\{\prod_l (1 - e^{-h\nu_l/kT})\right\}^{-1}$$

By (19–5), the number of ν_l in the range $\nu \pm \frac{1}{2}d\nu$ (for macroscopic V and two polarizations per "mode") is $8\pi V\nu^2\,d\nu/c^3$ and thus

$$\frac{F}{kT} = \frac{8\pi V}{c^3}\int_0^\infty \nu^2 \ln\left[1 - e^{-h\nu/kT}\right]d\nu$$

Whence,

$$F = -\frac{4\sigma T^4}{3c}V, \quad \text{where } \sigma = \frac{2\pi^5k^4}{15c^2h^3} = 5.67 \times 10^{-5}\text{ c.g.s.} \tag{6–53}$$

The remaining thermodynamic functions (see (2–57)) then follow from (6–30).

Planck's Distribution Law

Using (6–38) and (5–196), the mean number of photons in a given "mode", l, is

$$\langle n_l \rangle = \frac{\sum\limits_{(\text{all } n_j)} n_l \exp\left[-\sum\limits_j n_j h\nu_j/kT\right]}{\sum\limits_{(\text{all } n_j)} \exp\left[-\sum\limits_j n_j h\nu_j/kT\right]} = \frac{\sum\limits_{n_l} n_l \exp\left[-n_l h\nu_l/kT\right]}{\sum\limits_{n_l} \exp\left[-n_l h\nu_l/kT\right]}$$

$$\langle n_l \rangle = \frac{1}{e^{h\nu_l/kT} - 1} \tag{6–54}$$

There are $(8\pi V\nu^2/c^3)\,d\nu$ "modes" with frequencies $\nu \pm \frac{1}{2}d\nu$ and the energy per unit volume due to photons in this frequency range is therefore,

$$\rho(\nu)\,d\nu = \frac{(8\pi h/c^3)\nu^3}{e^{h\nu/kT} - 1}\,d\nu \tag{6–55}$$

(Planck's law). Integrating, the total energy per unit volume becomes $(4/c)\sigma T^4$ with the above definition of σ, in agreement with (2–56). From this result, it is readily shown that the power emitted per unit area (from a hole in the wall of an oven) is

$$\text{Emission} = P = \sigma T^4 \tag{6–56}$$

The mean energy of a photon follows from (6–55):

$$\langle h\nu \rangle = 3.828(kT)$$

THERMAL RADIATION FROM REAL BODIES: If a real body with temperature, T, absorbs only a fraction, ϵ, of incident thermal radiation (*also* with temperature, T), then by the zeroth law of thermodynamics (or by the symmetry of quantum transition probabilities) its thermal emission is only,

$$P = \epsilon\sigma T^4$$

Similar concepts are readily applied to each frequency component, $h\nu$, of the radiation.

For example, a finite mass of tenuous gas has, at frequency ν, an emissivity of the order of $\epsilon(\nu) = 1 - \exp[-L\mu(\nu)]$ where L is its thickness and $1/\mu(\nu)$ is the (absorption) mean free path of radiation (frequency ν) in the gas. If $\epsilon \ll 1$, the thermal emission is often conveniently treated by considering the power, P_{vol} emitted per unit *volume*. For a unit volume, $\mu(\nu)$ is the absorptivity and since the density of thermal radiation at the gas temperature T would be $\rho(\nu)$, we have

$$P_{\text{vol}} = \rho c\mu = 4\sigma T^4 \mu(\nu, T)\rho_1(\nu, T)$$

where ρ_1 is Planck's function (6–55) normalized to $\int \rho_1\,d\nu = 1$. This power, of course, is partly attenuated on its way out of the total mass of gas. See also (5–220).

4. IDEAL GASES

Ideal gases consist of N identical, non-interacting "molecules". By (5–28)–(5–29) the energy levels are

$$\left.\begin{aligned} E_{(j)} &= \sum_{\psi_r} n_r \epsilon_r \\ \Big(\sum_{\psi_r} n_r &= N\Big) \end{aligned}\right\} \tag{6–57}$$

where ϵ_r are the energy levels for a single molecule. By the symmetry postulate, (VIII) of Chapter 5, each set of occupation numbers, n_r, corresponds to a *single* wave function (essentially of the form, (6–43)), while the n_r themselves are restricted by

$$n_r = \begin{cases} 0, 1 \text{ (only) for Fermi–Dirac molecules} \\ \text{any integer} \geqslant 0, \text{ for Bose–Einstein molecules} \end{cases} \tag{6–58}$$

The partition function, (6–29), is difficult to evaluate directly, owing to the restriction $\sum n_r = N$, in (6–57), but the grand partition function, (6–33), may be verified to be (with $\beta = 1/kT$):

$$pV/kT = \ln Z_G = -\sigma \sum_{(\psi_r)} \ln\left[1 - \sigma e^{\beta(\mu - \epsilon_r)}\right] \tag{6–59}$$

where the sum extends over all single-particle states, r, and

$$\sigma = \begin{cases} -1, \text{ for Fermi–Dirac molecules} \\ 1, \text{ for Bose–Einstein molecules} \end{cases} \tag{6–60}$$

For the original N-particle system, μ is to be eliminated from (6–59) by using (6–36):

$$N = kT \left.\frac{\partial \ln Z_G}{\partial \mu}\right|_{T,V} = \sum_{\psi_r} \frac{1}{e^{(\epsilon_r - \mu)/kT} - \sigma} \tag{6–61}$$

Mean occupation numbers: From (6–38) and (6–57), it is easily seen formally that $\langle n_r \rangle = -kT\partial(\ln Z)/\partial\epsilon_r$ but by (6–29) and (6–37) the derivative is also equal to $\partial(\ln Z_G)/\partial\epsilon_r$ and hence

$$\langle n_r \rangle = \frac{1}{e^{(\epsilon_r - \mu)/kT} - \sigma} \tag{6–62}$$

Bose–Einstein Condensation

Setting $\sigma = +1$ in (6–59) and expanding the logarithms in series, one obtains (rigorously),

$$\left.\begin{aligned} \frac{pV}{kT} &= \sum_{l=1}^{\infty} \frac{1}{l} e^{\mu l/kT} Z_1\left(\frac{T}{l}\right) \\ \text{where} \quad & \\ Z_1\left(\frac{T}{l}, V\right) &= \sum_{\psi_r} e^{-l\epsilon_r/kT} \end{aligned}\right\} \tag{6–63}$$

Z_1 is the partition function for a single particle and is evaluated for structureless particles in (6–74), (6–75) below. When this result is substituted in (6–63) and in $N = [\partial(pV)/\partial\mu]_{T,V}$ it is found that the series for N has a finite sum at $\mu = 0$ but fails to converge for $\mu > 0$. Further details are sensitive to the approximation used for Z_1, but effectively as soon as the density, N/V, equals or exceeds* $2.61\ \lambda^{-3}$ then $\mu \doteq 0$ and p becomes nearly equal to $1.34\ \lambda^{-3}\ kT$, independent of N or V.

Degenerate Fermi Gas

When the spacing of the single-particle levels is large,

$$\epsilon_{r+1} - \epsilon_r \gg kT$$

the terms in (6–61) become very nearly unity for $\epsilon_r < \mu$ and very nearly zero for

* $\lambda = h(2\pi mkT)^{-1/2}$

$\epsilon_r > \mu$; this indicates that essentially all levels below the "Fermi level", μ, are filled and that few levels above μ are filled (as would be expected from the Pauli exclusion principle).

From (6–59), with $\sigma = -1$, if $\mathcal{N}(\epsilon)$ is the number of one-particle states with $\epsilon_r \leqslant \epsilon$,

$$\ln Z_G \doteq \int \frac{d\mathcal{N}}{d\epsilon} \ln\left[1 + e^{\beta(\mu-\epsilon)}\right] d\epsilon$$

Integrating by parts and using (8–13),

$$\frac{pV}{kT} = \ln Z_G = \beta \int_0^{\mu} \mathcal{N}(\epsilon')\, d\epsilon' + \frac{\pi^2}{6\beta} \mathcal{N}'(\mu) + \cdots \tag{6–64}$$

From (6–36) or by similar arguments applied to (6–61):

$$N = \mathcal{N}(\mu) + \frac{\pi^2}{6}(kT)^2 \mathcal{N}''(\mu) + \cdots = \mathcal{N}(\mu_0) \tag{6–65}$$

where the last equality defines μ_0 (the Fermi level at $T = 0$). Since $\mu N = G = U + pV - TS$, equations (6–36) and (6–64) show that

$$U = \mu N - \int_0^{\mu} \mathcal{N}(y)\, dy + \frac{\pi^2}{6}(kT)^2 \mathcal{N}'(\mu) + \cdots$$

Using
$$\mu N - \int_0^{\mu} = \mu \mathcal{N}(\mu_0) - \int_0^{\mu_0} - \int_{\mu_0}^{\mu}$$

one finds
$$U = U_0(\mu_0) + \frac{\pi^2}{6} \mathcal{N}'(\mu)(kT)^2 + \cdots \tag{6–66}$$

Thus the specific heat of a degenerate Fermi gas is

$$c_v = \frac{\pi^2}{3}\left[k\mathcal{N}'(\mu)\right] kT \tag{6–67}$$

This result explains why the conduction electrons in a metal contribute very little to the total specific heat. Assuming these electrons are essentially free, $\mathcal{N}$ may be evaluated from (5–95) with the results,

$$\left.\begin{aligned} c_v \text{ (per mole of electrons)} &= R\,\frac{\pi^2}{2}\left(\frac{kT}{\mu_0}\right) \\ \mu_0 &= \frac{h^2}{2m}\left[\frac{3}{8\pi}\frac{N}{V}\right]^{2/3} \end{aligned}\right\} \tag{6–68}$$

Electron Vapor Pressure

An electron with given momentum in the vapor phase will have greater total energy than one in the solid, say $\epsilon + \chi$ where ϵ is the corresponding energy in the metal. Since the chemical potential, μ, must be the same in both phases, while in the metal, $\mu \doteq \mu_0$, there follows (using an integral approximation to (6–61) and using (5–95) for the density-of-states),

$$\left(\frac{N}{V}\right)_{\text{vapor}} = 2(2\pi mkT/h^2)^{3/2}\, e^{-(\chi-\mu_0)/kT} \tag{6–69}$$

If this vapor is swept off by an electric field, the maximum current that the ("temperature limited") hot cathode can supply is

$$\left.\begin{aligned} J_{TL} &= \tfrac{1}{2}e\left(\frac{N}{V}\right)\langle|v_x|\rangle \\ &= e\,\frac{4\pi m}{h^3}\,(kT)^2\,e^{-(\chi-\mu_0)/kT} \end{aligned}\right\} \tag{6–70}$$

(Richardson equation).

Contact potentials, rectification, etc., are relatively simple consequences of properties of a degenerate Fermi "gas" of electrons. The main points to remember in such considerations are: (a) the energy levels of different materials must be measured on the same scale; (b) when this is done, the Fermi level (= chemical potential, μ) must be the same in all parts of the system; (c) if electrons tend to collect in a local region, this "charging" process shifts the energy levels themselves correspondingly to account for electrostatic potential energy.

Low-density Ideal Gases

By (6–61), low density requires $\exp(\mu/kT) \ll 1$. Combining (6–37) and (6–59) and expanding the logarithm in (6–59),

$$\mu\beta N + \ln Z = \ln Z_G \doteq e^{\mu\beta}\, Z_1$$

where Z_1 is the single-particle partition function. The distinction between Fermi–Dirac and Bose–Einstein "statistics" has disappeared,* for by (6–36) $N = Z_1 \exp(\mu\beta)$. Therefore on the one hand, $pV = kT \ln Z_G = NkT$, as expected for a classical ideal gas, while on the other hand,

$$\ln Z = N + N \ln(Z_1/N) \doteq \ln(Z_1^N/N!) \qquad \text{(low-density ideal gas)} \tag{6–71}$$

Thus, by (6–30), since $pV = NkT$,

$$G = -NkT \ln(Z_1/N) \tag{6–72}$$

which is useful for computing chemical equilibrium "constants" from (2–97).

The function, Z_1, will factor further if the single-molecule energy is a sum:

$$\epsilon = \epsilon_{\text{tran}} + \epsilon_{\text{rot}} + \epsilon_{\text{vib}} + \epsilon_{\text{elec}} + \epsilon_{\text{nucl}}$$

then

$$Z_1 = \zeta_{\text{tran}} \cdot \zeta_{\text{rot}} \cdot \zeta_{\text{vib}} \cdot \zeta_{\text{elec}} \cdot \zeta_{\text{nucl}} \tag{6–73}$$

where

$$\zeta_{\text{tran}} = \sum_{\epsilon_{tr}} g(\epsilon_{tr})\, e^{-\epsilon_{tr}/kT} \quad \text{etc.}$$

Thus, finally,

$$Z = (\zeta_{\text{tr}}^N/N!)\, \zeta_{\text{rot}}^N\, \zeta_{\text{vib}}^N\, \zeta_{\text{elec}}^N\, \zeta_{\text{nucl}}^N$$

Correspondingly, the various "extensive" thermodynamic quantities, S, U, H, G, F,

---

* If a second term is retained in the series expansions, one finds, $p/kT = (N/V)[1 - (\sigma\lambda^3 N/4\sqrt{2}\,V)]$, indicating the "clustering" tendency of Bose–Einstein particles and the "mutually repulsive" property of Fermi–Dirac particles.

C_p, C_v, etc., can all be decomposed by (6–71) and (6–73) into sums of translational,* rotational, $\cdots$ etc., contributions.

Translations: By (5–96)–(5–98),

$$\zeta_{\text{tr}} = \left\{ \sum_{n=-\infty}^{\infty} e^{-n^2(\pi\lambda^2 V^{-2/3})} \right\}^3; \quad \lambda = \frac{h}{\sqrt{2\pi mkT}} \tag{6–74}$$

which can be expressed as a theta function. If the sum is approximated by an integral, the result is the same as the classical approximation [$H = |\mathbf{p}|^2/2m$ in (6–47) with $N = 1$], namely,

$$\zeta_{\text{tr}} \doteq \frac{V}{h^3}(2\pi mkT)^{3/2} = \frac{V}{\lambda^3} \tag{6–75}$$

The corresponding translational contributions to thermodynamic quantities are then just those of a classical, ideal, monatomic gas. Per mole (using (6–30)),

$$\left.\begin{aligned} U^{\text{tr}} &= \tfrac{3}{2}RT; \quad C_v^{\text{tr}} = \tfrac{3}{2}R; \quad C_p^{\text{tr}} = \tfrac{5}{2}R \\ S^{\text{tr}} &= R \ln \zeta^{\text{tr}} - k \ln (N_0!) + \tfrac{3}{2}R \\ &= R[\ln (V/N_0\lambda^3) + \tfrac{5}{2}] \end{aligned}\right\} \tag{6–76}$$

The last result is called the Sackur–Tetrode formula. (N_0 = molecules/mole.)

Rotations: The factor ζ_{rot} for linear-top molecules can also be expressed as an elliptic function. Approximating sums by integrals and allowing for nuclear-spin degeneracies, $(2s_j + 1)$, one finds the semi-classical results:

$$\zeta_{\text{rot}}\zeta_{\text{nucl}} = \begin{cases} \dfrac{2IkT}{\sigma\hbar^2} \prod_i (2s_j + 1), \text{ linear} \\[2ex] \dfrac{\sqrt{ABC}\,(2\pi kT)^{3/2}}{\pi\sigma\hbar^3} \prod_i (2s_j + 1), \text{ polyatomic} \end{cases} \tag{6–77}$$

where I or A, B, C are the (principal) moments of inertia and σ is a "symmetry number", equal to the number of indistinguishable positions of the molecule (σ enters because postulate (VIII) of Chapter 5 restricts the rotational wave functions of a molecule with some indistinguishable nuclei).

The corresponding contributions to U and S are (per mole),

$$\left.\begin{aligned} U^{\text{rot}} &= \begin{cases} RT, \text{ linear} \\ \tfrac{3}{2}RT, \text{ polyatomic} \end{cases} \\ C_p^{\text{rot}} &= C_v^{\text{rot}} = U^{\text{rot}}/T \\ S^{\text{rot}} &= \begin{cases} R\left[1 + \ln\left(\dfrac{2IkT}{\sigma\hbar^2}\prod\right)\right], \text{ linear} \\[2ex] R\left[\tfrac{3}{2} + \ln\left(\dfrac{\sqrt{ABC}\,(2\pi kT)^{3/2}}{\pi\sigma\hbar^3}\prod\right)\right], \text{ polyatomic} \end{cases} \end{aligned}\right\} \tag{6–78}$$

where the nuclear spin factors, $(2s_j + 1)$, are represented by $\prod$. Since the latter cancel out in all processes not involving transmutations or isotope-separation, $\prod$ is frequently omitted.

---

* The function, $N - N \ln N$ in (6–71) is usually lumped with the translational contribution.

Vibrations: In the harmonic oscillator approximation, (5–156), the factor ζ_{vib} is merely a product of geometric series:

$$\zeta_{\text{vib}} = \prod_i \left\{ \frac{e^{-h\nu_i/2kT}}{1 - e^{-h\nu_i/kT}} \right\} \tag{6–79}$$

and per mole:

$$\left.\begin{aligned} U^{\text{vib}} &= N_0 \sum_i \frac{h\nu_i}{e^{h\nu_i/kT} - 1} + N_0 \sum_i \tfrac{1}{2} h\nu_i \\ S^{\text{vib}} &= R \sum_i \frac{h\nu_i/kT}{e^{h\nu_i/kT} - 1} - R \sum_i \ln\left[1 - e^{-h\nu_i/kT}\right] \end{aligned}\right\} \tag{6–80}$$

Electron states: Electronic states are seldom excited to appreciable extent unless chemical reactions are occurring. Usually, it is sufficient to take $\zeta_{\text{elec}} = g_{e0}$, the degeneracy of the ground electronic state. In "valence saturated" molecules (fully paired spins), $g_{e0} = 1$ or 2, according as the total number of electrons is even or odd (spin 0 or $\frac{1}{2}$). In diatomic molecules, $g_{e0} = 2S + 1$ for Σ states and $2(2S + 1)$ for all others; in atoms $g_{e0} = 2J + 1$. To this approximation,

$$U^{\text{elec}} = 0; \quad S^{\text{elec}} = R \ln g_{0e} \tag{6–81}$$

Mixtures of ideal gases: Since ideal gases do not interact, their energies (and energy levels) merely add, and (if the energy scales are consistent!) the partition functions therefore merely multiply; by (6–71),

$$Z_{\text{mix}} = \frac{(Z_{1A})^{N_A}}{N_A!} \times \frac{(Z_{1B})^{N_B}}{N_B!} \times \cdots \tag{6–82}$$

whence if x_j are the respective mole fractions (or molecule fractions, $N_A/\sum_\alpha N_\alpha$, etc.),

$$S_{\text{mix}} = \sum_j x_j S_j - R \sum_j x_j \ln x_j \tag{6–83}$$

in agreement with the entropy-of-mixing found in phenomenological thermodynamics.

Electromagnetic Properties

It is convenient to work with the electric and magnetic "susceptibilities" (or "polarizabilities"), χ_e and χ_m, per *molecule*, defined by

$$\frac{\mathbf{D} - \mathbf{E}}{4\pi} = \mathbf{P} = \frac{N}{V} \chi_e \mathbf{E}_L; \quad \frac{\mathbf{B} - \mathbf{H}}{4\pi} = \mathbf{M} = \frac{N}{V} \chi_m \mathbf{B}_L \tag{6–84}$$

where N/V is the number of molecules per unit volume and "L" signifies the average, "local" field seen by a molecule, including that due to its neighbors.

Lorentz suggested that these local fields are the same as those which would appear in a small (but macroscopic*) evacuated sphere cut in the medium *without disturbing the uniform polarization*, $\mathbf{P}$ or $\mathbf{M}$, of the remainder:

$$\mathbf{E}_L = \mathbf{E} + \frac{4\pi}{3}\mathbf{P}; \quad \mathbf{B}_L = \mathbf{B} - \frac{8\pi}{3}\mathbf{M} \tag{6–85}$$

* This simplifies the calculation but assumes that short-range correlations of molecular phenomena are at least statistically the same as the long-range correlations. (Note the analogy to (6–132) below.) Modifications have been proposed by Onsager and Van Vleck, which appear somewhat better supported by data for liquids and solids.

The relations between χ_e, χ_m and ϵ, μ are then (Clausius-Mosotti equations)

$$\frac{\epsilon - 1}{\epsilon + 2} = \frac{4\pi N}{3V}\chi_e; \quad \frac{\mu - 1}{\mu + 2} = \frac{4\pi N}{3V}\chi_m \tag{6–86}$$

Since the energy of a dipole, **p**, in a field, $\mathbf{E}_L$, is $-\mathbf{p}\cdot\mathbf{E}_L$, it follows from (6–38) and (6–71) that in an ideal gas, $\chi_e = \langle p_z\rangle/E_{Lz}$ is given by,

$$\chi_e = \frac{kT}{E}\frac{\partial \ln Z_1}{\partial E}; \quad \chi_m = \frac{kT}{B}\frac{\partial \ln Z_1}{\partial B} \tag{6–87}$$

where Z_1 is the one-molecule partition function and the subscript, L, has been dropped since it is now sufficient to consider an isolated molecule in an external field, **E** or **B**.

Low frequencies: A magnetic field changes the electronic energies of an atom as shown in (5–130). If only the ground electronic term is of importance, the net result is to multiply Z_1 by the factor,

$$\left.\begin{aligned} \zeta_B &= \frac{\sinh (J+\frac{1}{2})y}{\sinh \frac{1}{2}y} \\ \text{where} \quad kTy &= \frac{e\hbar}{2mc}BG = \frac{e\hbar}{2mc}B\left[1 + \frac{J(J+1)+S(S+1)-L(L+1)}{2J(J+1)}\right] \end{aligned}\right\} \tag{6–88}$$

whence, by (6–87), for a monatomic gas

$$\chi_m = \frac{kT}{B^2}y\{(J+\tfrac{1}{2})\coth[(J+\tfrac{1}{2})y] - \tfrac{1}{2}\coth \tfrac{1}{2}y\} \tag{6–89}$$

This is strongly field-dependent; for small fields or not too low temperatures,

$$\chi_m \doteq \frac{(e\hbar/2mc)^2}{3kT}J(J+1)G^2 \tag{6–90}$$

If the contribution, (6–89) vanishes,* then perturbations quadratic in B must be considered; with $\mathbf{A} = \frac{1}{2}(\mathbf{B}\times\mathbf{r})$ in (5–9), one finds,

$$\Delta E_k = \frac{e^2B^2}{8mc^2}\sum_i \langle k|x_i^2 + y_i^2|k\rangle$$

For a system in which (6–89) vanishes, $\langle x_i^2 + y_i^2\rangle = (2/3)\langle r_i^2\rangle$ where r_i is the distance of the ith particle from the center of mass of the system. The result (when only one electronic state of the molecule is of importance) is

$$\chi_m = \frac{-e^2}{6mc^2}\sum_i \langle r_i^2\rangle \tag{6–91}$$

which corresponds to diamagnetism ($\mu < 1$).

For electric susceptibilities, useful results are most readily obtained by semi-classical methods: If an (isolated) molecule has a permanent electric dipole moment,

---

* Most molecules, for example, have zero electronic orbital momentum and no unpaired spins in their ground states. (An important exception is O_2—ground state, ${}^3\Sigma_g^-$).

μ, and a polarizability, α (so that $\mathbf{p} = \boldsymbol{\mu} + \alpha\mathbf{E}$), an electric field along the z-axis will alter the partition function (6–47) by a factor,

$$\zeta_E = \iint \exp\left[\frac{-1}{kT}\left(-\mu E \cos\theta - \tfrac{1}{2}\alpha E^2\right)\right]\frac{\sin\theta\, d\theta\, d\phi}{4\pi}$$

where (θ, ϕ) is the direction of $\boldsymbol{\mu}$. By (6–87), then

$$\chi_e = \alpha + \frac{\mu}{E}\left[\coth\frac{\mu E}{kT} - \frac{kT}{\mu E}\right] \qquad (6\text{–}92)$$

For weak fields or not too low temperatures,

$$\chi_e \doteqdot \alpha + \frac{\mu^2}{3kT} \qquad (6\text{–}93)$$

(a result much used for molecular structure determination).

The d.c. polarizability, α, is given by setting $\nu = 0$ in (6–98) and (6–99) below; alternatively, a variational argument, due to Hylleraas and Hasse* shows (for the x–x component of the dyadic, α; similarly for the others),

$$\alpha_{xx} \doteqdot \frac{4nme^2}{\hbar^2}\{\langle(x_1 - \langle x\rangle)^2\rangle - (n-1)\langle(x_1 - \langle x\rangle)(x_2 - \langle x\rangle)\rangle\}^2 \qquad (6\text{–}94)$$

where n is the number of electrons in the molecule, x_1 and x_2 are "typical" electron coordinates and $\langle x\rangle$ is their mean (recall that ψ is anti-symmetric in all electrons in the molecule). Then,

$$\alpha = \langle\alpha\rangle = \tfrac{1}{3}\,\text{Trace}\ \alpha = \tfrac{1}{3}(\alpha_{xx} + \alpha_{yy} + \alpha_{zz}) \qquad (6\text{–}95)$$

For an atom, the second term in (6–94) vanishes and $\langle x^2\rangle = (1/3)\langle r^2\rangle$ so that,

$$\alpha \doteqdot \frac{4me^2}{9\hbar^2}\sum(\langle r_i^{\,2}\rangle)^2 \qquad (6\text{–}96)$$

Moreover, it is found empirically that the second term in (6–94) is usually small for molecules† as well (electrons are effectively localized) and that the total polarizability dyadic can be represented as a sum of those associated with each of the bonds in the molecule. (This fails for molecules which "resonate" between several bond-structures.)

High frequencies: Here, magnetic effects are minor. The average electric polarization induced by a high-frequency field in a molecule occupying a given state, I, can be obtained by taking the time-average of $\langle I|\sum_i e_i\mathbf{r}_i|I\rangle$, using the *perturbed* wavefunctions. From (19–78), (19–86) (with $V(t)$ given by (5–57) and recalling that $g_k \doteqdot \delta_{kI}$ for moderate t), the "in phase" component for state I is found to be $\alpha_I\mathbf{E}$, where

$$\alpha_I = \frac{2}{3h}\sum_{\psi_k}\frac{|\mu_{kI}|^2\,\nu_{kI}}{(\nu_{kI})^2 - \nu^2} \qquad (6\text{–}97)$$

---

* See "*Molecular Theory of Gases and Liquids*" by Hirschfelder, Curtiss and Bird (Wiley, 1954), pp. 941–951.

† London observed that the similarity between (6–94) and (5–161) then suggests that the van der Waals intermolecular potential is approximately, $U_{vdW} \doteqdot -[3\alpha_A\alpha_B I_A I_B/2(I_A + I_B)]R^{-6}$ where I_A and I_B are approximately the first ionization potentials of the two molecules.

Here,* $|\mu_{kI}|^2 = |\langle k|\sum_i e_i\mathbf{r}_i|I\rangle|^2$ (and ν_{kI} is defined in (5–67) while ν is the frequency of the applied field).

The mean polarizability is then

$$\chi_e \doteq \alpha = \left\{\sum_{\psi_I} \alpha_I e^{-E_I/kT}\right\} \Big/ \left\{\sum_{E_I} g_I e^{-E_I/kT}\right\} \tag{6–98}$$

A refinement of (6–97) allows for the exponential decay of ψ_I (that is, $g_k \doteq \delta_{kI}e^{-t/T}$; compare the discussion of line widths and line shapes, (5–71)–(5–78)). When this effect is combined with the absorption of the applied radiation (see (5–78)–(5–79)), the result can be expressed to good approximation as

$$\alpha_I = \frac{2}{3h}\sum_{\psi k}\frac{|\mu_{kI}|^2\,\nu_{kI}}{(\nu_{kI})^2 - \nu^2 + i\,(\nu/2\pi T_I)} \tag{6–99}$$

where T_I is the mean lifetime of state ψ_I (and the convention of electromagnetic theory, namely using a complex dielectric constant, $\epsilon' = \epsilon + (4\pi\sigma/i\omega)$ has been adopted by assigning all absorption to the conductivity, σ).

Optical rotation: If time-averaged magnetic-dipole terms (arising from gradients of **A**; compare (5–64)) are similarly evaluated, the main effect is to add to the average polarizations per molecule the terms,

$$\langle \delta\mathbf{p}\rangle = -\beta\frac{\partial\mathbf{H}}{\partial t}; \quad \langle\mathbf{m}\rangle = \beta\frac{\partial}{\partial t}(\mathbf{E} + \frac{4\pi}{3}\mathbf{P}) = \beta\frac{\partial\mathbf{E}_L}{\partial t}$$

where β is the thermal average (as in (6–98)) of β_I, defined by:

$$\beta_I = \frac{1}{3\pi h}\sum_{\psi_k}\frac{\mathrm{Im}\,\{\langle I|\sum e_i\mathbf{r}_i|k\rangle\langle k|\sum \frac{e_j}{2m_jc}\mathbf{r}_j \times \mathbf{p}_j|I\rangle\}}{(\nu_{kI})^2 - \nu^2}$$

(Here "Im" denotes "imaginary part of"). These relations imply, to first order in β. $\mathbf{D} = \epsilon\mathbf{E} - g\partial\mathbf{H}/\partial t$ and $\mathbf{B} = \mathbf{H} + g\partial\mathbf{E}/\partial t$ where $g = (4\pi N/3V)\beta(\epsilon + 2)$. It is then found that polarized plane waves in such a medium suffer a *rotation of the plane of polarization* by an angle, $\phi = 4\pi^2\nu^2 g/c$ per unit path length. (Symmetry arguments show that $\beta_I = 0 = g$ if the molecule is identical with its mirror image.)

5. Real Gases—Classical

To a good approximation, intermolecular forces merely add to the Hamiltonian function a term, $\Phi(\mathbf{q}_1, \mathbf{q}_2, \cdots, \mathbf{q}_N)$, independent of internal molecular coordinates. Thus by (6–47), using (6–71) and (6–75)

$$Z = \frac{(\zeta_i)^N}{\lambda^{3N}N!}\int\cdots\int \exp\left[\frac{-1}{kT}\Phi(\mathbf{q}_1, \cdots, \mathbf{q}_N)\right] d\mathbf{q}_1\cdots d\mathbf{q}_N \tag{6–100}$$

where ζ_i is the single-molecule "internal" partition function—that is, excluding translational kinetic energy. (λ is defined in (6–74) or (6–75).) In general, the $\mathbf{q}_k$

* If the molecule were not free to rotate, α_I and α should be replaced by dyadics, defined analogously in terms of the dyadic, $\langle I|\Sigma\, e_i\mathbf{r}_i|k\rangle\langle k|\Sigma\, e_i\mathbf{r}_i|I\rangle$.

include angle (orientation) variables as well as molecular center-of-mass positions (normalized so that when $\Phi = 0$, Z reduces to (6–71)).

Intermolecular forces are usually assumed to be additive:

$$\Phi(\mathbf{q}_1, \cdots, \mathbf{q}_N) = \sum_{1 \leqslant i < j \leqslant N} \phi(\mathbf{q}_i, \mathbf{q}_j) \tag{6–101}$$

It is then convenient to introduce Mayer's function,

$$f(\mathbf{q}_i, \mathbf{q}_j) = \exp\left[\frac{-1}{kT}\,\phi(\mathbf{q}_i, \mathbf{q}_j)\right] - 1 \tag{6–102}$$

which is nearly zero except when $\mathbf{r}_i \doteqdot \mathbf{r}_j$. In terms of this function,

$$e^{-\Phi/kT} = 1 + \sum_{i<j} f(\mathbf{q}_i, \mathbf{q}_j) + \sum_{i<j}\sum_{k<l} f(\mathbf{q}_i, \mathbf{q}_j) f(\mathbf{q}_k, \mathbf{q}_l) + \cdots \tag{6–103}$$

Mayer's "cluster integrals" are defined as

$$b_l(T, V) = \frac{1}{l!\,V} \int \cdots \int \sum_{(c)} [\textstyle\prod f(\mathbf{q}_i, \mathbf{q}_k)]\, d\mathbf{q}_1 \cdots d\mathbf{q}_l \tag{6–104}$$

where the sum, $\sum_{(c)}$, is over all *products*, $\prod f(\mathbf{q}_i, \mathbf{q}_j)$, corresponding to "clusters" of l molecules is the sense that: If each factor $f(\mathbf{q}_j, \mathbf{q}_k)$ of such a product is imagined to represent a physical link between molecules j and k, then a "cluster product" links all the molecules, $i = 1, 2, \cdots, l$, into a single, connected whole (in one way or another).*

Combinatorial arguments will then show that (6–100)–(6–104) may be cast in the form,

$$Z = \left(\frac{\zeta_i}{\lambda^3}\right)^N \sum{}'' \prod_l \frac{(Vb_l)^{m_l}}{m_l!} \tag{6–105}$$

in which the sum is over all sets of numbers, m_l, such that $\sum l m_l = N$. Using this condition, the grand partition function, (6–33), can then be written,

$$Z_G = \sum_{m_l} \prod_l [Vb_l\, \zeta_i^{\,l}\, e^{\mu l/kT}\, \lambda^{-3l}]^{m_l} \frac{1}{m_l!}$$

where the sum is now simply over all values of m_l; whence,

$$\frac{pV}{kT} = \ln Z_G = \sum_{l=1}^{\infty} \frac{Vb_l\, \zeta_i^{\,l}}{\lambda^{3l}}\, e^{l\mu/kT} \tag{6–106}$$

---

* Explicitly, the first three b are,

$$b_1 = 1 \qquad b_2 = \frac{1}{2V} \iint f(\mathbf{q}_1, \mathbf{q}_2)\, d\mathbf{q}_1\, d\mathbf{q}_2$$

$$b_3 = \frac{1}{6V} \iiint \{f_{12}f_{23} + f_{13}f_{23} + f_{13}f_{12} + f_{12}f_{23}f_{13}\}\, d\mathbf{q}_1\, d\mathbf{q}_2\, d\mathbf{q}_3$$

where $f_{ij} = f(\mathbf{q}_i, \mathbf{q}_j)$. The "linkages" corresponding to b_3 are

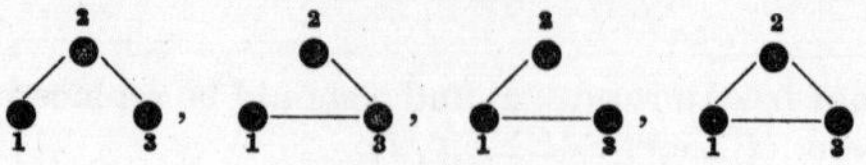

If N, the number of molecules, is fixed, μ must be eliminated between (6–106) and (6–36), or, letting

$$x = (\zeta_i/\lambda^3)e^{\mu/kT}$$

a parametric equation of state is

$$\left.\begin{aligned} p/kT &= \sum_{l=1}^{\infty} b_l x^l \\ N/V &= \sum_{l=1}^{\infty} l b_l x^l \end{aligned}\right\} \qquad (6\text{–}107)$$

A number of plausibility arguments have been advanced to indicate that (6–107) *predicts* condensation of vapor to liquid, but a completely rigorous proof* is still lacking.

Numerical results based on (6–107) have been obtained primarily at low densities; here it is customary and convenient to use the "virial expansion",

$$\frac{pV}{NkT} = 1 + \frac{B(T)}{V} + \frac{C(T)}{V^2} + \frac{D(T)}{V^3} + \cdots$$

wherein, from (6–107),

$$\left.\begin{aligned} B(T) &= -Nb_2 = \frac{-N}{2V}\iint f(\mathbf{q}_1, \mathbf{q}_2)\, d\mathbf{q}_1\, d\mathbf{q}_2 \\ C(T) &= -N^2(2b_3 - 4b_2{}^2) \\ D(T) &= -N^3(3b_4 - 18b_2b_3 + 20b_2{}^3) \end{aligned}\right\} \qquad (6\text{–}108)$$

Using (6–104) and (6–108), virial coefficients, etc., have been calculated for many special, assumed forms of the intermolecular potential, $\phi(\mathbf{q}_i, \mathbf{q}_j)$. Surprisingly good agreement with experiment over large ranges is obtained with the angle-independent Lennard–Jones 6–12 potential,

$$\phi(\mathbf{r}, \mathbf{r} + \mathbf{R}) = 4\epsilon[(\sigma/R)^{12} - (\sigma/R)^6] \qquad (6\text{–}109)$$

where ϵ and σ are constants characteristic of the gas. These have been fitted to data for many different gases and detailed numerical tables are available in the literature. (Naturally, this simple potential cannot be expected to suffice for strongly polar or very much elongated molecules.)

Radial distribution theory (*classical*)—an alternative formalism:

In (6–100), write $\mathbf{q}_i = (\mathbf{r}_i, \mathbf{\Omega}_i)$ where $\mathbf{\Omega}_i$ denotes the orientation of the ith molecule; then let $\mathbf{r}_i = V^{1/3}\mathbf{R}_i = L\mathbf{R}_i$ and use (6–30) in the form,

$$pV = \tfrac{1}{3}kT\frac{L}{Z}\left(\frac{\partial Z}{\partial L}\right)_T$$

and note that

$$L\frac{\partial}{\partial L}\Phi(L\mathbf{R}_i, \mathbf{\Omega}_i) = \sum_i \mathbf{r}_i \cdot \nabla_i \Phi(\mathbf{r}_i, \mathbf{\Omega}_i)$$

---

* In the sense of yielding, without any appeal to classical thermodynamics, $(\partial p/\partial V)_T = 0$ (at least in the limit $N \to \infty$ with V/N constant) for $T <$ some T_C and a finite range of V.

Wood and Alder have recently shown by machine-computations that hard-sphere molecules undergo a phase transition at about twice the close-packing volume and enter a condensed phase with volume larger than that for close packing.

The result is (using (6–48) as an abbreviation),

$$pV = NkT - \tfrac{1}{3}\langle \sum_i \mathbf{r}_i \cdot \nabla_i \Phi \rangle \tag{6–110}$$

(Classical virial theorem.)

It is now assumed that intermolecular forces are additive and independent of velocity and orientations:

$$\Phi = \tfrac{1}{2} \sum_{j \neq k} \phi(|\mathbf{r}_j - \mathbf{r}_k|) \tag{6–111}$$

Then (6–110) can be written,

$$pV = NkT - \tfrac{1}{6}N(N-1)\langle(\mathbf{r}_1 \cdot \nabla_1 + \mathbf{r}_2 \cdot \nabla_2)\phi(|\mathbf{r}_1 - \mathbf{r}_2|)\rangle$$

and using (6–48) again, the resulting equation of state is

$$pV = NkT - \frac{2\pi N(N-1)}{3V} \int_0^{(\infty)} g(r) \frac{\mathrm{d}\phi(r)}{\mathrm{d}r} r^3 \, \mathrm{d}r \tag{6–112}$$

where

$$g(|\mathbf{r}_1 - \mathbf{r}_2|) = \frac{\int e^{-\Phi/kT} V^2 \, \mathrm{d}\mathbf{r}_3 \cdots \mathrm{d}\mathbf{r}_N}{\int e^{-\Phi/kT} \, \mathrm{d}\mathbf{r}_1 \cdots \mathrm{d}\mathbf{r}_N} \tag{6–113}$$

which is called the *radial distribution function.* It is dimensionless and $\frac{1}{2}N^2 g(s)[4\pi s^2 \, \mathrm{d}s/V]$ is the number of molecule-pairs whose separation lies in the range $s \pm \frac{1}{2}\mathrm{d}s$. Either from this or by direct manipulations similar to the above,

$$U = N\langle E_{\text{int}} \rangle + \tfrac{3}{2}NkT + N(N-1)\frac{2\pi}{V} \int_0^{(\infty)} \phi(r) g(r) r^2 \, \mathrm{d}r \tag{6–114}$$

where $\langle E_{\text{int}} \rangle$ is the average internal energy of a molecule. It can also be shown that

$$kT \left.\frac{\partial(N/V)}{\partial p}\right|_T = 1 + \frac{4\pi N}{V} \int_0^{(\infty)} [g(r) - 1] r^2 \, \mathrm{d}r \tag{6–115}$$

Several methods of determining $g(s)$ for high densities have been proposed. For example, evaluating $\nabla_1 \ln g(|\mathbf{r}_1 - \mathbf{r}_2|)$ from (6–113) and taking the scalar product of the result with $(\mathbf{r}_1 - \mathbf{r}_2)$, it is not difficult to show,

$$kT \frac{\partial}{\partial r} \ln g(r) = -\frac{\mathrm{d}\phi(r)}{\mathrm{d}r} - \frac{\pi V^2/N(N-1)}{r^2 g(r)} \int_0^{(\infty)} \frac{\mathrm{d}}{\mathrm{d}s}\phi(s) \, \mathrm{d}s \int_{|s-r|}^{s+r} (s^2 + r^2 - t^2) n_3(r, s, t) t \, \mathrm{d}t$$

where n_3 is the triplet-distribution function defined by,

$$n_3(r_{12}, r_{13}, r_{23}) = N(N-1)(N-2) \frac{\int e^{-\Phi/kT} \, \mathrm{d}\mathbf{r}_4 \cdots \mathrm{d}\mathbf{r}_N}{\int e^{-\Phi/kT} \, \mathrm{d}\mathbf{r}_1 \cdots \mathrm{d}\mathbf{r}_N}$$

The "superposition approximation",

$$n_3(r, s, t) \doteqdot (N/V)^3 g(r) g(s) g(t)$$

or some similar "reasonable estimate" may then be substituted to obtain an equation in g alone. Numerical computations agree moderately well with experiment—better than do the "cell" or "hole" theories of liquids. It appears that the radial distribution function, $g(s)$, must be known to very high accuracy in order to obtain moderate accuracy in the thermodynamic results.

For low densities, the expansion (6–103) may be substituted in (6–113):

$$g(r_{12}) = \exp[-\phi(r_{12})/kT]\left\{1 + \frac{N}{V}\int \{1 - \exp[-\phi(r_{13})/kT]\}\{1 - \exp[-\phi(r_{23})/kT]\}\, d\mathbf{r}_3 + O\left(\frac{N^2}{V^2}\right)\right\}$$

where $r_{ij} = |\mathbf{r}_i - \mathbf{r}_j|$.

6. Solids

As a first approximation, a solid sample may be regarded as a gigantic molecule. The dominant factor in the partition function is then the vibration factor, given by (6–79),

$$-\ln Z_{\text{vib}} \doteqdot \sum_{\nu_i} \left[\frac{h\nu_i}{2kT} + \ln(1 - e^{-h\nu_i/kT})\right] \tag{6–116}$$

(in the harmonic oscillator approximation).

The lowest fundamental frequencies, ν_i, must be just ordinary macroscopic elastic vibrations. Debye suggested that the number of ν_i in the range, $\nu \pm \frac{1}{2}d\nu$, be approximated by (see (19–5)):

$$n(\nu)\,d\nu = \begin{cases} 3N(3\nu^2/\nu_D^3)\,d\nu, & \text{for } \nu \leqslant \nu_D \\ 0, & \text{for } \nu \geqslant \nu_D \end{cases} \tag{6–117}$$

where, since there must be $3N$ different ν_i in all,*

$$\frac{1}{\nu_D^3} = \frac{4\pi V}{9N}\left[\frac{1}{c_L^3} + \frac{2}{c_t^3}\right] \tag{6–118}$$

Here, c_L and c_t are the speeds of longitudinal and transverse acoustic waves (see (1–83), (1–84)).

Then from (6–116) and (6–30), the internal energy due to vibrations is

$$U_D = \tfrac{9}{8}Nk\Theta + 9NkT\left(\frac{T}{\Theta}\right)^3 \int_0^{\Theta/T} \frac{x^3\,dx}{e^x - 1} \tag{6–119}$$

where

$$\Theta = h\nu_D/k \quad \text{(Debye temperature)}$$

To U_D must be added the cohesive energy ("binding energy" in the giant-molecule analogue) which is a function of V only (compare (6–18)).

Debye equation of state: With the approximation (6–117), it follows from (6–116) and (6–30) that when the cohesive energy, $U_0(V)$ is added,

$$p = -\frac{d}{dV}U_0(V) + \gamma U_D/V \tag{6–120}$$

where

$$\gamma = -\frac{d(\ln \Theta)}{d(\ln V)} \tag{6–121}$$

From (6–120) and (2–33),

$$\alpha = K\gamma c_v/V \tag{6–122}$$

(Grueneisen's law.)

---

* Strictly, $3N - 6$. Here N is the number of atoms in the solid.

The atomic heat (per mole*) follows from (6–119),

$$c_v \doteq 9R\left(\frac{T}{\Theta}\right)^3 \int_0^{\Theta/T} \frac{x^4 e^x \, dx}{(e^x - 1)^2} \tag{6–123}$$

(To this must be added the specific heat, (6–67), of the conduction electrons, if any.)

For $T \gg \Theta$, equation (6–123) gives the classical result,† $c_v = 3R$ (Dulong and Petit's law); for $T \ll \Theta$, it gives the celebrated and well-established T^3-law:

$$c_v \doteq 9R\left(\frac{T}{\Theta}\right)^3 \frac{4\pi^4}{15} \tag{6–124}$$

Relations more precise than (6–117)–(6–124) require detailed calculation of the vibration spectrum, $n(\nu)$, on the basis of assumed interatomic forces. An important concept arising then is that of "optical"‡ branches, which are groups of very high-frequency vibrations corresponding to internal molecular vibrations. (Optical branches do not occur in monatomic crystals.)

Rather good agreement with exact calculations and with experiment can often be obtained merely by replacing an upper portion (typically $\frac{1}{3}$ to $\frac{1}{2}$) of the Debye spectrum by a lumped "optical branch", $n_0 = \alpha N \delta(\nu - \nu_0)$ with suitable parameters, α and ν_0. (The corresponding energy and specific heat follow immediately from (6–116).)

Order-Disorder Phenomena

Consider a binary alloy, $A + B$, in classical approximation. If $\phi_{\alpha\beta}$ is the energy of a bond between atoms of types, α, β, if ν *is the number of nearest neighbors* around each atom and if m is the number of A to B bonds in the entire crystal, then the cohesive energy may be written,

$$E = m\phi + \tfrac{1}{2}\nu(N_A \phi_{AA} + N_B \phi_{BB}) \tag{6–125}$$

where

$$\phi = \phi_{AB} - \tfrac{1}{2}(\phi_{AA} + \phi_{BB}) \tag{6–126}$$

and N_A, N_B are the number of A, B atoms respectively. The term, $m\phi$, in (6–125) represents the major effect of changing the arrangement of A and B atoms in the crystal and, to the extent that other energies (kinetic and "elastic") may be regarded as independent § of this term, the classical partition function (6–47) contains m only in the factor,

$$\zeta_0 = \sum_{\text{config}} e^{-m\phi/kT} = \sum_m g(m) e^{-m\phi/kT} \tag{6–127}$$

where $g(m)$ is the number of atomic arrangements (on the given lattice) consistent with m bonds of type A–B. Since $g(m)$ has not been exactly computed, further approximations are necessary:

Precipitation ($\phi > 0$): Consider a homogeneous phase with $N_A = \gamma N, N_B = (1 - \gamma)N$ and assume (since A and B tend to repel each other when $\phi > 0$) that the

* That is, per 6×10^{23} atoms of solid, irrespective of the chemical formula.

† The classical result follows directly from (6–49) for a collection of particles bound by harmonic forces.

‡ "Infrared" would be more accurate.

§ Admittedly a rather crude approximation.

main contribution to ζ_0 arises from completely random arrangements of A and B atoms in the homogeneous crystal. Then

$$\zeta_0 \doteqdot \binom{N}{\gamma N} \exp\left[-N\nu\gamma(1-\gamma)\phi/kT\right]$$

(the first factor is a binomial coefficient) and the contribution of order phenomena to the (Helmholtz) free energy is, by (6–29), using Stirling's formula,

$$F = kTN\left\{\gamma \ln \gamma + (1-\gamma)\ln(1-\gamma) + \frac{\nu\phi}{kT}\gamma(1-\gamma)\right\} \tag{6–128}$$

$$\equiv kTNf(\gamma) \quad \text{(say)}$$

Consider now two phases, 1, 2; for this system, $F = kT[N_1 f(\gamma_1) + N_2 f(\gamma_2)]$ and F is a minimum (fixed V, T), subject to the conditions, $N_1 + N_2 = N$ (fixed) and $N_1\gamma_1 + N_2\gamma_2 = \gamma N = N_A$ (fixed), when

$$f'(\gamma_1) = f'(\gamma_2) \quad \text{and} \quad f(\gamma_1) - f(\gamma_2) = (\gamma_1 - \gamma_2)f'(\gamma_1) \tag{6–129}$$

Since $f(\gamma)$ in (6–128) is symmetric about $\gamma = \frac{1}{2}$, these imply that γ_1 and γ_2 are each a root of $f'(\gamma) = 0$. Letting $\eta = 1 - 2\gamma_{1,2}$, so that $\eta = \pm 1$ for pure A or B phases, the condition, $f'(\gamma) = 0$, is

$$\eta = \tanh(\eta\nu\phi/2kT) \tag{6–130}$$

For $T < \nu\phi/2k$, this has two roots,* corresponding to separate A-rich and B-rich phases, while for $T > \nu\phi/2k$ the only root is $\eta = 0$ so that the "two" phases must then be identical. From this information, the "phase diagram" of the alloy is easily constructed.

The specific heat of precipitation may be estimated from (6–125) and $m \doteqdot N\nu\gamma(1-\gamma) = \frac{1}{4}N\nu(1-\eta^2)$.

These results apply, of course, only to the thermodynamically stable states whereas in practice (especially under rapid cooling) the atoms may be unable to move rapidly enough (even to form small grains of "pure" phases) and may thus be "frozen" in a high-temperature distribution. An example is ordinary tempered steel.

Ordering ($\phi < 0$): Consider an assembly with $N_A = N_B = \frac{1}{2}N$ and define a "short range order" parameter, σ, by

$$m = \tfrac{1}{4}N\nu(\sigma + 1) \tag{6–131}$$

$\sigma = 0$ for a random arrangement of atoms and $\sigma = 1$ for a perfectly orderly arrangement (the total number of bonds of any type is $\frac{1}{2}\nu N$). Also define a "long range order" parameter, S, as follows. When ordering is perfect, two sublattices will each be occupied by atoms of only one kind; for any actual configuration, let p be the fraction of sites on one of these sublattices which are occupied by A atoms. Since p and $p' = 1 - p$ refer to equivalent situations, define $S = 2p - 1$ (so that $S = 0$ for complete disorder and $S = \pm 1$ for perfect order).

For a given S, it is readily seen that, on the *average*, $m = \frac{1}{4}N\nu(1 + S^2)$. Thus it is reasonable to assume that, to a sufficient approximation, S and σ are related† by the Bragg–Williams assumption,

$$\sigma \doteqdot S^2 \tag{6–132}$$

* The root, $\eta = 0$, here represents a maximum of F and must be omitted.

† Strictly, this is not true. For example, take the perfectly ordered configuration and interchange A and B atoms in one half of the crystal; then $S = 0$ but $\sigma \doteqdot 1$.

The advantage is that the number of atomic configurations consistent with a given S is easily shown to be

$$g(S) = \binom{\frac{1}{2}N}{\frac{1}{2}Np}\binom{\frac{1}{2}N}{\frac{1}{2}N(1-p)} = \binom{\frac{1}{2}N}{\frac{1}{4}N(1+S)}^2 \tag{6–133}$$

Combining (6–127), (6–131)–(6–133),

$$\zeta_0 = \sum_S g(S) \exp (N\nu\,|\phi|\, S^2/4kT) \tag{6–134}$$

The terms of the sum are the relative probabilities of various values of S; compare (6–25)–(6–29). Since we have $\mathrm{d}g/\mathrm{d}S = -N \tanh^{-1} S$ (using Stirling's approximation, $\ln (N!) \doteqdot N \ln N$) the most probable value of S is a root of

$$S = \tanh\left(\frac{\nu|\phi|}{2kT} S\right) \tag{6–135}$$

For $T > T_c = \nu|\phi|/2k$, the only root is $S = 0$, corresponding to complete disorder, but as T drops below T_c, the ordering rapidly increases* to $S = \pm 1$.

The specific heat due to the order-disorder transformation follows from (6–125), (6–131), (6–132). In particular, $\int_0^{T_c} (c_v/T)\,\mathrm{d}T = Nk \ln 2$, as would be expected from the entropy of mixing; c_v suddenly drops from $3Nk/2$ to zero† at $T = T_c$, and finally $\int_0^{T_c} c_v\,\mathrm{d}T = \frac{1}{4}N\nu|\phi|$, as also follows from elementary energy considerations.

Vacancy and interstitial defects: Let E_v and E_i be the energies required to form a vacancy and an interstitial atom respectively. If a particular arrangement of N atoms entails N_v vacancies and N_i interstitials, there must be $N_L = N + N_v - N_i$ lattice sites over which the vacancies may be distributed and αN_L possible interstitial positions, where α is a constant characteristic of the lattice,

$$\alpha = \frac{\text{number of interstitial sites}}{\text{number of lattice sites}} \tag{6–136}$$

Thus the number of arrangements consistent with an energy, $N_vE_v + N_iE_i$, is given by

$$g(N_v, N_i) = \binom{N + N_v - N_i}{N_v}\binom{\alpha N + \alpha N_v - \alpha N_i}{N_i} \tag{6–137}$$

and the variables, N_v, N_i enter the partition function (primarily) through the factor,

$$\zeta = \sum_{N_v, N_i} g(N_i, N_v) \exp\left[-(N_vE_v + N_iE_i)/kT\right] \tag{6–138}$$

Using the same method as in passing from (6–134) to (6–135), the most probable values of N_v and N_i are found to satisfy,

$$\left.\begin{aligned} \frac{N_v}{N + N_v - N_i}\left\{1 - \frac{N_i}{\alpha(N + N_v - N_i)}\right\}^{\alpha} &= e^{-E_v/kT} \\ \frac{N_i}{N - N_i}\left\{1 - \frac{N_i}{\alpha(N + N_v - N_i)}\right\}^{-\alpha-1} &= \alpha e^{-E_i/kT} \end{aligned}\right\} \tag{6–139}$$

* In this range, the root, $S = 0$, represents the smallest term in (6–134). It may represent a metastable state in some cases.

† Experimentally, a rapid but not discontinuous change is found; this is probably connected specifically with the approximation (6–132).

Since, in a solid, N_v and N_i are very small compared to N,

$$N_v \doteqdot Ne^{-E_v/kT}; \qquad N_i \doteqdot \alpha Ne^{-E_i/kT} \tag{6–140}$$

(In some solids, E_i is so great, because of atomic size considerations, that interstitial sites are "never" occupied; vacancies, however, occur in virtually all solids.)

Ferromagnetism

Although wavefunctions which are symmetric in electron space coordinates usually have the lowest energy, there are a few cases where at least partially anti-symmetric wavefunctions are energetically favored; since the Pauli exclusion principle then requires some parallel alignment of spins, such substances at low temperatures will exhibit spontaneous magnetization arising from the electron magnetic moment. (Note that the mechanism is "electrostatic forces plus exclusion principle"; spin-spin magnetic forces are not only weak but have the wrong sign.)

The Ising model assumes that each lattice point contains the equivalent of an unpaired electron (magnetic moment, $\mu = e\hbar/2mc$, with two available spin states) and that interactions occur only between nearest neighbors with parallel alignment favored by an energy difference, ϕ. (In ferromagnets, $\phi > 0$.)

Bethe's treatment of this model focusses attention on groups of spins consisting of a central spin and all its nearest neighbors (ν in number). Denoting the central spin's state by $+(-)$ for alignment parallel to (against) the applied field, H, and denoting by m the number of its nearest neighbors aligned against H, the energies of the various possible types of groups are taken to be (with suitable choice of zero energy):

$$\begin{aligned} E(m, +) &= m\phi + 2\mu Hm + 2\mu H'm \\ E(m, -) &= (\nu - m)\phi + 2\mu H(m + 1) + 2\mu H'm \end{aligned} \tag{6–141}$$

where H' is an "inner field", as yet undetermined, which approximates the influence of the next-nearest neighbors. Since the situations $(m, \pm)$ can occur in $\binom{\nu}{m}$ ways, their probabilities are

$$p(m, +) = C\binom{\nu}{m}(xyz)^m; \qquad p(m, -) = C\binom{\nu}{m}x^{\nu-m}y^{m+1}z^m \tag{6–142}$$

where

$$x = e^{-\phi/kT}; \qquad y = e^{-2\mu H/kT}; \qquad z = e^{-2\mu H'/kT}; \qquad C = \text{normalizing constant}$$

Thus the probabilities of a given central spin are

$$p(+) = C(1 + xyz)^\nu; \qquad p(-) = Cy(x + yz)^\nu \tag{6–143}$$

But $p(-)$ must equal $\langle m\rangle/\nu$ since the central spin may be on any lattice point. The quantity, $\langle m\rangle$, is readily computed because, by (6–142),

$$mp(m, \pm) = z\frac{\partial}{\partial z}p(m, \pm)$$

and the resulting equation, $p(-) = \langle m\rangle/\nu$, may be written,

$$e^{-\phi/kT}\sinh\left[\frac{\mu}{kT}\left(\frac{\nu H'}{\nu - 1} + H\right)\right] = \sinh\left[\frac{\mu}{kT}\left(\frac{\nu - 2}{\nu - 1}H' + H\right)\right] \tag{6–144}$$

From this and (6–143), the magnetization,* M, is given by

$$\frac{M}{M_\infty} = \frac{p(+) - p(-)}{p(+) + p(-)} = \tanh\left[\frac{\mu}{kT}\left(\frac{\nu H'}{\nu - 1} + H\right)\right] \tag{6–145}$$

where $M_\infty = N\mu/V$ is the magnetization when all spins are aligned.

Eliminating H' between (6–145) and (6–144) yields M as a function of H and T. For $T < \Theta$, where

$$\Theta = \frac{\phi}{k\left|\ln\left(1 - \frac{2}{\nu}\right)\right|} \tag{6–146}$$

it is found that M is finite when $H = 0$ so that Θ is the "Curie temperature" of the ferromagnet. For $T > \Theta$, all three of M, H, H' approach zero together and from (6–145),

$$\left(\frac{\partial M}{\partial H}\right)_{H=0} = \frac{\mu M_\infty}{kT}\left[1 + \frac{\nu}{\nu - 1}\left(\frac{\partial H'}{\partial H}\right)_{H=0}\right]$$

The derivative, $\partial H'/\partial H$ for $H = 0 = H'$ can be evaluated from (6–144) and the resulting susceptibility per spin for $T > \Theta$ is

$$\chi_m \doteq \frac{V}{N}\left(\frac{\partial M}{\partial H}\right)_{H=0} = \frac{\mu^2/kT}{1 - \frac{1}{2}\nu[1 - e^{-\phi/kT}]} \tag{6–147}$$

For very large T, this approaches "Curie's law", $\chi_m = (\text{constant})/(T - \Theta_c)$, but with a Curie temperature, $\Theta_c = \nu\phi/2k$ different from (6–146).

Anti-ferromagnetism: In some solids, similar mechanisms favor an alternating, anti-parallel alignment of neighboring, net atomic spins; thus $\phi < 0$. The characteristic temperature, (6–146), is then negative, and (6–147) is valid for "all" temperatures (where quantum effects are not important). In this case, at high temperatures, $\chi_m = (\text{constant})/(T + \Theta_N)$ where $\Theta_N = \nu|\phi|/2k > 0$, and Θ_N is called the "Néel temperature". Near $T = \Theta_N$ (or somewhat below), χ_m has a maximum and there is some evidence that at 0°K, $\chi_0 \doteq \frac{2}{3}\chi_{\max}$.

Low temperatures (*Spin waves*): A quantum treatment of the above problem has been carried through only for very low temperatures (Bloch). The main result is that (6–144) and (6–145) should be replaced by

$$\frac{M}{M_\infty} = 1 - \frac{2.317}{2\pi^2 z}\left(\frac{kT}{\phi}\right)^{3/2}, \qquad \text{for } kT \ll \phi \tag{6–148}$$

where z is the number of atoms per unit cell. This result has been experimentally confirmed.

Domains, anisotropy and the *B–H* curve: The results (6–144)–(6–148) refer to single "domains". That is, in a large macroscopic specimen, the total magnetic energy, $\int (HB/8\pi)\, dV$, will be reduced if magnetic circuits can be closed within the specimen, thus reducing the external field. This tendency is counterbalanced by energy associated with misoriented spins on either side of the domain boundaries.

Experimentally, it is found that single crystals are more easily magnetized in some directions than in others; this "anisotropy energy" is presently thought to arise from spin-orbit coupling to the crystal fields.

---

* This is the magnetization within a domain and corresponds to the *saturation* magnetization of an ordinary, macroscopic sample.

Boundaries between domains ("Bloch walls") have a finite thickness determined by a balance between misorientation energy (ϕ, above) and the anisotropy energy of the transition region.

The B–H curve, commonly observed as H is increased from zero, is ascribed to initial growth of favorably oriented domains at the expense of others, first by reversible motions of the Bloch walls, and later by irreversible* wall motions; finally, the domain magnetizations are rotated against the anisotropy energy into complete alignment with the applied field as saturation is attained.

"Negative temperatures": It is possible to prepare some spin systems with net orientation opposite to an applied field; this situation, of course, is metastable but in special cases, its lifetime is long enough for a statistical theory to be meaningful. The entropy of such a system *decreases* with increasing energy, and the theory is formally equivalent to the usual theory, but with $T < 0$. The instability of such systems (there is always some coupling to lattice vibrations, etc.) is expressed by the fact that heat will always flow from a "negative-temperature" system to a positive-temperature system. In this sense, temperatures are ordered according to $(-1/T)$. The situation can, in principle, arise in any system whose internal energy has a finite upper bound, since then a sufficiently large internal energy requires nearly complete population of the highest state and hence nearly zero entropy.

7. Liquids

The basic theory of liquids is still in a state of flux, searching for a useful set of fundamental approximations. *Cell theories* virtually consider a liquid as a crystal, with each molecule "tied to" a lattice point, but able to move rather freely within its cell. Somewhat more realistic are *hole theories* which use the cell picture but allow a large proportion of empty cells into which a molecule from a neighboring cell may jump. At present writing, the radial distribution theory, (6–111)–(6–115), appears as promising an approach as any.

Dilute Solutions of Strong Electrolytes (*Debye Theory*)

Let the ions (into which the solute dissociates) have charge $\pm Ze$ and let there be $n_+ = n_- = n$ ions of each sign per unit volume. Consider the electrostatic potential, ϕ, about a particular positive ion. On the average, the remaining ions will be distributed according to Boltzmann's law: $dn_\pm = n \exp(\mp Ze\phi/kT)\, dV$ and if the solvent has dielectric constant, ϵ,

$$\nabla^2\phi = \frac{-4\pi}{\epsilon}\rho \doteqdot \frac{8\pi n Z^2 e^2}{\epsilon kT}\phi \tag{6–149}$$

Defining the *Debye length*:

$$l = \sqrt{\epsilon kT/8\pi n Z^2 e^2} \tag{6–150}$$

the appropriate solution of (6–149) is

$$\phi = \frac{Ze}{\epsilon r}e^{-r/l} = \frac{Ze}{\epsilon r} - \frac{Ze}{\epsilon r}(1 - e^{-r/l}) \tag{6–151}$$

wherein the last term is the potential due to ions other than the chosen (positive)

---

* Due to crystal imperfections. The Barkhausen effect is due to the walls "snapping" free of an imperfection.

one. The potential energy of the chosen ion is accordingly $(-Z^2e^2/\epsilon l)$; similarly a negative ion has the same potential energy. The total electrostatic energy is thus,

$$U_{\text{elec}} = -\frac{nVZ^2e^2}{\epsilon l} \tag{6–152}$$

For thermodynamic consequences, note that $G = G_0 + G_{\text{elec}} = U + pV - TS \doteqdot U - TS$ for condensed systems, wherein also $-S = (\partial G/\partial T)_p \doteqdot (\partial G/\partial T)_V$. Thus G and G_0 and hence G_{elec} satisfy: $G_i - T(\mathrm{d}G_i/\mathrm{d}T) \doteqdot U_i$ whence,

$$G_{\text{elec}} \doteqdot -\frac{2}{3}\frac{nVZ^2e^2}{\epsilon l}$$

When this is added to G_0, given by (2–105), arguments similar to (2–123) show that the freezing point depression, ΔT, and solute concentration, c, are related by (assuming the solid to be pure solvent; N_s = number of moles of liquid solvent),

$$2c\left[1 + \frac{N_sZ^2e^2}{3\epsilon kT}\frac{\partial(1/l)}{\partial N_s}\right] = \frac{-\Delta T|L|}{RT^2} \doteqdot 2c\left[1 - \frac{Z^2e^2}{6\epsilon kTl}\right]$$

C. STATISTICAL THEORIES—OFF EQUILIBRIUM

1. Fluctuations

Consider a macroscopic portion, $\mathscr{S}_1$, of a large system, $\mathscr{S}_t$. If R_1 is any (macroscopic) parameter of $\mathscr{S}_1$, the probability that R_1 lie in the range, $R_1 \pm \frac{1}{2}\mathrm{d}R_1$, (according to the material preceding (6–20)) is proportional to

$$\int_{R_1-\frac{1}{2}\mathrm{d}R_1}^{R_1+\frac{1}{2}\mathrm{d}R_1} \mathscr{N}_t(r)\,\mathrm{d}r = \mathscr{N}_t(R_1)\,\mathrm{d}R_1$$

where $\mathscr{N}_t(r)$ is the number of quantum states for the total system, $\mathscr{S}_t$, consistent with $R_1 = r$. Then by (6–28),

$$\mathscr{P}r(R_1 \pm \tfrac{1}{2}\mathrm{d}R_1) = \frac{\exp\,[S_t(R_1)/k]}{\int \exp\,[S_t(r)/k]\,\mathrm{d}r}\,\mathrm{d}R_1 \tag{6–153}$$

where $S_t(r)$ is the entropy of the *total* system when R_1 is held fixed at $R_1 = r$.

Similarly, for several variables: $P(r, s)\,\mathrm{d}r\,\mathrm{d}s = \text{constant} \cdot \exp\,[S_t(r, s)/k]\,\mathrm{d}r \cdot \mathrm{d}s$. One example of these results was encountered in (6–34)–(6–35) above.

Usually it is expedient to choose $\mathscr{S}_t$ as an isolated system, for then if $\Delta R_1 = R_1 - R_0$ where R_0 is the equilibrium value of R_1, we have, using a Taylor's series for S_1:

$$S_t = S_1 + S_2 = S_1(R_0) + \left.\frac{\partial S_1}{\partial R_1}\right|_0 \Delta R_1 + \frac{1}{2}\left.\frac{\partial^2 S_1}{\partial R_1^{\,2}}\right|_0 (\Delta R_1)^2 + \cdots + S_2(R_0) + \int_{R_0}^{R_1} (\delta Q_2/T_2)$$

If the environment, $\mathscr{S}_t - \mathscr{S}_1 = \mathscr{S}_2$, is sufficiently large, $T_2 \doteqdot$ constant and $\Delta Q_2 \doteqdot (\text{constant}) \cdot (\Delta R_1)$; but since $\mathscr{S}_t$ is isolated, $\mathrm{d}S_t \equiv 0$ and the linear terms in ΔR_1 must cancel:

$$S_t \doteqdot S_t(R_0) + \frac{1}{2}\left(\frac{\partial^2 S_1}{\partial R_1^{\,2}}\right)_0 (\Delta R_1)^2$$

and by (6–153),

$$\frac{1}{\langle(\Delta R_1)^2\rangle} \doteqdot \frac{-1}{k}\left(\frac{\partial^2 S_1}{\partial R_1{}^2}\right)_0 \tag{6–154}$$

where the derivative is evaluated at equilibrium and for the constraints imposed on S_1.

Similarly, if the constraints are such that several macroscopic variables R_m can fluctuate simultaneously,

$$\langle(\Delta R_i)(\Delta R_j)\rangle = k(\boldsymbol{\sigma}^{-1})_{ij}$$

where $\boldsymbol{\sigma}^{-1}$ is the inverse of the matrix,

$$\boldsymbol{\sigma}_{ij} = -(\partial^2 S/\partial R_i\,\partial R_j)_0$$

Often the derivative can be evaluated in general terms:

$$\left.\begin{array}{ll}
\text{For } V = \text{constant}, & \langle(\Delta U)^2\rangle \doteqdot kT^2 C_v \\
\text{For } p = \text{constant}, & \langle(\Delta H)^2\rangle \doteqdot kT^2 C_p \\
\text{For } V = \text{constant}, & \langle(\Delta T)^2\rangle \doteqdot kT^2/C_v \\
\text{For } T = \text{constant}, & \langle(\Delta V)^2\rangle \doteqdot kTVK_T \\
\text{For } V = \text{constant and for an ideal gas}, & \langle(\Delta p)^2\rangle \doteqdot kp^2/C_v \\
\multicolumn{2}{c}{(K_T = \text{isothermal compressibility})}
\end{array}\right\} \tag{6–155}$$

Note the arrangement of "extensive" quantities; in every case, the root-mean-square percentage fluctuation varies as the inverse square root of the size of the system.

2. The Onsager Relations (Irreversible Thermodynamics)

Let the index $j = 1, 2, 3, \cdots, n$ denote the quantum states available* to the system under the (equilibrium-denying) external constraints; let λ_{ij} be the corresponding transition probabilities per unit time. [$\lambda_{ij} = \lambda_{ji}$, at least to first order by (5–80).] Then if w_i is the probability that the system is in state, i,

$$\frac{\mathrm{d}w_i}{\mathrm{d}t} = \sum_j w_j\lambda_{ji} - w_i\sum_j \lambda_{ij} \tag{6–156}$$

Consider first a single macroscopic parameter, a, and let $\alpha_j = \langle\psi_j|a|\psi_j\rangle$ be its expectation value in state ψ_j. Thus $\langle a\rangle = \sum \alpha_i w_i$ and by (6–156),

$$\frac{\mathrm{d}\langle a\rangle}{\mathrm{d}t} = \sum_{i,j}\alpha_i(w_j - w_i)\lambda_{ij} = -\tfrac{1}{2}\sum_{i,j}(\alpha_j - \alpha_i)(w_j - w_i)\lambda_{ij} \tag{6–157}$$

For a given value of $\langle a\rangle$, the mean values of the w_i may be determined by noting that, for an ensemble of N duplicate systems, the number of states (of the ensemble) compatible with $N_i = w_i N$ is

$$\mathscr{N} = N!/\prod_i(N_i!)$$

* By (5–48)–(5–49), these are finite in number if the system is bounded in space and has a limited internal energy.

Using the restrictions, $\sum w_i = 1$, $\sum \alpha_i w_i = \langle a \rangle$, an argument similar to (6–20)–(6–25) shows that

$$\langle w_i \rangle = e^{A\alpha_i}/[\sum_j e^{A\alpha_j}]$$

where A is implicitly given as a function of $\langle a \rangle$ by

$$\langle a \rangle = \frac{\partial}{\partial A} \ln [\sum_j e^{A\alpha_j}] \tag{6–158}$$

The entropy of the system with a specified $\langle a \rangle$ is $(1/N)$ times that of the ensemble:

$$S(\langle a \rangle) = \frac{k}{N} \ln \mathcal{N} \doteq -k \sum w_j \ln w_j = -kA\langle a \rangle + k \ln [\sum_j e^{A\alpha_j}]$$

Thus, using (6–158),

$$\frac{dS}{dt} = -kA \frac{d\langle a \rangle}{dt} = \frac{\partial S}{\partial \langle a \rangle} \frac{d\langle a \rangle}{dt}$$

With these results, (6–157) becomes, after expanding* in a series in A,

$$\frac{d\langle a \rangle}{dt} = \frac{\partial S}{\partial \langle a \rangle} \frac{1}{2kn} \sum_{ij} (\alpha_i - \alpha_j)^2 \lambda_{ij} = C \frac{\partial S}{\partial \langle a \rangle} \tag{6–159}$$

("Phenomenological linear law".)

Similarly, with two macroscopic deviations, a and b, one finds

$$\frac{d\langle a \rangle}{dt} = \frac{\partial S}{\partial \langle a \rangle} L_{aa} + \frac{\partial S}{\partial \langle b \rangle} L_{ab}; \qquad \frac{d\langle b \rangle}{dt} = \frac{\partial S}{\partial \langle a \rangle} L_{ba} + \frac{\partial S}{\partial \langle b \rangle} L_{bb} \tag{6–160}$$

with

$$L_{ab} = L_{ba} = \frac{1}{2kn} \sum_{ij} (\alpha_j - \alpha_i)(\beta_j - \beta_i)\lambda_{ij} \tag{6–161}$$

(Onsager's reciprocal relation.)

3. Nyquist Theorems (Fluctuation-Dissipation Theorem)

Statement: If for any system an externally applied "force" (of any type), given by $V = V_0 \cos \omega t = \text{Re}\,(V_0 e^{i\omega t})$, causes a "response", $\dot{Q} = \text{Re}\,[V_0 Y(\omega) e^{i\omega t}]$ and entails energy absorption at a rate,

$$\text{Power absorbed} = \langle V\dot{Q} \rangle_{\text{avg}} = \tfrac{1}{2} V_0^2 G(\omega) \tag{6–162}$$

where

$$G(\omega) = \text{Re}\,[Y(\omega)]$$

then in thermal equilibrium the fluctuations of $\dot{Q}$ (without external excitation) have the following frequency spectrum,

$$\left.\begin{aligned} \langle (\dot{Q})^2 \rangle_f \, df &= 4\, G(2\pi f) \left[\frac{hf}{e^{hf/kT} - 1} + \tfrac{1}{2} hf \right] df \\ &\doteq 4kTG \, df, \quad \text{if} \quad hf \ll kT \end{aligned}\right\} \tag{6–163}$$

(The quantity $\langle (\dot{Q})^2 \rangle_f \, df$ may be defined as the mean of the square of the output of

---

* This step has not yet been fully justified; in a sense it is justified by experiments which indicate that (within limits) $d\langle a \rangle/dt$ is linear in $\partial S/\partial \langle a \rangle$.

an ideal filter which passes only those Fourier components of $\dot{Q}$ that lie in the range $f \pm \frac{1}{2}\mathrm{d}f$.)

Besides yielding the thermal (Johnson) noise of electrical circuits, the theorem connects acoustic impedance with gas–pressure fluctuations, Brownian motion with viscosity, etc. The first form of (6–163) has not yet been experimentally checked.

In the electrical case, with a constant resistance (megohms) at 300°K and an ideal filter of bandwidth, Δf, (megacycles), (6–163) becomes,

$$\sqrt{\overline{(V)^2}} = 128\sqrt{R_{M\Omega}\Delta f_{mc}} \quad \text{Microvolts} \tag{6–164}$$

PROOF: Let indices denote quantum states (not merely energy levels) and let $\zeta = \sum_j \exp(-E_j/kT)$. Then, by (6–38),

$$\langle(\dot{Q})^2\rangle = (1/\zeta)\sum_n e^{-E_n/kT}(\dot{Q}^2)_{nn}$$

but using (5–68),

$$(\dot{Q}^2)_{nn} = \sum_m \dot{Q}_{nm}\dot{Q}_{mn} = \sum_m (\omega_{mn})^2|Q_{nm}|^2$$

The portion of $\langle(\dot{Q})^2\rangle$ corresponding to "oscillation" at radian frequency, ω, may thus be written,

$$\begin{aligned}\langle(\dot{Q})^2\rangle_\omega &= (\omega^2/\zeta)\sum_{m,n} e^{-E_n/kT}\,|Q_{nm}|^2[\delta(\omega - \omega_{mn}) + \delta(\omega + \omega_{mn})] \\ &= (\omega^2/\zeta)(1 + e^{-\hbar\omega/kT})\sum_{E_m<E_n} e^{-E_m/kT}\,|Q_{nm}|^2\delta(\omega - \omega_{mn})\end{aligned}$$

On the other hand, if a perturbing "force", V, causes the system to change energy by $H \rightarrow H + VQ$, then with $V = V_0 \sin \omega t$, the transition probabilities per unit time are [for transitions with $\omega_{nm} \doteqdot \pm\omega$; compare (5–57)–(5–59)],

$$\left(\frac{V_0}{\hbar}\right)^2 |Q_{nm}|^2 \frac{\sin^2[\frac{1}{2}(\omega_{nm} \pm \omega)t]}{t(\omega_{nm} \pm \omega)^2} \doteqdot \left(\frac{V_0}{\hbar}\right)^2 |Q_{nm}|^2 \frac{\pi}{2}\,\delta(\omega_{nm} \pm \omega)$$

[Note that higher order terms would give rise to higher powers of V_0, contrary to the hypothesis, (6–162).] Recalling that the absorbed power changes sign with ω_{nm}, we have (near thermal equilibrium)

$$\text{Power absorbed} = \tfrac{1}{2}V_0^2 G(\omega) =$$

$$= \frac{\pi V_0^2\omega}{2\hbar\zeta}\sum_{m,n} e^{-E_n/kT}|Q_{nm}|^2[\delta(\omega + \omega_{nm}) - \delta(\omega - \omega_{nm})]$$

Thus:

$$G(\omega) = \frac{\pi\omega}{\hbar\zeta}(1 - e^{-\hbar\omega/kT})\sum_{E_m<E_n} e^{-E_m/kT}|Q_{nm}|^2\delta(\omega - \omega_{mn})$$

and comparison with the result for $\langle(\dot{Q})^2\rangle$ yields (6–163). (Recall that $\langle F\rangle_f\,\mathrm{d}f = \langle F\rangle_\omega\,\mathrm{d}\omega = 2\pi\langle F\rangle_\omega\,\mathrm{d}f$.)

4. Transport in Gases (Semi-Classical)

Basic Formalism

Consider a mixture of chemically different gases, possibly undergoing chemical reactions.* For brevity, let the index α identify both a specific chemical species

* Only reactions which proceed by two-body collisions can be explicitly treated by the following formalism.

and also (for polyatomic molecules) the internal quantum state. (Alternatively, regard molecules in different states of internal excitation as "chemically" different.)

Let $f_\alpha(\mathbf{r}, \mathbf{c}, t)\,dV\,dc_x\,dc_y\,dc_z$ be the number of molecules of type α located in a volume dV centered at position $\mathbf{r}$ and also having velocities only in the "volume" $d\mathbf{c} = dc_x\,dc_y\,dc_z$ centered on $\mathbf{c}$. (Note that f_α contains seven independent variables; unlike mean velocities defined later, $\mathbf{c}$ is entirely independent of $\mathbf{r}$ and therefore always commutes with $\boldsymbol{\nabla}$.) Let the external force on α molecules be $\mathbf{F}_\alpha$ and let

$$\boldsymbol{\nabla}_c = \hat{x}\frac{\partial}{\partial c_x} + \hat{y}\frac{\partial}{\partial c_y} + \hat{z}\frac{\partial}{\partial c_z} \tag{6–165}$$

At any given space point, $\mathbf{r}$, the rate of increase of f_α, namely $\partial f_\alpha/\partial t$, will be determined by:

(a) The net flow of molecules "α, $\mathbf{c}$" into dV, namely $-\boldsymbol{\nabla}\cdot(\mathbf{c}f_\alpha) = -\mathbf{c}\cdot\boldsymbol{\nabla}f_\alpha$.

(b) Acceleration of local molecules into or out of the range, $d\mathbf{c}$, by external forces. The net increase* is $(-1/m_\alpha)\boldsymbol{\nabla}_c\cdot(\mathbf{F}_\alpha f_\alpha)$.

(c) Accelerations, de-excitations, etc. of local molecules by intermolecular collisions. For the moment, denote by $\Gamma(\gamma\beta\to\alpha\delta)$ the rate at which molecules "α, $\mathbf{c}$" arise in dV because of collisions between γ and β molecules; denote by $\Gamma(\alpha\delta\to\gamma\beta)$ the corresponding rate for α molecules lost from the range $d\mathbf{c}$. (Note that the Γ's are functions of $\mathbf{r}$, $\mathbf{c}$, t.)

$$\frac{\partial f_\alpha}{\partial t} + \mathbf{c}\cdot\boldsymbol{\nabla}f_\alpha + \frac{1}{m_\alpha}\boldsymbol{\nabla}_c\cdot\mathbf{F}_\alpha f_\alpha = \sum\left[\Gamma(\gamma\beta\to\alpha\delta) - \Gamma(\alpha\delta\to\gamma\beta)\right] \tag{6–166}$$

This result assumes that only binary collisions are of importance, thus restricting the theory to low-density gases; it also assumes that collisions with the container walls are of minor importance so that the density must not be too low.

The Γ terms in (6–166) may be written in many ways, depending on the parameters used to describe the collisions. For clarity, we adopt a somewhat redundant notation; Let $P_{\gamma\beta;\alpha\delta}(\mathbf{g}, \mathbf{b};\ \mathbf{a}, \mathbf{d})\,d\mathbf{a}$ be the (differential) cross section† for a collision which starts with a γ molecule (velocity $\mathbf{g}$) and a β molecule (velocity $\mathbf{b}$) and produces a δ molecule and an α molecule with velocity in the range, $d\mathbf{a}$, centered on $\mathbf{a}$. (The velocity, $\mathbf{d}$, of the δ molecule is determined by $\mathbf{a}$, $\mathbf{b}$, $\mathbf{g}$ and conservation of momentum.)

With this notation, losses from the class (α, $\mathbf{c}$) occur at a local rate typified by (for collisions on δ, producing γ and β):

$$\Gamma(\alpha\delta\to\gamma\beta) = f_\alpha(\mathbf{r}, \mathbf{c}, t)\int|\mathbf{c}-\mathbf{c}'|\,f_\delta(\mathbf{r}, \mathbf{c}', t)\,d\mathbf{c}'\int P_{\alpha\delta;\gamma\beta}(\mathbf{c}, \mathbf{c}';\ \mathbf{c}'', \mathbf{c}''')\,d\mathbf{c}'''$$

Similarly‡

$$\Gamma(\gamma\beta\to\alpha\delta) = \iint|\mathbf{c}''-\mathbf{c}'''|\cdot f_\gamma'' f_\beta''' P_{\gamma\beta;\alpha\delta}(\mathbf{c}'', \mathbf{c}''';\ \mathbf{c}, \mathbf{c}')\,d\mathbf{c}''\,d\mathbf{c}'''$$

where f_γ'' denotes $f_\gamma(\mathbf{r}, \mathbf{c}'', t)$, etc.

---

* This is the (negative) "velocity divergence" of the "velocity current density", $(d\mathbf{c}/dt)\,f_\alpha$.

† Use of this description (essentially a probability concept) entails a fundamental *assumption* of "*molecular chaos*". Strictly, such an assumption is presumably unnecessary but no entirely rigorous way of avoiding it in all cases has yet been discovered. We are also assuming that the duration of a collision is negligible compared to the time between collisions (or that molecular spacing is much larger than molecular diameters).

‡ When $\gamma = \beta$, a factor of $\frac{1}{2}$ is needed to avoid counting collisions twice in the expressions shown for the Γ's. This then leads correctly to (6–169).

As anticipated by the notation, it is expedient to pair up those Γ terms which refer to collisions differing only by a time-reversal. Either by time-reversal symmetry of particle mechanics, or, more explicitly, from (5–82) and (5–85), it can be shown that with this interpretation:

$$|\mathbf{c}'' - \mathbf{c}'''| P_{\gamma\beta;\alpha\delta}(\mathbf{c}'', \mathbf{c}'''; \mathbf{c}, \mathbf{c}')\, d\mathbf{c}''' = |\mathbf{c} - \mathbf{c}'| P_{\alpha\delta;\gamma\beta}(\mathbf{c}, \mathbf{c}'; \mathbf{c}'', \mathbf{c}''')\, d\mathbf{c}' \tag{6–167}$$

With this result and abbreviating somewhat, we then have for the net local rate of gain of (α, $\mathbf{c}$) molecules due to collisions of the type $\gamma\beta \leftrightarrow \alpha\delta$,

$$\begin{aligned}\Gamma(\gamma\beta \rightarrow \alpha\delta) - \Gamma(\alpha\delta \rightarrow \gamma\beta) &= \left\{\frac{\partial}{\partial t}[f_\alpha(\mathbf{r}, \mathbf{c}, t)]\right\}_{\text{collisions}} \\ &= \iint [f_\gamma'' f_\beta''' - f_\alpha f_\delta'] |\mathbf{c} - \mathbf{c}'| P_{\alpha\delta;\gamma\beta}\, d\mathbf{c}'\, d\mathbf{c}''\end{aligned} \tag{6–168}$$

where the velocity argument, $\mathbf{c}'''$, of f_β''' is understood to be determined through conservation of momentum by the remaining velocities, $\mathbf{c}$, $\mathbf{c}'$, $\mathbf{c}''$. Recall that the space and time arguments of all the f's are $\mathbf{r}$ and t.

Combining (6–166) and (6–168) and being careful to count each type of collision only once,

$$\boxed{\frac{\partial f_\alpha}{\partial t} + \mathbf{c} \cdot \nabla f_\alpha + \frac{1}{m_\alpha} \nabla_c \cdot (\mathbf{F}_\alpha f_\alpha) = \tfrac{1}{2} \sum_{\beta\gamma\delta} \iint [f_\gamma'' f_\beta''' - f_\alpha f_\delta'] |\mathbf{c} - \mathbf{c}'| P_{\alpha\delta;\gamma\beta}\, d\mathbf{c}'\, d\mathbf{c}''} \tag{6–169}$$

(*Boltzmann's transport equation.*)

[When (6–169) is used to study transport of optical or of (high-energy) nuclear radiation ("α, γ"), the collision integrals simplify considerably since the scattering centers ("β, δ") may be considered fixed [$f_\delta' = f_0(\mathbf{r}, t)\delta(\mathbf{c}')$ etc.]; the loss integral becomes simply $(f_0 P_{\text{tot}}) c f_\alpha$ and $f_\beta''' = f_0$ can be taken outside the production integrals; the result is the simpler transport equation, (15–95).]

Quantum effects: Aside from effects on the cross sections, quantum mechanics also introduces into (6–169) a formal modification (due to symmetry requirements for wavefunctions):

$$[f_\gamma'' f_\beta''' - f_\alpha f_\delta'] \qquad \text{is replaced by}$$

$$[f_\gamma'' f_\beta'''(1 + \theta_\alpha f_\alpha)(1 + \theta_\delta f_\delta') - f_\delta f_\delta'(1 + \theta_\gamma f_\gamma'')(1 + \theta_\beta f_\beta''')] \tag{6–170}$$

where $\theta_\alpha = (h/m_\alpha)^3(\sigma/g_\alpha)$, where g_α is the statistical weight of α molecules and $\sigma = \pm 1$ is defined in (6–60). Although some results concerning quantum effects on the viscosity of gases at low temperatures have been obtained, these effects are presently screened by other theoretical complications, under experimentally accessible conditions.

Macroscopic Consequences

The mass density and number density of α molecules are

$$\frac{1}{m_\alpha} \rho_\alpha(\mathbf{r}, t) = n_\alpha(\mathbf{r}, t) = \int f_\alpha(\mathbf{r}, \mathbf{c}, t)\, d\mathbf{c} \tag{6–171}$$

For any function, $\psi(\mathbf{c})$, independent of $\mathbf{r}$ and t, let $\langle\psi\rangle_\alpha$ be its local average over α molecules:

$$\langle\psi\rangle_\alpha = \frac{1}{n_\alpha}\int f_\alpha(\mathbf{r}, \mathbf{c}, t)\psi(\mathbf{c})\, d\mathbf{c} \tag{6–172}$$

(a function of $\mathbf{r}$ and t). Multiply (6–169) by $m_\alpha\psi$, integrate over $\mathbf{c}$ and use the fact that f_α must vanish for sufficiently large $\mathbf{c}$.

$$\begin{aligned}\frac{\partial}{\partial t}(\rho_\alpha\langle\psi\rangle_\alpha) + \nabla\cdot(\rho_\alpha\langle\mathbf{c}\psi\rangle_\alpha) - n_\alpha\langle\mathbf{F}_\alpha\cdot\nabla_c\psi\rangle_\alpha \\ = \tfrac{1}{2}m_\alpha\sum_{\beta\gamma\delta}\iiint\psi(\mathbf{c})|\mathbf{c}-\mathbf{c}'|[f_\gamma''f_\beta''' - f_\alpha f_\delta']P_{\alpha\delta;\gamma\beta}\, d\mathbf{c}\, d\mathbf{c}'\, d\mathbf{c}''\end{aligned} \tag{6–173}$$

First set $\psi \equiv 1$; then the integral sum is $m_\alpha K_\alpha$ where K_α is the rate at which α molecules are created per unit volume (by "chemical" reaction). Thus,

$$\frac{\partial\rho_\alpha}{\partial t} + \nabla\cdot(\rho_\alpha\mathbf{v}_\alpha) = m_\alpha K_\alpha, \qquad \text{where} \qquad \mathbf{v}_\alpha = \langle\mathbf{c}\rangle_\alpha \tag{6–174}$$

Summing this over the internal molecular states for a given chemical species, A, gives the conservation equation for each chemical (in the true sense); if there are no chemical reactions occurring, $K_A \equiv 0$. In any case, since mass is always conserved,

$$\sum m_\alpha K_\alpha = 0$$

(as may also be derived from (6–176) below) and

$$\frac{\partial\rho}{\partial t} + \nabla\cdot(\rho\mathbf{v}) = 0, \qquad \text{where} \qquad \mathbf{v} = \frac{1}{\rho}\sum\rho_\alpha\mathbf{v}_\alpha \tag{6–175}$$

The quantity, $\mathbf{c} - \mathbf{v}$, is often called the "peculiar velocity" (of a molecule) and $\langle\mathbf{c} - \mathbf{v}\rangle_\alpha = \mathbf{v}_\alpha - \mathbf{v}$ is called the "diffusion velocity" (of component α).

If (6–173) is summed over α, then the quadruple sum of integral terms can be symmetrized by interchanging dummy indices and integration-variables, using (6–167) and averaging the results; the integral terms then take the form,

$$\begin{aligned}\tfrac{1}{8}\sum_{\alpha\beta\gamma\delta}\iiint[m_\alpha\psi + m_\delta\psi' - m_\gamma\psi'' - m_\beta\psi'''] \\ \times [f_\gamma''f_\beta''' - f_\alpha f_\delta']|\mathbf{c}-\mathbf{c}'|P\, d\mathbf{c}''\, d\mathbf{c}'\, d\mathbf{c}\end{aligned} \tag{6–176}$$

(where ψ' denotes $\psi(\mathbf{c}')$ etc.).

Setting $\psi(\mathbf{c}) = \mathbf{c}$, the integral terms therefore sum to zero by conservation of momentum in every collision. The remaining part of (6–173) summed over α then gives precisely the fluid *equations of motion*, (1–66), with the body force and stress tensor defined by

$$\begin{aligned}\mathbf{f} &= \sum_\alpha n_\alpha\langle\mathbf{F}_\alpha\rangle_\alpha \\ \mathfrak{P} &= \rho\mathbf{v}\mathbf{v} - \sum_\alpha\rho_\alpha\langle\mathbf{c}\mathbf{c}\rangle_\alpha = -\sum_\alpha\rho_\alpha\langle(\mathbf{c}-\mathbf{v})(\mathbf{c}-\mathbf{v})\rangle_\alpha\end{aligned} \tag{6–177}$$

Similarly, setting $\psi(\mathbf{c}) = \frac{1}{2}|\mathbf{c}|^2 + e_i(\alpha)$ where $e_i(\alpha)$ is the internal energy *per unit mass* of an α molecule, the sum of (6–173) over α again leads to vanishing integral terms

(6–176) and the result is the energy-conservation equation, (1–70), with the internal ("thermodynamic") energy-per-unit-mass and the heat-flux defined by

$$\left.\begin{aligned} e &= \frac{1}{\rho} \sum_{\alpha} \rho_\alpha \{\tfrac{1}{2}\langle|\mathbf{c} - \mathbf{v}|^2\rangle_\alpha + e_i(\alpha)\} \\ \mathbf{Q} &= \sum_{\alpha} \rho_\alpha \{\tfrac{1}{2}\langle(\mathbf{c} - \mathbf{v})|\mathbf{c} - \mathbf{v}|^2\rangle_\alpha + \langle \mathbf{c} - \mathbf{v}\rangle_\alpha e_i(\alpha)\} \end{aligned}\right\} \tag{6–178}$$

It is also convenient to define a local (kinetic*) temperature:

$$\tfrac{3}{2}kT = \left[\frac{1}{\sum_\alpha n_\alpha}\right] \sum_\alpha \tfrac{1}{2}\rho_\alpha \langle|\mathbf{c} - \mathbf{v}|^2\rangle_\alpha \tag{6–179}$$

These results connect the macroscopic properties of gaseous mixtures with the microscopic, molecular model as soon as the Boltzmann equations, (6–169), have been solved for $f_\alpha(\mathbf{r}, \mathbf{c}, t)$. This ideal program has been only approximately carried through.

Isolated System (The H-Theorem)

The equilibrium solution of the Boltzmann equation (6–169) is known from (6–51) but may also be derived by considering the (entropy) function,

$$\begin{aligned} -S(\mathbf{r}, t) &= \sum_\alpha \int f_\alpha(\mathbf{r}, \mathbf{c}, t) \ln [f_\alpha(\mathbf{r}, \mathbf{c}, t)]\, d\mathbf{c} \\ &= \sum_\alpha n_\alpha \langle \ln f_\alpha \rangle_\alpha \end{aligned}$$

Evaluating $\partial S/\partial t$ from (6–169) and noting that f_α vanishes for sufficiently large $\mathbf{c}$, one finds:

$$\begin{aligned} -\frac{\partial S}{\partial t} &+ \nabla \cdot \{\sum_\alpha n_\alpha \langle \mathbf{c} \ln f_\alpha\rangle_\alpha\} \\ &= \tfrac{1}{2} \sum_{\alpha\beta\gamma\delta} \iiint [1 + \ln f_\alpha](f_\gamma'' f''' - f_\alpha f_\delta')|\mathbf{c} - \mathbf{c}'|\, P_{\alpha\delta;\gamma\beta}\, d\mathbf{c}\, d\mathbf{c}'\, d\mathbf{c}'' \end{aligned}$$

Symmetrizing as in (6–176), this may be written,

$$\begin{aligned} \frac{\partial S}{\partial t} &+ \nabla \cdot \mathbf{J}_s \\ &= \tfrac{1}{8} \sum_{\alpha\beta\gamma\delta} \iiint \left[\ln\left(\frac{f_\gamma'' f_\beta'''}{f_\alpha f_\delta'}\right)\right] (f_\gamma'' f_\beta''' - f_\alpha f_\delta')|\mathbf{c} - \mathbf{c}'|\, P_{\alpha\delta;\gamma\beta}\, d\mathbf{c}\, d\mathbf{c}'\, d\mathbf{c}'' \end{aligned} \tag{6–180}$$

Since $\{(z - 1) \ln z\} \geqslant 0$ for positive z, the rate of creation of S per unit volume is necessarily non-negative and in an isolated system, *each integrand* on the right side of (6–180) must eventually vanish.† At equilibrium, therefore, $\ln f_\alpha$ is conserved during collisions and must‡ have the form,

$$\ln f_\alpha(\mathbf{r}, \mathbf{c}, t) = A_\alpha m_\alpha + \mathbf{B}_\alpha \cdot \mathbf{c} m_\alpha + C_\alpha[\tfrac{1}{2}m_\alpha c^2 + m_\alpha e_i(\alpha)] \tag{6–181}$$

* If the molecules are such that change of internal energy during collisions is improbable, then the "kinetic" and "internal" temperatures will be different except when the gas is in thermal equilibrium. Even the kinetic temperatures of different types of particles can be different.

† S is bounded since, if f_α decreases more slowly than e^{-Ac^2}, the integral, $\langle \ln f_\alpha\rangle_\alpha$, is less than $\langle Ac^2\rangle_\alpha$ which is essentially the mean kinetic energy.

‡ The only collision invariants of the form, $\psi(\mathbf{c})$, are mass, momentum and energy (and their linear combinations); otherwise, the final velocities after a collision would be overdetermined.

16

which is the Maxwell–Boltzmann distribution, (6–51), with a superposed "fluid" velocity. (Note that this proof depends on the assumption of "molecular chaos" introduced through (6–168).)

Similarly, the Fermi–Dirac or the Bose–Einstein distribution functions (6–62) cause the quantum-theoretic integrands, (6–170) to vanish.

Approximations

For conditions not too far from equilibrium and involving only moderate gradients, the f_α should be approximately a Maxwell distribution,* (6–51), with a superposed drift velocity, $\mathbf{v}_\alpha(\mathbf{r}, t)$, and a varying temperature, $T(\mathbf{r}, t)$. Calling this distribution $f_\alpha{}^0$, the common approximation consists in setting

$$f_\alpha = f_\alpha{}^0(1 + \phi_\alpha + \cdots) \tag{6–182}$$

and assuming $|\phi_\alpha(\mathbf{r}, \mathbf{c}, t)| \ll 1$. The resulting integral equation† for ϕ_α is then solved by successive approximations. This program becomes rather tedious even for monatomic gases and only the simpler results are given below. These results refer primarily to monatomic gases, but, actually, the internal excitations of polyatomic molecules affect only the heat fluxes (to good approximation) and appropriate corrections are indicated where needful. (Results for complex mixtures and results to second approximation (in (6–182)) are also available; the latter are called **Burnett equations**.)

Notation

For collisions between molecules of two given species (i, j) with relative velocity, g, let

$$Q_{ij}^{(l)}(g) = \int \sigma_{\text{com}}(g, \theta_c)[1 - (\cos\theta_c)^l]\, d\Omega_{\text{com}} = \langle 1 - (\cos\theta_c)^l \rangle \sigma_s \tag{6–183}$$

where σ_s is the total scattering cross section and θ_c is the center-of-mass scattering angle (= angle between initial and final *relative* laboratory velocities, often called the "deflection angle").

[$Q_{ij}^{(1)}$ is often called the "transport cross section", since it essentially determines the diffusion coefficient in (6–189) below.]

Then let‡

$$\Upsilon_{ij}^{(l,s)}(T) = \int_0^\infty e^{-\gamma}\, \gamma^{s+1}\, Q_{ij}^{(l)}(g)\, d\gamma \tag{6–184}$$

where

$$\gamma = \tfrac{1}{2}\mu g^2/kT; \qquad \mu = m_i m_j/(m_i + m_j)$$

(μ is the reduced mass; $kT\gamma$ is the center-of-mass kinetic energy.) Note that

$$\Upsilon^{(l,s+1)} = T\frac{d\Upsilon^{(l,s)}}{dT} + (s + 2)\Upsilon^{(l,s)} \tag{6–185}$$

---

* The interior of a shock-wave transition is better described by a weighted sum of two Maxwell distributions.

† There are also auxiliary conditions on ϕ_α which arise because the density, temperature and drift velocity which define the Maxwell factor, $f_\alpha{}^0$, must be the same for f_α. Thus $\int f_\alpha{}^0 \phi_\alpha\, d\mathbf{c} = 0$; $\Sigma\, m_\alpha \int \mathbf{c}\, f_\alpha{}^0 \phi_\alpha\, d\mathbf{c} = 0$; $\tfrac{1}{2}\Sigma\, m_\alpha \int |\mathbf{c} - \mathbf{v}_\alpha|^2 f_\alpha{}^0 \phi_\alpha\, d\mathbf{c} = 0$.

‡ Another common notation is $\Omega^{(l,s)} = \Upsilon^{(l,s)}\sqrt{kT/8\pi\mu}$. The Υ are mean cross sections (with various weighting factors).

(Subscripts are often omitted when the meaning is clear.) For rigid-sphere molecules of diameter σ,

$$\Upsilon^{(l,s)} = \pi\sigma^2(s+1)!\left[1 - \frac{1}{2}\,\frac{1+(-1)^l}{l+1}\right] \qquad (6\text{–}186)$$

For a Lennard–Jones "6–12" potential, (6–109), the Υ vary from about twice the values (6–186)—for the same σ—when $kT = \frac{1}{2}\epsilon$ to about half these values when $kT = 100\epsilon$. The two sets are about equal near $kT = 2.5\epsilon$.

Diffusion and Thermal Diffusion

It is found that for a binary mixture, the velocities (6–174) satisfy*

$$\mathbf{v}_1 - \mathbf{v}_2 = -\frac{n^2}{n_1 n_2}\mathscr{D}[\mathbf{d}_1 + k_T \nabla \ln T] \qquad (6\text{–}187)$$

where $n = n_1 + n_2$ and

$$\mathbf{d}_1 = -\mathbf{d}_2 = \nabla(n_1/n) + (n_1/n)[1 - (nm_1/\rho)](\nabla \ln p) - (n_1 m_1/p\rho)[(\rho/m_1)\mathbf{F}_1 - n_1\mathbf{F}_1 - n_2\mathbf{F}_2] \qquad (6\text{–}188)$$

The diffusion coefficient is given (to within a few percent†) by

$$\mathscr{D} = \frac{3\sqrt{2\pi}}{8}\sqrt{\frac{kT(m_1+m_2)}{m_1 m_2}}\,\frac{1}{(n_1+n_2)\Upsilon_{12}^{(1,1)}} \qquad (6\text{–}189)$$

The second-order correction to (6–189) introduces the factor (due to Kihara),

$$f_{\mathscr{D}} = 1 + \frac{[(2\Upsilon_{12}^{(1,2)}/\Upsilon_{12}^{(1,1)}) - 5]^2}{(8\Upsilon_{12}^{(2,2)}/\Upsilon_{12}^{(1,1)}) + 40}$$

on the right-hand side. This correction factor is, in fact, exact for inverse-fourth-power intermolecular forces (Maxwell) or for a Lorentz mixture ($m_1 \ll m_2$ *and* $n_1 \ll n_2$) but for the extreme case of an ionized gas it does not agree with the second-order correction derived by Chapman and Cowling—compare (6–203) below.

Thermal diffusion is essentially a second-order effect and the general formula for the "thermal diffusion ratio", k_T, is exceedingly complex. For isotopic mixtures (that is, when all molecules have the same interactions) and for $(\Delta m/m) < 0.3$, a simpler formula is adequate:

$$k_T \doteqdot \frac{15[\Upsilon^{(2,2)} + 5\Upsilon^{(1,1)}][2\Upsilon^{(1,2)} - 5\Upsilon^{(1,1)}]}{\Upsilon^{(2,2)}[8\Upsilon^{(2,2)} - 20\Upsilon^{(1,2)} + 4\Upsilon^{(1,3)} + 55\Upsilon^{(1,1)}]}\left(\frac{m_1 - m_2}{m_1 + m_2}\right)\left(\frac{n_1 n_2}{n^2}\right) \qquad (6\text{–}190)$$

Viscosity

The stress tensor (6–177) is found to have the form, $\mathfrak{P} = -p\mathbf{1} + 2\eta\mathfrak{V}'$, where $\mathfrak{V}'$ is the symmetric, non-dilational part of $\nabla\mathbf{v}$ (see (1–87)). The coefficient of viscosity for a pure gas is (to about one percent),

$$\eta = \frac{5}{4}\,\frac{\sqrt{\pi m k T}}{\Upsilon^{(2,2)}} \qquad (6\text{–}191)$$

* $\mathscr{D}$ is the same coefficient that appears in (6–11) and (6–13). Thus if $\nabla T = 0$, (6–187) and the conservation equations (6–174) etc., imply $\partial n_i/\partial t = (\partial/\partial x)(\mathscr{D}\,\partial n_i/\partial x)$.

† As regards approximations made in the *theory*. Also, the error is much greater for the extreme case of ionized gases, which are discussed later.

For mixtures, an accurate semi-empirical relation is (with $x_i = n_i/n$, the mole fractions):

$$\eta = \sum_i x_i \left\{\frac{x_i}{\eta_i} + 1.385 \frac{RT}{pM_i} \sum_{k \neq i} \frac{x_k}{\mathscr{D}_{ik}}\right\}^{-1} \tag{6–192}$$

In polyatomic gases, the value of η is not greatly changed, but the stress tensor acquires an additional term, $\kappa(\nabla \cdot \mathrm{v})\mathbf{1} = -\kappa(\mathrm{d}\ln\rho/\mathrm{d}t)\mathbf{1}$, which arises from the time-delay required to change internal molecular excitations. This effect is small, however. (At high densities, another mechanism produces a bulk viscosity in both monatomic and polyatomic gases—see later.)

The second-order correction to (6–191) introduces the factor,

$$f_\eta = 1 + \frac{3}{49}\left[\frac{\Upsilon^{(2,3)}}{\Upsilon^{(2,2)}} - \frac{7}{2}\right]^2$$

on the right side of (6–191).

Thermal Conductivity

The heat flux (6–178) is found to be given* by $\mathbf{Q} = -K\nabla T$, where (to a few percent),

$$K = \frac{25}{8}\frac{\sqrt{\pi mkT}}{\Upsilon^{(2,2)}}\left(\frac{C_v}{M}\right) = \frac{15}{4}\frac{R}{M}\eta \tag{6–193}$$

for a monatomic gas. (C_v/M = specific heat per gram.) For a polyatomic gas (Eucken correction; to account for internal excitation energies),

$$K \doteqdot \left[\frac{C_v}{M} + \frac{9}{4}\frac{R}{M}\right]\eta \tag{6–194}$$

The formulas for mixtures are very complicated. An empirical rule is

$$\frac{1}{K_{\text{mix}}} = \frac{1}{\eta_{\text{mix}}}\left(\frac{n_1}{n}\sqrt{\frac{\eta_1}{K_1}} + \frac{n_2}{n}\sqrt{\frac{\eta_2}{K_2}}\right)^2 \tag{6–195}$$

The second-order correction to (6–193) introduces the factor,

$$f_K = 1 + \frac{2}{21}\left[\frac{\Upsilon^{(2,3)}}{\Upsilon^{(2,2)}} - \frac{7}{2}\right]^2$$

on the right side of (6–193).

It has been found that the formulas (6–184)–(6–194) reproduce experimental results quite accurately for a large number of gases if the Lennard–Jones potential, (6–109), is used. For polar gases, better agreement is obtained with the Krieger potential, which is obtained by adding the quantity, $(-2\mu^2/r^3)$ to (6–109), where the effective mean dipole moment, μ, can be varied to fit the data.

5. Dense Gases

For idealized *hard sphere* molecules, only two-body collisions are of importance even at very high densities; thus the Boltzmann equation may be used at all densities. The theory for such as gas (due to Enskog) actually fits empirical data for real gases quite accurately. We merely sketch the basic method and quote the results.

* In a "stationary" system. The general expression for $\mathbf{Q}$ agrees with the predictions of phenomenological thermodynamics.

The finite size of the hard-sphere molecules (diameter, σ) has two effects: (I) the centers of a colliding pair are located at different space-points and (II) collisions occur more frequently by a factor $Y(\rho)$ than for point molecules at the same density. These effects may be incorporated in (6–168) and (6–169) by replacing* $f(\mathbf{r}, \mathbf{c}, t)f(\mathbf{r}, \mathbf{c}', t)$ by

$$f(\mathbf{r}, \mathbf{c}, t)f(\mathbf{r} + \sigma\hat{k}, \mathbf{c}', t)\, Y(\mathbf{r} + \tfrac{1}{2}\sigma\hat{k})$$

(where $\hat{k}$ is a unit vector along the collision axis) and similarly for other expressions of this type. If these expressions are expanded in a Taylor's series (in σ) to second order, the entire theory in (4) can be carried through as before (although the manipulations are lengthier and more involved).

The final results are (y and b_0 are given below):

Viscosity (η_0 is the value, (6–191)):

$$\eta = \eta_0 \frac{b_0}{V}\left[\frac{1}{y} + \frac{4}{5} + 0.761y\right] \tag{6–196}$$

Bulk Viscosity (adding a term, $\kappa(\nabla \cdot \mathbf{v})\mathbf{1}$ to $\mathfrak{P}$):

$$\kappa = \eta_0(b_0/V)1.002y \tag{6–197}$$

Thermal Conductivity (including an Eucken correction for internal energy of real molecules):

$$K = \frac{R\eta_0}{M}\frac{b_0}{V}\left[\left(\frac{C_v}{R} + \frac{9}{4}\right)\frac{1}{y} + \frac{9}{2} + 2.83y\right] \tag{6–198}$$

Diffusion in a binary mixture ($\mathscr{D}_0$ given in (6–189)):

$$\frac{1}{\mathscr{D}} = \frac{1}{\mathscr{D}_0}\left[1 + \tfrac{2}{3}\pi n_1\sigma_1^3\left(\frac{\sigma_1 + 4\sigma_2}{4\sigma_1 + 4\sigma_2}\right) + \tfrac{2}{3}\pi n_2\sigma_2^3\left(\frac{4\sigma_1 + \sigma_2}{4\sigma_1 + 4\sigma_2}\right) + \cdots\right]$$

Self-diffusion:

$$\mathscr{D} = \mathscr{D}_0 \frac{b_0}{yV} \tag{6–199}$$

In (6–196)–(6–199), the quantities, b_0 and y for hard-sphere molecules are simply $(2/3)N\pi\sigma^3$ and $(pv/RT) - 1$ respectively. For real gases, however, these quantities must be estimated from data. Enskog suggested that (v = volume per mole)

$$y \doteqdot \frac{v}{RT}\left[p + \left.\frac{\partial U}{\partial V}\right|_T\right] - 1 = \frac{v}{R}\left.\frac{\partial p}{\partial T}\right|_V - 1 \tag{6–200}$$

(wherein $(\partial U/\partial V)_T$ may be regarded as the "internal pressure" due to molecular attractions). The value of the constant, b_0, is then determined by the requirement that as $V \to \infty$ the quantity $Y = yV/b_0 \to 1$. The agreement with high-pressure data is then very good for such gases as N_2 and CO_2.

6. Ionized Gases (Plasmas)

Because Coulomb forces have such long range, the concepts of two-body collisions and short collision-durations have no validity for ionized gases; indeed, the quantities, $Q^{(l)}$, in (6–183) fail to converge. Nevertheless, approximate results may be derived

* We consider only a chemically pure monatomic gas so that the subscript, "α," may be omitted.

by the artifice of assuming that the Coulomb forces are cut off beyond a certain distance by the mutual cancellation of fields from many charges. The Debye theory of electrolytic solutions, especially (6–151), suggests that the effective cut-off distance is the Debye length, which for electrons and ions of charge Ze is (by similar arguments),

$$l = \sqrt{kT/4\pi(Z+1)n_e e^2} \tag{6–201}$$

where n_e is the number of electrons per unit volume. (Over regions greater than about this size, the plasma must become electrically neutral.)

If the Coulomb forces are cut off at ranges greater than l, (6–183) and (5–126) give (for collisions between ions and electrons)

$$Q_{ei}^{(m)} = 2\pi \left(\frac{Ze^2}{\mu g^2}\right)^2 \int_{-1}^{\cos\theta_0} \frac{1-x^m}{(1-x)^2}\,dx$$

where the cut-off-scattering-angle, θ_0, is obtained by setting the classical projected distance of closest approach (the "impact parameter") equal to l:

$$l\mu g^2/Ze^2 = \cot \tfrac{1}{2}\theta_0 = \sqrt{(1+x)/(1-x)}$$

Thus one finds

$$Q_{ei}^{(1)} = 2\pi(Ze^2/\mu g^2)^2 \ln\,[1 + (l\mu g^2/Ze^2)^2]$$

$$Q_{ei}^{(2)} = 4\pi(Ze^2/\mu g^2)^2 \left\{\ln\,[1 + (l\mu g^2/Ze^2)^2] - \frac{1}{1+(Ze^2/l\mu g^2)^2}\right\}$$

Substitution into (6–184) then leads to integrals of the form, $\int_0^\infty e^{-\gamma}\gamma^n \ln\,[1 + y^2\gamma^2]\,d\gamma$ which for large y are asymptotic to $n!\ln(y)^2 + 2\,\Gamma'(n+1)$. Thus,

$$\begin{aligned} \Upsilon^{1,s} &\sim 4\pi(s-1)!\left(\frac{Ze^2}{2kT}\right)^2 \ln\frac{y}{\gamma_s} \\ \Upsilon^{2,s} &\sim 8\pi(s-1)!\left(\frac{Ze^2}{2kT}\right)^2 \ln\frac{y}{\gamma_s\sqrt{e}} \end{aligned} \tag{6–202}$$

where

$$y = 2kTl/Ze^2; \qquad \gamma_s = \exp\,[-\Gamma'(s)/\Gamma(s)]$$

With these results, the first-order diffusion coefficient for electrons in low-density plasmas are easily evaluated. However, in this rather extreme case, the second order correction* increases the result by a factor of about four (but higher order corrections have been found to be much smaller). The result for infinitely heavy ions is

$$\mathscr{D}_{ei} = \frac{(2kT)^{5/2}/Z(Z+1)e^4\sqrt{\pi m_e}}{\pi n_e \ln\Lambda} \tag{6–203}$$

where m_e is the electron mass and†

$$\Lambda = (3/2Ze^3)\sqrt{k^3T^3/\pi n_e} \tag{6–204}$$

---

* Using formulas of Chapman and Cowling. This result has been checked by Spitzer and Haerm (*Phys. Rev.*, **89,** 977 (1953)) using a different formalism but essentially the same cut-off procedure.

† Quantum mechanical diffraction effects at high temperatures reduce Λ by the factor $100\sqrt{42/T}$ when $T > 4.2 \times 10^5$ deg K.

If an electric field, $\mathbf{E}$, is applied to the plasma, it follows either from (6–15) or from (6–187), (6–188) and (6–175) (with $\mathbf{v} = 0$ and uniform T, p, n_e) that the electrical conductivity, σ, is equal to $[n_e e^2(Z+1)/kT]\mathscr{D}_{ei}$ and thus with heavy ions,

$$\sigma = \frac{2}{\pi}\frac{(2kT)^{3/2}/e^2\sqrt{\pi m_e}}{Z \ln \Lambda} = \frac{T^{3/2}}{3800 Z \ln \Lambda}\ \text{mho/cm} \tag{6–205}$$

For lighter nuclei, the conductivity is decreased: $\sigma' = \gamma_E \sigma$ where

for $Z =$	1	2	4	16	(∞)
$\gamma_E =$	0.582	0.683	0.785	0.923	(1)

When a strong magnetic field is also impressed on the plasma, the bending of electron paths causes a further decrease in conductivity when the current is perpendicular to $\mathbf{B}$, namely, $\sigma_\perp'' = (0.259)\sigma'$.

The theory of thermal conductivity* is similar in that the general formulas for mixtures must be used merely to obtain the correct Z-dependence, and second-order corrections are needed to obtain the proper numerical factors. For heavy ions (and no electric *field*; compare below) the thermal conductivity is

$$K = 20\left(\frac{2}{\pi}\right)^{3/2}\frac{k(kT)^{5/2}/e^4\sqrt{m_e}}{Z \ln \Lambda}$$

$$= 4.67 \times 10^{-12}\frac{T^{5/2}}{Z \ln \Lambda}\frac{\text{cal}}{\text{sec cm °C}}$$

Actually, the electrical and heat flow currents are strongly coupled:

$$\mathbf{J} = \sigma\mathbf{E} + \alpha\nabla T; \qquad \mathbf{Q} = -\beta\mathbf{E} - K'\nabla T$$

where $\alpha \doteqdot (3k/2e)\sigma$ and $\beta \doteqdot (4kT/e)\sigma$. When the electric *current* vanishes,

$$K_{\text{eff}} = K' - (\beta\alpha/\sigma) = \epsilon K' \doteqdot \tfrac{2}{5}K$$

For lighter nuclei, $K' = AK$ where

for $Z =$	1	2	4	16	∞
$A =$	0.225	0.356	0.513	0.791	1
$\epsilon =$	0.419	0.410	0.401	0.396	0.4

Slightly Ionized Gases

If ionization is slight, the charged particles affect only electromagnetic phenomena and the electrons dominate by virtue of their lighter mass. Since an electromagnetic radiation wave has $\mathbf{B} = \mathbf{E}$, electric forces on the electrons are larger than the magnetic forces by a factor, v/c. Hence we may neglect magnetic forces, except those arising from an externally applied magnetic field.

---

* Presumably, as for neutral gases, these results are correct only if the particles have no internal energy states; that is, the gas should be *fully* ionized.

No Magnetic Field:

In an electric field, $\mathbf{E} = E\hat{x} \cos \omega t$, the distribution function for electrons $f(\mathbf{v}, t)$ satisfies a transport equation analogous to (6–169).

$$\frac{\partial f}{\partial t} + \frac{eE}{m} \cos \omega t \frac{\partial f}{\partial v_x} = \left(\frac{Df}{Dt}\right)_{\text{coll.}}$$

where it is assumed that the wavelength of the field is sufficiently great that space-variations of f need not be taken into account. When E vanishes, $f = f_0(v)$ where, since $\partial f_0/\partial t = 0$, we also have $(Df_0/Dt)_{\text{coll.}} = 0$. If E is not too great we may adopt the approximation, $f = f_0(v) + (eE/m)g(\mathbf{v}, t)$. Then to first order,

$$\frac{\partial g}{\partial t} + \cos \omega t \frac{\partial f_0}{\partial v_x} = -\nu(v)\, g(\mathbf{v}, t)$$

where $\nu(v)$ is the mean collision frequency for electrons of speed v. To the same approximation, $g(\mathbf{v}, t)$ would be expected to depend linearly on the cosine of the angle between $\mathbf{E}$ and $\mathbf{v}$ and to contain both in-phase and quadrature components:

$$g(\mathbf{v}, t) = v_x[g_c(v) \cos \omega t + g_s(v) \sin \omega t]$$

Substituting above, observing that the sine and cosine are independent (e.g. multiply by $\cos \omega t$ and average over one cycle) and recalling that f_0 depends only on v, we obtain,

$$\nu g_s = \omega g_c\,; \qquad (1/v)(\partial f_0/\partial v) = -\nu g_c - \omega g_s$$

It follows that the electric current is given by

$$\begin{aligned} J_x &= n_e e \langle v_x \rangle \\ &= (n_e e^2 E/m) \iiint v_x^2 (g_c \cos \omega t + g_s \sin \omega t)\, d\mathbf{v} \end{aligned}$$

where n_e is the number of electrons per unit volume and the normalization, $4\pi \int v^2 f_0\, dv = 1$ has been adopted). Integrate over the direction of $\mathbf{v}$, substitute for g_c and g_s and integrate by parts.

$$\frac{J}{E} = \frac{4\pi n_e e^2}{3m} \int f_0(v) \frac{\partial}{\partial v} \left(\frac{\nu(v) \cos \omega t + \omega \sin \omega t}{[\nu(v)]^2 + \omega^2} v^3 \right) dv$$

In particular, if the collision frequency ν is independent of v (i.e. if the collision cross section varies as $1/v$), the integral becomes merely the normalizing integral for f_0. In the complex-number notation of electromagnetic theory, this result may be expressed either in terms of a complex conductivity:

$$\sigma = \frac{n_e e^2/m}{\nu + i\omega} \qquad (\epsilon = 1)$$

or in terms of a real conductivity and dielectric constant:

$$\sigma = \frac{(n_e e^2/m)\nu}{\nu^2 + \omega^2} \qquad \epsilon = 1 - \frac{4\pi n_e e^2/m}{\nu^2 + \omega^2}$$

These results are frequently used to interpret radio propagation in the ionosphere. With n_e given as a function of position, (3–77) and the equation following it may be used to trace the paths of rays. Note that for $\omega \gg \nu$ (microwaves) the radio reflectivity of the gas will depend primarily on (n_e/ω^2) and may be used to measure electron densities. The quantity $\sqrt{(4\pi n_e e^2/m)}$ is known as the "plasma (angular) frequency".

Strong Applied Magnetic Field:

If the applied magnetic field, $\mathbf{B}_0$, is sufficiently strong, magnetic forces will dominate over collision effects and each electron will follow a path given approximately by

$$i\omega\mathbf{v} = d\mathbf{v}/dt = (e/m)[\mathbf{E} + (\mathbf{v}/c) \times \mathbf{B}_0]$$

where the complex notation of harmonic time-dependence is justified since $\mathbf{B}_0$ is independent of time. The solution of this equation is given by (10–15):

$$\mathbf{v}_0 = \frac{e}{i\omega m} \left[1 - \left(\frac{\omega_c}{\omega}\right)^2 \right]^{-1} \left\{ \mathbf{E} + \mathbf{E} \times \mathbf{B}_0 \frac{\omega_c}{i\omega B_0} - (\mathbf{E} \cdot \mathbf{B}_0)\mathbf{B}_0 \left(\frac{\omega_c}{\omega B_0}\right)^2 \right\}$$

where $\omega_c = eB_0/mc$ is the "cyclotron" (angular) frequency. The velocity $\mathbf{v}_0$ is superposed on any random initial velocities which the electrons may possess and is executed in phase by all the electrons together. Since the random velocities contribute no electric current, $\mathbf{J} = n_e e\mathbf{v}_0 = \boldsymbol{\sigma} \cdot \mathbf{E}$ where $\boldsymbol{\sigma}$ is a tensor conductivity. The harmonic form of Maxwell's first equation can then be written,

$$\nabla \times \mathbf{B} = (i\omega/c)[4\pi\boldsymbol{\sigma}/i\omega + \mathbf{1}] \cdot \mathbf{E} = (i\omega/c)\boldsymbol{\epsilon} \cdot \mathbf{E}$$

where $\boldsymbol{\epsilon}$ is a tensor dielectric constant. Collecting all these results, we have

$$\boldsymbol{\epsilon} = \mathbf{1} + \frac{4\pi n_e e^2/m}{\omega_c^2 - \omega^2}\left[\mathbf{1} - \frac{\mathbf{B}_0\mathbf{B}_0}{B_0^2}\left(\frac{\omega_c}{\omega}\right)^2 + \frac{\omega_c}{i\omega B_0}\mathfrak{B}_0\right]$$

where $\mathfrak{B}_0$ is the tensor form of the operator, $(-\mathbf{B}_0 \times)$, namely $e^{ijk}B_{0k}$ [see (10–67)].

The theory following (3–70) may now be applied with this explicit form for $\boldsymbol{\epsilon}$. In particular, if $\mathbf{B}_0 = \mathbf{B}_0\hat{z}$ then

$$\boldsymbol{\epsilon} = \mathbf{1} + \frac{4\pi n_e e^2/m}{\omega_c^2 - \omega^2}\begin{array}{c|c|c} 1 & \omega_c/i\omega & 0 \\ \hline -\omega_c/i\omega & 1 & 0 \\ \hline 0 & 0 & 1 - (\omega_c/\omega)^2 \end{array}$$

The eigenvalues and eigenvectors are

$$\epsilon_+ = 1 - \frac{4\pi n_e e^2/m}{\omega(\omega - \omega_c)} \qquad \mathbf{e}_+ = (\hat{x} + i\hat{y})/\sqrt{2}$$

$$\epsilon_- = 1 - \frac{4\pi n_e e^2/m}{\omega(\omega + \omega_c)} \qquad \mathbf{e}_- = (\hat{x} - i\hat{y})/\sqrt{2}$$

$$\epsilon_z = 1 - 4\pi n_e e^2/m\omega^2 \qquad \mathbf{e}_z = \hat{z}$$

In particular, waves propagated along $\mathbf{B}_0$ split into two circularly polarized components with different phase velocities and the final result is found to depend on whether the wave propagates along or counter to the direction of $\mathbf{B}_0$ (Faraday rotation, non-reciprocal). To first order, collisions of frequency ν merely cause $i\omega$ to be replaced by $i\omega + \nu$ throughout.

7. Chemical Reaction Kinetics (Eyring Theory)

We consider only reactions in gases.* Empirically, many reactions proceed at a rate nearly proportional to $p^n \exp(-B/T)$. This suggests that the reaction (or its slowest step) proceeds by n-body collisions but that only collisions with a total kinetic energy at least kB are effective. Thus kB (commonly written ΔH) is called the "activation energy" and a reaction is termed "bimolecular" if $n = 2$, etc. (The word "reaction" usually denotes, in this context, "rate-determining step in the reaction".)

Actual calculation of reaction rates is a formidable quantum-mechanical problem, but the following formalism indicates the manner in which the rate "constants" depend upon more easily estimated properties of the molecules.

Consider the pseudo-molecule ("complex") formed *during* a collision of the type in question. The equations of motion (classical or quantum) of such a system are equivalent to the frictionless motion of a mass-point over a multi-dimensional surface.† In this surface, there will obviously be (at least) two long "valleys"

---

* In solids, the rate of reaction is usually determined primarily by the relatively slow diffusion of reactants (or intermediate products) through the "solvent". In dilute solutions, the result, (6–207) below, is a fair approximation if the reaction is not diffusion-controlled.

† Diagonalize the kinetic energy and change the coordinate scales so that $\sum_k (p_k^2/2m_k) \to (\frac{1}{2}m^\ddagger) \sum_k \dot{R}_k^2$; the remaining portion of the Hamiltonian, $\Phi(R_1, \cdots, R_n)$, is then the effective potential. This step is primarily an expository device which aids in defining the concepts used later and indicates how they may be estimated.

wherein the atoms of the complex are formed into (normal) molecules of reactants or of products respectively (with arbitrarily large intermolecular separations). Connecting these "valleys" will be a particular path (which leads across a "pass") entailing a minimum potential energy barrier; distance along this path is called "the reaction coordinate", and this coordinate is unique in the sense that displacement in this direction induces no such restoring forces (or vibrations) as occur in other coordinate directions, even in the vicinity of the "pass".

Consider now the statistical assembly of such complexes, representing (say) a unit volume of gas. The ensemble may be described by an ensemble of equivalent mass-points on the potential surface. Let $n^\ddagger$ be the number of these points lying in the "pass" (the number of "*activated* complexes"). The number of reactions per unit time is then,

$$R = \frac{\kappa n^\ddagger}{w} \langle v \rangle = \frac{\kappa n^\ddagger}{w} \sqrt{\frac{kT}{2\pi m^\ddagger}}$$

where w is the length of the reaction coordinate in the activated region ("pass"), $m^\ddagger$ is the effective mass of the complex, and κ is a transmission coefficient of the order of $\frac{1}{2}$ to 1 (unless electronic transitions are required during the collision).

Either by elementary calculations or by using (6–72) and (2–97): If c_j is the mole-fraction of reactant, j, and if there are a total of r reactants (allowing repetitions; N_0 is Avogadro's number)

$$\frac{c^\ddagger}{\prod_j c_j} = \frac{Z_1{}^\ddagger}{\prod_j (Z_1)_j} N_0^{r-1} = \frac{(Z_1{}^\ddagger)'}{\prod_j (Z_1)_j} N_0^{r-1} \frac{w}{h} \sqrt{2\pi m^\ddagger kT}$$

where $(Z_1)_j$ are the (one-molecule) partition functions of the reactants and where $(Z_1{}^\ddagger)'$ is the partition function (with the same energy-zero) for the activated complex, *excluding* the degree of freedom along the reaction coordinate (which has been treated as a one-dimensional box in this equation).

With these relations, $(n^\ddagger/w\sqrt{m^\ddagger})$ cancels out and the reaction rate may be expressed entirely in terms of the concentrations of reactants:

$$\frac{R}{n_{\text{tot}}} = R' = k' \prod_j c_j \tag{6–206}$$

$$k' = \kappa \frac{kT}{h} \frac{(Z_1{}^\ddagger)'}{\prod_j (Z_1)_j} N_0^{r-1} \tag{6–207}$$

(k' is called the "specific reaction rate"). This result is more commonly written, using (6–72) again,

$$k' = \kappa \left(\frac{kT}{h}\right) e^{-\Delta G^\ddagger/RT} = \kappa \left(\frac{kT}{h}\right) e^{-\Delta H^\ddagger/RT} e^{-\Delta S^\ddagger/R} \tag{6–208}$$

wherein $\Delta H^\ddagger$ is the "activation enthalpy" (essentially the potential barrier) and $\Delta S^\ddagger$ is the "entropy of activation" (omitting the reaction coordinate); $\Delta S^\ddagger$ can often be estimated from simple geometric considerations concerning the number of degrees of freedom, etc., in the pre-collision state and the activated (colliding) state.

Note that the form of the activated complex can*not* necessarily be inferred from the overall chemical reaction. For example, the combination of any two *atoms* $A + B \rightarrow AB$ proceeds primarily by three-body collisions of the form, $A + B + C \rightarrow AB + C$. Despite the rarity of three-body collisions, this mechanism is strongly favored ($\kappa \approx 1$) because it can readily dissipate the excess AB vibrational energy by transfer to kinetic energy of C. Most atomic re-combination reactions are of this type. [In the process $A + B \rightarrow AB$, conservation of momentum and energy entail four equations in three unknowns (the final velocity components) and there is no solution except under very special initial conditions.]

8. Solids

Atomic Rearrangements—Formalism

A solid is, in a sense, the antithesis of a gas in that interatomic forces act unceasingly and atomic displacements are rare events. The formalism* is correspondingly different. The lattice of atomic sites will be considered fixed and position vectors, $\mathbf{r}$, will refer only to such *sites*. (If interstitial "impurity atoms" are to be considered, all interstitial sites imbedded in the primary lattice must be included as possible sites in the full lattice.)

Let $P(A, B, \cdots, Z|\mathbf{r}_1, \mathbf{r}_2, \cdots, \mathbf{r}_n)$ denote the probability that (at any instant) the lattice sites $\mathbf{r}_1, \mathbf{r}_2, \cdots, \mathbf{r}_n$ are occupied by atoms of (chemical) type $A, B, \cdots, Z$ *respectively*. We shall also denote such a *series* of types collectively by $\mathscr{E}$ (for "environment") and the corresponding *series* of position vectors by $\boldsymbol{\xi}$. The various P functions are not independent; for example,

$$P(A, B|\mathbf{r}, \mathbf{R}) = \sum_{\mathscr{E}} P(A, B, \mathscr{E}|\mathbf{r}, \mathbf{R}, \boldsymbol{\xi}) \tag{6–209}$$

(where the sum is over all series $\mathscr{E}$ with (any) fixed, specific length).

Let $R(A, B, \mathscr{E}|\mathbf{r}, \mathbf{r} + \boldsymbol{\delta}, \boldsymbol{\xi})$ denote the rate at which (neighboring) atoms, A and B, (located at $\mathbf{r}$ and $\mathbf{r} + \boldsymbol{\delta}$, respectively) interchange positions when their environment is specified by $\mathscr{E}$ and $\boldsymbol{\xi}$. (Usually the environmental description need only include the nearer neighbors and usually R is appreciable only when either A or B represents a vacancy.)

Then if $\boldsymbol{\delta}$ represent a vector from any site to a nearest neighbor,

$$\frac{\partial}{\partial t} P(A|\mathbf{r}) = \sum_{C} \sum_{\mathscr{E}} \sum_{\boldsymbol{\delta}} \{P(C, A, \mathscr{E}|\mathbf{r}, \mathbf{r} + \boldsymbol{\delta}, \boldsymbol{\xi}) R(C, A, \mathscr{E}|\mathbf{r}, \mathbf{r} + \boldsymbol{\delta}, \boldsymbol{\xi}) - P(A, C, \mathscr{E}|\mathbf{r}, \mathbf{r} + \boldsymbol{\delta}, \boldsymbol{\xi}) R(A, C, \mathscr{E}|\mathbf{r}, \mathbf{r} + \boldsymbol{\delta}, \boldsymbol{\xi})\} \tag{6–210}$$

Similarly, $(\partial/\partial t)P(A, B|\mathbf{r}, \mathbf{R})$ is given by a triple sum over four terms involving the next higher-order P's such as $P(A, B, C, \mathscr{E}| \cdots)$ etc., etc.

If only (atom $\leftrightarrow$ vacancy) interchanges are important,†

$$\frac{\partial}{\partial t} P(A|\mathbf{r}) = \sum_{\boldsymbol{\delta}} \sum_{\mathscr{E}} \{P(V, A, \mathscr{E}|\mathbf{r}, \mathbf{r} + \boldsymbol{\delta}, \boldsymbol{\xi}) R(V, A, \mathscr{E}|\mathbf{r}, \mathbf{r} + \boldsymbol{\delta}, \boldsymbol{\xi}) - P(A, V, \mathscr{E}|\mathbf{r}, \mathbf{r} + \boldsymbol{\delta}, \boldsymbol{\xi}) R(A, V, \mathscr{E}|\mathbf{r}, \mathbf{r} + \delta, \boldsymbol{\xi})\} \tag{6–211}$$

$$\frac{\partial}{\partial t} P(V|\mathbf{r}) = -\sum_{A} \frac{\partial}{\partial t} P(A|\mathbf{r}) \tag{6–212}$$

The rates, $R(A, V, \mathscr{E})$, can be estimated from reaction-rate theory: to pass from $\mathbf{r}$ to $\mathbf{r} + \boldsymbol{\delta}$, the atom A must overcome a potential barrier, $E_0(\mathscr{E})$; when on top of

* Compare: G. H. Vineyard, *Phys. Rev.* **102,** 981 (1956).

† Empirically, this seems to be rather generally true. This is reasonable in view of the large distortion (and consequent energy barrier) entailed by a direct interchange of two atoms.

the barrier (in transit), the atom may be considered as an activated "complex" in the sense of (6–207), according to which the specific rate constant is, using (6–79),

$$k' \doteq (kT/h)[1 - e^{-h\nu/kT}]e^{h\nu/2kT}e^{-E_0(\mathscr{E})/kT} \qquad (6\text{–}213)$$

where ν is the vibration frequency which is missing (becomes the reaction coordinate) in the activated state. If, as is usually true, $h\nu \ll kT$, we may write, setting $E^{\ddagger} = E_0 - \frac{1}{2}h\nu$,

$$R(A, V, \mathscr{E}|\cdots) = \nu \exp[-E^{\ddagger}(\mathscr{E})/kT] \qquad (6\text{–}214)$$

An admittedly crude but fruitful further assumption is

$$P(A, B, \cdots Z|\mathbf{r}_1, \mathbf{r}_2, \cdots \mathbf{r}_n) \doteq P(A|\mathbf{r}_1)P(B|\mathbf{r}_2)\cdots P(Z|\mathbf{r}_n) \qquad (6\text{–}215)$$

Volume Diffusion

If the concentration of B atoms is everywhere small, the only important terms in (6–211) will be of the form, $P(V, A, \cdots, A)$ or $P(V, B, A, \cdots, A)$. Using (6–214) and (6–215) and the equivalence of atomic sites, we may write,

$$\frac{\partial}{\partial t}P(B|\mathbf{r}) = \nu P(V|\mathbf{r}) \exp[-E^{\ddagger}/kT]\{\sum_{\boldsymbol{\delta}} P(B|\mathbf{r} + \boldsymbol{\delta}) - cP(B|\mathbf{r})\} \qquad (6\text{–}216)$$

where c is the number of nearest-neighbor sites, $\mathbf{r} + \boldsymbol{\delta}$. If a is the mean nearest-neighbor spacing, expansion of $P(B|\mathbf{r} + \boldsymbol{\delta})$ in series (and averaging over the various sites if necessary*) gives,

$$\frac{\partial}{\partial t}P_B = \mathscr{D}\nabla^2 P_B; \qquad \mathscr{D} = a^2\nu P(V|\mathbf{r})e^{-E^{\ddagger}/kT} \qquad (6\text{–}217)$$

For interstitial diffusion (that is if B atoms are "small enough to fit in the holes of the A lattice"), $P(V|\mathbf{r})$ refers to interstitial sites and is therefore nearly unity:

$$\mathscr{D} \doteq a^2\nu e^{-E^{\ddagger}/kT} \qquad \text{(interstitial)}$$

Otherwise, $P(V|\mathbf{r})$ refers to vacant A-sites and (at thermodynamic equilibrium) is given by (6–140):

$$\mathscr{D} \doteq a^2\nu e^{-(E_v + E^{\ddagger})/kT} \qquad \text{(vacancy)}$$

The activation energies for diffusion, E_v, $E^{\ddagger}$ may be estimated from sublimation and elastic (distortion) energies.

Grain-boundary and surface diffusion: In many solid samples, solute atoms diffuse more readily between, rather than through crystal grains. Also, diffusion over a free surface occurs still more readily, presumably because it involves breaking only about half as many bonds as does volume diffusion; indeed, the activation energies are about half those in (6–217). Activation energies for grain-boundary diffusion usually lie between those for surface and volume diffusion.

Ionic Conduction

In ionic crystals, electrical conductivity seems to arise from motions of ions, induced by the electric field but taking place through either the vacancy or the

---

* Strictly, $\mathscr{D}$ in (6–217) is probably a tensor in crystalline materials, but the present experimental data seldom justify such accuracy.

interstitial mechanisms, which characterize volume diffusion. Thus, by (6–15), the electrical conductivity is

$$\sigma = \frac{e^2}{kT}[n_+Z^2_+\mathscr{D}_+ + n_-Z_-{}^2\mathscr{D}_-]$$

where $eZ_\pm$ are the charges on the ions, $n_\pm$ are their numbers per unit volume, and $\mathscr{D}_\pm$ are the corresponding diffusion coefficients.

Order-Disorder Kinetics*

We consider a two-component, A_nB_m, alloy and conceptually divide the lattice into a sublattice of N_α different α-sites on which the N_A different A atoms "belong" and a sublattice of N_β different β-sites on which the N_B different B atoms "should" reside, in the ordered state. (Note that N_A is only approximately equal to N_α because of vacancies; $N_V \neq 0$.) We assume that all nearest-neighbors around an α-site are β-sites (and conversely) and that all α-sites are crystallographically equivalent as are all β-sites.

Assuming spatial homogeneity, $P(A|\mathbf{r})$ is then the same for all α-sites and we denote this common value by $P(A|\alpha)$; similarly for $P(V|\beta)$, etc. With $j = A, B,$ or V:

$$N_\alpha P(j|\alpha) + N_\beta P(j|\beta) = N_j, \qquad \text{a constant} \tag{6–218}$$

and

$$P(A|\alpha) + P(B|\alpha) + P(V|\alpha) = 1 = P(A|\beta) + P(B|\beta) + P(V|\beta) \tag{6–219}$$

These are four independent relations, so that only two of the six P are independent.

If c_α is the number of nearest-neighbor (β) sites around an α-site, equations (6–211) and (6–215) take a form typified by,

$$\frac{1}{c_\alpha}\frac{d}{dt}P(A|\alpha) = P(V|\alpha)P(A|\beta)\mathscr{R}_{A\alpha} - P(A|\alpha)P(V|\beta)\mathscr{R}_{A\beta} \tag{6–220}$$

where

$$\left.\begin{aligned}\mathscr{R}_{A\alpha} &= \sum_{\mathscr{E}} P(\mathscr{E}|\boldsymbol{\xi})R(VA\mathscr{E}|\alpha\beta\boldsymbol{\xi})\\ \mathscr{R}_{A\beta} &= \sum_{\mathscr{E}} P(\mathscr{E}|\boldsymbol{\xi})R(AV\mathscr{E}|\alpha\beta\boldsymbol{\xi})\end{aligned}\right\} \tag{6–221}$$

Note that these $\mathscr{R}$ coefficients depend on the P's.

The degree of (long range†) order is measured by,

$$S = \frac{P(A|\alpha) - N_A/N}{1 - N_A/N} = \frac{N_\beta}{N_B + N_V}[P(A|\alpha) - P(A|\beta)] \tag{6–222}$$

(where $N = N_\alpha + N_\beta = N_A + N_B + N_V$, the total number of sites).

By (6–220) and its analogue for $P(A|\beta)$,

$$\frac{N_B + N_V}{N_\beta}\frac{dS}{dt} = (c_\alpha + c_\beta)[P(V|\alpha)P(A|\beta)\mathscr{R}_{A\alpha} - P(A|\alpha)P(V|\beta)\mathscr{R}_{A\beta}] \tag{6–223}$$

Now since $P(V|\alpha) \leqslant N_V/N \ll P(A|\alpha)$, the derivative of $P(V|\alpha)$ cannot be comparable to that of $P(A|\alpha)$ or S for more than a brief instant. It should therefore be a fair

---

* This section is adapted from: G. H. Vineyard, *Phys. Rev.*, **102,** 981 (1956).

† The short-range order parameter is related to $\langle P(A, B|\mathbf{r}, \mathbf{R})\rangle$ but (6–215) essentially assumes that the long- and short-range orders are related as in the Bragg–Williams theory, (6–131)–(6–132).

approximation to set $(\partial/\partial t)[P(A|\alpha) + P(B|\alpha)] \doteqdot 0$, which implies, by (6–220) and its analogue for $P(B|\alpha)$,

$$\frac{P(V|\alpha)}{P(V|\beta)} \doteqdot \frac{P(A|\alpha)\mathscr{R}_{A\beta} + P(B|\alpha)\mathscr{R}_{B\beta}}{P(A|\beta)\mathscr{R}_{A\alpha} + P(B|\beta)\mathscr{R}_{B\alpha}} \doteqdot \frac{N_V - N_\beta P(V|\beta)}{N_\alpha P(V|\beta)} \tag{6–224}$$

Using this to eliminate $P(V|\cdots)$ from (6–223) and noting that *for stoichiometric composition* $(N_A/N_B = N_\alpha/N_\beta)$, since $N_V \ll N_A, N_B$

$$\left.\begin{aligned} P(A|\alpha) &\doteqdot f_\alpha + Sf_\beta; \quad & P(B|\alpha) &\doteqdot f_\beta(1-S) \\ P(A|\beta) &\doteqdot f_\alpha(1-S); \quad & P(B|\beta) &\doteqdot f_\beta + Sf_\alpha \end{aligned}\right\}$$

where

$$f_\alpha = \frac{N_\alpha}{N} \doteqdot \frac{N_A}{N}; \quad f_\beta = \frac{N_\beta}{N} \doteqdot \frac{N_B}{N} \tag{6–225}$$

it is found, after considerable algebra that, finally,

$$\frac{dS}{dt} = \frac{N_V}{N}(c_\alpha + c_\beta)$$

$$\times \frac{f_\alpha f_\beta(1-S)^2\mathscr{R}_{A\alpha}\mathscr{R}_{B\beta} - (f_\alpha + Sf_\beta)(f_\beta + Sf_\alpha)\mathscr{R}_{A\beta}\mathscr{R}_{B\alpha}}{(1-S)f_\alpha f_\beta(\mathscr{R}_{A\alpha} + \mathscr{R}_{B\beta}) + f_\alpha(f_\alpha + Sf_\beta)\mathscr{R}_{A\beta} + f_\beta(f_\beta + Sf_\alpha)\mathscr{R}_{B\alpha}} \tag{6–226}$$

Here the $\mathscr{R}$ depend on S through the environmental probabilities in (6–221). This dependence may be estimated by using (6–214), (6–215) and (6–225) in the definitions (6–221). The activation energy $E^\ddagger(\mathscr{E})$ in (6–214), for example, may be assumed to contain a term varying linearly with the number of A–A (or A–B or B–B) bonds in the various possible configurations, $AV\mathscr{E}$, etc. The sums over $\mathscr{E}$ in (6–221) can then be evaluated by the binomial theorem.

In this way, (6–226) may be reduced to the form, $dS/dt = F(S, T)$ which directly indicates the behavior of the system, even though it is not readily integrated in closed form. Namely, for given (sufficiently low) T, the order parameter, S, has stable (or at least metastable) values where $F(S, T) = 0$ and $\partial F/\partial S < 0$. When displaced slightly from such a state, the system will return exponentially with a time constant equal to $[-\partial F/\partial S]^{-1}$. Preliminary numerical calculations* of relaxation rates for Cu_3Au show good agreement with experiment, using values of the parameters roughly indicated by other data.

Properties Due to Electrons

Formalism: The electrons in a crystalline solid form a (degenerate, Fermi) gas with an unusual distribution of quantum states; see (5–102)–(5–110). Because of the non-uniqueness of the state-labels (wave numbers), **k**, and the multiple-valuedness of the energy, $E(\mathbf{k})$, several conventions for labeling are possible. One convenient convention is that $|\mathbf{k}|$ is unrestricted and that $E(\mathbf{k})$ increases† ("in the large") with increasing $|\mathbf{k}|$.

Let $f(\mathbf{r}, \mathbf{k}, t)\, dV\, d\mathbf{k}$ denote the number of electrons located in a (small but macroscopic) volume dV centered at $\mathbf{r}$ and having wave numbers in $d\mathbf{k}$ centered on $\mathbf{k}$.

---

* G. H. Vineyard, *op. cit.*

† Another common convention ("reduced zone scheme") is to choose always the smallest of the equivalent **k** and to introduce an index to indicate which of the multiple values of $E(\mathbf{k})$ is intended. Since transitions between bands are rare, the distinction is usually merely one of notation.

If the solid is subjected to an electric field, $\mathscr{E}$, then, using (5–110), the transport equation (analogous to (6–169)) which determines f is

$$\frac{\partial f}{\partial t} + \mathbf{v} \cdot \nabla f + \frac{e}{\hbar} \mathscr{E} \cdot \nabla_k f = \left(\frac{\partial f}{\partial t}\right)_{\text{collisions}} \tag{6–227}$$

where $\mathbf{v}$ is essentially an abbreviation (see (5–107)):

$$\mathbf{v} = \frac{1}{\hbar} \nabla_k E(\mathbf{k})$$

"Umklapp" collisions: Since the energy can actually take many values for each $\mathbf{k}$, the above single-value *convention* requires consideration of collisions wherein the "momentum" change, $\Delta\mathbf{k}$, is equal to a reciprocal lattice vector. (Pictorially, $\mathbf{k}$ jumps—to preserve the label convention—from one face of a Brillouin zone to a diametrically opposite face.)

The relaxation time, τ, may be *defined* by

$$\left(\frac{\partial f}{\partial t}\right)_{\text{collisions}} = \frac{f_0 - f}{\tau(\mathbf{k}, \mathbf{r})} \tag{6–228}$$

where $f_0(\mathbf{r}, \mathbf{k})$ is the equilibrium distribution with $\mathscr{E} = 0$ and local temperature $T(\mathbf{r})$; that is f_0 is given by (6–62).

Conductivity in general: The electric current density, $\mathbf{J}$, is $\int e\mathbf{v}f\, d\mathbf{k} = \int e\mathbf{v}(f - f_0)\, d\mathbf{k}$, since $\mathbf{J}$ vanishes in the equilibrium state, $f = f_0$. From (6–227) and (6–228), if conditions are spatially uniform ($\nabla f = 0$), it follows that the electrical conductivity dyadic is

$$\left.\begin{aligned} \boldsymbol{\sigma} &= -\frac{e^2}{\hbar} \int \tau \mathbf{v} \nabla_k f\, d\mathbf{k} = \frac{e^2}{\hbar} \int f \nabla_k(\tau\mathbf{v})\, d\mathbf{k} \\ &= n \frac{e^2}{\hbar^2} \langle \nabla_k[\tau \nabla_k E] \rangle \doteq ne^2\tau/m^* \end{aligned}\right\} \tag{6–229}$$

where the second form follows from integration by parts (since f vanishes, with our convention, for sufficiently large $\mathbf{k}$); $n = \int f\, d\mathbf{k}$ is the number of electrons per unit volume and m^* is the effective mass, (5–108).

Approximations: When conditions are not too far from equilibrium, we may set

$$f = f_0 - g \tag{6–230}$$

where f_0 is an "equilibrium" distribution, (6–62) and depends on $\mathbf{r}$ and $\mathbf{k}$ only through $T(\mathbf{r})$ and $E(\mathbf{k})$ respectively. On the left side of (6–227) we may neglect g and from the form, (6–62), of f_0 we obtain, in a steady state,

$$\left(\frac{\partial f}{\partial t}\right)_{\text{coll}} = \left[e\mathscr{E} \cdot \mathbf{v} - (\mathbf{v} \cdot \nabla T) \frac{E - \mu}{T}\right] \frac{\partial f_0}{\partial E} = \frac{g}{\tau} \tag{6–231}$$

where μ is the Fermi energy (chemical potential) of the electrons.

The current density, $\mathbf{J}$, is $\int e\mathbf{v}f\, d\mathbf{k} = -\int e\mathbf{v}g\, d\mathbf{k}$ and if τ is assumed to be independent of the direction, $\mathbf{k}/|\mathbf{k}|$, the integral may be converted to an integral over the energy, E, by introducing $\mathscr{N}(E)$, the number of states* with energy *below* (and equal to) E:

$$\mathbf{J} = -e \int \tau \mathbf{v}\mathbf{v} \cdot \left[e\mathscr{E} - \frac{E-\mu}{T} \nabla T \right] \mathscr{N}' \frac{\partial f_0}{\partial E} \, dE \tag{6-232}$$

Similarly, the heat-current density, $n\langle E\mathbf{v}\rangle$, is given by

$$\mathbf{Q} = -\int \tau E \mathbf{v}\mathbf{v} \cdot \left[e\mathscr{E} - \frac{E-\mu}{T} \nabla T \right] \mathscr{N}' \frac{\partial f_0}{\partial E} \, dE \tag{6-233}$$

In these equations, $\mathbf{v}\mathbf{v}$ should be interpreted as an average over all $\mathbf{k}$ for each given $E = E(\mathbf{k})$. Now (integrating by parts and) using the Fermi form, (6–62), for f_0 and expanding the integral by (8–13),

$$\mathbf{J} \doteqdot e^2\mathscr{E} \cdot \{\tau \mathbf{v}\mathbf{v} \mathscr{N}'\}_{E=\mu} - \frac{\pi^2}{3} ek^2T(\nabla T) \cdot \left\{ \mathbf{v}\mathbf{v}\tau\mathscr{N}'' + \mathscr{N}' \frac{\partial}{\partial E} (\tau \mathbf{v}\mathbf{v}) \right\}_{E=\mu} \tag{6-234}$$

Similarly, replacing τ by $E\tau/e$,

$$\mathbf{Q} \doteqdot \mu \mathbf{J} - \frac{\pi^2}{3} k^2 T \, \nabla T \cdot \{\mathbf{v}\mathbf{v} \, \tau \mathscr{N}'\}_{E=\mu} \tag{6-235}$$

From the first term of (6–234), the (isothermal) electrical conductivity dyadic is

$$\boldsymbol{\sigma} \doteqdot e^2(\tau \mathbf{v}\mathbf{v} \mathscr{N}')_{E=\mu} \tag{6-236}$$

and from (6–235) the (electron) thermal conductivity for zero electric current is

$$\mathfrak{K} \doteqdot \left(\frac{\pi^2 k^2}{3e^2} T \right) \boldsymbol{\sigma} \tag{6-237}$$

which is the Wiedemann–Franz law. (Thermoelectric "coupling" effects are not given accurately by these equations; higher approximations are necessary.)

For a cubic crystal, the (average) $\langle v_i v_j \rangle$ at any energy must be $\langle v_x{}^2 \rangle \delta_{ij} = (1/3)\langle v^2 \rangle \delta_{ij}$ and $\boldsymbol{\sigma}$ reduces to a simple number,

$$\sigma = \frac{e^2}{3} (\tau v^2)_{E=\mu} \mathscr{N}'(\mu) \tag{6-238}$$

If the electron-states near $E = \mu$ are "nearly free," that is if $E = \hbar^2 k^2 / 2m_\mu$, then† $\mathscr{N} \propto E^{3/2}$ so that $\mathscr{N}' = 3\mathscr{N}/2E$ while $\mathscr{N}(\mu) = n$. Thus

$$\sigma \doteqdot ne^2\tau/m_\mu \tag{6-239}$$

where m_μ is the effective mass of electrons near the Fermi level, μ.

Computation of τ: To a first approximation, the relaxation *rates* (or transition probabilities) due to various types of collision are additive:

$$\frac{1}{\tau} \doteqdot \sum \frac{1}{\tau_i} \tag{6-240}$$

and the resistivity, $1/\sigma$, can therefore be evaluated for each process separately. In each case, $\tau_i(\mathbf{k})$, must be computed from its definition (6–228) using (6–227) or

* Per unit volume of the crystal and including spin states; some authors write $2\mathscr{N}(E)$ for this. The simple introduction of $\mathscr{N}' = d\mathscr{N}/dE$ as in (6–232) is not appropriate for semi-conductors, which are discussed later.

† Compare (5–95).

(6–231) with the quantum mechanical expression ((6–168) with (6–170)) for $\partial f/\partial t$ due to the collisions in question.

Impurity or defect scattering (residual resistivity): Vacant atomic sites, interstitial atoms, impurity atoms, or dislocations all introduce irregularities in the otherwise periodic crystalline potential and therefore act as fixed scattering centers for electron waves. The factors, θ_β, θ_γ (for the scattering centers) in (6–170) can be set equal to zero and the terms in θ_α, θ_δ (for the electrons) then cancel; thus (6–170) actually reduces to the classical form in this case. For each type of scattering center (5–82) then shows directly* that (in the spatially uniform case and assuming random placement of the scattering centers, n_i per unit volume):

$$\left.\frac{\partial f(\mathbf{k})}{\partial t}\right|_{\text{coll}(i)} = \frac{2\pi n_i}{\hbar}\sum_{\mathbf{k}'} |\langle\mathbf{k}'|w_i|\mathbf{k}\rangle|^2\{f(\mathbf{k}') - f(\mathbf{k})\}\delta(E - E') \tag{6–241}$$

where $w_i(\mathbf{r})$ is the perturbing potential due to a scattering center of type i. Since $(\partial f/\partial t)_{\text{coll}} = 0$ when $f = f_0$, the approximations (6–230) and (6–231) give,

$$\frac{-g}{\tau_i} = e\mathscr{E}\cdot\mathbf{v}\,\frac{\partial f_0}{\partial E} = \frac{2\pi n_i}{\hbar}\sum_{\mathbf{k}'} |\langle\mathbf{k}'|w_i|\mathbf{k}\rangle|^2[g(\mathbf{k}') - g(\mathbf{k})]\delta(E - E') \tag{6–242}$$

For $E \doteq \mu$ and if $\mathbf{v} \doteq \hbar\mathbf{k}/m_\mu$ (nearly spherical energy surfaces), a solution of the second half is $g =$ (constant) $\times$ $(e\mathscr{E}\cdot\mathbf{v})(\partial f_0/\partial E)_\mu$. Then, taking the z-axis along $\mathscr{E}$,

$$\left(\frac{1}{\tau_i}\right)_{E=\mu} = \frac{2\pi n_i}{\hbar}\sum_{\mathbf{k}'} |\langle\mathbf{k}'|w_i|\mathbf{k}\rangle|^2\left[1 - \frac{k_z'}{k_z}\right]\delta(E' - \mu) \tag{6–243}$$

which may be written† in terms of the scattering cross section for electrons near the Fermi level, $\sigma_i(\mu)$,

$$\left(\frac{1}{\tau_i}\right)_{E=\mu} = n_i v(\mu)\langle 1 - \cos\theta\rangle\sigma_i(\mu) \tag{6–244}$$

Thus, according to (6–239), this type of scattering leads to a resistivity which is independent of temperature. In real materials, this "residual" component dominates at very low temperatures.

Thermal scattering: At ordinary temperatures, the crystal lattice is continually disturbed by thermal vibrations, most of which are highly organized and may be regarded as thermally excited acoustic waves. The potential seen by the electrons (when only one such wave is excited) is then approximately $(\delta\mathbf{r})\cdot\nabla V_0$ where $V_0(\mathbf{r})$ is the periodic, perfect-crystal potential‡ and $\delta\mathbf{r}$ is the atomic displacement due to the acoustic wave.

To treat the statistical assembly of waves, they may be described by a formalism such as (5–195)–(5–201) or, alternatively, the wave-functions of the entire solid may be employed: $\psi = \psi_{(\text{nucl})}\cdot\psi_{(\text{elec})}$; in either case, the nuclear displacements, $\delta\mathbf{r}$, become operators with "harmonic oscillator" matrix elements, (5–198), connecting lattice states with differing numbers of "phonons" (acoustic wave quanta). Subsequent manipulations are analogous to (6–241)–(6–244) if it is assumed that the phonon occupation numbers have their equilibrium (Bose–Einstein) values, but the details are

---

* In more detail: The density of *states* is approximately $\rho(E) = G(E)f(\mathbf{k})$ for some G (if the deviation of f from equilibrium is small) but G cancels in (6–241), owing to the factor $\delta(E - E')$ which arises because the massive fixed scattering centers absorb very little energy from the light electrons.

† Recall that $\int d\mathbf{k} = \int d\Omega(mk/\hbar^2)\,dE$.

‡ More precisely, ∇V_0 should be replaced by a function which more accurately describes the actual change in crystalline electron potential due to small atomic displacements.

considerably more complicated. The phonon spectrum is usually approximated by a Debye spectrum, (6–117) and (6–118).

By these methods, it has been found that at high temperatures only dilational (longitudinal) sound waves are effective, that elastic scattering predominates ($E = E'$ for the electrons) and that, for monovalent metals, the electrical conductivity is

$$\sigma \doteqdot \frac{4e^2}{\pi^3\hbar^3}\frac{Mk\Theta^2}{T}(3\pi^2 n)^{-1/3} \tag{6–245}$$

where M is the mass of one atom, n is the number of atoms per unit volume, Θ is the Debye temperature of the solid, and k is Boltzmann's constant. Similarly, assuming* thermal equilibrium of phonons at low temperatures, it has been found that if $T_1 \ll \Theta \ll T_2$,

$$\frac{\sigma_2}{\sigma_1} \doteqdot 500\left(\frac{T_1}{\Theta}\right)^4 \frac{T_1}{T_2} \tag{6–246}$$

(Originally derived by F. Bloch.)

An excellent empirical fit, agreeing with the above, was discovered by Grueneisen:

$$\rho = \frac{1}{\sigma} = (\text{constant}) \times T^5 \int_0^{\Theta/T} \frac{x^5 e^{-x}\,dx}{(1-e^{-x})^2} \tag{6–247}$$

(for the *lattice* resistivity—that is with the residual resistivity subtracted off).

Semi-Conductors

In a semi-conductor, the allowed electronic energy bands are either completely filled or completely empty except for very small deviations due to thermal excitation or to impurity atoms.† The main qualitative difference in the theory is that the *free carriers* act as if they obeyed *classical statistics*, as we now show.

A general situation is shown in the sketch. (Note that donor and acceptor states are localized in space and electrons or holes in such levels cannot take part in conduction.)

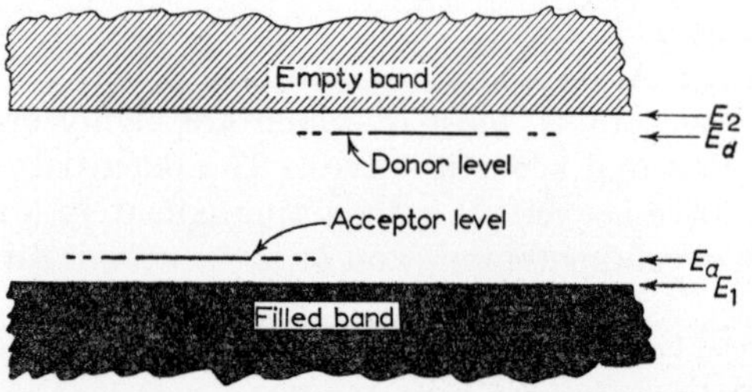

Near the band edges, $E(\mathbf{k})$ has an extremum and, if the crystal is approximately isotropic, $E(\mathbf{k})$ must be quadratic in $|\mathbf{k}|$; see (5–105). It then follows‡ that near the band edges (and per unit volume) the number of states per unit dE is

$$\mathcal{N}_i'(E) = \frac{1}{2\pi^2}\left(\frac{2m_i}{\hbar^2}\right)^{3/2}|E - E_i|^{1/2} \tag{6–248}$$

* Peierls has pointed out that this is probably not justified and that the (empirically correct) T^5 law is actually difficult to understand theoretically.

† Or to vacancies, excess (interstitial) atoms, etc. The deviations caused by these agencies are so slight that the electrons contribute no appreciable specific heat or thermal conductivity. They can only be detected electrically or optically.

‡ Compare (5–95).

where i denotes the band edge in question. Thus the number, n_e, of electrons in the "empty" band is, according to the Fermi distribution, (6–62), (observing that n_e must be very small)

$$n_e = \int_{E_2}^{(\infty)} \frac{\mathcal{N}_2' \, dE}{e^{(E-\mu)/kT}+1} \doteq e^{(\mu-E_2)/kT} \int_0^{(\infty)} \mathcal{N}_2'(x) e^{-x/kT}\, dx$$

$$n_e = 2(2\pi m_e kT/h^2)^{3/2}\, e^{-(E_2-\mu)/kT} \tag{6–249}$$

Similarly, the number of *holes* (vacancies) in the lower band is

$$n_h = 2(2\pi m_h kT/h^2)^{3/2}\, e^{-(\mu-E_1)/kT} \tag{6–250}$$

We note immediately the useful relation,

$$n_e n_h = 4(2\pi\sqrt{m_e m_h}\, kT/h^2)^3\, e^{-(E_2-E_1)/kT} \tag{6–251}$$

To locate the Fermi energy, μ, let $n_d(n_a)$ be the number of donor (acceptor) atoms per unit volume. The number of donor *ions*, n_d^+, is then

$$n_d^+ = n_d - \frac{n_d}{e^{(E_d-\mu)/kT}+1} = \frac{n_d}{1+e^{-(E_d-\mu)/kT}} \tag{6–252}$$

and similarly,

$$n_a^- = \frac{n_a}{e^{(E_a-\mu)/kT}+1} \tag{6–253}$$

Conservation of electrons (electrical neutrality) requires,

$$n_e + n_a^- = n_h + n_d^+ \tag{6–254}$$

which, upon inserting (6–249)–(6–253), becomes a quartic equation in exp (μ/kT). If $n_a = 0 = n_d$, we have immediately $\mu = \frac{1}{2}(E_1+E_2) + \frac{3}{4}kT \ln(m_h/m_e) \doteq \frac{1}{2}(E_1+E_2)$. (This and similar results further justify the approximations in (6–249) and (6–250).)

The conductivity (or, more conveniently, the mobilities, μ_e and μ_h) can be computed by formalisms similar to those outlined above. The only essential difference is the effectively classical statistics of the free carriers (because $|E_i - \mu|/kT \gg 1$). The result for thermal lattice scattering is* [notation: see (6–245).]

$$\mu_{e,h} = \frac{2^{1/2}\,6^{1/3}}{4\pi^{5/6}} \frac{\hbar^2 k^2 \Theta^2 M}{a(m_{e,h})^{5/2}(kT)^{3/2}C^2} \tag{6–255}$$

where a is the spacing of unit cells and C depends on the detailed wave functions, (5–102):

$$C = \frac{\hbar^2}{2m}\int |\nabla u|^2\, d\tau$$

Its numerical value is about 1 to 10 electron volts. The corresponding conductivity is*

$$\sigma = e^2[n_e\mu_e + n_h\mu_h] \tag{6–256}$$

Ionized donor or acceptor atoms introduce additional scattering. Using (6–244) and methods similar to (6–201)–(6–202) (except that the Coulomb field is reduced by the dielectric constant, ϵ, of the solid), one finds for the ion scattering,*

$$\mu_{e,h} = \frac{4\epsilon^2(2kT/\pi)^{3/2}}{n_i e^4 \sqrt{m_{e,h}}} \ln[1 + (3\epsilon kT/e^2 n_i^{1/3})^2] \tag{6–257}$$

* We use the definition, mobility = average velocity per unit *force*; much of the literature uses velocity per unit *field*. The latter is $e\mu_e$ in our notation.

where n_i is the total number of (singly charged) ions per unit volume (for charge Ze, replace e^2 by Ze^2).

When the two types of mobility (6–255) and (6–257) are comparable, they must be combined according to (6–240) to obtain the net mobility.

Diffusion: Since the charge carriers effectively obey classical statistics, (6–15) applies*

$$\mathscr{D}_e = \mu_e kT; \qquad \mathscr{D}_h = \mu_h kT \tag{6–258}$$

Non-equilibrium carrier concentrations (introduced by electrodes or light, for example) have surprisingly long lifetimes (this, indeed, is necessary for transistor action) but the situation appears too complex for a useful theory of such lifetimes.

Thermal Conductivity of the Lattice

In insulators and semi-conductors, virtually all the heat flow is carried by lattice vibrations. An infinite, perfect lattice with purely harmonic interatomic forces would have infinite thermal conductivity since the normal vibration modes do not interact and thus have infinite mean free paths. Anharmonic force terms are the dominant interaction mechanism at high temperatures.

The formalism again involves a Boltzmann transport equation. We give only the results: In a perfect crystal, only "Umklapp" collisions are effective. At *high temperatures*:

$$K_U = (\text{constant})/T \tag{6–259}$$

At low temperatures:

(a) In an infinite, perfect crystal:

$$K_U = (\text{constant}) \exp(b\,\Theta/T) \tag{6–260}$$

where Θ is the Debye temperature of the material and $b \doteqdot \frac{1}{2}$.

(b) In a finite perfect crystal (or for grain-boundary scattering):

$$K = (\text{constant})T^3 \tag{6–261}$$

(c) For scattering by point imperfections:

$$K = (\text{constant})/T \tag{6–262}$$

(d) Isotope scattering:

$$K = (\text{constant})T \tag{6–263}$$

(e) Dislocation scattering:

$$K = (\text{constant})T^2 \tag{6–264}$$

In general, several of these processes may act simultaneously and both the theoretical and the experimental situations become quite involved. Some of the formulas above can be understood qualitatively by setting $K = \lambda v C_v/3$ where v is the speed of sound (= phonons), C_v is the specific heat per unit volume ($\int C_v\, dT$ = phonon energy density) and λ is the phonon mean free path.

9. Liquids

A Classical Formalism

If a system (with N particles) is represented by a statistical assembly of many such systems,† the state of each individual system may be specified by a $6N$ dimensional

* We use the definition, mobility = average velocity per unit *force*; much of the literature uses velocity per unit *field*. The latter is $e\mu_e$ in our notation.

† An assumption of "molecular chaos".

vector, $(\mathbf{r}_1, \mathbf{r}_2, \cdots, \mathbf{r}_N, \mathbf{p}_1, \mathbf{p}_2, \cdots, \mathbf{p}_N) = (\mathbf{r}^N, \mathbf{p}^N)$, and the ensemble may be described by a *density* or distribution function, $f(\mathbf{r}^N, \mathbf{p}^N, t)$, giving the density of such system-points in the "space" $(\mathbf{r}^N, \mathbf{p}^N)$. [In equilibrium, $f = C \exp[-H(\mathbf{r}^N, \mathbf{p}^N)/kT]$, according to (6–48).]

Since the number of system-points is constant, we have the conservation relation,

$$\begin{aligned}\frac{\partial f}{\partial t} &= -\sum_{k=1}^{N}\left[\nabla_{\mathbf{r}_k}\cdot\left(\frac{d\mathbf{r}_k}{dt}f\right) + \nabla_{\mathbf{p}_k}\cdot\left(\frac{d\mathbf{p}_k}{dt}f\right)\right] \\ &= \sum_{k=1}^{N}\left[-\frac{\mathbf{p}_k}{m_k}\cdot\nabla_{\mathbf{r}_k}f + (\nabla_{\mathbf{r}_k}H)\cdot(\nabla_{\mathbf{p}_k}f)\right]\end{aligned} \tag{6–265}$$

The last equality (Liouville's theorem) follows from Hamilton's equations of motion, (1–52).

The mean value of any function, $\alpha(\mathbf{r}^N, \mathbf{p}^N)$, is given by

$$\langle\alpha\rangle = C\left\{\int\!\!\int \alpha f\, d\mathbf{r}^N\, d\mathbf{p}^N\right\}; \quad \frac{1}{C} = \int\!\!\int f\, d\mathbf{r}^N\, d\mathbf{p}^N$$

(The usual convention is $C = 1/N$.) From (6–265), since $f = 0$ for sufficiently large $\mathbf{r}_k$ or $\mathbf{p}_k$,

$$\frac{d\langle\alpha\rangle}{dt} = \sum_k\left\langle\frac{\mathbf{p}_k}{m_k}\cdot\nabla_{\mathbf{r}_k}\alpha\right\rangle - \sum_k\langle\nabla_{\mathbf{p}_k}\cdot[\alpha\nabla_{\mathbf{r}_k}H]\rangle \tag{6–266}$$

Choosing various specific forms for the function α gives the usual macroscopic equations for continuous media, namely (1–54), (1–66), (1–71). If

$$H = \frac{1}{2m}\sum_k|\mathbf{p}_k|^2 + \sum_{i<k}\phi(|\mathbf{r}_i - \mathbf{r}_k|)$$

it may be shown in this way that the stress tensor, $\mathfrak{P} = \mathfrak{P}_k + \mathfrak{P}_\phi$, and the heat flux, $\mathbf{Q} = \mathbf{Q}_K + \mathbf{Q}_\phi$, are given by

$$\mathfrak{P}_k = m\int\left(\frac{\mathbf{p}}{m} - \mathbf{v}\right)\left(\frac{\mathbf{p}}{m} - \mathbf{v}\right)f^{(1)}(\mathbf{r}, \mathbf{p}, t)\, d\mathbf{p}$$

$$\mathfrak{P}_\phi = -\tfrac{1}{2}\left(\frac{\rho}{m}\right)^2\int\frac{d\phi(R)}{dR}\, g(\mathbf{r}, \mathbf{R}, t)\,\frac{\mathbf{R}\mathbf{R}}{R}\, d\mathbf{R}$$

$$\mathbf{Q}_k = \tfrac{1}{2}m\int\left|\frac{\mathbf{p}}{m} - \mathbf{v}\right|^2\left(\frac{\mathbf{p}}{m} - \mathbf{v}\right)f^{(1)}(\mathbf{r}, \mathbf{p}, t)\, d\mathbf{p}$$

$$\mathbf{Q}_\phi = \tfrac{1}{2}\int\left[\phi(R)\mathbf{1} - \frac{d\phi(R)}{dR}\frac{\mathbf{R}\mathbf{R}}{R}\right] \cdot\left\{\boldsymbol{j}(\mathbf{r}, \mathbf{r} + \mathbf{R}, t) - \frac{\rho^2}{m}\mathbf{v}\, g(\mathbf{r}, \mathbf{R}, t)\right\} d\mathbf{R}$$

where $\mathbf{v}$ is the (macroscopic) fluid velocity, ρ is the fluid density, and

$$f^{(1)}(\mathbf{r}, \mathbf{p}, t) = \sum_k\langle\delta(\mathbf{r}_k - \mathbf{r})\delta(\mathbf{p}_k - \mathbf{p})\rangle$$

$$g(\mathbf{r}, \mathbf{R}, t) = \left(\frac{m}{\rho}\right)^2\int\!\!\int f^{(2)}(\mathbf{r}, \mathbf{r} + \mathbf{R}, \mathbf{p}, \mathbf{p}', t)\, d\mathbf{p}\, d\mathbf{p}'$$

(where):

$$f^{(2)}(\mathbf{r}, \mathbf{r}', \mathbf{p}, \mathbf{p}', t) = \sum_{k\neq j}\langle\delta(\mathbf{r}_j - \mathbf{r})\delta(\mathbf{r}_k - \mathbf{r}')\delta(\mathbf{p}_j - \mathbf{p})\delta(\mathbf{p}_k - \mathbf{p}')\rangle$$

and

$$\boldsymbol{j}(\mathbf{r}, \mathbf{r} + \mathbf{R}, t) = \int\!\!\int \mathbf{p} f^{(2)}(\mathbf{r}, \mathbf{r} + \mathbf{R}, \mathbf{p}, \mathbf{p}', t)\, d\mathbf{p}\, d\mathbf{p}'$$

In equilibrium, these results reduce to (6–111)–(6–115). To evaluate the transport coefficients, the distribution, f, or at least $f^{(2)}$ must be estimated by approximately solving (6–265) or some approximation thereto. One such program has been formally carried through but numerical comparison with experiment is still incomplete, so that the adequateness of its approximations cannot yet be judged.

Semi-Empirical Relations

Viscosity: Consider a liquid subject to a shearing force, F, (per unit area). Imagine that the liquid molecules form a lattice and consider the rate at which a molecule squeezes past its neighbors. When the work done against F is added to the equilibrium $\Delta G^{\ddagger}$ of (6–208), the net velocity of flow of molecules in one lattice plane relative to their neighbors is found to be

$$v = (2akT/h)\, e^{-\Delta G^{\ddagger}/RT} \sinh (F/2nkT)$$

where a is the lattice spacing ($\doteqdot n^{-1/3}$) and n is the number of molecules per unit volume. By definition, the viscosity, η, is then

$$\eta = \frac{hFe^{\Delta G^{\ddagger}/RT}}{2kT \sinh (F/2nkT)} \doteqdot nhe^{\Delta G^{\ddagger}/RT} \qquad (6\text{–}267)$$

With complex hydrocarbon molecules, $\Delta G^{\ddagger}$ has sudden transitions, apparently at temperatures (or volumes) where new types of molecular motion become possible. However, for simple liquids it is found empirically that (as might be suspected),

$$\Delta G^{\ddagger} \doteqdot (\Delta H_{\text{vap}} - RT_{\text{vap}})/2.45 = \Delta U_{\text{vap}}/2.45$$

where ΔH = heat of vaporization and ΔU = internal energy change at vaporization.

For mixtures (empirically),

$$\ln \eta = \frac{n_1 \ln \eta_1 + n_2 \ln \eta_2}{n_1 + n_2} \qquad (6\text{–}268)$$

Diffusion: By similar arguments, the coefficient of self-diffusion is approximately,

$$\mathscr{D} = a^2(kT/h)e^{-\Delta G^{\ddagger}/kT}$$

There are few measurements of self-diffusion and similar arguments for mixtures give only order-of-magnitude agreement with experiment.

Thermal conductivity: According to (6–6) and (6–9), the thermal conductivity, K, of a gas is $(1/3)nc_v\lambda\langle v\rangle$. For a monatomic liquid, $c_v \doteqdot 3k$, including potential ("lattice vibration") energy; $\lambda \doteqdot n^{-1/3}$ and the effective energy transport velocity, $\langle v\rangle$, may be estimated from the ratio of the speed of sound c (in the liquid) to that in the gas. Thus one expects,

$$K = n^{2/3}\, kc\sqrt{8c_v/\pi c_p} \quad \text{(monatomic)} \qquad (6\text{–}269)$$

An Eucken correction for the rotational energies (only) of polyatomic liquids gives,

$$K = 2.80\, kn^{2/3}\, c\sqrt{c_v/c_p} \quad \text{(polyatomic)} \qquad (6\text{–}270)$$

These results are remarkably accurate (~10%) for many liquids and have the correct temperature dependence at normal pressures, but they are high by about a factor of two near 12,000 atm pressure.

PART II

MATHEMATICS

SCOPE

This part emphasizes material not readily available in compact, handbook form. Most of the information normally contained in tables of integrals or in recent compilations of the properties of special functions has been omitted. Many sections contain a mere list of results; some include a condensed but connected discussion.

REMARK

To forestall any misplaced hope for purely "theoretical" answers to all questions, no scientist should be unaware of Goedel's humbling theorem of symbolic logic. In effect, the theorem states that in every system of formal logic there always exist propositions which can be neither proved nor disproved within the system. In particular, either such a proposition, or equally well its denial, could be appended to the axioms of the system without generating any contradictions, but the new system so formed would contain new undecidable propositions.

CHAPTER 7

ALGEBRA

Mathematical Induction:

If a proposition $\mathscr{P}(n)$ contains an integer parameter, $n = 1. 2, 3, \cdots$ (or several such parameters), it is true for all n if: $\mathscr{P}(1)$ is true and $\mathscr{P}(n-1)$ [and/or all earlier $\mathscr{P}(n')$] implies $\mathscr{P}(n)$.

Partial Fractions

If the polynomial, $p(x)$ has distinct roots, $x_1, \cdots, x_n$ then, if the degree of ϕ is less than that of p

$$\frac{\phi(x)}{p(x)} = \sum_{i=1}^{n} \frac{A_i}{x - x_i}$$

where (obviously):

$$A_i = \lim_{x \to x_i} (x - x_i) \frac{\phi(x)}{p(x)} = \frac{\phi(x_i)}{p'(x_i)} \qquad (7\text{–}1)$$

If the root x_α has multiplicity m, then the corresponding term in (7–1) is replaced by

$$\sum_{j=1}^{m} \frac{B_{m-j}}{(x - x_\alpha)^j}$$

where if

$$\frac{p(x)}{(x - x_\alpha)^m} = q(x)$$

then

$$B_k = \frac{\phi^{(k)}}{k!q} - \sum_{j=0}^{k-1} \frac{B_j}{(k-j)!} \frac{q^{(k-j)}}{q}$$

(evaluated at $x = x_\alpha$).

ROOTS OF POLYNOMIALS

Cubics

$$x^3 - 3ax^2 + 3bx - c = 0$$

Let*

$$\cos \phi = \frac{a^3 - \frac{3}{2}ab + \frac{1}{2}c}{(a^2 - b)^{3/2}}$$

The roots are all real if and only if this expression is real and lies between ± 1. If $a^2 = b$, the roots are $x = a + (c - a^3)^{1/3}$; otherwise

$$x_k = a + 2\sqrt{a^2 - b} \cos \left(\frac{\phi + 2\pi k}{3} \right) \qquad (7\text{–}2)$$

* To compute square-roots on a desk computer: If x is an approximate root of S (e.g. found by slide rule) then a better root is

$$x' = (S + x^2)/2x$$

which (by mentally doubling x) can be obtained in one operation on a desk computer. The number of significant figures doubles with each iteration.

Quartics

$$ax^4 + bx^3 + cx^2 + dx + e = 0$$

1. Set $x = z - (b/4a)$ to obtain,

$$z^4 + pz^2 + qz + r = 0$$

which, for *any* u, is equivalent to:

$$\left(z^2 + \frac{u}{2}\right)^2 - \left[(u - p)z^2 - qz + \left(\frac{u^2}{4} - r\right)\right] = 0 \qquad (7\text{–}3)$$

2. Therefore, solve for u:

$$q^2 = 4(u - p)\left(\frac{u^2}{4} - r\right)$$

that is,

$$u^3 - pu^2 - 4ru + (4pr - q^2) = 0$$

and let a solution be u_0.

3. Then (7–3) is reduced to biquadratic form ($\alpha^2 = u_0 - p;\ \beta = -q/2\alpha$):

$$(z^2 + \alpha z + \beta + \tfrac{1}{2}u_0)(z^2 - \alpha z - \beta + \tfrac{1}{2}u_0) = 0 \qquad (7\text{–}4)$$

Descartes' Rule of Signs

$$x^n + a_1 x^{n-1} + \cdots + a_i x^{n-i} + \cdots + a_n = 0 \qquad (7\text{–}5)$$

$$\begin{Bmatrix}\text{Number of positive}\\ \textit{real}\text{ roots}\end{Bmatrix} = \begin{Bmatrix}\text{Number of sign changes}\\ \text{in the sequence, } a_i\end{Bmatrix} - 2m$$

where m is a non-negative integer, where multiple roots are counted according to their multiplicity, and where vanishing a_i are ignored. Note that judicious changes of variable will often locate the roots unambiguously.

Bounds on Roots

In (7–5),

$$\text{each real root} \leqslant 1 + G^{1/k}$$

where G is the magnitude of the "most negative" coefficient, that is $G = \max\limits_{(a_i<0)} (|a_i|)$, and where k is the index of the first negative coefficient, that is $j < k$ implies $a_j \geqslant 0$.

In (7–5) consider the quantities, $1 + |a_i| \{\sum' a_j\}^{-1}$, for any $a_i < 0$, and where the summation is over positive coefficients which precede it, that is, with $a_0 = 1$,

$$\textstyle\sum' = \sum\limits_j (j < i;\ a_j > 0)$$

The largest of these quantities is larger than any real root.

If in (7–5) we have

$$|a_p| > 1 + \sum_{k \neq p} |a_k|$$

(for some one value of p), then there are p roots outside the unit circle, $|x| \geqslant 1$, in the complex plane. (The converse, however, is false). Moreover, *these* roots lie in the region,

$$|a_1 + x| \leqslant \sum_{2}^{n} |a_k|$$

and also in

$$|x| < 1 + |a_p| \quad \text{if} \quad 1 \neq p \neq n$$

$$|x| < |a_n| \qquad \text{if} \quad p = n$$

(*Math. Reviews* **17,** 597 (1956).)

In (7–5) the number of roots with positive real *part* equals the number of sign changes in the sequence,

$$1,\ D_1,\ D_1D_2,\ D_2D_3, \cdots, D_kD_{k+1}, \cdots, D_{n-2}D_{n-1},\ a_n.$$

where D_k is the determinant,

$$D_k = \begin{vmatrix} a_1 & 1 & 0 & 0 & 0 & \cdots & 0 \\ a_3 & a_2 & a_1 & 1 & 0 & \cdots & 0 \\ a_5 & a_4 & a_3 & a_2 & a_1 & \cdots & . \\ \cdot & & & & & & \cdot \\ \cdot & & & & & & \cdot \\ \cdot & & & & & & \cdot \\ a_{2k-1} & \cdots & \cdots & \cdots & \cdots & \cdots & a_k \end{vmatrix} \tag{7–6}$$

(Modified "Routh's Criterion".)

A polynomial, all of whose roots have negative real parts, is called a "Hurwitz polynomial".

Computation of Roots

1. An easily remembered, efficient method is "cut and try" plus evaluation of the derivative. [If r is an approximate root and e the required correction: $p(r + e) = 0 = p(r) + ep'(r) + \cdots$ whence $e \doteq -p(r)/p'(r)$.] This also can be used with any function. (Newton's method.)

2. Graeffe's root-squaring method: If the roots of $p(x) = 0$ are desired, then $p(x)p(-x) = 0$ is also of order n in the variable $y = x^2$ and the roots are the squares of those desired. Repetition of this operation separates the roots further and further. Eventually, $y_i \doteq a_i/a_{i-1}$ and the original roots can be found except for sign, which must be determined in some other way. The method often converges even with equal roots; if not, the failure to converge is soon obvious and this information can be used in various ways.

Polynomials With Common Roots

1. **Eliminants:** Two polynomials, $p(x)$, $q(x)$ have (*at least*) one root in common if *and only if* the determinant of the coefficients of x^i in the following $n + m$ equations vanishes.

$$x^j p(x) = 0, \qquad j = 0, 1, \cdots, \text{(degree of } q \text{ less 1)}$$

$$x^k q(x) = 0, \qquad k = 0, 1, \cdots, \text{(degree of } p \text{ less 1)}.$$

2. **Euclidean algorithm:** The greatest common divisor [the product of the common factors $(x - r_i)$] of $P_1(x)$ and $P_2(x)$ may be systematically found as follows. Let P_1 have greater degree than P_2 (or the same degree). Divide P_1 by P_2 to obtain a polynomial remainder, P_3; continue dividing P_{i-1} by P_i to obtain a polynomial remainder P_{i+1}. The last non-vanishing remainder is the greatest common divisor of $P_1(x)$ and $P_2(x)$.

Curve-fitting (Interpolation)

A polynomial which takes the value y_i at $x = x_i$ is obviously given by:

$$y = \sum_{i=1}^{n} \left[y_i \prod_{j \neq i} \frac{x - x_j}{x_i - x_j} \right] \tag{7–7}$$

Special forms, however, are often more useful in special cases. These may be conveniently derived by manipulations on the determinant form:

$$\begin{vmatrix} y_1 & \cdots\cdots & y_n & y \\ 1 & \cdots\cdots & 1 & 1 \\ x_1 & \cdots\cdots & x_n & x \\ x_1^2 & \cdots\cdots & x_n^2 & x^2 \\ \cdot & & \cdot & \cdot \\ \cdot & & \cdot & \cdot \\ \cdot & & \cdot & \cdot \\ x_1^{n-1} & \cdots\cdots & x_n^{n-1} & x^{n-1} \end{vmatrix} = 0 \tag{7–8}$$

(also manifestly correct for $x = x_i$: $\cdots y(x_i) = y_i$).

Another frequently convenient form is

$$y = y_1 + (x - x_1)\{a_2 + (x - x_2)[a_3 + \cdots (x - x_n)] \cdots\}$$

where the a_i can be evaluated by setting x equal to $x_1, x_2, x_3, \cdots$ successively. This "nested" form has the advantage that an extra point, x_{n+1}, can always be added without recomputing any of the earlier a_i.

Least-squares polynomial: If the number n of points x_i is very large, it is often desirable to obtain a polynomial $P(x)$ of low degree, $k < n$, which is nevertheless fitted to *all* of the data, $y(x_i) = y_i$. One method is to minimize the mean square error, $(1/n) \sum [y_i - P(x_i)]^2$. Use (9–7.5) with the notaticn,

$$(p, q) = (1/n) \sum_{1}^{n} p(x_i)\, q(x_i)$$

(and with the initial conditions $p_{-1} = 0$, $p_0 = 1$) to generate $k + 1$ "orthonormal" polynomials, $p_\alpha(x)$ (completely determined by the points x_i). The required $P(x)$ is then [compare (9–9)]

$$P(x) = \sum_{\alpha=0}^{k} (y, p_\alpha) p_\alpha(x)$$

and its mean square error is $(y, y) - \sum_{\alpha} (y, p_\alpha)^2$.

[Note: It can be shown that in the present case $(xp_\alpha, p_{\alpha-1}) = 1$, which somewhat simplifies (9–7.5).]

Curve-fitting With Rational Functions:

To determine the coefficients in

$$y(x) = \frac{a_0 x^n + a_1 x^{n-1} + \cdots + a_n}{b_0 x^n + b_1 x^{n-1} + \cdots + b_n} \tag{7–9}$$

such that $y(x_i) =$ a given y_i, multiply through by the denominator and adjoin the corresponding equations with $x = x_i$, $y = y_i$. The eliminant (equation eliminating the a_i and b_j) is then,

$$0 = \begin{vmatrix} 1, & y, & x, & xy, & x^2, & x^2y, & \cdots, x^n, & x^ny \\ 1, & y_1, & x_1, & x_1y_1, & x_1^2, & x_1^2y_1, & \cdots, x_1^n, & x_1^ny_1 \\ \cdot & & & & & & & \cdot \\ \cdot & & & & & & & \cdot \\ \cdot & & & & & & & \cdot \\ 1, & y_k, & x_k, & x_ky_k, & x_k^2, & x_k^2y_k, & \cdots, x_k^n, & x_k^ny_k \end{vmatrix} \tag{7-10}$$

which is the desired relation.

A frequently more convenient form is based on the continued fraction,

$$y = a_1 + \frac{x - x_1|}{|\ a_2} + \frac{x - x_2|}{|\ a_3} + \cdots$$

which leads to the following prescription, in which the conditions $y(x_1) = y_1, \cdots, y(x_n) = y_n$ are successively satisfied by

$$y = \frac{p_n(x)}{q_n(x)} = \frac{a_np_{n-1}(x) + (x - x_{n-1})p_{n-2}(x)}{a_nq_{n-1}(x) + (x - x_{n-1})q_{n-2}(x)}$$

where

$$a_n = (x_n - x_{n-1})\frac{y_nq_{n-2}(x_n) - p_{n-2}(x_n)}{p_{n-1}(x_n) - y_nq_{n-1}(x_n)}$$

and, at the start,

$$p_0 \equiv 1, \quad q_1 \equiv 1, \quad p_1 \equiv y_1, \quad q_2 \equiv a_2 = (x_2 - x_1)/(y_2 - y_1)$$

SOME FINITE SERIES

$$\sum_{i=0}^{n} x^i = \frac{x^{n+1} - 1}{x - 1}$$

$$\sum_{i=0}^{n} i = \tfrac{1}{2}n(n + 1)$$

$$\sum_{i=0}^{n} i^2 = \tfrac{1}{6}n(n + 1)(2n + 1)$$

$$\sum_{i=0}^{n} i^3 = \tfrac{1}{4}n^2(n + 1)^2$$

$$\sum_{i=0}^{n} i^4 = \frac{n}{30}[6n^4 + 15n^3 + 10n^2 - 1]$$

$$\sum_{i=0}^{n} i^p = \frac{(n + B)^{p+1} - B^{p+1}}{p + 1} + n^p$$

where, after expansion, replace B^k by B_k (Bernoulli numbers as defined below.)

$$\sum_{i=0}^{n} (2i + 1) = (n + 1)^2$$

$$\sum_{i=1}^{n} \frac{1}{i(i + 1)} = \frac{n}{n + 1}$$

$$\sum_{i=0}^{n} i[(i + 1)^l - i^l + i^{l-1}] = n(n + 1)^l$$

Bernoulli Numbers

(This definition is common but several others are also frequently used.)

$$\frac{x}{e^x - 1} = \sum_{n=0}^{\infty} \frac{B_n x^n}{n!} \tag{7–11}$$

Thus, $B_{2k+3} = 0$; the only odd-order non-vanishing B_n is $B_1 = -\frac{1}{2}$. The numbers satisfy the schematic recursion formula:

$$(B + 1)^n = B^n \qquad (B^k \to B_k; \qquad n \neq 1)$$

Some values:

$$B_0 = 1, \quad B_1 = -\frac{1}{2}, \quad B_2 = \frac{1}{6}, \quad B_4 = \frac{-1}{30}, \quad B_6 = \frac{1}{42}$$

$$B_8 = \frac{-1}{30}, \quad B_{10} = \frac{5}{66}, \quad B_{12} = \frac{-691}{2730}, \quad B_{14} = \frac{7}{6}, \quad B_{16} = \frac{-3617}{510}$$

Further relations:

$$\frac{(-1)^{k+1}(2\pi)^{2k} B_{2k}}{2(2k)!} = \zeta(2k) = \sum_{n=1}^{\infty} \frac{1}{n^{2k}}$$

$$\frac{(2^{2k} - 2)\pi^{2k} B_{2k}}{(-1)^{k+1} 2(2k)!} = \sum_{n=0}^{\infty} \frac{(-1)^n}{(n + 1)^{2k}}$$

Multinomial Theorem:

$$(a_1 + a_2 + \cdots + a_N)^n = \sum_{i_1 + \cdots + i_N = n} \frac{(n!) a_1^{i_1} a_2^{i_2} \cdots a_N^{i_N}}{(i_1!)(i_2!) \cdots (i_N!)} \tag{7–12}$$

Binomial Theorem ($N = 2$):

$$(a + b)^n = \sum_{i=0}^{n} \binom{n}{i} a^{n-i} b^i \tag{7–13}$$

where

$$\binom{x}{i} = \binom{x}{x-i} = \frac{x!}{i!(x - i)!} = \frac{x(x - 1) \cdots (x - i + 1)}{i!}, \qquad \text{if } i \geqslant 0,$$

The latter form is valid for negative or positive x. It is convenient to define

$$\binom{x}{i} = 0 \quad \text{for} \quad i < 0; \qquad \binom{n}{i} = 0 \quad \text{if} \quad i > n$$

(where n is a positive integer). These binomial coefficients have many surprising properties; the following is a collection of such identities.

Reversion:

$$\binom{-x}{v} = (-1)^v \binom{x + v - 1}{v}$$

Recursion:

$$\binom{x + y}{n} = \sum_{i=0}^{n} \binom{x}{i} \binom{y}{n - i}$$

(Note the special cases $y = 1$ and $y = x$.)

$$\binom{n + 1}{k + 1} = \sum_{i=0}^{n-k} \binom{n - i}{k}$$

$$\sum_{i=0}^{n} \binom{n}{i} (\pm 1)^i = (1 \pm 1)^n = \begin{cases} 2^n \\ 0 \end{cases}$$

$$\sum_{i=0}^{n} \binom{2n}{2i} = 2^{2n-1}$$

$$\sum_{i=0}^{n} i \binom{n}{i} x^i (1-x)^{n-i} = nx$$

$$\sum_{i=k}^{n} \binom{n}{i}\binom{i}{k}(-1)^i = (-1)^n \delta_{nk}$$

where $\delta_{nn} = 1$ and $\delta_{nk} = 0$ if $n \neq k$.

$$\sum_{i=0}^{m} \binom{x+i}{i} = \binom{x+m+1}{m}$$

$$\sum_{i=k}^{n} \binom{n+1}{i+1}\binom{i}{k}(-1)^{i-k} = 1$$

$$\binom{l}{n} \sum_{i=0}^{l} i^n \binom{l}{i} (-1)^i = (l!)(-1)^l \delta_{nl}$$

$$\sum_{i=l}^{n} \binom{i}{l}\binom{n}{i} x^i (1-x)^{n-i} = \binom{n}{l} x^l$$

$$\sum_{i=0}^{n} (-1)^i \binom{n}{i}\binom{ns-is}{r} = s^n \delta_{nr}$$

$$\sum_{i=t}^{n} (-1)^i \binom{n}{i}\binom{i}{m} = \binom{n}{m}\binom{n-m-1}{t-m-1}$$

$$\sum_{i=0}^{n} (-1)^i \binom{n}{i}\binom{n-i}{k-i} = 0$$

$$\sum_{i=0}^{n} (-1)^i i \binom{n}{i} = 0$$

$$\sum_{i=0} \binom{n}{i+k}\binom{m}{i} = \binom{n+m}{n-k}$$

$$\sum_{i=1}^{n} (-1)^{n-i} \binom{n}{i}\binom{m+i}{m+1} = \binom{m}{n-1}$$

$$\sum_{i=0}^{k} \binom{n+k-i-1}{k-i}\binom{m+i-1}{i} = \binom{n+m+k-1}{k}$$

$$\sum_{i=0}^{k} (-1)^i \binom{n}{i} = (-1)^k \binom{n-1}{k}$$

$$\sum_{i=1}^{n} \binom{n}{i}\frac{(-1)^i}{i} = -\sum_{1}^{n} \frac{1}{i}$$

$$\sum_{i} (-1)^i \binom{m+n}{m+i}\binom{l+m}{l+i}\binom{n+l}{n+i} = \frac{(m+n+l)!}{m!n!l!}$$

$$\sum_{i=0}^{n-1}\left[\binom{u}{i}\Big/\binom{v}{i}\right] = \frac{v+1}{v-u+1}\left\{1 - \left[\binom{u}{n}\Big/\binom{v+1}{n}\right]\right\}$$

$$\sum_{i=1}^{n} \frac{(-1)^{i-1}(n+i-1)!}{(i!)^2(n-i)!} = \frac{1}{n}$$

$$\sum_{i=0}^{n} (-1)^i \frac{\binom{n}{i}\binom{u}{i}}{\binom{n-u-1}{i}} = \frac{2^n\Gamma(1+u-n)\sqrt{\pi}}{\Gamma(1+u-\frac{1}{2}n)\,\Gamma(\frac{1}{2}-\frac{1}{2}n)}$$

Methods of Proof

(a) If only one or two parameters are involved, mathematical induction works well (and will often rigorously establish a guess based on a few trial cases).

(b) More generally, one can choose a "clever" function, expand it in several ways, and either compare coefficients or assign special values to the variables. Thus, for example

$$(x+y+1)^m = \sum_l \binom{m}{l}(x+y)^l = \sum_{l,k}\binom{m}{l}\binom{l}{k}x^k y^{l-k}$$

and setting $y = -1$ and comparing the coefficients of x^i, there results

$$\sum_l \binom{n}{l}\binom{l}{k}(-1)^l = (-1)^n\delta_{nk}$$

If integer factors occur in the desired expression, it will often prove expedient to integrate or differentiate a rational function.

(c) The properties of hypergeometric series may also be used to advantage. (The last three results may be proven in this manner.)

PERMUTATIONS AND COMBINATIONS

Definition

A permutation of a set of objects (say $x_1, x_2, \cdots, x_n$) is an *ordering* (arrangement in a row) of these objects. Often, the objects are conceived as given in a "natural order" and one speaks of a *re*-ordering—a special case of which is then the "identity" permutation which leaves the objects in natural order.

An *even* permutation is one which does not change the sign of the expression

$$\prod_{i<j}(x_j - x_i)$$

An *odd* permutation does change the sign.

Theorems

1. There are a total of $n!$ permutations on n objects—one half of these are "even" and one-half "odd". If two permutations differ by a simple interchange (of only one pair of objects), one must be even and the other odd.

2. Arrangements with repetition: If a total of n objects is made up of i_1 identical objects of "type 1" plus i_2 objects of "type 2", etc., so that $i_1 + i_2 + \cdots + i_l = n$,

then the number of *distinct* ("different looking") arrangements of all n objects (in a row, say) is

$$\frac{n!}{(i_1!)(i_2!)\cdots(i_l!)}$$

(compare (7–12); proof: permutations of identical objects do not produce a "different arrangement").

3. From a supply of n objects, all different, one can:

—select m objects (ignoring the order) in $\binom{n}{m}$ ways

—select *and* arrange m objects in $m!\binom{n}{m} = \dfrac{n!}{(n-m)!}$ ways

4. From an unlimited supply of n different *types* of object, one can

—select m objects (ignoring the order) in $\binom{n+m-1}{m}$ ways

—select *and* arrange m objects in n^m ways.

5. The number of "partitions" of n into s summands (with different orders of *distinct* numbers considered different "partitions") is $\binom{n-1}{s-1}$ = number of ways of placing $s - 1$ bars in the $n - 1$ spaces between n dots.

Ignoring the order of the summands leads to a much more complicated function, $p(n)$, which satisfies the recursion relation,

$$\sum_k (-1)^k p[n - \tfrac{1}{2}k - \tfrac{3}{2}k^2] + \sum_l (-1)^l p[n + \tfrac{1}{2}l - \tfrac{3}{2}l^2] = p(n)$$

where $p(0) = 1$ and each sum extends over a range such that the argument of p is non-negative and $\leqslant n \neq 0$. (Tables of $p(n)$ for n up to 600 exist.)

ELEMENTARY TOPOLOGY

1. *Euler Formula:* In any polyhedron (enclosing a finite, three-dimensional volume)

$$\#\text{ edges} = \#\text{ faces} + \#\text{ corners} - 3 + \text{connectivity} \qquad (7\text{–}14)$$

where # denotes "number of" and:

Connectivity = the *maximum* number of cuts (first one must be a closed curve; later ones may only join two points of earlier ones) which can be made so that only the last one separates the surface into two pieces. (If the surface has connectivity C it is topologically equivalent to a sphere with $C - 1$ "handles.")

2. In n dimensions, the quantities $\sum_{i=0}^{n-1} (-1)^i \alpha_i$ are topological invariants (as in (7–14) above) if α_i are the number of elements of dimension i. For n-dimensional "spheres" the value of this sum is $1 - (-1)^n$.

3. In any network (not necessarily planar) with n nodes and l links (each joining two nodes), the number of *independent* meshes, m, is

$$m = l - n + 1 \qquad (7\text{–}15)$$

This is also the maximum number of links which can be cut (or removed) *without* separating the network into two unconnected nets.

4. *Fixed-point theorems:*

(a) Any continuous mapping of (interior and boundary of) a circle onto itself sends at least one point into itself.

(b) In any continuous mapping of the surface of a sphere onto itself, either at least one point goes into its diametrically opposite point or there are at least two fixed points.

Boolean Algebra

An isomorphism of Boolean algebra onto arithmetic: If we set up the following correspondence between non-negative real numbers and Boolean "truth values",

$$x = 0 \leftrightarrow \text{Boolean "}x\text{ is false"}$$

$$x > 0 \leftrightarrow \text{Boolean "}x\text{ is true"}$$

then we have

$$xy \leftrightarrow \text{Boolean "}x\text{ and }y\text{"}$$

$$x + y \leftrightarrow \text{Boolean "}x\text{ or }y\text{ (or both)"}$$

$$\text{Integral part of } [(1 + x)^{-1}] \leftrightarrow \text{Boolean "not }x\text{"}$$

and Boolean algebra is thereby mapped onto the algebra of non-negative real numbers if we adjoin the extra rules:

$$x^2 = x = Ax$$

$$x + A = A = 1$$

(where A is any positive numerical coefficient). Thus, for example, $(x + y)(x + z) = x + yz$.

Often, in programming for automatic computing machines, the "propositions" to be tested for truth or falsity take the form, "$Z > 0$". These may be incorporated in the above by using as the corresponding Boolean variable

$$z = Z + |Z|.$$

NOMOGRAPHS

Nomographs are graphical diagrams which serve to perform a calculation by aligning a straight edge across various printed scales.

A single application of a straight edge serves to determine one quantity from two others. Quite generally, if u_1, u_2, u_3 are the variables and if the three scales are defined by the parametric curves,

$$C_i \quad : \quad \begin{cases} x = f_i(u_i) \\ y = g_i(u_i) \end{cases} \qquad i = 1, 2, 3 \tag{7–16}$$

then a straight edge solves the equation,

$$\begin{vmatrix} f_1(u_1) & g_1(u_1) & 1 \\ f_2(u_2) & g_2(u_2) & 1 \\ f_3(u_3) & g_3(u_3) & 1 \end{vmatrix} = 0 \tag{7–17}$$

(Determinantal form of the equation for a line through three points.)

Thus, to construct a nomograph for solving a given equation, the steps are:

(a) Cast the equation into determinant form, $D = 0$.

(b) By manipulations which do not alter the (zero) value of the determinant,* rearrange so that unity appears everywhere in the third column and only one variable appears in each row. (If the latter is impossible, see below under "Several Equations.")

(c) Plot the curves C_i (defined by comparison with the general form (7–16), (7–17) above) and mark on each the corresponding values of the u_i.

EXAMPLE: $UV = W$ may be written, $\log U + \log V = \log W$, and is then readily handled by three parallel log scales. The following, however, gives a linear scale for W

$$\begin{vmatrix} U & 1 & 0 \\ W & V & 0 \\ 0 & 0 & 1 \end{vmatrix} = 0 = \begin{vmatrix} U & 1 & 0 \\ W & V & 1 \\ 0 & 0 & 1 \end{vmatrix} = \begin{vmatrix} U & 1 & 0 \\ 0 & V & 1 \\ -W & 0 & 1 \end{vmatrix} = \begin{vmatrix} U & 1 & 1 \\ 0 & V & (V+1) \\ -W & 0 & 1 \end{vmatrix} = \begin{vmatrix} U & 1 & 1 \\ 0 & \dfrac{V}{V+1} & 1 \\ -W & 0 & 1 \end{vmatrix}$$

(The manipulations are: add row-3 to row-2; subtract W (col-3) from col-1; add col-2 to col-3; divide row-2 by $V + 1$.) The last is the required form (compare (7–16) and (7–17) to construct the scales). If U and V are both positive, it is convenient to shift the W scale into the region $x > 0$; to do this, add "A times col-3 minus A times col-2" to col-1:

$$0 = \begin{vmatrix} U & 1 & 1 \\ \dfrac{A}{V+1} & \dfrac{V}{V+1} & 1 \\ A - W & 0 & 1 \end{vmatrix} = \begin{vmatrix} \alpha\beta U & 1 & 1 \\ \dfrac{A\beta}{V+\beta} & \dfrac{V}{V+\beta} & 1 \\ A - \alpha W & 0 & 1 \end{vmatrix}$$

where the last form is obviously equivalent since $UV = W$ can be written $(\alpha\beta U)(V/\beta) = \alpha W$. This is the often-used "N diagram."

More than three variables (one equation): An additional determinant (corresponding to an additional alignment) is needed for each variable in excess of three. The principles are illustrated by the case of four variables (one equation). Cast the equation into a form where only two variables appear on each side and define a fifth variable by

$$z = F(u_1, u_2) = G(u_3, u_4)$$

(where the latter equality is the original equation). Now construct determinant forms of the two relations, $z = F$ and $z = G$, and manipulate each into the standard form (7–17) with the additional restriction that the row containing (only) z must be identical in the two determinants. If this is possible, the curve so defined, $x = h(z)$, $y = H(z)$, is a *pivot curve* on which the two straight alignment lines must cross. It is drawn in on the diagram along with the other four, but (unless values of z are desired) need carry no labels.

EXAMPLE: $(UV + R)e^S = T$. The product UV must be obtained by the "N" diagram (last example) since then R is conveniently added by a scale parallel to

---

* Such operations are: Adding any row (or column) to any other row (or column, respectively), multiplying any row or column by any function, reflection in the main diagonal, interchanging any two rows or any two columns.

that of $W = UV$. The product $e^S(UV + R)$ can then be obtained by another "N" diagram (with e^S replacing "V" but with the scale *labeled* with values of S). Schematically:

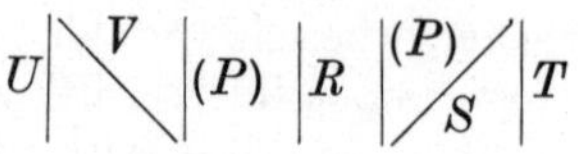

where (P) denotes a pivot line. Formally, we have used the decomposition,

$$UV = W; \qquad R + W = f; \qquad fg = T; \qquad (g = e^S)$$

Several equations: Such situations may, of course, be treated with several nomographs, but considerable advantage in use can often be realized by superposing them in convenient forms. (The pivot curve technique is a special case where an extra equation was artificially introduced.) The general principles are based on the simple facts,

(a) Three points x_i, y_i lying on a line satisfy

$$\begin{vmatrix} x_1 & y_1 & 1 \\ x_2 & y_2 & 1 \\ x_3 & y_3 & 1 \end{vmatrix} = 0$$

(b) The relations $x = f(u, v)$ and $y = g(u, v)$ define a "grid" of u, v curves in the x, y plane.

Example: The form (7–17) may be unattainable in certain cases, but it may be possible to make the first two rows correct while the third row involves both u_2 and u_3. The first two rows then define curves as before while the third defines a grid from which (using the given value of u_2 again) one may read the value of u_3.

CHAPTER 8

DIFFERENTIATION AND INTEGRATION

DIFFERENTIATION

Some Elementary Formulas

$$D^n(uv) = \sum_{i=0}^{n} \binom{n}{i} (D^i u)(D^{n-i} v) \tag{8-1}$$

where $D = \mathrm{d}/\mathrm{d}x$.
(Proof: by induction.) Therefore, if $P(D)$ is a polynomial in $D = \mathrm{d}/\mathrm{d}x$,

$$P(D)[uv] = \sum_{i=0}^{n} \frac{1}{i!} (D^i u)[P^{(i)}(D)v]$$

$$\frac{\mathrm{d}y}{\mathrm{d}x} = \frac{\mathrm{d}y}{\mathrm{d}u}\frac{\mathrm{d}u}{\mathrm{d}x}; \quad \frac{\mathrm{d}^2y}{\mathrm{d}x^2} = \frac{\mathrm{d}^2y}{\mathrm{d}u^2}\left(\frac{\mathrm{d}u}{\mathrm{d}x}\right)^2 + \frac{\mathrm{d}y}{\mathrm{d}u}\frac{\mathrm{d}^2u}{\mathrm{d}x^2}$$

$$\frac{\mathrm{d}^2y}{\mathrm{d}x^2} = -\frac{\mathrm{d}^2x}{\mathrm{d}y^2}\left(\frac{\mathrm{d}x}{\mathrm{d}y}\right)^{-3} \qquad \boxed{\frac{\mathrm{d}}{\mathrm{d}x} = \frac{\mathrm{d}u}{\mathrm{d}x}\frac{\mathrm{d}}{\mathrm{d}u}}$$

Radius of curvature:

$$\frac{1}{R} = \frac{|y''|}{[1 + (y')^2]^{3/2}} \tag{8-2}$$

A Note on Scale Transformations

In physics literature, it is common to use a given symbol to denote a given physical quantity. This, however, leads to a (usually not serious) discrepancy with common *functional* notation. Thus if $I(x)$ denotes a physical quantity depending on x, then if we wish to use $y = g(x)$ as the independent quantity, the *same* physical I is then often denoted by $I(y)$—whereas the strictly correct notation is $I(x) = I(g^{-1}(y)) = H(y)$, say. For example, if $I(x) = Ax$ and $y = bx$, then $I(y)$ in mathematical literature always denotes Ay whereas in physics literature it frequently denotes Ay/b.

Partial Derivatives

1. It is important to remember that:

$\dfrac{\partial f}{\partial z}$ *is an incomplete symbol. It's definition depends upon the context.*

If we have written $f = f(x, y, z)$ then it is *implied* that the differentiation is for constant x and y, but, by itself and out of context, the meaning of $\partial f/\partial z$ is *not* specified.

The common usages of Physics (whereby one prefers to use the same symbol for the same quantity expressed in terms of various sets of independent variables) are especially likely to lead to confusion on this score. Hence the emphasis in modern thermodynamics on writing $(\partial S/\partial p)_T$, for example, to distinguish it from $(\partial S/\partial p)_V$, etc.

2. The relation,

$$df = \sum_{i=1}^{n} \frac{\partial f}{\partial x_i}\, dx_i \quad \text{if} \quad f = f(x_1, x_2, \cdots, x_n)$$

(wherein each $\partial f/\partial x_i$ is defined as the partial derivative for constant $x_1, x_2, \cdots, x_{i-1}, x_{i+1}, \cdots, x_n$) *is always valid provided f is completely determined by specifying* $x_1 \cdots x_n$. Its validity is *not* affected if additional relations between the x_i are adjoined so that they are no longer independent—provided that the definitions of $\partial f/\partial x_i$ are not changed, of course.

This principle will in general yield all the special formulas for changes of variables, etc., when it is carefully applied, keeping in mind the many possible definitions of "$\partial f/\partial z$". Also useful is the fact that two equal expressions in *independent* "variables," dx_k, must be equal term by term.

3. Volume differentials:

$$\left.\begin{aligned} dx_1\, dx_2 \cdots dx_n &= \left|\frac{\partial(x_1, x_2, \cdots, x_n)}{\partial(y_1, y_2, \cdots, y_n)}\right| dy_1\, dy_2 \cdots dy_n \\ &= dy_1\, dy_2 \cdots dy_n \,\text{Det}\left(\frac{\partial x_i}{\partial y_j}\right) \end{aligned}\right\} \tag{8–3}$$

(Proof: see (21–7).)

Euler's Theorem

This is typified by:

$$\left.\begin{aligned} &\text{If} & f(Ax, Ay, Az, t) &= A^n f(x, y, z, t) \\ &\text{Then} & x\frac{\partial f}{\partial x} + y\frac{\partial f}{\partial y} + z\frac{\partial f}{\partial z} &= nf(x, y, z, t) \end{aligned}\right\} \tag{8–4}$$

and conversely. (Proof: (a) differentiate the first relation with respect to A and set $A = 1$, (b) write out the general solution of the second equation.)

Euler's Theorem for Operators

If Λ is an operator which replaces x_i by λx_i and if L is an operator with the property that for all functions $f(x_1, x_2, \cdots)$,

$$\Lambda L f = \lambda^n L \Lambda f \tag{8–5}$$

Then with $\mathscr{V} = \sum_i x_i \dfrac{\partial}{\partial x_i}$

$$\mathscr{V} L - L \mathscr{V} = nL \tag{8–6}$$

(Proof: Write out the hypothesis as $L(\lambda x) f(\lambda x) = \lambda^n L(x) f(\lambda x)$, differentiate with respect to λ and set $\lambda = 1$.)

Lagrange Multipliers

To maximize (or minimize) $f(x_1, x_2, \cdots, x_n)$ subject to m restrictions, $g_\alpha(x_1, x_2, \cdots, x_n) = 0$: The coefficient of each dx_i must vanish in the expressions,

$$df + \sum_{\alpha=1}^{m} \lambda_\alpha\, dg_\alpha = \sum_{i=1}^{n} dx_i \left[\frac{\partial f}{\partial x_i} + \sum_{\alpha=1}^{m} \lambda_\alpha \frac{\partial g_\alpha}{\partial x_i}\right] = 0 \tag{8–7}$$

where the functions, λ_α, are m (initially undetermined) "multipliers".

[Proof: Since the λ_α are arbitrary functions, they may be *chosen* to make the first m brackets vanish; using these relations, the last $(n - m)$ of the x_i may be taken as independent and $df = 0 = dg_\alpha$ then requires that each of the remaining brackets vanish.]

Differentiation of Integrals

$$\frac{d}{dx}\int_{\phi(x)}^{\psi(x)} f(x, t)\, dt = \psi'(x)f(x, \psi(x)) - \phi'(x)f(x, \phi(x)) + \int_{\phi(x)}^{\psi(x)} \frac{\partial}{\partial x} f(x, t)\, dt \qquad (8\text{–}8)$$

REMARKS:

(a) If f has a singularity at one end of the integration range, it is helpful to introduce a new variable such that the corresponding limit becomes a constant.

(b) If f has a discontinuity in slope anywhere, it is best to split the integral into two parts at that point before applying (8–8).

INTEGRATION

Pappas' Theorems

A solid generated by the revolution of any plane, *closed* curve about an axis in its plane (possibly tangent to, but not cutting across the curve) has:

Surface = [perimeter of (full) curve] × [circumference of circle described by center-of-mass of the (full) *curve**]

Volume = [area enclosed by curve] × [circumference of circle described by center-of-mass of the *area* enclosed by the curve†]

Methods of Integration

The following table shows variable-substitutions which will convert integrands of the type indicated into rational functions of the simple variable, u. The latter, of course, may then be integrated by expanding the integrand in partial fractions, (7–1).

Table 8.1

If integrand is a rational function of:	Set u =	Then
e^x	e^x	$dx = \dfrac{du}{u}$
$\sin x, \cos x$ (also $\sin 2x, \sin 3x, \cdots$ etc.)	$\tan \frac{1}{2}x$	$\sin x = \dfrac{2u}{1+u^2}$; $\cos x = \dfrac{1-u^2}{1+u^2}$; $dx = \dfrac{2du}{1+u^2}$; $\left(e^{ix} = \dfrac{1+iu}{1-iu}\right)$
$\sinh x, \cosh x$	$\tanh \frac{1}{2}x$	$\sinh x = \dfrac{2u}{1-u^2}$; $\cosh x = \dfrac{1+u^2}{1-u^2}$; $dx = \dfrac{2du}{1-u^2}$; $\left(e^{x} = \dfrac{1+u}{1-u}\right)$

* That is, the center-of-mass is the same as that of a wire-model of the curve.

† That is, the center-of-mass is the same as that of a flat plate bounded by the curve.

Table 8.1 (*contd.*)

If integrand is a rational function of:	Set $u =$	Then
$x,\ \sqrt{ax^2+2bx+c}$ (See also special cases below.)	$x\sqrt{a}+\sqrt{ax^2+2bx+c}$	$x=\dfrac{u^2-c}{2(b+u\sqrt{a})}$; $\sqrt{ax^2+2bx+c}=\dfrac{u^2\sqrt{a}+2bu+c\sqrt{a}}{2(b+u\sqrt{a})}$; $dx=\sqrt{ax^2+2bx+c}\,\dfrac{du}{b+u\sqrt{a}}$
$x,\ \sqrt{ax+b},\ \sqrt{cx+d}$	$\sqrt{cx+d}$	$cx=u^2-d$; $\sqrt{ax+b}=\sqrt{\dfrac{a}{c}u^2-\dfrac{ad}{c}+b}$; $dx=\dfrac{2u\,du}{c}$
$x,\ [(ax+b)/(cx+d)]^{1/n}$ (Note case $c=0$)	$\left[\dfrac{ax+b}{cx+d}\right]^{1/n}$	$x=(b-du^n)/(cu^n-a)$; $dx=nu^{n-1}[(ad-bc)/(cu^n-a)^2]\,du$
$x,\ [c+(a+bx)^{1/m}]^{1/n}$	$[c+(a+bx)^{1/m}]^{1/n}$	$bx=(u^n-c)^m-a$; $dx=\dfrac{mn}{b}(u^n-c)^{m-1}u^{n-1}\,du$
$x,\ \sqrt{1-x^2}$	$\sqrt{\dfrac{1-x}{1+x}}$	$x=\dfrac{1-u^2}{1+u^2}$; $\sqrt{1-x^2}=\dfrac{2u}{1+u^2}$; $dx=\dfrac{-4u\,du}{(1+u^2)^2}$
$x,\ \sqrt{a+bx-x^2}$	$\dfrac{\sqrt{a+bx-x^2}-\sqrt{a}}{x}$	$x=\dfrac{b-2u\sqrt{a}}{1+u^2}$; $\sqrt{a+bx-x^2}=\dfrac{bu+\sqrt{a}-u^2\sqrt{a}}{1+u^2}$ $dx=2\,\dfrac{u^2\sqrt{a}-bu-\sqrt{a}}{(1+u^2)^2}\,du$
$x,\ \sqrt{(x-a)(x-b)}$	$\sqrt{\dfrac{x-a}{x-b}}$	$x=\dfrac{bu^2-a}{u^2-1}$; $\sqrt{(x-a)(x-b)}=\dfrac{u(b-a)}{u^2-1}$ $dx=\dfrac{2(a-b)u\,du}{(u^2-1)^2}$
$x,\ \sqrt{(x-\alpha)(\beta-x)}$	$\sqrt{\dfrac{x-\alpha}{\beta-x}}$	$x=\dfrac{\beta u^2+\alpha}{1+u^2}$; $\sqrt{(x-\alpha)(\beta-x)}=\dfrac{u(\beta-\alpha)}{1+u^2}$ $dx=\dfrac{2(\beta-\alpha)u\,du}{(1+u^2)^2}$

Principal-value of an Integral (Cauchy)

If the integrand, $f(x)$, is infinite at $x = c$, then the (Cauchy) principal-value of the integral of f across any range including c is defined by,

$$\text{princ. val.} \int_a^b f(x)\,dx = \lim_{\epsilon \to 0} \left[\int_a^{c-\epsilon} f\,dx + \int_{c+\epsilon}^b f\,dx \right]$$

and similarly when there are several singularities of f in the range of integration.

Elliptic Integrals

If R denotes a *rational* function, $\int R[y, \sqrt{P(y)}]\,dy$ is an elliptic integral if $P(y)$ is a cubic or quartic polynomial (with no multiple roots). *If* the roots of $P(y)$ can be found, the integral can be reduced to tabulated standard forms as follows.

1. If $P(y)$ is cubic, set $y = z^2 + r$ where r is a root of P.
2. By setting $y = A(z + B)/(z + 1)$, convert the integrand to the form, $R[z, \sqrt{\pm(z^2 + C)(z^2 + D)}]$. (All of A, B, C, D real.)
3. Write R in the form, $R_1(z^2, \sqrt{\ }) + zR_2(z^2, \sqrt{\ })$. The second term can be integrated by setting, $z^2 = u$.
4. Write R_1 in the form, $F(z^2) + [G(z^2)/\sqrt{\ }]$. The first term leads to a rational integral.
5. Using Table 8.2, introduce a new variable, x, such that

$$\frac{dz}{\sqrt{\pm(z^2 + C)(z^2 + D)}} = \frac{c\,dx}{\sqrt{(1 - x^2)(1 - k^2x^2)}}$$

with $x^2 < 1$ over the range of integration. Let

$$G(z^2) = \frac{f(x^2)}{g(x^2)}; \qquad X = \sqrt{(1 - x^2)(1 - k^2x^2)}$$

where f and g are polynomials.

Table 8.2

Form of $\pm(z^2 + C)(z^2 + D)$	Let $k^2 =$	To achieve $x^2 < 1$, let $z^2 =$ either	or	$c =$
$+(z^2 - a^2)(z^2 - b^2)$ where $a^2 < b^2$	a^2/b^2	$(ax)^2$	$(b/x)^2$	$\pm 1/b$
$(z^2 + a^2)(z^2 + b^2)$ where $a^2 < b^2$	$1 - (a/b)^2$	$(ax)^2/(1 - x^2)$	$(b/x)^2 - b^2$	$\pm 1/b$
$+(z^2 + a^2)(z^2 - b^2)$	$a^2/(a^2 + b^2)$	$b^2/(1 - x^2)$	$(a/kx)^2 - a^2$	$\pm k/a$
$-(z^2 + a^2)(z^2 - b^2)$	$b^2/(a^2 + b^2)$	$b^2(1 - x^2)$	$(akx)^2/(1 - k^2x^2)$	$\pm k/b$
$-(z^2 - a^2)(z^2 - b^2)$ where $a^2 < b^2$	$1 - (a/b)^2$	$b^2(1 - k^2x^2)$	$a^2/(1 - k^2x^2)$	$\pm 1/b$

6. If $g(x^2)$ is not of the form $(1 - x^2)^n(1 - k^2x^2)^m$, then the final results will involve integrals of the third kind. Tables of these are not available, but if the integral is "complete" (limits $x = 0$ and 1 [or -1 and 1]), it can be expressed in terms of integrals of the first and second kinds (see below).

7. The simplest way to complete the reduction is: If

$$g(x^2) = C(1 - x^2)^n(1 - k^2x^2)^m(x^2 - \gamma_1)^{n_1}(x^2 - \gamma_2)^{n_2} \cdots (x^2 - \gamma_N)^{n_N},$$

then set

$$\int \frac{f(x^2)\,dx}{g(x^2)X} = \frac{xp(x^2)X}{g_2(x^2)} + A_0\int \frac{dx}{X} + A_2\int \frac{x^2\,dx}{X} + \sum_{j=1}^{N} B_j\int \frac{dx}{X(x^2 - \gamma_j)}$$

where the coefficients can be evaluated by (differentiating and) comparing powers of x^2 on both sides, and where

$$g_2(x^2) = \frac{g(x^2)}{\prod_j (x^2 - \gamma_j)} \qquad p(x^2) = \text{polynomial.*}$$

The connection with standard notation is then:

$$F(\phi, k) = \int_0^{\sin\phi} \frac{dx}{X}; \quad \frac{1}{k^2}[F(\phi, k) - E(\phi, k)] = \int_0^{\sin\phi} \frac{x^2\,dx}{X}$$

$$\Pi(\phi, c, k) = \int_0^{\sin\phi} \frac{dx}{(1 + cx^2)X}; \quad \mathbf{K}(k) = F\left(\frac{\pi}{2}, k\right); \quad \mathbf{E}(k) = E\left(\frac{\pi}{2}, k\right)$$

(These are often written with $x = \sin\psi$; then $dx/X = d\psi/\sqrt{1 - k^2\sin^2\psi}$.) F and E are tabulated as also are Jacobi's zeta function:

$$Z(\phi, k) = E(\phi, k) - [\mathbf{E}/\mathbf{K}]F(\phi, k)$$

and Heuman's lambda function:

$$\Lambda(\beta, k) = \frac{2}{\pi}\{\mathbf{K}(k)E(\beta, k') + \mathbf{E}(k)F(\beta, k') - \mathbf{K}(k)F(\beta, k')\}$$

where

$$k' = \sqrt{1 - k^2}$$

Inequalities useful for visualizing these functions:

$$0 \leqslant Z(\phi, k) \leqslant Z(\phi, 1) \leqslant 1$$

$$Z(\phi, 0) = Z(0, k) = Z\left(\frac{\pi}{2}, k\right) = 0 \quad (k \neq 1)$$

$$\Lambda(\beta, 1) = \frac{2}{\pi}\beta \leqslant \Lambda(\beta, k) \leqslant \sin\beta = \Lambda(\beta, 0)$$

* The highest power appearing in p is x^{2P} where

$$P = \text{Max}(F, G + 1) - N - 2$$

where x^{2F} and x^{2G} are the highest powers in f and g respectively. If P is negative, set $p = 0$.

Although $\Pi(\phi, c, k)$ is not tabulated, the following relations hold when $\phi = \pi/2$:

For $c > 0$:

$$\Pi\left(\frac{\pi}{2}, a^2, k\right) = \frac{\mathbf{K}(k)}{1+a^2} + \frac{\pi a[1 - \Lambda(\beta, k)]}{2\sqrt{(k^2+a^2)(1+a^2)}}; \quad \text{where } \sin\beta = \frac{1}{\sqrt{1+a^2}}$$

For $(-k^2) < c < 0$:

$$\Pi\left(\frac{\pi}{2}, -a^2, k\right) = \mathbf{K}(k) + \frac{a\mathbf{K}(k)Z(\beta, k)}{\sqrt{(1-a^2)(k^2-a^2)}}; \quad \text{where } \sin\beta = a/k$$

For $(-1) < c < -k^2$:

$$\Pi\left(\frac{\pi}{2}, -a^2, k\right) = \frac{\pi a \Lambda(\beta, k)}{2\sqrt{(a^2-k^2)(1-a^2)}}; \quad \text{where } \sin\beta = \frac{1}{a}\sqrt{\frac{a^2-k^2}{1-k^2}}$$

For $c < -1$ (Cauchy principle-value of the original integral):

$$\Pi\left(\frac{\pi}{2}, -a^2, k\right) = \frac{-a\mathbf{K}(k)Z(\beta, k)}{\sqrt{(a^2-1)(a^2-k^2)}}; \quad \text{where } \sin\beta = 1/a.$$

Moreover, there is the following relation for general ϕ (which is of immediate use if $(-k^2) < c < 0$ but holds for arbitrary complex parameters).

$$\Pi(\phi, c, k) = F(\phi, k) + \frac{\sqrt{-c}}{\sqrt{(1+c)(k^2+c)}}\left\{F(\phi, k)Z(\beta, k) + \tfrac{1}{2}\ln\frac{\theta_0[(F_\phi - F_\beta)/2\mathbf{K}]}{\theta_0[(F_\phi + F_\beta)/2\mathbf{K}]}\right\}$$

where $F_\phi = F(\phi, k)$, $F_\beta = F(\beta, k)$ and $\sin\beta = (\sqrt{-c}/k)$ and θ_0 is another tabulated function.*

Another relation of this type, of value when $c < -1$, is

$$\Pi(\phi, c, k) = \frac{-\sqrt{-c}}{\sqrt{(1+c)(k^2+c)}}\left\{F(\phi, k)Z(A, k) + \tfrac{1}{2}\ln\frac{\theta_1[(F_A - F_\phi)/2\mathbf{K}]}{\theta_1[(F_A + F_\phi)/2\mathbf{K}]}\right\}$$

where $\sin A = 1/\sqrt{-c}$ and the remaining notation is analogous to the above.*

* As a check on notation,

$$\theta_0(v) = \sum_{n=-\infty}^{\infty} (-1)^n q^{n^2} e^{2\pi i n v}; \qquad \theta_1(v) = 2\sum_{n=0}^{\infty} (-1)^n q^{(n+\frac{1}{2})^2} \sin[\pi(2n+1)v]$$

where q is determined by k (and is often written $q = e^{i\pi\tau}$). Although this notation seems to be universal, we quote two forms of the relation:

$$\sqrt{k} = \frac{2\sum_{n=0}^{\infty} q^{(n+\frac{1}{2})^2}}{\sum_{n=-\infty}^{\infty} q^{n^2}}; \qquad q = \exp\left[-\pi\mathbf{K}(\sqrt{1-k^2})/\mathbf{K}(k)\right]$$

Some Useful Integrals

$$\int_{t_0}^{t} f(\tau_1) \int_{t_0}^{\tau_1} f(\tau_2) \cdots \int_{t_0}^{\tau_{n-1}} f(\tau_n)\, \mathrm{d}\tau_1\, \mathrm{d}\tau_2 \cdots \mathrm{d}\tau_n = \frac{1}{n!}\left[\int_{t_0}^{t} f(x)\, \mathrm{d}x\right]^n \tag{8–9}$$

$$\int_{t_0}^{t} \mathrm{d}\tau_1 \int_{t_0}^{\tau_1} \mathrm{d}\tau_2 \int_{t_0}^{\tau_2} \cdots \int_{t_0}^{\tau_n} f(x)\, \mathrm{d}x = \frac{1}{n!}\int_{t_0}^{t} f(y)(t-y)^n\, \mathrm{d}y \tag{8–10}$$

Dirichlet's integral: If $i_j > 0$ and $p_j > 0$ then

$$\int \cdots \iint_{R_p} x_1^{i_1-1} x_2^{i_2-1} \cdots x_n^{i_n-1}\, \mathrm{d}x_1\, \mathrm{d}x_2 \cdots \mathrm{d}x_n$$

$$= \frac{C^{\alpha}\Gamma\left(\dfrac{i_1}{p_1}\right)\Gamma\left(\dfrac{i_2}{p_2}\right)\cdots\Gamma\left(\dfrac{i_n}{p_n}\right)}{p_1 p_2 \cdots p_n \Gamma(\alpha+1)} \tag{8–11}$$

where
$$\alpha = \frac{i_1}{p_1} + \frac{i_2}{p_2} + \cdots + \frac{i_n}{p_n}$$

and the integration region, R_p, is defined by

$$R_p: \qquad x_j \geqslant 0 \quad \text{and} \quad \sum_{i=1}^{n} (x_i)^{p_i} \leqslant C.$$

Miscellaneous

$$\int_0^{\infty} \frac{x^n\, \mathrm{d}x}{e^x - 1} = n!\zeta(n+1) \tag{8–12}$$

(where ζ is Riemann's zeta function).

$$\int_0^{\infty} \frac{h(x)\, \mathrm{d}x}{1+e^{x-y}} = [\pi D \operatorname{cosec} \pi D] \int_0^{y} h(z)\, \mathrm{d}z, \quad \text{where } D = \frac{\mathrm{d}}{\mathrm{d}y}$$

$$= \int_0^{y} h(z)\, \mathrm{d}z + \frac{\pi^2}{6} h'(y) + \frac{7\pi^4}{360} h'''(y) + \cdots \tag{8–13}$$

[Proof: see (13–50)–(13–52).]

Integrals involving functions which satisfy second-order differential equations:

(1). If $Y(x)$ is a solution of $\mathscr{D}[Y] \equiv F_0(x)\dfrac{\mathrm{d}^2 Y}{\mathrm{d}x^2} + F_1(x)\dfrac{\mathrm{d}Y}{\mathrm{d}x} + F_2(x)Y = 0$ then for *arbitrary* $f(x)$:

$$\int^{x} \frac{Y(u)}{F_0(u)}\left[\exp \int_{\alpha}^{u} \frac{F_1}{F_0}\right] \mathscr{D}[f(u)]\, \mathrm{d}u = \left[\exp \int_{\alpha}^{x} \frac{F_1}{F_0}\right] \cdot \left[Y\frac{\mathrm{d}f}{\mathrm{d}x} - f\frac{\mathrm{d}Y}{\mathrm{d}x}\right] \tag{8–14}$$

(Proof: differentiate)

Example: If J_ν is (any) Bessel function of order ν and $f(x)$ is arbitrary,

$$\int^{x} J_\nu(x)\left[xf'' + f' + \left(x - \frac{\nu^2}{x}\right)f\right] \mathrm{d}x = x[J_\nu f' - fJ_\nu'] \tag{8–15}$$

(2). If $Y_0(x)$ satisfies $\mathscr{D}[Y_0] = 0$ as above, then

$$\int^x \frac{1}{[Y_0(x)]^2} \exp\left[-\int_\beta^x \frac{F_1}{F_0}\,dx\right] dx$$

can be expressed in terms of $[c_1 Y_1(x) + c_2 Y_2(x)]/Y_0(x)$ where the numerator is the general solution of $\mathscr{D}[Y] = 0$.

(3). If $z'' + \sigma z = 0$ and $y'' + \rho y = 0$ then

$$\int^x [\sigma(x) - \rho(x)]y(x)z(x)\,dx = zy' - yz' \tag{8–16}$$

Schwarz's inequality: If $\rho(x) \geqslant 0$ in the integration range, then for any $f(x)$ and $g(x)$:

$$\left|\int \rho f g^*\,dx\right|^2 \leqslant \left[\int \rho |f|^2\,dx\right]\left[\int \rho |g|^2\,dx\right] \tag{8–17}$$

[equality only if $f(x) =$ (constant) $g(x)$].

More generally, if R is any linear operator [that is, $R(af + bg) = aRf + bRg$] such that for any $f(x)$

$$\int \rho(Rf)f^*\,dx \geqslant 0 \qquad \text{(therefore real)}$$

Then

$$\left|\int \rho g^*(Rf)\,dx\right|^2 \leqslant \left[\int \rho f^*(Rf)\,dx\right] \cdot \left[\int \rho g^*(Rg)\,dx\right] \tag{8–18}$$

(equality only if $f = Ag$).

These are special cases of results for unitary function-spaces. They are a consequence of the fact that in each case the quantity on the right is non-negative when f is replaced by $f + \lambda g$ for all complex constants, λ.

Methods of Evaluating Definite Integrals

1. Differentiate or integrate with respect to a parameter (which can be *introduced* if necessary).

2. Use

$$\int_0^\infty \psi(s)\mathscr{L}\{\phi(t)\}\,ds = \int_0^\infty \mathscr{L}\{\psi(t)\}\phi(s)\,ds \tag{8–19}$$

where $\mathscr{L}$ denotes the operation of taking the Laplace transform. A similar relation holds for any integral transform with a symmetric kernel and an integration range equal to (or greater than) that of the desired integral.

3. If

$$\psi(t) = \int_0^\infty \phi(xt)h(x)\,dx$$

then

$$\mathscr{L}\{\psi(t)\} = \int_0^\infty f(s/x)\,\frac{h(x)}{x}\,dx \tag{8–20}$$

where

$$f(s) = \mathscr{L}\{\phi(t)\}$$

4. Provided $a < 1$ and $x^aQ(x) \to 0$ at $|x| = 0$ and ∞ (in the *complex* plane) then

$$\text{(Principal value)} \int_0^\infty x^{a-1}Q(x)\, dx = \frac{\pi}{\sin \pi a} \sum_i r_i - \pi \cot \pi a \sum_k r_k' \qquad (8\text{–}21)$$

where

r_i = residues of $(-z)^{a-1}Q(z)$ at poles not on the positive real axis.
r_i' = residues of $(+z)^{a-1}Q(z)$ at poles on the positive real axis.

Reduction of (arbitrary) volume integrals to surface integrals or of surface integrals to line integrals is possible if an appropriate differential equation can be solved:
By Gauss' and Stokes' Theorems,

$$\left.\begin{aligned} \iiint f(\mathbf{r})\, dV &= \oint\!\!\oint \mathbf{a} \cdot d\boldsymbol{\sigma}; \quad \text{where} \quad \nabla \cdot \mathbf{a} = f(\mathbf{r}) \\ \iint f(\mathbf{r})\, d\sigma &= \oint \mathbf{a} \cdot d\mathbf{l}; \quad \text{where} \quad \hat{n} \cdot (\nabla \times \mathbf{a}) = f(\mathbf{r}) \end{aligned}\right\} \qquad (8\text{–}22)$$

(For at least formal solutions, see (10–51).)

Asymptotic Evaluations

(1). If an integral contains a parameter (that is, defines a function of that parameter) then one can often obtain expressions valid at extreme values of the parameter by rather straightforward methods. These generally consist in noting limiting forms of the integrand and then obtaining bounds on the error incurred by using such approximations. If the process is repeated on the successive correction terms, the result is often an asymptotic series (that is, a series which is divergent but useful for computation). Judicious *integration by parts* is a very commonly useful device in this regard.

(2). If $F(t) \to A$ as $t \to 0$ or ∞. Then

$$sf(s) = s \int_0^\infty e^{-st}F(t)\, dt \to A \text{ as } s \to \infty \text{ or } 0 \text{ (respectively)}$$

(3). If $h'(a) = 0$ and $h''(a) < 0$ then as $k \to \infty$

$$\int_a^b \phi(x)e^{kh(x)}\, dx \sim \phi(a)e^{kh(a)}\sqrt{\frac{-\pi}{2kh''(a)}} \qquad (8\text{–}23)$$

$$\int_a^b (x - a)\phi(x)e^{kh(x)}\, dx \sim \frac{-\phi(a)e^{kh(a)}}{kh''(a)} \qquad (8\text{–}24)$$

(4). *Saddle Point Method* (*"Steepest Descents"*)
Strictly, this method applies to asymptotic evaluations for an integral of the form*

$$I(p) = \int_C e^{-pf(w)}\phi(w)\, dw$$

for large values of p. Here C is any path in the complex w plane. The idea is to deform the path C so that it passes through a "saddle" in the graph of $|\exp[-pf(w)]|$

* If the parameter p appears in other forms, a change of the variable of integration will often yield the above form.

and then passes as quickly as possible into very deep "valleys" of the graph so that the main contribution to $I(p)$, for large p, comes from the region of the saddle. The technique can be systematized as follows.

(a) Locate the "saddles" by finding the roots of

$$\frac{d}{dw} f(w) = 0$$

Choose any such root, w_0, as seems convenient for the following.

(b) Find the "path of steepest descent", defined by the curve:*

$$\text{Im}\,[f(w)] = \text{Im}\,[f(w_0)]$$

Choose a root w_0 and branches of this curve such that $\text{Re}\, f \geqslant 0$ throughout, and deform the integration path (see (12–10) and discussion there) to coincide with the path of steepest descent—taking due account of any singularities in f or ϕ, of course.

(c) Change the variable of integration to obtain integrals of the form of Laplace transforms:

$$I(p) = A_1 \int_0^\infty e^{-pu} F_1(u)\, du + A_2 \int_0^\infty e^{-pv} F_2(v)\, dv + \cdots$$

(d) Finally, use standard theorems for the asymptotic behavior of Laplace transforms to obtain an asymptotic series for $I(p)$. A rather general theorem of this type is:

THEOREM: If $F(t)$ *has* a Laplace transform and if $F(t) \sim \sum_0^\infty a_i t^{\lambda_i}$ as $t \to 0^+$ (where $-1 < \lambda_0 < \lambda_1 < \cdots$) in the sense that

$$\lim_{t \to 0^+} t^{-\lambda_n} \left[F(t) - \sum_0^{n-1} a_i\, t^{\lambda_i} \right] = a_n$$

Then

$$\int_0^\infty e^{-pt} F(t)\, dt \sim \sum_0^\infty a_i \frac{\Gamma(\lambda_i + 1)}{p^{\lambda_i + 1}} \quad \text{as } |p| \to \infty \tag{8–25}$$

in the sense that

$$\lim_{|p| \to \infty} p^{\lambda_n + 1} \left\{ \int_0^\infty e^{-pt} F(t)\, dt - \sum_0^{n-1} a_i \frac{\Gamma(\lambda_i + 1)}{p^{\lambda_i + 1}} \right\} = a_n \Gamma(\lambda_n + 1)$$

provided that $|\arg p| < \frac{\pi}{2}$; moreover, the limit is approached uniformly for all p with equal real parts.

NOTE: In applications of this theorem, the range of usefulness of the second series is governed by the "radius of convergence" of the series for $F(t)$. Hence it is often expedient, when possible, to remove singularities of $F(t)$ which lie near $t = 0$ in the complex t plane before applying the theorem. Thus, nearby poles of $F(t)$ can be subtracted and their contributions to $I(p)$ evaluated explicitly.

(5). *Lower Bound* for an integral: Consider

$$I(x) = \int_x^b e^{g(x)}\, dx$$

---

* "Im" denotes "imaginary part of"; "Re" denotes "real part of".

where g'' is continuous [and, if $b = \infty$, where $(g')^2 \geqslant 2g''$] for all x-values involved. Let $v(x)$ be arbitrary except that $v(b) = 0$ and define $J(x)$ by

$$\frac{e^{g(x)}}{J(x)} = \frac{1}{v^2}\int_x^b [(v')^2 + \tfrac{1}{4}(vg')^2 - \tfrac{1}{2}v^2g'']\,dx - \tfrac{1}{2}g'$$

Then*

$$J(x) \leqslant I(x) \qquad \text{and} \qquad \frac{d(I-J)}{dx} \leqslant 0$$

By suitable choice of v (minimizing the integral term), $J(x)$ can often be made to approximate $I(x)$ very closely.

Numerical Integration

Notation:

$$y_k = f(a + k\delta), \quad k = 0, 1, 2, \cdots, n$$

$$\text{with } a + n\delta = b; \quad \text{also} \quad a < \xi < b$$

Trapezoidal Rule:

$$\int_a^b f(x)\,dx = \frac{\delta}{2}\left(y_0 + y_n + 2\sum_1^{n-1} y_k\right) - R_n \tag{8–26}$$

$$R_n = \frac{n\delta^3}{12} f''(\xi)$$

Simpson's Rule:

$$\int_a^b f(x)\,dx = \frac{\delta}{3}\left(y_0 + y_n + 2\sum_{\substack{\text{even}\\ i}} y_i + 4\sum_{\substack{\text{odd}\\ i}} y_i\right) - R_n \tag{8–27}$$

$$R_n = \frac{n\delta^5}{90} f^{(4)}(\xi)$$

Some more complicated rules are given below, but it is usually more profitable to invest the extra labor in using more points (smaller δ) in the simpler rules.

Rapidly varying functions: It is sometimes useful to observe that

$$\int f(x)\,dx = \int xf(x)\,d(\ln x)$$

This enables one to use $x_j = a^j x_0$ in the above rules. Note also that if $xf(x)$ is plotted on semi-log graph paper, a planimeter will then measure $\int f\,dx$. Similarly

$$\int f(x)\,dx = xf - \int xf\,d(\ln f)$$

is also sometimes useful.

Graphical method: Cut out the graph and weigh.

Theory of the planimeter: If a point, $\mathbf{r}$, traverses a closed plane curve, enclosing an area, a, then (compare the definition of the vector product)

$$\oint \mathbf{r} \times d\mathbf{r} = 2\hat{n}a$$

---

* Duffin and Serbyn, *Jour. Math. & Phys.*, **37**, 162 (1958).

where $\hat{n}$ is a vector normal to the plane of the curve. If at all times $\mathbf{r} = \mathbf{A} + \mathbf{B}$ (where $\mathbf{A}$ and $\mathbf{B}$ have constant lengths) and the "tail" of $\mathbf{A}$ is held fixed at $\mathbf{r} = 0$, then

$$2\hat{n}a = \oint \mathbf{A} \times \mathrm{d}\mathbf{A} + \oint \mathbf{B} \times \mathrm{d}\mathbf{B} + \oint \mathbf{A} \times \mathrm{d}\mathbf{B} + \oint \mathbf{B} \times \mathrm{d}\mathbf{A}$$

The first term represents the net area swept out by $\mathbf{A}$ and the second the net area which $\mathbf{B}$ would sweep out if its orientation changed in the same way but its "tail" were fixed; since both $\mathbf{A}$ and $\mathbf{B}$ return to their initial positions, these terms vanish.

$$2\hat{n}a = \oint \mathrm{d}(\mathbf{A} \times \mathbf{B}) + 2\oint \mathbf{B} \times \mathrm{d}\mathbf{A} = 2\oint \mathbf{B} \times \mathrm{d}\mathbf{A}$$

and thus a wheel at the tail of $\mathbf{B}$ and mounted on $\mathbf{B}$ as axle (thus measuring $\mathbf{dA}$ projected normal to $\mathbf{B}$) will rotate by an amount proportional to the area, a, as the tip of $\mathbf{B}$ traverses the curve.

More accurate rules: By (7–7),

$$\int_a^b f(x)\rho(x)\,\mathrm{d}x \doteq \sum_1^m f(x_j)\left[\frac{1}{F'(x_j)}\int_a^b \frac{F(x)\rho(x)}{x - x_j}\,\mathrm{d}x\right]$$

where $F(x) = \prod_1^m (x - x_j)$.

If $\rho \equiv 1$ and the x_j are equally spaced, this is the Newton–Cotes formula, of which the Trapezoidal and Simpson's rules are special cases.

If the x_j are chosen so that $\int_a^b \rho(x)F(x)x^{k-1}\,\mathrm{d}x = 0$ for $k = 1, 2, 3, \cdots, m$ then (as is easily seen) the rule is exact for polynomials of degree $\leqslant 2m$. Whence follow:

Gauss formula: $F(x) = P_m(x) \quad (a = -1, b = 1, \rho \equiv 1)$

Radeau formula: $F(x) = (1 - x^2)P_m{}'(x), \quad (a = -1, b = 1, \rho \equiv 1)$

Riez formula: $F(x) = L_m(x) \quad (a = 0, b = \infty, \rho = e^{-x})$

(In all these cases, $\dfrac{1}{F'}\displaystyle\int \frac{F\rho}{x - x_j}\,\mathrm{d}x$ can be evaluated in terms of tabulated functions.)

Bounds on errors: If the rule, $\int_a^b f(x)\rho(x)\,\mathrm{d}x \doteq \sum_0^m c_i f(x_i)$ is exact when f is a polynomial of degree $\leqslant n$, then

$$\text{error} = \int_a^b f^{(n+1)}(x)K_{(n)}(x)\,\mathrm{d}x$$

where

$$(n!)K_{(n)}(x) = \sum_{x_i \leqslant x} c_i(x_i - x)^n - \int_a^x (y - x)^n\rho(y)\,\mathrm{d}y$$

$$= \int_x^b (y - x)^n\rho(y)\,\mathrm{d}y - \sum_{x_i \geqslant x} c_i(x_i - x)^n = -n!\,K'_{(n+1)}$$

(Proof: integrate n times by parts.) This result is especially useful for obtaining error limits in terms of the *low* derivatives of f—which are more easily estimated.

19

MODERN INTEGRATION THEORIES IN PHYSICS

In applied mathematics or physics, one can seldom specify what "integral" one is using;—certainly not Riemann's definition, usually. More often one means either (a) the inverse of a differentiation or (b) the area under a graph. Both of these concepts can be made precise (although this fact was not realized until "recently") and *both*, when this is done, give precisely the Lebesgue (*definition* of an) integral.

The advantage of this modern theory of the integral is that the integral exists for a wider class of functions and therefore equations of the type $\lim \int \cdots = \int \lim \cdots$ can be proved under less restrictive conditions. (Of course, all the old counter-examples, where $\lim \int \cdots \neq \int \lim \cdots$, are still valid; the theory cannot alter facts.)

One theorem of this type (which could not be proved using the Riemann definition of an integral) is:

$$\int_a^b \left\{ \sum_1^\infty u_k(t) \right\} \mathrm{d}t = \sum_1^\infty \int_a^b u_k(t)\, \mathrm{d}t$$

in the following cases

(a) If all $u_k(t) \geqslant 0$ (in the range a to b), then the above holds in the sense that either the two expressions are equal or else both diverge.

(b) If for all N, $\sum_1^N |u_k| < F(t)$ where $\int_a^b F\, \mathrm{d}t < \infty$, then if the series $\sum u_k$ converges (for all t in the integration range), the above is true.

The Stieltjes integral is another new *definition* of an old concept. Roughly, instead of considering $\int f(x)\alpha'(x)\, \mathrm{d}x$, one writes it as $\int f(x)\, \mathrm{d}[\alpha(x)]$ and then defines *this* directly. The definition is deceptively similar to Riemann's definition; the fundamental difference lies in the fact that it applies even when $\mathrm{d}\alpha/\mathrm{d}x$ does not exist:

If the limit:

$$\lim_{\delta \to 0} \sum_{i=0}^{n-1} f(\xi_i)[\alpha(x_{i+1}) - \alpha(x_i)]$$

wherein:

$$a = x_0 < x_1 < x_2 < \cdots < x_{n-1} < x_n = b$$
$$\delta = \text{Maximum of } (x_{i+1} - x_i)$$
$$x_i \leqslant \xi_i \leqslant x_{i+1}$$

—if this limit exists independently of the choice of the x_i, ξ_i then the limit is called the Stieltjes integral of $f(x)$ with respect to $\alpha(x)$ from a to b and is denoted by

$$\int_a^b f(\alpha)\, \mathrm{d}\alpha(x)$$

One application lies in treating distributions (of electric charge, say) which are continuous, $\rho(x)$, over some ranges and contain point concentrations, q_i, as well. By letting $\alpha(x)$ be the total (charge) in the region $x' < x$, one obtains a convenient single expression for "integrals" over such charge distributions:

$$\int f(x)\rho(x)\, \mathrm{d}x + \sum f(x_i)q_i = \int f(x)\, \mathrm{d}\alpha(x)$$

Such methods can be used to evade any use of the Dirac delta-function in one-dimensional problems, but they cannot readily be extended to problems in spaces of dimension two or greater.

Roughly, the Stieltjes integral exists whenever α and f have no common discontinuities (i.e. discontinuities at the same value of x) and one is piece-by-piece continuous while the other has bounded variation. ("Bounded variation" means roughly that the arc-length of the graph is finite in any finite range of x.)

The Stieltjes definition can be further generalized* to obtain the Lebesgue–Stieltjes (definition of an) integral. This concept shares the properties of both the Lebesgue and Stieltjes definitions. For example, even if α is not continuous, we still have

$$\int_a^b \left\{\sum_1^\infty u_k(x)\right\} \mathrm{d}\alpha(x) = \sum_1^\infty \int_a^b u_k(x)\,\mathrm{d}\alpha(x)$$

if all $\sum_1^N |u_k(x)| < F(x)$ where $\int_a^b F(x)\,\mathrm{d}x < \infty$.

The relations among the various definitions of integrals may be indicated schematically by:

Lebesgue–Stieltjes
↙ ↘
Lebesgue Stieltjes
↘ ↙
Riemann

where an arrow indicates that the upper definition exists in all cases when the lower definition exists (and, of course, gives the same numerical answer).

The Delta Function

The "delta function" arises in attempts to find a genuine function which behaves under integration in the way the Kronecker symbol, δ_{ij}, behaves under summation. No such function actually exists—even with the most general definition of the process of integration which has yet been devised—but the concept is nevertheless of use in formal manipulations (which, for example, can lead to answers that, once known, can be justified by other methods). The properties of this strictly non-existent function are:

$$\delta(x) = 0 \text{ for all } x \neq 0; \qquad \int_{-|a|}^{|b|} \delta(x)\,\mathrm{d}x = 1 \tag{8–28}$$

If these properties were compatible, it would then follow,

$$\int_{-|a|}^{|b|} f(x)\delta(x)\,\mathrm{d}x = f(0); \qquad \int_a^b f(x)\delta(x-y)\,\mathrm{d}x = \begin{cases} f(y), & \text{if } a < y < b \\ 0, & \text{otherwise} \end{cases} \tag{8–29}$$

In such formal manipulations, one must be careful to observe that the variable of integration must match that in the argument of δ; thus

$$\int_a^b f(x)\delta(g(x)-z)\,\mathrm{d}x = \int \frac{f}{g'}\,\delta(g-z)\,\mathrm{d}g = \begin{cases} (f/g')_{g=z}, \text{ if } g(x) = z \\ \text{for some } x \text{ in } (a, b) \\ 0, \quad \text{otherwise} \end{cases} \tag{8–30}$$

---

* The basic idea is to define a generalized "length with respect to $\alpha(x)$" for an interval $x_1 < x < x_2$. This "length" is taken (with certain refinements) to be:

$$\text{"length } (x_1, x_2)\text{"} = \alpha(x_2) - \alpha(x_1)$$

and this concept is then inserted into the Lebesgue general theory of areas ("measure theory").

Some of these formal manipulations can be justified by:

Schwartz's Theory of Distributions

A "distribution" in the sense of this theory is (not a function but) a linear functional, that is, *an operator* which converts a function to a number. Every (summable) function, $f(\mathbf{r})$, defines such an operator, F, by:

$$F\phi(\mathbf{r}) = \iiint_{-\infty}^{\infty} f(\mathbf{r})\phi(\mathbf{r})\, d\mathbf{r} \tag{8-31}$$

Not every operator, however, need be associated with a function. For example, if $F\phi(\mathbf{r}) = \phi(0)$, then no corresponding $f(\mathbf{r})$ exists—except in the heuristic sense, $f(\mathbf{r}) = \delta(\mathbf{r})$.

To qualify as a "distribution", a (linear) operator *need* be applicable only to a very narrow class of functions, called $\mathscr{D}$, namely functions which are infinitely differentiable everywhere and which vanish outside a closed, bounded region. [Example: $\phi(\mathbf{r}) = \exp[1/(r^2 - b^2)]$ for $r < b$ (and $\phi \equiv 0$ for $r \geqslant b$) belongs to $\mathscr{D}$ for any b.]

To be a distribution, a linear operator, L, must be continuous in the rather weak sense that: (only) if all $\phi_j(\mathbf{r})$ vanish outside a common closed, bounded region and (with $n \geqslant 0$) all $\phi_j^{(n)}(\mathbf{r}) \to 0$ uniformly in $\mathbf{r}$ (but not necessarily in n) then the numbers $L\phi_j$ must converge to zero. Any such linear, continuous operator is a "distribution".

The derivative of a distribution is *defined* by

$$\left(\frac{\partial L}{\partial x}\right)\phi = -L\left(\frac{\partial \phi}{\partial x}\right) \tag{8-32}$$

and since ϕ need only be one of the special class, $\mathscr{D}$ above, $\partial\phi/\partial x$ exists and is also such a function. Thus any distribution is differentiable infinitely often *by definition.* It is a theorem (albeit not very deep) that L can always be integrated in a sense inverse to (8–32). In one dimension, if I_0 is one such integral, so that $dI_0/dx = L$, then any other integral equals $I_0 + C$ where $C\phi \equiv \int_{-\infty}^{\infty} C\phi(x)\, dx$.* Similarly, $\partial I/\partial x = L$ has many solutions, any two of which satisfy $(\partial/\partial x)(I_1 - I_2) = 0$.

A far from trivial theorem is that the differentiation (8–32) is "continuous" in a certain topological sense: A sequence of distributions L_j is said to converge to zero† if $L_j\phi \to 0$ for all $\phi(\mathbf{r})$ in $\mathscr{D}$ and if also this convergence is *uniform* over any set of ϕ which (are in $\mathscr{D}$ and) vanish outside a common bounded, closed region and have bounded derivatives of all orders [that is, $\partial^{(a+b\cdots)}\phi/\partial x_1^a\, \partial x_2^b \cdots < M(a, b, \cdots)$ for all $\mathbf{r}$ and all ϕ of the set]. With this convention, it may be proven that, if the sequence L_j converges‡ to L, then $\partial L_j/\partial x$ converges to $\partial L/\partial x$ (and similarly for all derivatives). This shows that differentiation [in the sense of (8–32)] under summations, integrations or other limiting operations is always allowable—*when* working with distributions.

Caution: The theorem applies only to the distributions and not (in general) to their corresponding functions. For example, if $f_m(x) = (1/m) \cos mx$, then $f_m \to 0$ but $f_m^{(\text{iv})}(x) = m^3 \cos mx$ do not approach zero in any sense, even though the theorem states that the corresponding distributions, $F_m^{(\text{iv})}$ defined by (8–32), converge to the zero operator (at least over $\mathscr{D}$; that is, "$F_m^{(\text{iv})}\phi \to 0$" is proven only when ϕ is a member of the special class of functions, $\mathscr{D}$).

Multiplication of Distributions:

(1) "Tensor product": If L and M operate on functions of *different* variables, $\mathbf{r}$ and $\mathbf{R}$, then $LM = ML$ is well-defined and $LM[\phi(\mathbf{r}, \mathbf{R})] = L[M\phi(\mathbf{r}, \mathbf{R})] = M[L\phi(\mathbf{r}, \mathbf{R})]$.

(2) If L and M operate over the same set of base functions, then LM in general has no sense. [Compare $[\delta(\mathbf{r})]^2$ or $\delta(\mathbf{r}) \cdot \delta'(\mathbf{r})$.] But if $f(\mathbf{r})$ is infinitely differentiable then FL exists and indeed $FL\phi = L(F\phi) = L(f\phi)$ and $(FL)' = F'L + L'F$.

---

* Define I_0 by $I_0(d\phi/dx) = L\phi$ so that $I_0\psi$ is defined whenever ψ is a derivative; for some ϕ_0 such that $\int_{-\infty}^{\infty} \phi_0(x)\, dx \neq 0$, let $I_0\phi_0 = \int_{-\infty}^{\infty} \phi_0\, dx$; since any $\phi = a\phi_0 + d\phi_1/dx$ for some unique ϕ_1, I_0 is thereby completely defined.

† The L_j converge to T if $(L_j - T)$ converge to 0.

‡ In particular, the L_j converge if the associated $l_j(\mathbf{r})$ converge and are summable $[\int|l_j| < \infty]$ on a closed, bounded region.

DIVISION:

Division is not defined in general, but in one dimension, division by analytic functions is meaningful. Thus $XT = S$ has the solution $T = S/X + C\boldsymbol{\delta}$ in the sense that if $T\phi(x) = S\{[\phi(x) - \phi(0)]/x\} + C\phi(0)$ then $S\phi = T(x\phi) = (TX)\phi$. (As always, the relation need hold only when ϕ is in $\mathscr{D}$.) Division by higher powers of x or (X) introduces the distributions, $\boldsymbol{\delta}'$, $\boldsymbol{\delta}''$, $\cdots$ defined by (8–32). Similarly for division by any simple function with "analytic" zeros.

In more than one dimension results are limited. One useful result is that $(a^2 - r^2)^m T = 0$ has solutions, $T = \sum_1^{m-1} (\nabla^2)^q T_q$ where each T_q operates only on the angle-variables of $\mathbf{r}$ (that is, T_q operates over the "projected" space, $\mathbf{r}/r$).

CONVOLUTIONS:

Corresponding to functional relations of the type, $h(x) = \int_{-\infty}^{\infty} l(x - u)m(u)\, du$, one may define a convolution, $L * M$, by

$$(L * M)\phi = L_x[M_y\phi(x + y)]$$

where subscripts are used to indicate the variable over which a distribution operator acts. The definition fails unless at least one of L or M decreases sufficiently rapidly as $x \to \pm\infty$ (in the sense, for example, that $L_x\phi(x + b)$ decreases as $b \to \pm\infty$). One easily verifies that, within such limitations: $L * M = M * L$; $L * \boldsymbol{\delta} = L$; $J * (L * M) = (J * L) * M$; $(L * M)' = L' * M = L * M'$.

INTEGRAL TRANSFORMS:

The Fourier transform of a distribution may be defined as

$$\mathscr{F}(L) = L(e^{2\pi i\omega x})$$

which is a *function* of ω (not a distribution).

Similarly, provided that "$L = 0$ for $x < 0$" (that is, provided $L\phi = 0$ whenever ϕ vanishes in $x < 0$), its Laplace transform may be defined as

$$\mathscr{L}(L) = \lambda(p) = L(e^{-px})$$

One has (if L and M both "vanish for $x < 0$"): $\mathscr{L}(L * M) = \lambda(p) \cdot \mu(p)$, etc. Note that, by (8–32),

$$\mathscr{L}(L') = L'(e^{-px}) = pL(e^{-px}) = p\lambda(p)$$

(The usual "extra" term, $l(0^+)$, as in (13–7), here appears on the left-hand side as a term, $l(0)\boldsymbol{\delta}$, in L'.)

REMARKS:

The lack of true algebraic properties for distributions is something of a handicap. However, with this theory it is possible to regard some relations [such as $\nabla^2\phi - \partial^2\phi/\partial t^2 = -4\pi\,\delta(\mathbf{r})$] as having a precise meaning for "*distributions*" rather than for functions. If the final solution is a distribution which corresponds to a function,* then this associated function may be regarded as the required solution, although it may even fail to possess derivatives which appear in the original equation.

Heuristic example: The potential of a point charge, $\phi_0 = 1/r$, is the solution of "$\nabla^2\phi = -4\pi\,\delta(\mathbf{r})$" and we may interpret the "density", $\delta(\mathbf{r})$, as the distribution (operator), $\boldsymbol{\delta}[\psi(\mathbf{r})] = \psi(0)$. Now, in the same sense, a *dipole*, $\mathbf{p}$ (located at $\mathbf{r} = 0$), is associated with the operator $P\psi =$ "$\iiint \rho\psi$" $= (\mathbf{p} \cdot \nabla\psi)_{r=0}$. It is not difficult to show that $P = -\mathbf{p} \cdot \nabla\boldsymbol{\delta}$ in the sense of (8–32). Hence, interpreting all quantities as distributions, $\nabla^2\phi = -4\pi P$ must have the solution, $\phi = -\mathbf{p} \cdot \nabla\phi_0 = +\mathbf{p} \cdot \mathbf{r}/r^3$.

---

* It has been proved that every distribution is some derivative, (8–32), of another distribution which does correspond to a (summable) function.

CHAPTER 9

INFINITE SERIES

Taylor's Series

$$f(\mathbf{r}+\mathbf{a}) = e^{\mathbf{a}\cdot\nabla} f(\mathbf{r}) \tag{9-1}$$

where the exponential operator is defined by its power series and

$$\nabla = \left(\frac{\partial}{\partial r_1}, \frac{\partial}{\partial r_2}, \cdots, \frac{\partial}{\partial r_n}\right)$$

In one dimension, the remainder after the term in $d^n f/dx^n$ is (if $d^n f/dx^n$ is continuous in $r \leqslant x \leqslant r + a$ and its derivative, in turn, exists for $r < x < r + a$):

$$R_n = \frac{a^{n+1}}{(n+1)!} f^{(n+1)}(r + a\theta) \tag{9-2}$$

where $0 < \theta < 1$. This much is true (although not necessarily very helpful) even for "non-analytic" functions such as e^{-1/x^2}—(whose Taylor's series, about $x = 0$, is $0 + 0 + 0 + 0 + \cdots$).

Terminology: Asymptotic Series

Asymptotic series are series which *diverge* but which are nevertheless useful, in the sense that: A finite number of terms gives a numerical value whose error is known. For practical purposes, asymptotic series are finite expansions plus a remainder whose maximum magnitude is known. Note that the error can*not* be made arbitrarily small with such series. Nevertheless, the error is often so small that asymptotic series are often of far greater accuracy than other practical expressions.

Methods for Summing a Series

1. To sum $\sum_{-\infty}^{\infty} N(n)$, consider $\oint_{C_n} \pi(\cot \pi z)N(z)\, dz$ where C_n is a square path with corners at $(n + \frac{1}{2})(\pm 1 \pm i)$; on C_n $\cot \pi z$ is bounded, and hence, in particular, if $|zN(z)| \to 0$ as $|z| \to \infty$ and if $N(z)$ has poles p_i (not integers) with residues R_i, then

$$\sum_{-\infty}^{\infty} N(n) = -\pi \sum_i R_i \cot(\pi p_i) \tag{9-3}$$

which is a *finite* sum if $N(z)$ has a finite number of poles. Similarly, use $\pi/(\sin \pi z)$, $\pi/(\cos \pi z)$, $\pi \tan \pi z$ to treat $\sum(-1)^n N(n)$, $\sum(-1)^n N(n + \frac{1}{2})$, $\sum N(n + \frac{1}{2})$ respectively. Often (9–3) may be (strictly) inapplicable but can be used to *guess* the value of the sum, which value may then be provable in some other way.

2. If $f(z)$ is an "integral" (= "entire") function,* whose zeros are $z_1, z_2, \cdots$ and if

* That is, a function which is analytic everywhere except at $z = \infty$.

(as is easily achieved) $f(0) \neq 0$ and $|f(z)| \leqslant K \exp(|z|^\alpha)$ (for some constant K and all z), then for any $k \geqslant [\alpha] + 1$ [= the largest integer $\leqslant \alpha + 1$],

$$\sum_1^\infty \frac{1}{(z_n)^k} = \frac{-1}{(k-1)!}\left\{\left(\frac{d}{dz}\right)^k \ln f(z)\right\}_{z=0} \tag{9–4}$$

This in turn may be evaluated from the coefficients of the power series for $f(z)$.

EXAMPLE: $f(z) = (\sin z)/z$ shows that

$$\sum_1^\infty \frac{1}{n^2} = \frac{\pi^2}{6}; \qquad \sum_1^\infty \frac{1}{n^4} = \frac{\pi^4}{90}; \qquad \text{etc.}$$

3. *Poisson's Formula*:

$$\tfrac{1}{2}f(0) + \sum_1^\infty f(nx) = \frac{1}{x}\left\{\tfrac{1}{2}g(0) + \sum_1^\infty g(2\pi n/x)\right\} \tag{9–5}$$

where

$$g(y) = 2\int_0^\infty f(t) \cos yt \, dt = F(iy) + F(-iy)$$

if $F(p)$ is the Laplace transform of $f(t)$. A rigorous condition sufficient for the validity of (9–5) is that $g(0)$ exist (as a Lebesgue integral) and $f(x)$ be continuous and steadily decreasing to zero as $x \to \infty$ (or be the difference of two such functions).

Orthogonal Functions

A common notation, based on a vector (unitary space) analogy (see Chapter 18) is, with some specific $\rho(x) \geqslant 0$ in the region of integration, R,

$$(f, g) = \int_R f^* g \rho \, dx; \qquad \|f\|^2 = (f, f) \tag{9–6}$$

("dot product" and "length squared"). The Schwarz inequality then reads,

$$|(f, g)|^2 \leqslant |(f, f)| \cdot |(g, g)| \tag{9–7}$$

("$\cos^2 \theta_{fg} \leqslant 1$").

A set of functions $\phi_1, \phi_2, \phi_3, \cdots$ is called "orthogonal" if $(\phi_i, \phi_j) = 0$ (when $i \neq j$). If also $(\phi_i, \phi_i) = 1$ for all i, the set is called "orthonormal".

If $f_1, f_2, f_3, \cdots$ are independent functions (that is $\sum_1^k c_i f_i \equiv 0$ only if all $c_i = 0$), they may be "orthonormalized" by setting,

$$\phi_1 = f_1/\sqrt{(f_1, f_1)}$$

$$\phi_2 = \text{"}f_2\text{—Projection of } f_2 \text{ along } \phi_1\text{"} = N\left[f_2 - \phi_1 \frac{(\phi_1, f_2)}{(\phi_1, \phi_1)}\right]$$

where N is adjusted to make $(\phi_2, \phi_2) = 1$; similarly each ϕ_n is formed by subtracting from f_n all its projections along earlier ϕ_i.

ORTHONORMAL POLYNOMIALS can be generated more readily by the recursion formula:

$$p_{n+1}(x) = N_n\{xp_n(x) - (p_n, xp_n)p_n(x) - (p_{n-1}, xp_n)p_{n-1}(x)\} \tag{9–7.5}$$

[N_n is adjusted to make $(p_{n+1}, p_{n+1}) = 1$]

with the "initial conditions", $p_{-1} = 0$ and $(p_0)^{-2} = (1, 1) = \int \rho\, dx$. (Proof: Induction.) Since an arbitrary polynomial can be expressed as a sum of the form, $\Sigma\, a_i p_i(x)$, each $p_n(x)$ is orthogonal to *any* polynomial of degree less than n. See also (9–27).

It is also useful to observe that, for any constant a, the *kernel polynomials*,

$$K_n(a, x) = \sum_0^n p_i^*(a) p_i(x)$$

are orthogonal with respect to the weight–function, $\rho'(x) = (x - a)\rho(x)$ and that if $P(x)$ is an arbitrary polynomial of degree at most n, we have $(K_n, P) = P(a)$, so that in this sense K_n acts like the delta function, $\delta(x - a)/\rho(a)$.

Several variables: If $\phi_i(x)$ and $\psi_i(y)$ are orthogonal in $a \leqslant x \leqslant b$ and in $c \leqslant y \leqslant d$ respectively, then the products $\phi_i(x)\psi_j(y) = \Phi_{ij}(x, y)$ are orthogonal in the rectangle, $a \leqslant x \leqslant b$, $c \leqslant y \leqslant d$. Similarly for more variables. If the two-dimensional region is not rectangular, consider:

Change of region: If $\phi_i(\mathbf{r})$ are orthogonal in a region, $\mathscr{R}$ and if the function $\mathbf{R} = \mathbf{R}(\mathbf{r})$ maps $\mathscr{R}$ onto a region, $\mathscr{R}'$, then the functions,

$$\psi_i(\mathbf{R}) = \left| \frac{\partial(x_1, x_2, \cdots)}{\partial(X_1, X_2, \cdots)} \right|^{1/2} \phi_i(\mathbf{r}) \tag{9–8}$$

(Jacobian determinant) are orthogonal in $\mathscr{R}'$. In particular, $\mathscr{R}'$ may be the same as $\mathscr{R}$, but the ψ's "distorted versions" of the ϕ's.

Expansions in Orthonormal Functions, $\phi_i(x)$

(Even if the ϕ_i are not complete:)

(1). The minimum value of

$$\int_R \left| f(x) - \sum_1^n a_j \phi_j(x) \right|^2 \rho(x)\, dx$$

is given by

$$a_k = (\phi_k, f) = \int_R \phi_k^* f \rho\, dx \tag{9–9}$$

That is, the "Fourier coefficients" give the best mean-square approximation even when only a finite number of terms are taken.

(2). Always,

$$\sum_1^{(\infty)} |a_k|^2 \leqslant (f, f) = \int_R |f|^2 \rho\, dx \tag{9–10}$$

(Proof: evaluate the integral preceeding (9–9).) Bessel inequality; useful for proving convergence.

(3). If also $b_k = (\phi_k, g)$ then

$$\sum_1^{(\infty)} |a_k b_k^*| \leqslant \tfrac{1}{2}(f, f) + \tfrac{1}{2}(g, g) \tag{9–11}$$

and if the set ϕ_k is "complete" (equality in (9–10)) then

$$\sum_1^{\infty} a_k^* b_k = (f, g)$$

EXAMPLES:

(1). *Fourier Series:*

(a) In $|x| < \pi$

$$f(x) = \tfrac{1}{2}a_0 + \sum_1^\infty a_n \cos nx + \sum_1^\infty b_n \sin nx$$

$$a_n = \frac{1}{\pi}\int_{-\pi}^{\pi} f(x) \cos nx \, dx; \quad b_n = \frac{1}{\pi}\int_{-\pi}^{\pi} f(x) \sin nx \, dx \tag{9–12}$$

(b) In $0 < x < \pi$, define $f(-x)$ as $\pm f(x)$ and use (9–12) or (9–13):

(c) In $|x| < \pi$

$$f(x) = \sum_{-\infty}^{\infty} \alpha_n e^{inx}; \qquad \alpha_n = \frac{1}{2\pi}\int_{-\pi}^{\pi} e^{-inx} f(x) \, dx \tag{9–13}$$

(d) In $0 < x < l$,

$$f(x) = \sum_{-\infty}^{\infty} \beta_n e^{2\pi inx/l}; \quad \beta_n = \frac{1}{l}\int_0^l e^{-2\pi inx/l} f(x) \, dx \tag{9–14}$$

(*e*) "Almost-Periodic" Functions: A function, $f(x)$, is called "almost-periodic" if it is continuous in the range $-\infty < x < \infty$ and if: Given any $\epsilon > 0$, one can find an L such that *any* interval of length L contains (at least) one number w such that for *all* x:

$$|f(x + w) - f(x)| < \epsilon$$

(f is not only "nearly" periodic but the periods are also "nearly" integral multiples of some number.)

The sums, products, and uniformly convergent limits of almost-periodic functions are again almost-periodic. For any almost-periodic function

$$a(\lambda) = \lim_{T\to\infty} \frac{1}{T}\int_0^T f(x) e^{-i\lambda x} \, dx \tag{9–15}$$

exists and is, in fact, equal to zero for all but a denumerable set of values, λ_i.

With these λ_i, the "Fourier series",

$$f(x) = \sum_i a(\lambda_i) e^{i\lambda_i x} \tag{9–16}$$

converges uniformly for all x—with any ordering of the terms if no two λ_i are rational multiples of each other.

(2). *Legendre Series:*

(a) In $|x| \leqslant 1$,

$$f(x) = \sum_{n=0}^{\infty} c_n P_n(x)$$

$$c_n = (n + \tfrac{1}{2})\int_{-1}^{1} f(x) P_n(x) \, dx = \frac{2n+1}{n! 2^{n+1}}\int_{-1}^{1} f^{(n)}(t)(1 - t^2)^n \, dt \tag{9–17}$$

(b) On the surface of a sphere,

$$F(\theta, \phi) = \sum_{l=0}^{\infty} \sum_{m=-l}^{l} a_{lm} e^{im\phi} P_l^m(\cos\theta)$$

$$a_{lm} = \frac{2l+1}{4\pi}\frac{(l-m)!}{(l+m)!}\int_0^{2\pi} d\phi' \int_0^{\pi} F(\theta', \phi') e^{-im\phi} P_l^m(\cos\theta') \sin\theta' \, d\theta' \tag{9–18}$$

(c) Some special cases:

$$\left.\begin{aligned} r<1:\quad & \sum_0^\infty r^n P_n(\cos\theta) = \\ r>1:\quad & \sum_0^\infty r^{-n-1} P_n(\cos\theta) = \end{aligned}\right\} \frac{1}{\sqrt{1-2r\cos\theta+r^2}} \tag{9–19}$$

$$\sum_0^\infty \frac{(-r)^l\, P_l(\cos\theta)}{l!} = e^{-r\cos\theta} J_0\,(r\sin\theta) \tag{9–20}$$

$$\left.\begin{aligned} & \sum_0^\infty (2l+1)\, P_l(z) Q_l(t) = \frac{1}{t-z} \\ & \sum_0^\infty (2l+1)\, P_l(z) P_l(t) = 2\delta(t-z) \end{aligned}\right\} \tag{9–21}$$

(3). *Some Frequently Useful Series*

$$e^{ikz} = e^{ikr\cos\theta} = \frac{2\pi}{\sqrt{2kr}} \sum_0^\infty i^l \sqrt{2l+1}\, J_{l+\frac12}(kr) \sqrt{\frac{2l+1}{4\pi}}\, P_l(\cos\theta) \tag{9–22}$$

$$\frac{e^{ik|\mathbf{r}-\mathbf{r}'|}}{|\mathbf{r}-\mathbf{r}'|} = i\pi \sum_0^\infty (l+\tfrac12)\, \frac{H^{(1)}_{l+\frac12}(kr_>)}{\sqrt{r_>}} \frac{J_{l+\frac12}(kr_<)}{\sqrt{r_<}}\, P_l(\cos\theta) \tag{9–23}$$

where $r_<$ is the smaller of r and r', and similarly $r_>$ is the greater; and $\cos\theta = \mathbf{r}\cdot\mathbf{r}'/rr'$.

"MOMENT" SEQUENCES

It is sometimes expedient to calculate, for an unknown function, $f(x)$, the quantities:

$$\mu_n = \int_{-\infty}^{\infty} x^n f(x)\, dx \tag{9–24}$$

While these "moments" do not always determine the function completely* (even when all μ_i, $i = 0, 1, 2, 3, \cdots, \infty$ are known), the degree of restriction on f is surprisingly high and often adequate—especially if it is known that $f(x) \geqslant 0$ for all x.

The usefulness of "moments" for practical computations lies in their economy; within limits, the entire graph of a function can be specified approximately by relatively few numbers.

General Theorems (valid if $f(x) \geqslant 0$ for all x):

1. If the values of $\mu_0, \mu_1, \cdots, \mu_{2n}$ are known then any two functions $f_1(x)$ and $f_2(x)$ with these given first $2n+1$ moments are limited by,

$$\left| \int_{-\infty}^{x} f_1(u)\, du - \int_{-\infty}^{x} f_2(u)\, du \right| \leqslant \frac{1}{\sum_0^n [p_k(x)]^2} \equiv \rho_n(x) \tag{9–25}$$

where the polynomials $p_k(x)$ can be constructed (knowing only the first $2n+1$ moments) from the requirements,

$$\int_{-\infty}^{\infty} p_k(x)\, p_l(x) f(x)\, dx = \delta_{kl} \tag{9–26}$$

* For example, the function: $g(t) = 0$ for $t < 0$, $g(t) = e^{-(t^{1/4})} \sin(t^{1/4})$ for $t > 0$, has vanishing moments of all orders and hence could be added to any function without changing the values of the μ_i. However, if f is known to vanish outside a finite interval, it is uniquely determined by the full infinite set of moments.

In fact,

$$p_k(x) = \text{constant} \times \begin{vmatrix} \mu_0, & \mu_1, & \cdots, & \mu_{k-1}, & 1 \\ \mu_1, & \mu_2, & \cdots, & \mu_k, & x \\ \mu_2, & \mu_3, & \cdots, & \mu_{k+1}, & x^2 \\ \cdot & & & & \cdot \\ \cdot & & & & \cdot \\ \cdot & & & & \cdot \\ \mu_k, & \mu_{k+1}, & \cdots, & \mu_{2k-1}, & x^k \end{vmatrix} \tag{9–27}$$

The p_k can also be generated by (9–7.5) wherein $(p, P) = \int pPf\, dx$ can be evaluated in terms of the μ_i.

2. If c and d are two consecutive zeros of $p_n(x)$, then when $c < x < d$ (and other conditions as in (9–25)),

$$\left| \int_{-\infty}^{x} f_1(n)\, du - \int_{-\infty}^{x} f_2(u)\, du \right| \leqslant \rho_n(c) + \rho_n(d) \tag{9–28}$$

3. If all μ_i (the infinite set) are known, then $f(x)$ is unique if and only if $\sum_0^\infty |p_k(x)|^2 = \infty$ for some one value of x.

4. A check relation:

$$\frac{\mu_n \, \mu_k}{(\mu_{(n+k)/2})^2} \geqslant 1 \tag{9–29}$$

(The Schwarz inequality.) Note that this ratio, being independent of the substitution, $f(x) \to Af(bx)$ is more characteristic of the "basic nature" of $f(x)$ than are the μ_n.

These theorems hold even when $f(x)$ includes delta-functions. (A rigorous formulation then involves the Stieltjes definition of an integral.) For this reason, (9–25) and (9–28) are rather conservative error-estimates since the class of "admissable" functions in a physical problem is usually strongly restricted by continuity and some required asymptotic behavior.

To "Reconstruct" a Function from its Moments

For this task, an embarrassingly wide range of possibilities exists. Virtually any trial function can be assumed provided that it has a sufficient number of adjustable parameters which can be fixed to make its moments agree with the given ones.

However, the accuracy of the final result is usually improved greatly if other information concerning the general behavior of $f(x)$ is "forced in". For example, it may be known on physical grounds that $f(x) \geqslant 0$ everywhere; or that $f \equiv 0$ for $x < 0$; or that $f(x) \doteqdot ax^k$ near $x = 0$; or that $f \doteqdot (A/x)e^{-x}$ as $x \to \infty$, etc. If the trial functions are also required to have such known properties, the end result of such additional restrictions will almost always be a great improvement in accuracy and the removal of considerable ambiguity.

1. When an even number, $2N$, of moments, $\mu_0, \mu_1, \cdots, \mu_{2N-1}$ is known, a useful method of "forcing in" desired features is to assume:

$$f(x) = \sum_{i=1}^{N} \frac{\alpha_i}{\beta_i} G\left(\frac{x}{\beta_i}\right) \tag{9–30}$$

where G has been chosen to have the desired properties. If one defines,

$$\frac{1}{\nu_k} = \frac{1}{\mu_k} \int_{-\infty}^{\infty} G(t) t^k \, dt \tag{9–31}$$

then the β_i in (9–30) are the roots of $P_N(\beta) = 0$ where $P_N(x)$ is defined by (9–26) or (9–27) but with ν_k substituted for μ_k. In terms of these same modified polynomials, the remaining parameters in (9–30) are given by

$$\frac{1}{\alpha_j} = \sum_{k=0}^{N-1} |P_k(\beta_j)|^2 = \int_{-\infty}^{\infty} \frac{P_N(t)f(t)\,dt}{(t-\beta_j)P_N'(\beta_j)} \tag{9–32}$$

(where the last form can be evaluated since the μ_k are known, even though $f(t)$ is not).

All the constants α_i, β_i in (9–30) will be real and positive if and only if (the function G is such that) the coefficients of $P_N(x)$ alternate in sign; equivalently, if and only if all determinants of the form $\|\nu_{i+j}\|$ and $\|\nu_{i+j+1}\|$ (where $i, j = 0, 1, 2, \cdots, k$ with $k < N$) are positive.

2. When an odd number, $2N - 1$, of moments is given, the above procedure may be modified by arbitrarily assigning one of the constants, β_i—or assigning it a value on physical grounds; $\sqrt{\mu_2/\mu_0}$ often indicates a "natural" scale for the independent variable.

The parameters α_i, β_i will be real and positive when the same conditions as before are satisfied (that is, those which are applicable).

3. If $f(x)$ is known to be non-negative for all x, and if the μ_k are known for $k = 0, 1, 2, \cdots, 2N$, then any solution, $f(x)$, has the property that its "Hilbert transform" satisfies,*

$$\int_{-\infty}^{\infty} \frac{f(x)\,dx}{z-x} = \frac{\mu_0}{z} + \frac{\mu_1}{z^2} + \cdots + \frac{\mu_{2N}}{z^{2N+1}} + R(z) \tag{9–33}$$

where $R(z)$ has the property

$$\lim_{|z|\to\infty} z^{2N+1} R(z) = 0$$

in any sector, $\epsilon \leqslant \arg z \leqslant \pi - \epsilon$.

Conversely, if we choose such a function, $g(z)$, which is analytic in $\mathrm{Im}(z) > 0$ and which has non-positive imaginary part there, then its (inverse) Hilbert transform (namely, $f(x) = (1/\pi)^2 \int_{-\infty}^{\infty} (z-x)^{-1} g(z)\,dz$) has moments μ_k.

4. When a large number of moments is available, the following is much simpler than the foregoing methods (but is more likely to introduce errors at large values of x). Choose a function $G(x)$ with the desired asymptotic properties. If polynomials $Q_i(x)$ are constructed [see material following (18–38)] such that

$$[x^n, Q_i] \equiv \int_{-\infty}^{\infty} x^n Q_i(x) G(x)\,dx = \delta_{ni}$$

then a function having moments μ_i is

$$f(x) = G(x) \sum \mu_j Q_j(x)$$

5. Functions not defined for negative x: In this case, instead of (9–24),

$$\mu_n = \int_0^{\infty} x^n f(x)\,dx \tag{9–34}$$

Since we may define a new function, $F(x) = f(|x|)$ in the range $-\infty$ to ∞, whose odd

* The infinite series always diverges, but it is an asymptotic series.

moments all vanish and whose even moments are twice those of f, it follows that *f is essentially determined by its even moments alone.* (Similarly, considering $G(x) = (x/|x|) f(|x|)$, it follows that f is also determined by its odd moments alone.)

By such devices, the theorems given above for functions defined on $(-\infty, \infty)$ can be used for functions defined only on $(0, \infty)$. Note that if information on the odd moments is to be used, theorems requiring "$f \geqslant 0$" cannot be applied (except as hints).

CHAPTER 10

VECTOR ANALYSIS

Geometric Definitions

Physical laws are naturally expressed in terms of "arrows" in ordinary three-dimensional space and this geometric picture is the main advantage of vector notation. (A minor advantage is economy.) The actual location of a vector is not usually specified by its symbol. The symbol is a name only for the length and direction of a vector and the location must be inferred from the context, if it is of importance, or indicated by additional symbols.

Vectors are added by placing* the terms tip to tail and drawing a new vector, the sum, from the free tip to the free tail. (The sum is independent of the order of the terms.)

$\mathbf{a} \cdot \mathbf{b}$ is a *number*, the scalar or "dot" product, defined to be $ab \cos \theta$ where a and b are the lengths of $\mathbf{a}$ and $\mathbf{b}$ and θ is the angle between their directions.

$x\mathbf{a}$ denotes a *vector* x-times as long as $\mathbf{a}$ and having the same direction if $x > 0$ and opposite direction if $x < 0$.

$\mathbf{a} \times \mathbf{b}$ is a *vector*, the vector product, whose length is $ab \sin \theta$ and whose direction is perpendicular to the plane of $\mathbf{a}$ and $\mathbf{b}$, on the side towards which the right thumb points when the fingers of the right hand point from the tip of $\mathbf{a}$ to the tip of $\mathbf{b}$ with the wrist lying at the common tail of $\mathbf{a}$ and $\mathbf{b}$:

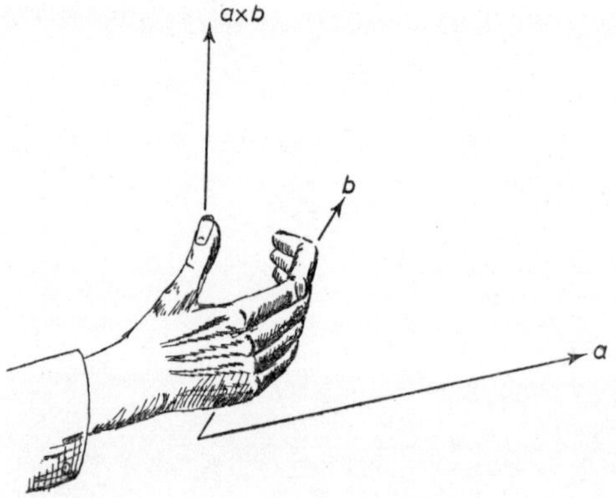

Note that $\mathbf{a} \times \mathbf{b} = -\mathbf{b} \times \mathbf{a}$.

Although most non-trivial theorems in vector analysis are conveniently proved by introducing Cartesian coordinates, the *geometric* ideas are the prime feature of vector analysis and are vital to its effective application.

The special notation for vectors (overlying half-arrow "⇀" or underline or bold-face type etc.) is sometimes dropped when no confusion can arise.

* In all motions of this sort, the direction and magnitude are held fixed as the vector is moved.

Analytic-Geometry Definitions

If Cartesian coordinates are introduced, **a** *is regarded as an abbreviation for* (a_x, a_y, a_z), where the latter are the coordinates of the tip of **a** when its tail is placed at the origin; more generally, a_x is the length of the projection of **a** on the x-axis. If $\hat{x}$ is a vector of *unit* length pointing along the positive x-axis, then $a_x = \hat{x} \cdot \mathbf{a}$.

(The component-list is sometimes more conveniently written in a column, $\begin{pmatrix} a_x \\ a_y \\ a_z \end{pmatrix}$; standard matrix-notation can then be more readily adjoined.)

To see the equivalence of the following definitions to the earlier geometric definitions, it is simplest to select special coordinates such that one vector is along a coordinate axis, etc. Alternatively, one can write: $\mathbf{a} = a_x\hat{x} + a_y\hat{y} + a_z\hat{z}$ and use the obvious properties of unit-length axis-vectors, $\hat{x}$, $\hat{y}$, $\hat{z}$.

$$\mathbf{a} + \mathbf{b} = (a_x + b_x, a_y + b_y, a_z + b_z) \tag{10–1}$$

$$\alpha\mathbf{a} = (\alpha a_x, \alpha a_y, \alpha a_z) \tag{10–2}$$

$$\mathbf{a} \cdot \mathbf{b} = a_x b_x + a_y b_y + a_z b_z \tag{10–3}$$

$$a = |\mathbf{a}| = \sqrt{\mathbf{a} \cdot \mathbf{a}} \tag{10–4}$$

$$\mathbf{a} \times \mathbf{b} = -\mathbf{b} \times \mathbf{a} = \hat{x}(a_y b_z - a_z b_y) + \hat{y}(a_z b_x - a_x b_z) + \hat{z}(a_x b_y - a_y b_x) \tag{10–5}$$

(in right-handed* coordinates **only**)

Note the cyclic order of the coordinates in the positive terms, xyz, yzx, zxy.

Basic Theorems

All algebraic rules hold in manipulating vectors, *except* that:

$$\mathbf{a} \times \mathbf{b} = -\mathbf{b} \times \mathbf{a}$$

$$\mathbf{a} \times (\mathbf{b} \times \mathbf{c}) \neq (\mathbf{a} \times \mathbf{b}) \times \mathbf{c}$$

(There is no division operation; $\mathbf{a} \cdot \mathbf{b} = \mathbf{a} \cdot \mathbf{c}$ does *not* imply $\mathbf{b} = \mathbf{c}$—as is geometrically obvious.)

$$\boxed{\mathbf{a} \cdot (\mathbf{b} \times \mathbf{c}) = (\mathbf{a} \times \mathbf{b}) \cdot \mathbf{c}} \quad \text{(often written } \mathbf{a} \times \mathbf{b} \cdot \mathbf{c} \text{ or } \mathbf{abc}) \tag{10–6}$$

$$\boxed{\mathbf{a} \times (\mathbf{b} \times \mathbf{c}) = \mathbf{b}(\mathbf{a} \cdot \mathbf{c}) - \mathbf{c}(\mathbf{a} \cdot \mathbf{b})} \tag{10–7}$$

$$|\mathbf{a} \times \mathbf{b}|^2 = a^2 b^2 - (\mathbf{a} \cdot \mathbf{b})^2 \tag{10–8}$$

$$\left.\begin{matrix}\text{Projection of } \mathbf{b} \\ \text{parallel to } \mathbf{a}\end{matrix}\right\} = \mathbf{a}\left(\frac{\mathbf{a} \cdot \mathbf{b}}{a^2}\right) \tag{10–9}$$

$$\left.\begin{matrix}\text{Projection of } \mathbf{b} \\ \text{perpendicular to } \mathbf{a}\end{matrix}\right\} = \frac{\mathbf{a} \times (\mathbf{b} \times \mathbf{a})}{a^2} = \mathbf{b} - \mathbf{a}\left(\frac{\mathbf{a} \cdot \mathbf{b}}{a^2}\right) \tag{10–10}$$

$$(\mathbf{a} \times \mathbf{b}) \cdot (\mathbf{c} \times \mathbf{d}) = (\mathbf{a} \cdot \mathbf{c})(\mathbf{b} \cdot \mathbf{d}) - (\mathbf{a} \cdot \mathbf{d})(\mathbf{b} \cdot \mathbf{c}) \tag{10–11}$$

---

* That is $\hat{x} \times \hat{y} = \hat{z}$; in left-handed coordinates, the signs must be inverted. Some formal theories consider the analytic definition basic and speak of an "axial" vector which reverses its sign on reflection of coordinates.

Volume of parallelepiped with edges **a**, **b**, **c**

$$= \mathbf{a} \times \mathbf{b} \cdot \mathbf{c} = \mathbf{a} \cdot \mathbf{b} \times \mathbf{c} = \begin{vmatrix} a_x & a_y & a_z \\ b_x & b_y & b_z \\ c_x & c_y & c_z \end{vmatrix} \tag{10–12}$$

Solutions of Some Vector Equations

$$\left.\begin{aligned}(\mathbf{x} \cdot \mathbf{c}) &= p \\ (\mathbf{x} \times \mathbf{a}) &= \mathbf{b}\end{aligned}\right\}: \qquad \mathbf{x} = \frac{\mathbf{c} \times \mathbf{b} + p\mathbf{a}}{\mathbf{a} \cdot \mathbf{c}} \tag{10–13}$$

(Here $\mathbf{a} \cdot \mathbf{b} = 0$ if the original equations are possible.)

$$\left.\begin{aligned}\mathbf{x} \cdot \mathbf{a} &= \alpha \\ \mathbf{x} \cdot \mathbf{b} &= \beta \\ \mathbf{x} \cdot \mathbf{c} &= \gamma\end{aligned}\right\}: \qquad \mathbf{x} = \frac{\alpha\mathbf{b} \times \mathbf{c} + \beta\mathbf{c} \times \mathbf{a} + \gamma\mathbf{a} \times \mathbf{b}}{\mathbf{a} \cdot \mathbf{b} \times \mathbf{c}} \tag{10–14}$$

$$\mathbf{x} + \mathbf{b} \times \mathbf{x} = \mathbf{a}: \qquad \mathbf{x} = \frac{\mathbf{a} + \mathbf{a} \times \mathbf{b} + (\mathbf{a} \cdot \mathbf{b})\mathbf{b}}{1 + b^2} \tag{10–15}$$

$$\mathbf{a} \times \mathbf{x} + \mathbf{b}(\mathbf{c} \cdot \mathbf{x}) = \mathbf{d}: \qquad \mathbf{x} = \frac{\mathbf{d} \times \mathbf{b}}{\mathbf{a} \cdot \mathbf{b}} + \mathbf{a}\left[\frac{\mathbf{a} \cdot \mathbf{d} + \mathbf{c} \cdot \mathbf{b} \times \mathbf{d}}{(\mathbf{a} \cdot \mathbf{c})(\mathbf{a} \cdot \mathbf{b})}\right] \tag{10–16}$$

$$\mathbf{p} = x\mathbf{a} + y\mathbf{b} + z\mathbf{c}: \begin{cases} x = \dfrac{\mathbf{p} \cdot \mathbf{b} \times \mathbf{c}}{\mathbf{a} \cdot \mathbf{b} \times \mathbf{c}} \\[2ex] y = \dfrac{\mathbf{p} \cdot \mathbf{c} \times \mathbf{a}}{\mathbf{a} \cdot \mathbf{b} \times \mathbf{c}} \\[2ex] z = \dfrac{\mathbf{p} \cdot \mathbf{a} \times \mathbf{b}}{\mathbf{a} \cdot \mathbf{b} \times \mathbf{c}} \end{cases} \tag{10–17}$$

$$\mathbf{p} = x(\mathbf{b} \times \mathbf{c}) + y(\mathbf{c} \times \mathbf{a}) + z(\mathbf{a} \times \mathbf{b}):$$

$$x = \frac{\mathbf{p} \cdot \mathbf{a}}{\mathbf{a} \cdot \mathbf{b} \times \mathbf{c}}, \quad y = \frac{\mathbf{p} \cdot \mathbf{b}}{\mathbf{a} \cdot \mathbf{b} \times \mathbf{c}}, \quad z = \frac{\mathbf{p} \cdot \mathbf{c}}{\mathbf{a} \cdot \mathbf{b} \times \mathbf{c}} \tag{10–18}$$

Rotations

If all of space is rotated about an axis along $\boldsymbol{\delta}$ and by an angle of δ radians (clockwise, looking out along $\boldsymbol{\delta}$ and not necessarily less than 2π), then $\mathbf{r}$ goes into $\mathbf{r}'$ where

$$\mathbf{r}' = \mathbf{r} + \boldsymbol{\delta} \times \mathbf{r}\,\frac{\sin\delta}{\delta} + \boldsymbol{\delta} \times (\boldsymbol{\delta} \times \mathbf{r})\,\frac{1 - \cos\delta}{\delta^2} \tag{10–19}$$

The inverse, of course, is given by changing the sign of $\boldsymbol{\delta}$. (Proof: resolve $\mathbf{r}$ into a sum of two vectors, one parallel to and one perpendicular to $\boldsymbol{\delta}$.)

Differentiation (Total)

If a vector changes with the value of a variable, t, as is often denoted by $\mathbf{a} = \mathbf{a}(t)$—where, for example, t may be time or arc-length on a curve—then we define

$$\frac{\mathrm{d}}{\mathrm{d}t}\,\mathbf{a}(t) = \left(\frac{\mathrm{d}a_x}{\mathrm{d}t}, \frac{\mathrm{d}a_y}{\mathrm{d}t}, \frac{\mathrm{d}a_z}{\mathrm{d}t}\right) = \lim_{\Delta \to 0} \frac{\mathbf{a}(t + \Delta) - \mathbf{a}(t)}{\Delta} \tag{10–20}$$

Note that $\mathbf{a} \cdot (\mathrm{d}\mathbf{a}/\mathrm{d}t)$ can be zero even though $\mathrm{d}\mathbf{a}/\mathrm{d}t \neq 0$.

Space curves: If s = arc length and the curve is $\mathbf{r} = \mathbf{r}(s)$ [where $\mathbf{r}$ is conceived as always having its tail at the origin; thus $\mathbf{r} = (x, y, z)$], then

$$\text{Unit tangent vector} = \boldsymbol{\tau} = \frac{\mathrm{d}\mathbf{r}}{\mathrm{d}s} \tag{10–21}$$

$$\frac{\mathrm{d}^2\mathbf{r}}{\mathrm{d}s^2} = \frac{\mathbf{R}}{R^2} \tag{10–22}$$

where R is the radius of curvature and $\mathbf{R}$ points perpendicular to the curve in the direction of greatest (concave) curvature.

$$\text{“curvature”}, c = \left|\frac{\mathrm{d}^2\mathbf{r}}{\mathrm{d}s^2}\right| = 1/R$$

$$\text{“torsion”}, T = \frac{\mathrm{d}\mathbf{r}}{\mathrm{d}s} \cdot \left(\frac{\mathrm{d}^2\mathbf{r}}{\mathrm{d}s^2} \times \frac{\mathrm{d}^3\mathbf{r}}{\mathrm{d}s^3}\right)\frac{1}{c^2} \tag{10–23}$$

Serret-Frenet Formulas

If we define,

$$\boldsymbol{\tau} = \frac{\mathrm{d}\mathbf{r}}{\mathrm{d}s} \qquad \text{(“tangent”)}$$

$$\boldsymbol{\nu} = \frac{1}{c}\frac{\mathrm{d}^2\mathbf{r}}{\mathrm{d}s^2} \qquad \text{(“principal normal”)}$$

$$\boldsymbol{\beta} = \boldsymbol{\tau} \times \boldsymbol{\nu} \qquad \text{(“binomial”)}$$

then,

$$\left.\begin{aligned} \frac{\mathrm{d}\boldsymbol{\tau}}{\mathrm{d}s} &= c\boldsymbol{\nu} \\ \frac{\mathrm{d}\boldsymbol{\nu}}{\mathrm{d}s} &= -c\boldsymbol{\tau} + T\boldsymbol{\beta} \\ \frac{\mathrm{d}\boldsymbol{\beta}}{\mathrm{d}s} &= -T\boldsymbol{\nu} \end{aligned}\right\} \tag{10–24}$$

Rigid Motions

Consider a rigid body in arbitrary motion. Let $\mathbf{r}_\alpha$ denote the position vector (drawn from an origin fixed in space) of a point “α” of the body and let $\mathbf{v}_\alpha = \mathrm{d}\mathbf{r}_\alpha/\mathrm{d}t$ be its velocity. Then at every *instant* and for all α, β,

$$\frac{\mathrm{d}}{\mathrm{d}t}|\mathbf{r}_\alpha - \mathbf{r}_\beta|^2 = 0 = (\mathbf{v}_\alpha - \mathbf{v}_\beta) \cdot (\mathbf{r}_\alpha - \mathbf{r}_\beta) \tag{10–25}$$

In particular, writing $\mathbf{v}_\alpha \cdot (\mathbf{r}_\alpha - \mathbf{r}_i) = \mathbf{v}_i \cdot (\mathbf{r}_\alpha - \mathbf{r}_i)$ for $i = 1, 2, 3$ and any $\mathbf{r}_i$ which are not coplanar, we see from (10–14) that all $\mathbf{v}_\alpha$ are determined if any three are given. Thus the following solution of (10–25)

$$\mathbf{v}_\alpha = \mathbf{u} + \boldsymbol{\omega} \times \mathbf{r}_\alpha \tag{10–26}$$

must be unique if it in turn can be solved for $\mathbf{u}$ and $\boldsymbol{\omega}$ with $\alpha = 1, 2, 3$. These are nine linear numerical equations for the six components of $\mathbf{u}$ and $\boldsymbol{\omega}$; but there exist three independent relations of the form (10–25) between them and there is consequently one non-zero solution $\mathbf{u}$, $\boldsymbol{\omega}$.

For any arbitrary rigid motion, (10–26) *holds for suitable* $\mathbf{u}(t)$ *and* $\boldsymbol{\omega}(t)$. [$\mathbf{u}(t)$ is evidently the velocity of the point presently located at the origin.] Setting $\mathbf{r}'_\alpha = \mathbf{r}_\alpha + \mathbf{a}$, in (10–26), we find:

$\boldsymbol{\omega}(t)$ *is independent of shifts of origin.*

In particular, taking $\mathbf{a} = \omega^{-2}[\boldsymbol{\omega} \times \mathbf{u}]$, one finds $\mathbf{u}' = \omega^{-2}(\boldsymbol{\omega} \cdot \mathbf{u})\boldsymbol{\omega}$ so that, with this particular origin, $\mathbf{u}$ is parallel to $\boldsymbol{\omega}$. That is:

The motion (10–26) *can always be regarded* (*for an element of time* d*t*) *as a screw-motion.*

Moving Coordinates

The actual transformation equations can be obtained from (10–19) and (10–26), but these are seldom of great interest in themselves. More useful are the *transformation laws for velocities and accelerations.* These can be expressed more simply than the coordinate transformations. It should be noted that here *time plays a dual role*: on the one hand, it is a parameter which specifies the coordinate transformation (at the moment) while on the other hand, quite independently, it specifies the arbitrary motion of, say, a mass point along an arbitrary space curve.

First let **f** be any "free" vector (as opposed to a field of vectors). It can be expressed either in fixed coordinates (x, y, z) or in moving coordinates (ξ, η, ζ) which we also take to be Cartesian but unrestricted as to motions. Thus

$$\mathbf{f} = f_x\hat{x} + f_y\hat{y} + f_z\hat{z} = f_\xi\hat{\xi} + f_\eta\hat{\eta} + f_\zeta\hat{\zeta}$$

then

$$\frac{d\mathbf{f}}{dt} = \hat{x}\frac{df_x}{dt} + \hat{y}\frac{df_y}{dt} + \hat{z}\frac{df_z}{dt} = \hat{\xi}\frac{df_\xi}{dt} + \hat{\eta}\frac{df_\eta}{dt} + \hat{\zeta}\frac{df_\zeta}{dt} + f_\xi\frac{d\hat{\xi}}{dt} + f_\eta\frac{d\hat{\eta}}{dt} + f_\zeta\frac{d\hat{\zeta}}{dt}$$

To evaluate the last three terms, we use (10–26) where, because $\hat{\xi}, \hat{\eta}, \hat{\zeta}$ are drawn from the moving coordinate origin,* $\mathbf{u} = 0$.

$$\frac{d\hat{\xi}}{dt} = \boldsymbol{\omega} \times \hat{\xi}, \qquad \frac{d\hat{\eta}}{dt} = \boldsymbol{\omega} \times \hat{\eta}, \qquad \frac{d\hat{\zeta}}{dt} = \boldsymbol{\omega} \times \hat{\zeta}$$

Thus

$$\boxed{\frac{d\mathbf{f}}{dt} = \frac{d_r\mathbf{f}}{dt} + \boldsymbol{\omega} \times \mathbf{f}} \tag{10–27}$$

where the notation, d_r/dt has been used to denote the derivative obtained by differentiating only the (ξ, η, ζ) *components* of **f**—it is what a "moving geometer" would call $d\mathbf{f}/dt$. Note that the translational motion of the coordinates does not appear *explicitly* in (10–27). The angular velocity, $\boldsymbol{\omega}$, is, of course, in general a function of t.

* More completely, if $\mathbf{r}_\xi$ locates the tip of $\hat{\xi}$ relative to $x = 0 = y = z$, and if $\mathbf{r}_0$ does the same for the origin of the moving coordinates, then $\hat{\xi} = \mathbf{r}_\xi - \mathbf{r}_0$ and

$$\frac{d\hat{\xi}}{dt} = \mathbf{v}_\xi - \mathbf{v}_0 = \boldsymbol{\omega} \times (\mathbf{r}_\xi - \mathbf{r}_0) = \boldsymbol{\omega} \times \hat{\xi}$$

by (10–26).

Similarly, it can be shown that for vector and scalar *fields*, $\mathbf{a}(\mathbf{r}, t)$ and $\phi(\mathbf{r}, t)$,

$$\frac{\partial \phi}{\partial t} = \frac{\partial_r \phi}{\partial t} - \mathbf{u} \cdot \nabla \phi \tag{10–28}$$

$$\frac{\partial \mathbf{a}}{\partial t} = \frac{\partial_r \mathbf{a}}{\partial t} - (\mathbf{u} \cdot \nabla)\mathbf{a} + \boldsymbol{\omega} \times \mathbf{a} = \frac{\partial_r \mathbf{a}}{\partial t} - \nabla \times (\mathbf{a} \times \mathbf{u}) - \mathbf{u}(\nabla \cdot \mathbf{a}) + \boldsymbol{\omega} \times \mathbf{a} \tag{10–29}$$

where the ∇ operator is defined and discussed below.

Vector Differentiation (Partial)

Almost all commonly required partial differentiations can be expressed in terms of the vector operator,*

$$\text{Grad} = \nabla = \hat{x}\frac{\partial}{\partial x} + \hat{y}\frac{\partial}{\partial y} + \hat{z}\frac{\partial}{\partial z} \tag{10–30}$$

Thus $\nabla\phi$—the "gradient of ϕ"—is a *vector* pointing in the direction of most rapid increase of ϕ and having magnitude, $\partial\phi/\partial s$ where s is distance in that direction; $\mathbf{a} \cdot \nabla\phi = a(\partial\phi/\partial s_a)$ where s_a is distance along $\mathbf{a}$.

Note that $\hat{x} = \nabla x$ and that in general a unit vector perpendicular to surfaces, $\phi(r) = \text{constant}$, is given by $(\nabla\phi)/|\nabla\phi|$. Commonly occurring expressions,

$$\text{"Laplacian"} = \nabla^2 = \nabla \cdot \nabla = \frac{\partial^2}{\partial x^2} + \frac{\partial^2}{\partial y^2} + \frac{\partial^2}{\partial z^2} \tag{10–31}$$

$$\text{"Divergence of } \mathbf{a}\text{"} = \nabla \cdot \mathbf{a} = \frac{\partial a_x}{\partial x} + \frac{\partial a_y}{\partial y} + \frac{\partial a_z}{\partial z} \tag{10–32}$$

$$\text{"Curl of } a\text{"} = \nabla \times \mathbf{a} \tag{10–33}$$

The second is a number; the last is a vector.

Manipulation of ∇

To reform an expression involving ∇, first write it as a sum of terms wherein only one variable is to be differentiated in each (use a subscript c to denote the "constant" factors, for example). *Then* rearrange the terms to obtain another form where the order of the various factors alone makes clear what is to be differentiated in each term.

EXAMPLE: $\nabla \cdot (\mathbf{a} \times \mathbf{b}) = \nabla \cdot \mathbf{a} \times \mathbf{b}_c + \nabla \cdot \mathbf{a}_c \times \mathbf{b} = \mathbf{b}_c \cdot \nabla \times \mathbf{a} - \nabla \cdot \mathbf{b} \times \mathbf{a}_c = \mathbf{b}_c \cdot \nabla \times \mathbf{a} - \mathbf{a}_c \cdot \nabla \times \mathbf{b}$ whence:

$$\nabla \cdot (\mathbf{a} \times \mathbf{b}) = \mathbf{b} \cdot (\nabla \times \mathbf{a}) - \mathbf{a} \cdot (\nabla \times \mathbf{b}) \tag{10–34}$$

Similarly

$$\nabla \cdot (\phi\mathbf{a}) = \phi\nabla \cdot \mathbf{a} + \mathbf{a} \cdot \nabla\phi \tag{10–35}$$

$$\nabla \times (\phi\mathbf{a}) = \phi\nabla \times \mathbf{a} - \mathbf{a} \times (\nabla\phi) \tag{10–36}$$

$$\nabla \times (\nabla\phi) \equiv 0 \tag{10–37}$$

$$\nabla \cdot (\nabla \times \mathbf{a}) \equiv 0 \tag{10–38}$$

$(\mathbf{b} \cdot \nabla)\mathbf{a}$ = the (first order) change in $\mathbf{a}$ when one moves a distance b along $\mathbf{b}$

$$= \tfrac{1}{2}[\nabla \times (\mathbf{a} \times \mathbf{b}) + \nabla(\mathbf{a} \cdot \mathbf{b}) - \mathbf{a}(\nabla \cdot \mathbf{b}) + \mathbf{b}(\nabla \cdot \mathbf{a}) - \mathbf{a} \times (\nabla \times \mathbf{b}) - \mathbf{b} \times (\nabla \times \mathbf{a})] \tag{10–39}$$

---

* The gradient operator, commonly read "grad"; the notation, $\frac{\partial}{\partial \mathbf{r}}$, is also used for this operator.

Here, the notation $(\mathbf{b}\cdot\nabla)\mathbf{a}$ denotes a vector whose x-component is $\mathbf{b}\cdot\nabla a_x$, etc.

By *definition*, (note the formal similarity to (10–7).)

$$\nabla^2\mathbf{a} = \nabla(\nabla\cdot\mathbf{a}) - \nabla\times(\nabla\times\mathbf{a}) \tag{10–40}$$

[In Cartesian coordinates **only**, $\nabla^2\mathbf{a} = \hat{x}\nabla^2 a_x + \hat{y}\nabla^2 a_y + \hat{z}\nabla^2 a_z$]

$$\nabla\times(\mathbf{a}\times\mathbf{b}) = (\mathbf{b}\cdot\nabla)\mathbf{a} - (\mathbf{a}\cdot\nabla)\mathbf{b} + \mathbf{a}\nabla\cdot\mathbf{b} - \mathbf{b}\nabla\cdot\mathbf{a} \tag{10–41}$$

$$\nabla(\mathbf{a}\cdot\mathbf{b}) = (\mathbf{a}\cdot\nabla)\mathbf{b} + (\mathbf{b}\cdot\nabla)\mathbf{a} + \mathbf{a}\times(\nabla\times\mathbf{b}) + \mathbf{b}\times(\nabla\times\mathbf{a}) \tag{10–42}$$

$$\nabla f(\phi) = \frac{\mathrm{d}f}{\mathrm{d}\phi}\nabla\phi \tag{10–43}$$

$$\nabla^2 f(\phi) = \frac{\mathrm{d}f}{\mathrm{d}\phi}\nabla^2\phi + \frac{\mathrm{d}^2 f}{\mathrm{d}\phi^2}|\nabla\phi|^2 \tag{10–44}$$

$$\nabla^2(\phi\psi) = \phi\nabla^2\psi + 2\nabla\phi\cdot\nabla\psi + \psi\nabla^2\phi \tag{10–45}$$

Note the analogy of the last three relations to (8–1) and other elementary rules for ordinary functions.

In general, whenever an operator operates on a vector, care must be taken to evaluate its *effect on the coordinate basis vectors*. Only in rectangular coordinates are these ($\hat{x}$, $\hat{y}$, $\hat{z}$) independent of position.

Vector Integrals

If a vector is a function of a variable, t, then its integral is defined as three scalar integrals:

$$\int \mathbf{a}(t)\,\mathrm{d}t = \left(\int a_x(t)\,\mathrm{d}t,\ \int a_y(t)\,\mathrm{d}t,\ \int a_z(t)\,\mathrm{d}t\right) \tag{10–46}$$

Often a vector is a function of space-position; then integrals over volumes, surfaces, or curves are defined in obvious analogy to (10–46).

A special notation is useful for certain frequently occurring integrals in which particular components of the vector are to be integrated:

"Line integral":

$$\int_C \mathbf{a}\cdot\mathrm{d}\mathbf{s} \quad \text{means} \quad \int_C (\mathbf{a}\cdot\hat{\tau})\,\mathrm{d}s \qquad \text{(a number)}$$

where $\hat{\tau}$ is a unit vector parallel to the curve C and s is arc length along C.

"Surface integral":

$$\iint_S \mathbf{a}\cdot\mathrm{d}\boldsymbol{\sigma} \quad \text{means} \quad \iint_S \mathbf{a}\cdot\hat{n}\,\mathrm{d}\sigma \qquad \text{(a number)}$$

where $\hat{n}$ is a unit vector normal to the surface, S, and $\mathrm{d}\sigma$ is an element of area on S.

Integration-By-Parts for Vector Integrals

Gauss' theorem:

$$\boxed{\iiint_V (\nabla\cdot\mathbf{a})\,\mathrm{d}V = \iint_S \mathbf{a}\cdot\mathrm{d}\boldsymbol{\sigma}} \tag{10–47}$$

where the surface S is the boundary of the volume V and $d\boldsymbol{\sigma}$ points outward from V (and normal to S).

Stokes' theorem:

$$\boxed{\iint_S (\nabla \times \mathbf{a}) \cdot d\boldsymbol{\sigma} = \int_C \mathbf{a} \cdot d\mathbf{s}} \tag{10–48}$$

where the curve C is the border of the surface S and $d\mathbf{s}$ is tangent to C and points in the direction such that $(d\mathbf{s} \times d\boldsymbol{\sigma})$ points outward from S.

These two theorems also apply in any number of dimensions, with appropriate changes of notation and definitions. The volumes and surfaces must be simply-connected unless certain restrictions are placed on the spatial variation of $\mathbf{a}$. *Green's theorems* are special cases of these—especially (10–47) with $\mathbf{a} = \psi\nabla\phi - \phi\nabla\psi$.

[Proofs of (10–47) and (10–48) consist essentially in dividing the volume or surface into a large number of very small pieces and observing that the theorems hold (to first order) over each small piece, while the integrals over interior boundaries cancel.]

When these theorems are applied to very small V and S, the physical meanings of $\nabla \cdot \mathbf{a}$ and $\nabla \times \mathbf{a}$ respectively are brought out. Thus the "divergence", $\nabla \cdot \mathbf{a}$, measures the extent to which the vectors $\mathbf{a}(\mathbf{r})$ diverge from an elemental volume; if $\mathbf{a}$ is a net current per unit area, $(\nabla \cdot \mathbf{a})\, dV$ measures the *net* flow out of dV. The "curl", $\nabla \times \mathbf{a}$, has a less direct meaning but roughly indicates the extent to which the vectors, $\mathbf{a}(\mathbf{r})$ tend to form closed loops. The direction of $\nabla \times \mathbf{a}$ is perpendicular to such loops.

Some special consequences: By taking the scalar ("dot") product of various vectorial integrals with an *arbitrary, constant* vector, the above theorems yield many non-too-obvious results. Thus*

$$\iiint_V (\nabla \times \mathbf{a})\, dV = -\iint_S \mathbf{a} \times d\boldsymbol{\sigma} \tag{10–49}$$

$$\iiint_V (\nabla\phi)\, dV = \iint_S \phi\, d\boldsymbol{\sigma} \tag{10–50}$$

Any vector-function of position, which is defined throughout all space and which approaches zero like $1/r$ at large distances, r, from the origin, can be split into a sum of two vectors with, respectively, vanishing curl and vanishing divergence:

$$\left.\begin{aligned} &\mathbf{a}(\mathbf{r}) = \mathbf{c} + \mathbf{d}; \qquad \nabla \times \mathbf{c} = 0; \qquad \nabla \cdot \mathbf{d} = 0 \\ &\text{where} \\ &\mathbf{c}(\mathbf{r}) = -\nabla_r \iiint_{-\infty}^{\infty} \frac{\nabla_{r'} \cdot \mathbf{a}(\mathbf{r}')}{4\pi|\mathbf{r} - \mathbf{r}'|}\, dV' \\ &\mathbf{d}(\mathbf{r}) = \nabla_r \times \iiint_{-\infty}^{\infty} \frac{\nabla_{r'} \times \mathbf{a}(\mathbf{r}')}{4\pi|\mathbf{r} - \mathbf{r}'|}\, dV' \end{aligned}\right\} \tag{10–51}$$

---

* Proof of (10–49): $\mathbf{e} \cdot \iiint \nabla \times \mathbf{a}\, dV = \iiint \mathbf{e} \cdot \nabla \times \mathbf{a}\, dV = \iiint (\mathbf{e} \times \nabla) \cdot \mathbf{a}\, dV = -\iiint \nabla \times \mathbf{e} \cdot \mathbf{a}\, dV = -\iiint \nabla \cdot (\mathbf{e} \times \mathbf{a})\, dV = -\iint \mathbf{e} \times \mathbf{a} \cdot d\boldsymbol{\sigma} = -\mathbf{e} \cdot \iint \mathbf{a} \times d\boldsymbol{\sigma}$ in the first and last expressions, $\mathbf{e}$, may be canceled since it is arbitrary (as well as constant).

These are called "Helmholtz integrals". (Proof: Apply Gauss' theorem to the region, $\epsilon \leqslant |\mathbf{r} - \mathbf{r}'| \leqslant D$, and let $D \to \infty$ and $\epsilon \to 0$.) If finite regions are considered, the resolution of $\mathbf{a}$ is still possible but the formulas become rather complicated and involve boundary integrals as well.

In particular (10–51) is an explicit formula for:

—ϕ if $\nabla^2\phi$ is known over *all* space

—$\mathbf{a}$ if $\nabla \times \mathbf{a}$ and $\nabla \cdot \mathbf{a}$ are known over all space.

Note also that

—$\nabla \cdot \mathbf{a} = 0 = \nabla \times \mathbf{a}$ if (and only if) $\mathbf{a} = \nabla\phi$ where $\nabla^2\phi = 0$.

Curvilinear Coordinates

All vector relations are "geometric" or "physical" relations which are independent of any coordinate systems (even though Cartesian coordinates are a help in establishing theorems). Herein lies their power and their conciseness.

Yet for specific problems vector relations must usually be broken down into their three numerical relations. In the commonly used coordinates (cylindrical, spherical, ellipsoidal—and in general any with orthogonal coordinate surfaces), geometric intuition is usually reliable for ordinary vectors, but expression with "∇" are less easily expressed in their components. The use of Gauss' or Stokes' theorems, applied to small volumes bounded by coordinate surfaces, is then the simplest guide—short of consulting standard mathematical handbooks.

(The general theory of arbitrary coordinate transformations—especially non-orthogonal coordinates—constitutes tensor analysis.)

Linear, Non-orthogonal Coordinates

Such coordinates are sometimes convenient in the theory of crystals (and form a basis for the concepts behind the general tensor analysis).

If we choose three vectors $\mathbf{u}_i$ which are not orthogonal, we can still expand an arbitrary vector in terms of them,

$$\mathbf{a} = \sum_n a_n \mathbf{u}_n$$

but $a_j \neq \mathbf{a} \cdot \mathbf{u}_j$ and moreover $\mathbf{a} \cdot \mathbf{b} \neq \sum a_k b_k$. The advantage of any such coordinates would appear to have been lost. However, if we define "reciprocal coordinates",

$$\mathbf{v}_1 = \frac{\mathbf{u}_2 \times \mathbf{u}_3}{\mathbf{u}_1 \cdot \mathbf{u}_2 \times \mathbf{u}_3}, \quad \mathbf{v}_2 = \frac{\mathbf{u}_3 \times \mathbf{u}_1}{\mathbf{u}_1 \cdot \mathbf{u}_2 \times \mathbf{u}_3}, \quad \mathbf{v}_3 = \frac{\mathbf{u}_1 \times \mathbf{u}_2}{\mathbf{u}_1 \cdot \mathbf{u}_2 \times \mathbf{u}_3} \tag{10–52}$$

then

$$\boxed{\mathbf{u}_i \cdot \mathbf{v}_j = \delta_{ij}} \tag{10–53}$$

and

$$\left.\begin{aligned} \mathbf{a} &= \sum_i a_i \mathbf{u}_i = \sum a_j^{\dagger} \mathbf{v}_j \\ a_i &= \mathbf{a} \cdot \mathbf{v}_i; \qquad a_j^{\dagger} = \mathbf{a} \cdot \mathbf{u}_j \\ \mathbf{a} \cdot \mathbf{b} &= \sum_i a_i b_i^{\dagger} = \sum a_i^{\dagger} b_i \end{aligned}\right\} \tag{10–54}$$

Thus *in non-orthogonal coordinates*, it is still possible to speak of the "components" of a vector provided we *introduce two types of components*, a_i and $a_i^{\dagger}$. These may be used interchangeably to describe the vector, $\mathbf{a}$, (either set determines the other) but in scalar products the two kinds must always be "mixed", one type for one vector and the other for the other; in vector addition, however, the two types must never be mixed. This is an essential, unavoidable complication, entailed by using non-orthogonal basis vectors. (But it may be more than compensated if the physical symmetry of a problem is thereby preserved.)

Tensors (Dyadics)

Tensor concepts in full generality are best handled by index-notation, but one simple case (dyadics), adequate for most of classical physics, is often expressed in an extension of vector notation.

Definition

A three-dimensional, second-order *tensor* (dyadic) $\mathfrak{T}$ is a set of *nine components* (numbers), T_{ij}, such that either of the "scalar products":

$$\sum_i a_i T_{ij} = b_j \qquad (\text{written } \mathbf{a} \cdot \mathfrak{T} = \mathbf{b}) \tag{10–55}$$

$$\sum_j T_{ij} c_j = d_i \qquad (\text{written } \mathfrak{T} \cdot \mathbf{c} = \mathbf{d}) \tag{10–56}$$

is a *vector*.

[From some abstract points of view—"vector = set of three numbers"—, this definition would say only that $\mathfrak{T}$ is a set of nine numbers. From a geometric or physical point of view, however, a vector has a "geometric reality"—which is formally expressed by the way in which its components change when the coordinate system is changed. In this sense, the definition of $\mathfrak{T}$ *implies* a corresponding "geometric reality" for $\mathfrak{T}$—namely that its components, T_{ij}, transform as do products of a pair of vector components, $a_i b_j$.]

EXAMPLE: The flux (current) of a numerical density, ρ, is the vector, $\rho\mathbf{v}$, where $\mathbf{v}$ is the local "fluid" velocity; the flux of a *vector* quantity $\mathbf{a}$ (momentum density, $\rho\mathbf{v}$, for example) is a tensor, $\mathfrak{T} = \mathbf{av}$ or $T_{ij} = a_i v_j$; the vector (T_{xx}, T_{xy}, T_{xz}) thereby becomes the flux of the number, a_x. Similarly, the three gradients, ∇a_x, ∇a_y, ∇a_z, of the components of a vector $\mathbf{a}$ can be assembled to a tensor, $\nabla\mathbf{a}$.

Further Notations:

$$\mathbf{ab} \text{ for the tensor } a_i b_j \tag{10–57}$$

$$\mathfrak{T} \cdot \mathfrak{S} \text{ for the tensor } \sum_k T_{ik} S_{kj} \tag{10–58}$$

$$(\mathfrak{T} \cdot \mathfrak{S} \neq \mathfrak{S} \cdot \mathfrak{T})$$

$$\mathfrak{T} : \mathfrak{S} = \mathfrak{S} : \mathfrak{T} \text{ for the } \textit{number} \sum_i \sum_k T_{ik} S_{ki} \tag{10–59}$$

$$\nabla \cdot \mathfrak{T} \text{ for the vector } \sum_i \frac{\partial T_{ik}}{\partial x_i} \tag{10–60}$$

$$\text{Trace } (\mathfrak{T}) \text{ for the number } \sum_i T_{ii} \tag{10–61}$$

These notations lose their value when the order of writing can no longer make clear the summations (dot products) which are intended. Index notation is then clearer. Some "theorems":

$$T_{ij} = \hat{\imath} \cdot \mathfrak{T} \cdot \hat{\jmath} \qquad (T_{xy} = \hat{x} \cdot \mathfrak{T} \cdot \hat{y}) \tag{10–62}$$

A (3-dimensional, 2nd-order) tensor can always be written (in many ways) in the form:

$$\mathfrak{T} = \mathbf{ab} + \mathbf{cd} + \mathbf{ef} \tag{10–63}$$

Indeed, if $\mathfrak{T} \cdot \hat{x} = \mathbf{a}$, $\mathfrak{T} \cdot \hat{y} = \mathbf{b}$, $\mathfrak{T} \cdot \hat{z} = \mathbf{c}$, then $\mathfrak{T} = \mathbf{a}\hat{x} + \mathbf{b}\hat{y} + \mathbf{c}\hat{z}$; similarly, if $\hat{x} \cdot \mathfrak{T} = \boldsymbol{\alpha}$ etc., then $\mathfrak{T} = \hat{x}\boldsymbol{\alpha} + \hat{y}\boldsymbol{\beta} + \hat{z}\boldsymbol{\gamma}$.

The determinant (formed from the components) of $\mathfrak{T}$ can be written, with arbitrary **a**, **b**, **c**:

$$|\mathfrak{T}| = \frac{(\mathfrak{T} \cdot \mathbf{a}) \cdot (\mathfrak{T} \cdot \mathbf{b}) \times (\mathfrak{T} \cdot \mathbf{c})}{\mathbf{a} \cdot \mathbf{b} \times \mathbf{c}} \tag{10–64}$$

The tensor, $\mathfrak{T} = \mathbf{ab} - \mathbf{ba}$, is connected with the vector product, $\mathbf{c} = \mathbf{a} \times \mathbf{b}$ as follows,

$$c_x = T_{yz} = -T_{zy}; \quad c_y = T_{zx} = -T_{xz}; \quad c_z = T_{xy} = -T_{yx} \tag{10–65}$$

In "spaces" of dimension different from three, **c** has no analogue, but $\mathfrak{T}$ can always be defined.

Gauss' theorem:

$$\iiint\limits_V (\nabla \cdot \mathfrak{T})\, dV = \iint\limits_S d\boldsymbol{\sigma} \cdot \mathfrak{T} \tag{10–66}$$

(note the order). This is readily proved from the vector theorem by considering $\mathbf{f} = \mathfrak{T} \cdot \mathbf{a}$ where **a** is an *arbitrary* constant vector.

A Note on Converting to Index Notation

The vector product, $\mathbf{a} \times \mathbf{b}$, and the curl, $\nabla \times \mathbf{f}$, are concepts peculiar to three-dimensional space: Thus the ith component of $\mathbf{a} \times \mathbf{b}$ is $a_j b_k - a_k b_j$ *where* $i \neq j \neq k \neq i$. This concept is most readily adapted to index notation by introducing the quantities, e^{ijk}, defined by

$$e^{ijk} = \begin{cases} 0, \text{ unless } i, j, k \text{ are all different} \\ 1, \text{ if } (i, j, k) \text{ is an even permutation of } (1, 2, 3) \\ -1, \text{ if } (i, j, k) \text{ is an odd permutation of } (1, 2, 3) \end{cases}$$

Then $\mathbf{c} = \mathbf{a} \times \mathbf{b}$ becomes

$$c_i = \sum_{j,k} e^{ijk} a_j b_k \tag{10–67}$$

and $\mathbf{u} = \nabla \times \mathbf{f}$ becomes

$$u_i = \sum_{jk} e^{ijk} \frac{\partial}{\partial x_j} f_k \tag{10–68}$$

N-Dimensional "Spaces"

Throughout this chapter, we spoke of real, three-dimensional space. In many problems, more than three independent variables enter (for example x, y, z *and* time, t). It is then often expedient to generalize the three-space concepts, **by analogy**.

Thus, a set of n numbers, $(a_1, a_2, a_3, \cdots, a_n)$, can be called a "vector in n-space". The phrase, "sphere in 4-space", can be used to denote the relation, $x^2 + y^2 + z^2 + t^2 = R^2$, where R may be called the "radius" of the "sphere". The scalar product of two "vectors" can be defined as $\mathbf{a} \cdot \mathbf{b} = a_1 b_1 + a_2 b_2 + \cdots + a_n b_n$, and so on and on and on. (The vector-product, however, has no direct analogue and is not defined.)

The entire concept does **not** presume that the reader can **visualize** such "spaces". The geometric terminology is used only as an *analogy* for two reasons: Concepts can be introduced without lengthy, distracting definitions. The terminology often reliably *suggests* relations and theorems not otherwise easily suspected—nor easily remembered.

CHAPTER 11

DETERMINANTS AND MATRICES

THE theory of linear equations in several variables can be based on the special case where the number of variables equals the number of equations,

$$\sum_{j=1}^{n} \alpha_{ij} x_j = b_i \qquad \text{where} \qquad i = 1, 2, \cdots, n \tag{11-1}$$

A decisive role in the theory is played by a certain function of the coefficients, α_{ij}. This function, defined in (11–3) below, is called the "determinant" and is usually written (in full) as a square array between two vertical bars; α_{IJ} is placed in the Ith row of the array and the Jth column (as the α's would appear when (11–1) is written out in full as n separate equations). This row-column ("RC") notation, α_{IJ}, is now standard and virtually universal. The *array itself* is called a *matrix* and is often denoted by a single letter such as α; the determinant is then denoted by $|\alpha|$ or Det (α).

Summation Convention

In any one (product) term, if an index (j) is repeated, the symbol, $\sum_j$, is understood before that term. The range of this sum is the full range of possible values for j. In short, *repeated indices are understood to be summed over all possible values.* (Thus in (11–1) the summation sign would be omitted.)

We shall occasionally insert the "$\sum$" symbol to emphasize the presence of such repeated indices, but it is strictly unnecessary.

If an expression of this type contains a repeated index which is *not to be summed, a capital letter is used* for that index.

Kronecker delta:

$$\delta_{ij} = \begin{cases} 1, & \text{if} \quad i = j \\ 0, & \text{if} \quad i \neq j \end{cases} \tag{11-2}$$

This symbol acts as a "substitution operator" in summed expressions:

$$\delta_{ij} a_j = a_i; \qquad b_i \delta_{ij} a_j = b_i a_i = \text{“}\mathbf{b} \cdot \mathbf{a}\text{”}.$$

Definition of a Determinant

(For actual computation, other methods are more efficient; see below.)

$$\text{Det}\,(\alpha_{ij}) = |\alpha_{ij}| = |\alpha| = \sum e^{i_1 i_2 \cdots i_n} \alpha_{1i_1} \alpha_{2i_2} \cdots \alpha_{ni_n} \tag{11-3}$$

where

$$e^{i_1 i_2 \cdots i_n} = \begin{Bmatrix} 0, \text{ unless } i_1, \cdots, i_n \text{ are all different} \\ +1, \text{ if } (i_1, \cdots, i_n) \text{ is an } \textit{even} \text{ permutation of } (1, 2, \cdots, n) \\ -1, \text{ if } (i_1, \cdots, i_n) \text{ is an } \textit{odd} \text{ permutation of } (1, 2, \cdots, n) \end{Bmatrix} \tag{11-4}$$

Properties of the $e^{i_1 \cdots i_n}$ symbol which follow directly from (11–4) are,

$$\sum e^{i_1 \cdots i_n} \quad e^{i_1 \cdots i_n} = n! \tag{11-5}$$

$$\frac{1}{(n-1)!} \sum e^{I i_2 \cdots i_n} e^{J i_2 \cdots i_n} = \delta_{IJ} = \begin{cases} 0 & \text{if} \quad I \neq J \\ 1 & \text{if} \quad I = J \end{cases} \tag{11-6}$$

Also from (11–4),

$$|\alpha| e^{i_1 \cdots i_n} = \sum e^{j_1 \cdots j_n} \alpha_{i_1 j_1} \alpha_{i_2 j_2} \cdots \alpha_{i_n j_n} \tag{11–7}$$

and thus from (11–5)

$$|\alpha|(n!) = \sum e^{i_1 \cdots i_n} e^{j_1 \cdots j_n} \alpha_{j_1 i_1} \alpha_{j_2 i_2} \cdots \alpha_{j_n i_n} \tag{11–8}$$

From the definitions (11–3) or (11–8), it readily follows that:

A determinant is unchanged in value by reflection in its diagonal (interchanging α_{ij} with α_{ji}; "transposing" the matrix).

A determinant vanishes when:

1. all elements of a row (or of a column) vanish
2. one row (or column) is a common multiple of another row (or column respectively)
3. any row (or column) is a sum of multiples of other rows (or columns respectively).

A determinant is unchanged in value by adding a multiple of a row (or column) to another row (or column respectively)

Interchange of two rows or columns changes only the sign of a determinant.

Multiplying a row (or column) through by c multiplies the determinant by c. (Multiplying all elements by c multiplies the determinant by c^n.)

Differentiation

From (11–3), if $\alpha_{ij} = \alpha_{ij}(x)$, then $(\mathrm{d}/\mathrm{d}x)|\alpha|$ = the sum of (n) determinants of which the Ith contains $\mathrm{d}\alpha_{Ij}/\mathrm{d}x$ in its Ith row (and α's elsewhere) = the analogous sum by columns.

Practical Calculation of Determinants

For small determinants, the following is easy to remember and quite efficient. The object is to reduce the determinant to triangular form by operations which do not change its value:

1st Step: From the Rth row $(R > 1)$, subtract multiples of the first row so as to make all of the first column, except α_{11}, vanish.

Jth Step: Subtract multiples of the Jth row from the rows below it so as to leave zeros in the Jth column below the diagonal.

In this way, all elements below the diagonal are made to vanish; the determinant is then just the product of the elements on the diagonal:

$$\mathrm{Det}\,(\alpha) = \mathrm{Det}\,(\beta) = \prod_I \beta_{II}$$

A systematic, abbreviated version of this method is given in (11–26) and (11–27) below.

Cofactors

Cofactors are defined as $(-1)^{I+J}$ times* the determinant obtained by striking out the row and column containing α_{IJ}. These cofactors are here denoted by A_{JI} (note the inverted order of the indices†). From (11–8), we see that they may also be defined by,

$$(n-1)!A_{JI} = \sum e^{Ii_2 \cdots i_n} e^{Jj_2 \cdots j_n} \alpha_{i_2 j_2} \alpha_{i_3 j_3} \cdots \alpha_{i_n j_n} \tag{11–9}$$

This is also the coefficient of α_{IJ} in the expansion of $|\alpha|$ itself.

---

* The signs, $(-1)^{I+J}$, form a checkerboard pattern in the array.

† Often, however, A_{jk} is used to denote the cofactor of α_{jk}.

From (11–6), (11–7) and (11–9) follows the fundamental relation ("development of $|\alpha|$ by elements of the Kth row or Ith column"):

$$\boxed{\sum \alpha_{Kj}A_{jI} = \delta_{IK}\,|\alpha| = \sum A_{Il}\alpha_{lK}} \tag{11–10}$$

which holds for *any* square array (matrix). (Cramer's rule.) The matrix A_{ji} is called the "*adjoint*" of α.

Solution of (11-1)

From (11–10) a solution of (11–1) is, if $|\alpha| \neq 0$

$$x_j = |\alpha|^{-1} \Sigma\, A_{jk} b_k \tag{11–11}$$

(not useful for actual computation if $n \geqslant 4$, about). A simple proof that this solution is *unique* is given later (just preceding (11–21)). In particular, if all $b_i = 0$ in (11–1), the only solution is: all $x_j = 0$.

Further theory, for the case $|\alpha| = 0$, is simplest in matrix notation.

Multiplication of Determinants

The (matrix) product of two arrays is defined by

$$\sigma_{ij} = \Sigma\, \alpha_{ik}\beta_{kj} \tag{11–12}$$

Substituting this in the definition (11–3) and using (11–7),

$$|\sigma| = |\alpha| \cdot |\beta| \tag{11–13}$$

That is, the determinant of a matrix product equals the product of the determinants of the factors; determinants multiply together by the rule (11–12).

Matrices

A matrix has already been defined as an *array* of numbers, α_{ij}, where the "element" α_{ij} appears in the ith row and the jth column. We now allow the number of rows to differ from the number of columns. Thus in (11–1), x_i and b_j can be regarded as matrices with a single column. (Non-square matrices have no determinants; none is defined.)

We use small Greek letters $\alpha, \beta, \gamma, \cdots$ to denote matrices in general. Two special matrices, however, are denoted by 0 and I:

$$I_{ij} = \delta_{ij} = \begin{cases} 0 & \text{if} \quad i \neq j \\ 1 & \text{if} \quad i = j \end{cases} \tag{11–14}$$

$$0_{ij} = 0 \qquad \text{(all elements are zero)}$$

"I" is the matrix analogue of "1" and "0" the analogue of zero; indeed, directly from (11–14),

$$\alpha I = I\alpha = \alpha; \qquad 0 + \alpha = \alpha + 0 = \alpha$$

Algebra of Matrices

For purely ad hoc reasons, operations on matrices are defined as follows to yield new *arrays* of numbers.

Addition:

$$\alpha + \beta = \sigma \qquad \text{means} \qquad \alpha_{ij} + \beta_{ij} = \sigma_{ij} \tag{11–15}$$

that is, add the elements in corresponding "boxes"; α and β must have the same "shape". (However, a common convention with square matrices is to write $a + \alpha$ when $aI + \alpha$ is intended.)

Multiplication by a number:

$$\alpha = k\beta \qquad \text{means} \qquad \alpha_{ij} = k\beta_{ij} \tag{11–16}$$

that is, multiply all elements by the number, k.

Multiplication of matrices:

$$\gamma = \alpha\beta \qquad \text{means} \qquad \gamma_{ij} = \sum \alpha_{ik}\beta_{kj} \tag{11–17}$$

(note the position of the repeated index). The number of rows in β must equal the number of columns in α; otherwise, multiplication is undefined. In terms of the arrays as they appear when written out: To find γ_{ij}, take the "scalar product" (the sum of the products of successive corresponding elements) of the ith row of α and the jth column of β. Schematically:

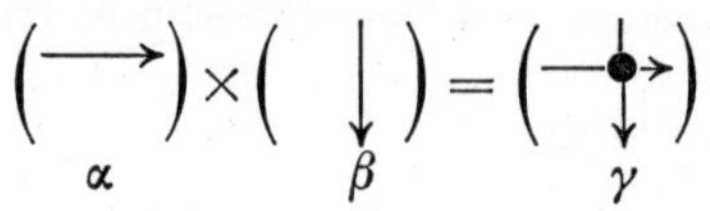

Differentiation:

$$\gamma = \frac{\mathrm{d}}{\mathrm{d}t}\alpha \qquad \text{means} \qquad \gamma_{ij} = \frac{\mathrm{d}}{\mathrm{d}t}\alpha_{ij} \tag{11–18}$$

that is, differentiate each element. Similarly for integration.

It is readily verified that, *except for*:

$$\alpha\beta \neq \beta\alpha, \tag{11–19}$$

all the ordinary rules of algebra hold also for matrices with these definitions. (There is no "division," and "I" acts like "1".) One need only *guard against rearranging the factors in a product.*

Inverse of a Matrix

It is *sometimes* possible to introduce division, of a sort, for square matrices (only). *If* there exists an array, "α^{-1}" with the property,

$$\alpha\alpha^{-1} = I \tag{11–20}$$

then α^{-1} is called the inverse of α and we also have $(\alpha^{-1})\alpha = I$ (see (11–10)). [A simple example of a matrix with no inverse is the "projection operator", defined by $P\mathbf{a} = (\mathbf{a} \cdot \mathbf{b})\mathbf{b}$, or $P_{ik} = b_i b_k$; it is geometrically obvious that a projection of a vector on $\mathbf{b}$ does not specify the original vector.]

From (11–10) and (11–13) we find:

A (square) matrix, α, has an inverse if and only if $|\alpha| \neq 0$, and an explicit (though not the most useful) formula for it is given by (11–10).

If an inverse exists, it is unique (Proof: Let α^{-1} denote the inverse given by (11–10); then if $\alpha\beta = I$: $\beta = I\beta = \alpha^{-1}\alpha\beta = \alpha^{-1}$ and similarly if $\beta\alpha = I$.)

Differentiating (11–20), we obtain the useful result,

$$\frac{\mathrm{d}}{\mathrm{d}t}(\alpha^{-1}) = -\alpha^{-1}\frac{\mathrm{d}\alpha}{\mathrm{d}t}\alpha^{-1} \tag{11–21}$$

Powers of a (square) matrix may now be defined by $\alpha^2 = \alpha\alpha$ etc., and $\alpha^{-2} = \alpha^{-1}\alpha^{-1}$ etc., where all the usual rules hold by virtue of $\alpha\alpha^{-1} = \alpha^{-1}\alpha$.

Note that

$$(\alpha\beta)^{-1} = \beta^{-1}\alpha^{-1} \tag{11–22}$$

Sub-Matrices

Mentally "partition" a matrix into an array of smaller matrices. One can regard the full compound array as a "supermatrix"—a matrix whose *elements* themselves are matrices (not necessarily square nor all of the same shape).

It is easily checked that the algebraic operations all remain unaltered in the sense that the definitions, (11–15)–(11–18), are now to be interpreted as (sub-)*matrix* addition and multiplication. That is, these interpretations lead to the same result as the original interpretation. (For example, $\sum_{j=1}^{n} \alpha_{ij}\beta_{jk} = \sum_{j=1}^{J} \alpha_{ij}\beta_{jk} + \sum_{l=J}^{n} \alpha_{il}\beta_{lk}$ and this is true for $1 \leqslant i \leqslant I$ and also for $I \leqslant i \leqslant n$, etc., etc.)

"Rank" of a Matrix

If a "*minor*" of α denotes the determinant of (any square) sub-matrix obtained by deleting any set of rows and columns, then the "*rank*" of α (or of $|\alpha|$) is defined as the *dimension* (number of rows or columns) *of the largest non-vanishing minor.*

LEMMA:

The rank of a (matrix) product, (11–12), is no greater than the rank of either factor. (Proof: (11–3) shows that any k-dimensional minor of σ can be expressed as a sum of k-dimensional minors of (say) β, each multiplied by a polynomial in the elements of α.)

THEOREM:

If the (partitioned) matrix, $\begin{array}{c|c} \epsilon & \beta \\ \hline \gamma & \delta \end{array}$, where the minor $|\epsilon|$ has dimension r, has rank r and if $|\epsilon| \neq 0$, then:

$$\delta = \gamma(\epsilon^{-1})\beta \tag{11–23}$$

PROOF:

Since $|\epsilon| \neq 0$, we can define an array:

$$\begin{Vmatrix} I & 0 \\ -\gamma\epsilon^{-1} & I \end{Vmatrix} \cdot \begin{Vmatrix} \epsilon & \beta \\ \gamma & \delta \end{Vmatrix} \cdot \begin{Vmatrix} I & -\epsilon^{-1}\beta \\ 0 & I \end{Vmatrix} = \begin{Vmatrix} \epsilon & 0 \\ 0 & (\delta - \gamma\epsilon^{-1}\beta) \end{Vmatrix}$$

which, by the lemma, has rank at most r. But since $|\epsilon| \neq 0$, the rank is at least r, and thus is precisely r. Therefore, every element of $\delta - \gamma\epsilon^{-1}\beta$ must vanish.

(Note that the matrices β and γ are in general not square and thus need have no determinants.)

Solution of (11-1) when $|\alpha| = 0$:

Let the rank of α be $r > 0$ (if $r = 0$, then $\alpha = 0$ and the situation is obvious). If necessary, renumber the (column matrices) x_j and b_i so that the upper left corner of α contains an r-by-r submatrix, ϵ, with $|\epsilon| \neq 0$. Then "partition" x and b similarly:

$$x = \begin{pmatrix} y \\ z \end{pmatrix} \quad \text{and} \quad b = \begin{pmatrix} c \\ d \end{pmatrix}$$

where y and c each have r members. Then:

$$\begin{Vmatrix} \epsilon & \beta \\ \gamma & \delta \end{Vmatrix} \cdot \begin{pmatrix} y \\ z \end{pmatrix} = \begin{pmatrix} c \\ d \end{pmatrix}$$

where, by the theorem, $\delta = \gamma\epsilon^{-1}\beta$.

The above reads, more explicitly,

$$\epsilon y + \beta z = c$$

$$\gamma y + \delta z = d$$

From the first equation, $y = \epsilon^{-1}c - \epsilon^{-1}\beta z$ and hence $\gamma y = \gamma\epsilon^{-1}c - \gamma\epsilon^{-1}\beta z = \gamma\epsilon^{-1}c - \delta z$ but this is not, in general consistent with the second relation. Hence, the equations are inconsistent unless

$$d = \gamma\epsilon^{-1}c$$

If this condition is satisfied, then

$$x = \begin{pmatrix} \epsilon^{-1}c \\ 0 \end{pmatrix}$$

is one solution and we may obtain other solutions by adding to it any solution of $\alpha x = 0$, that is, any $\begin{pmatrix} y \\ z \end{pmatrix}$ with $y = -\epsilon^{-1}\beta z$. Since z has $(n - r)$ members, these extra solutions have $(n - r)$ parameters. That is to say, $(n - r)$ such solutions can be taken as basic and all others expressed (linearly) in terms of them:

There are $(n - r)$ linearly-independent solutions if the consistency condition, $d = \gamma\epsilon^{-1}c$, is fulfilled; otherwise there are none.

More or Fewer Variables Than Equations

This case may be treated by "extending" α by adding additional rows or columns, consisting entirely of zeros, as required to obtain a square matrix, α'. If the number of variables is greater than the number of equations, the previous theory can be applied directly (additional b_i, also zeros, are added). In particular, if the rank of α' is n, the consistency conditions are always satisfied and the number of linearly independent solutions equals the number of variables minus the number of equations plus one.

If there are more equations than variables, then additional "dummy" variables x_j must be adjoined; since the corresponding elements of α' are all zero, these dummy variables play no role in the final solutions but merely serve to make the earlier theory applicable. If the rank of α' is equal to the number of original variables, and if the consistency conditions are satisfied, there are many "extended solutions" but these all have the same values for the original variables, and the original equations have a unique solution.

Practical Calculation of Inverse Matrices

For matrices of low order, Cramer's rule, (11–10), may be used. In particular:

To invert a *two-by-two* matrix: Interchange the diagonal elements, change the signs of the off-diagonal elements, and divide the array by its determinant.

When n is greater than about 3 or 4, (11–10) rapidly becomes exceedingly tedious and the following abbreviated, systematic method (based on reduction to triangular form*) is about the most efficient.

Crout's Method of Matrix Inversion

The solution of

$$\sum_{c=1}^{n} A_{rc}x_c = A_{r,n+1} \tag{11–24}$$

is†

$$x_r = B_{r,n+1} - \sum_{k=r+1}^{n} B_{rk}x_k \tag{11–25}$$

also

$$\text{Det}\,(A_{rc}) = \prod_i B_{ii} \tag{11–26}$$

where†

$$B_{rc} = \begin{cases} A_{rc} - \sum_{k=1}^{c-1} B_{rk}B_{kc}, \text{ below and on the diagonal } (r \geqslant c) \\ \dfrac{1}{B_{rr}}\left[A_{rc} - \sum_{k=1}^{r-1} B_{rk}B_{kc}\right], \text{ above the diagonal } (r < c) \end{cases} \tag{11–27}$$

If A is symmetric, the second half can be replaced by

$$B_{rc} = \frac{B_{cr}}{B_{rr}}, \text{ above the diagonal if } A_{kl} = A_{lk} \tag{11–28}$$

(except when $c = n + 1$). By (11–26) division by zero will occur only if the matrix A is singular.

Note that the B's can each be generated (recursively, row by row, left to right) in one operation on a standard desk computer. The summation limits in (11–27) are then "automatic" in the sense that terms beyond the proper limits have not yet been computed. Similarly, the x_i are found from (11–25) by working backwards from $x_n = B_{n,n+1}$ and the limits again are "automatic". In practical computation, it is wise to arrange the B matrix below the A matrix and make up paper strips (for each B row) which carry the B_{rk} factors of (11–27) aligned (in column form) with the corresponding B_{kc}. Similarly, a row-strip carrying the x_i is useful both in computing the x's and in checking by substitution back into (11–24). Note that the $A_{r,n+1}$ column is carried along as part of the A matrix and generates a corresponding "extra" column of B. Additional extra columns may be added if several sets of equations with the same A matrix are to be solved; these may be treated by "blind use" of (11–27) with no consideration of whether or not a column is an "extra".

---

* Specifically, in the notation of (11–27) below, define the "lower triangular" and "upper triangular" matrices:

$$L_{rc} = \begin{cases} B_{rc}, & \text{if } r \geqslant c \\ 0, & \text{if } r < c \end{cases} \qquad U_{rc} = \begin{cases} 0, & \text{if } r > c \\ 1, & \text{if } r = c \\ B_{rc}, & \text{if } r < c \end{cases}$$

Then: $A = LU$ and $A^{-1} = U^{-1}L^{-1}$

† A sum with lower limit greater than the upper limit is a zero. Thus, $x_n = B_{n,n+1}$ and the first column of B is identical with the first column of A; the first row of B (beyond B_{11}) is the first row of A divided by A_{11}.

Continuous check: It is strongly recommended that a check column be adjoined. In the A matrix it is a column of row-sums, $A_{rC} = \sum_j A_{rj}$, and is treated as a part of A to generate a corresponding column, B_{rC}, of B. Then the check relation,

$$B_{rC} = 1 + \sum_{c>r} B_{rc} \tag{11–29}$$

may be applied after each row of B is computed. In this manner, errors can be caught quickly and localized.

The inverse of A can be found by adjoining the entire unit matrix, I, as n "extra" columns of A. The n sets of solutions, $x_i^{(n)}$, then form (as columns) the inverse, A^{-1}.

If A is symmetric (as can sometimes be achieved by changing variables etc.) the labor of finding A^{-1} is reduced by about a factor of four by using (11–28) and:

$$\left.\begin{aligned} (A^{-1})_{sl} = (A^{-1})_{ls} = \frac{\delta_{ls}}{B_{ss}} - \sum_{j=s+1}^{n} B_{sj}(A^{-1})_{lj} \\ \textit{provided } l \geqslant s \quad \text{and} \quad A_{pq} = A_{qp} \end{aligned}\right\} \tag{11–30}$$

from which A^{-1} can be obtained by working backwards from the element, $(A^{-1})_{nn}$, (row by row from right to left and bottom to top). Check: $\sum_j (A^{-1})_{rj} A_{jC} = 1$ where A_{rC} are the row-sums of A.

Biorthogonalization

If the rows of A are regarded as vectors, u_i, the columns of A^{-1} form a set of vectors, v_i, which are biorthogonal to the u_i. Consequently [M. R. Hestenes, *Jour. Soc. Ind. Appl. Math.*, **6**, 51 (1958)], the algorithm following (18–38) of Chapter 18 can be used to compute the inverse of a matrix. Although this method involves at least 50% more computation than Crout's method, it has the advantage that, if round-off errors are serious, the algorithm can be repeated (using the results of the first application as a starting point for the second) to improve the accuracy. (Two applications almost always suffice.) In the notation of Chapter 18, we also have (if $v_i^{(0)} = u_i$)

$$(\text{Det } A)^2 = \prod_{k=1}^{n} (u_k, v_k^{(k-1)})$$

so that division-by-zero indicates that A is singular. Moreover, when this occurs, the complex conjugate of the corresponding $v_k^{(k-1)}$ is a solution of $Ax = 0$.

Iterative Methods

Automatic machines compute rapidly but their storage may be limited. In such cases, iteration may be the most efficient method of solving $Ax = b$. Each cycle replaces an approximate set of x_i by

$$x_i' = x_i + C_i\{b_i - \sum_{j=1}^{i-1} A_{ij}x_j' - \sum_{j=i}^{n} A_{ij}x_j\}$$

where, if A is Hermitian and positive definite, it can be proved that the method converges if and only if the C_i are chosen in the range, $0 < C_i < 2/A_{ii}$. The best values of the C_i usually lie near $2/A_{ii}$. [More generally: If L is the lower triangle of A omitting the diagonal, if U is the upper triangle including the diagonal of A, and if D is a diagonal matrix with elements $1/C_i$, the method is equivalent to $(L + D)x' = (D - U)x + b$ and (therefore) converges if and only if all roots y_j of Det $[yL + U + (y - 1)D] = 0$ have complex magnitudes less than unity.]

Manifestly, the C_i could in principle be chosen to give the correct answers in one cycle, but the problem in practice is to achieve even reasonably rapid convergence; it is usually wise to provide for altering the C_i.

Operation and Storage Counts

Method and Problem	Additions	Multiplications*	Divisions*	Minimum Storage
Crout, $Ax = b$	$\frac{n}{6}(n-1)(2n+5)$ each		$\frac{1}{2}n(n+1)$	$n(n+1)$
Crout, A^{-1}	$\frac{n}{6}(n-1)(8n-1)$ each		$\frac{1}{2}n(3n-1)$	$2n^2$
Crout, A^{-1} sym. A	$\frac{n}{6}(n-1)(2n-1)$	$\frac{n}{3}(n^2-1)$	$\frac{1}{2}n(n+1)$	$\frac{1}{2}n(n+1)$
Biorthog. A^{-1}	$2n^2(n-1)$	$2n^3 - n^2$	n^2	$2n^2$
Iteration $Ax = b$ *per cycle*	$\{n(n+1)\}$	$\{n(n+1)\}$	$\{0\}$	Data + n

Terminology

The following concepts will be especially useful in later chapters. They apply to non-square as well as square matrices.

Transpose:

$$\alpha^{tr} \qquad \text{definition:} \qquad (\alpha^{tr})_{ij} = \alpha_{ji} \tag{11-31}$$

that is, reflect all the elements in the diagonal,

Conjugate:

$$\alpha^* \qquad \text{definition:} \qquad (\alpha^*)_{ij} = (\alpha_{ij})^* \tag{11-32}$$

that is, take the complex conjugate of each element.

Hermitian Conjugate:

$$\alpha^\dagger \qquad \text{definition:} \qquad \alpha^\dagger = \alpha^{tr*} \tag{11-33}$$

that is, reflect and take conjugates.

Properties:

$$(\alpha\beta)^{tr} = \beta^{tr}\alpha^{tr}; \qquad (\alpha\beta)^\dagger = \beta^\dagger\alpha^\dagger; \qquad \textit{but} \qquad (\alpha\beta)^* = \alpha^*\beta^* \tag{11-34}$$

$$(\alpha^{-1})^{tr} = (\alpha^{tr})^{-1}; \qquad (\alpha^{-1})^\dagger = (\alpha^\dagger)^{-1}; \qquad \textit{and} \qquad (\alpha^{-1})^* = (\alpha^*)^{-1} \tag{11-35}$$

If ξ is a column matrix, ξ^{tr} and $\xi^\dagger$ are row matrices.

(The notation used above is common but not universal; the transpose is often indicated by a prime.)

Further terminology:

Hermitian matrix:	$\alpha^\dagger = \alpha$	$(\therefore \lvert\alpha\rvert$ real)	(11-36)
Unitary matrix:	$\alpha^\dagger = \alpha^{-1}$	$(\therefore \lvert\alpha\rvert = \pm 1)$	(11-37)
Symmetric matrix:	$\alpha^{tr} = \alpha$		(11-38)
Anti-Symmetric:	$\alpha^{tr} = -\alpha$	$(\therefore \lvert\alpha\rvert = 0)$	(11-39)
Orthogonal matrix:	$\alpha^{tr} = \alpha^{-1}$		(11-40)

The last is used mainly when it is understood that α is real ($\alpha^* = \alpha$) and it is then equivalent to "unitary."

A product of unitary matrices is unitary.

A sum of Hermitian matrices is Hermitian.

Only the "symmetrized" product, $\frac{1}{2}(\alpha\beta + \beta\alpha)$, of Hermitian matrices, α and β, is in general again Hermitian.

The symmetric and anti-symmetric parts of a matrix are $\frac{1}{2}(\alpha + \alpha^{tr})$ and $\frac{1}{2}(\alpha - \alpha^{tr})$ respectively.

A matrix is called *normal* if it can be written in the form, $\mu^\dagger\delta\mu$, where μ is unitary and δ is (complex-) diagonal.

---

* The number of divisions can be reduced to n in every case by storage of appropriate reciprocals. The number of multiplications is then increased accordingly.

A matrix α is said to be *positive definite* if, for every (non-zero) column vector, ξ,

$$\xi^\dagger \alpha \xi > 0$$

If equality is also allowed, α is said to be positive *semidefinite*.

Miscellaneous Theorems

$$|\alpha|^2 = |\text{Det}\,(\alpha)|^2 \leqslant \prod_{i=1}^{n} \left(\sum_{k=1}^{n} |\alpha_{ik}|^2 \right) \tag{11–41}$$

(That is, the volume enclosed by the vectors $\boldsymbol{\alpha}_{i.}$ is less than the product of lengths of the $\boldsymbol{\alpha}_{i.}$.)

$$\text{If } \alpha_{ik} = (a_i)^{k-1} \quad \text{then} \quad |\alpha| = \prod_{l<k} (a_k - a_l) \tag{11–42}$$

where the a_i are n arbitrary numbers. (The elements of α^{-1} involve "symmetric polynomials" of a_i divided by $|\alpha|$.) Compare (7–7) and (7–8).

$$\begin{vmatrix} a_1 a_2 \cdots\cdots a_n \\ a_2 a_3 \cdots\cdots a_1 \\ a_3 a_4 \cdots\cdots a_2 \\ \vdots\ \vdots \qquad\quad \vdots \\ a_n a_1 \cdots\cdots a_{n-1} \end{vmatrix} = (-1)^{\frac{1}{2}(n-1)(n-2)} \prod_{k=0}^{n-1} [a_1 + a_2\omega^k + a_3\omega^{2k} + \cdots\cdots + a_n\omega^{(n-1)k}]$$

$$\text{where} \quad \omega = e^{2\pi i/n} \tag{11–43}$$

$$\text{If } \alpha_{ij} = \frac{1}{a_i + b_j}$$

$$|\alpha| = \frac{\prod\limits_{j>k} (a_j - a_k)(b_j - b_k)}{\prod\limits_{i} \prod\limits_{l} (a_i + b_l)} \tag{11–44}$$

Polar Decomposition: An arbitrary matrix can always be written in the form

$$\alpha = \eta\mu \qquad (\text{or } \alpha = \mu'\eta')$$

where μ is unitary and is unique while η is Hermitian and positive semidefinite. If α^{-1} exists, η is also unique.

Mini-Max Theorem

For any real (square or non-square) matrix, α, there exists a vector x_i (column matrix) with the properties

$$x_i \geqslant 0, \qquad \sum_i x_i = 1$$

and at least one of:

$$\sum_i x_i \alpha_{ij} \geqslant 0 \quad \text{for all } j; \qquad \sum_j \alpha_{ij} x_j \leqslant 0 \quad \text{for all } i \tag{11–45}$$

also there exist other vectors which reverse at least one of the inequalities (for, consider the matrix, $-\alpha$).

Transcendental Functions of Matrices

Functions of a (square) matrix may be defined by power series if the requisite powers exist and if the corresponding sequence of arrays converges element by element. Example:

$$e^\alpha = \sum_0^\infty \frac{1}{k!} \alpha^k$$

Convergence: If all $\alpha_{ij} < M$, then the elements of α^k are easily seen (by induction on (11–12)) to be each less than $n^{k-1}M^k$ where n is the number of rows and columns in α. Hence every element in the array-series is less than $(1/n)e^{nM}$. The series therefore converges for all finite α.

Note that

$$e^{\alpha}e^{\beta} \neq e^{\alpha+\beta}$$

unless $\alpha\beta = \beta\alpha$.

[Another, less general definition for $f(\alpha)$ is suggested by the expansion of α in projection operators (see Chapter 18, Unitary Spaces). The definitions are equivalent whenever both are applicable.]

Cayley–Hamilton Theorem

If α is any (square) matrix, the determinant, $|\alpha - xI|$, is an ordinary polynomial, $p(x)$, in x. The full theory of this important concept is deferred to Chapter 18 (Unitary Spaces) but the following is valid for an arbitrary (square) matrix and serves to express high powers of a matrix in terms of its lower powers.

$$\text{If } p(x) = |\alpha - xI| \quad \text{then*} \quad p(\alpha) = 0 \tag{11–46}$$

Proof: If $\beta = \alpha - xI$ and B is the adjoint of β (matrix of the adjoint determinants of the elements of β) then by (11–10) $\beta B = |\beta| I$; that is, $\alpha B - xB = p(x)I$. By definition of B, it can be written,

$$B = B_0 + xB_1 + x^2B_2 + \cdots + x^{n-1}B_{n-1};$$

and let

$$p(x) = a_0 + xa_1 + x^2a_2 + \cdots + x^{n-1}a_{n-1} + x^na_n$$

Substituting these above and equating like powers of the (arbitrary) variable, x, one finds (defining $B_{-1} = 0 = B_n$) that $\alpha B_i - B_{i-1} = a_iI$ for all i. Multiplying these relations by α^i and adding gives (11–46).

High powers of a matrix tend to approach a limiting form. The precise result is given in (11–47) but for most matrices, it should be pointed out, the result is essentially

$$\alpha^n \sim C^n\beta \quad \text{as} \quad n \to \infty$$

where C is a numerical constant and β is a certain matrix independent of n.

Sylvester's Theorem

If $x_1, x_2, \cdots$ are the *distinct* roots of $|\alpha - xI| = 0$ and if x_j has multiplicity J, then for all n,

$$\alpha^n = \sum_j \frac{1}{(J-1)!}\left[\frac{d^{J-1}}{dx^{J-1}} \frac{x^n\beta(x)}{\prod_{s\neq j}(x - x_s)^S}\right]_{x=x} \tag{11–47}$$

where

$$\beta(x) = \text{adjoint matrix of } (xI - \alpha)$$

In particular if $|\alpha - xI| = 0$ has no multiple roots then

$$\alpha^n = \sum_j (x_j)^n \prod_{i\neq j} \frac{x_iI - \alpha}{x_i - x_j} \tag{11–48}$$

Stronger results for matrices with non-negative elements are listed in Chapter 20 under "Markov Chains".

---

* The constant term, a_0, in $p(\alpha)$ is to be interpreted as a_0I.

For a two-by-two matrix, an explicit formula is
If

$$\sigma = (\alpha_{11} + \alpha_{22})/2\sqrt{|\alpha|} \quad \text{and} \quad |\alpha| \neq 0$$

then

$$\alpha^n = |\alpha|^{\frac{1}{2}(n-1)} U^*_{n-1}(\sigma)\alpha - |\alpha|^{\frac{1}{2}n} U^*_{n-2}(\sigma) I \tag{11-49}$$

where

$$U_n{}^*(x) = \frac{\sin[(n+1)\cos^{-1} x]}{\sqrt{1-x^2}}$$

(an associated Tchebycheff polynomial). If $|\alpha| = 0$ then $\alpha^n = (\alpha_{11} + \alpha_{22})^{n-1}\alpha$. (Proofs: induction.)

"Trace" of a Matrix

$$\text{Trace}(\alpha) = \sum_i \alpha_{ii} \tag{11-50}$$

Hidden by this notation are the facts that

$$\begin{aligned} \text{Trace}(\alpha\beta) &= \text{Trace}(\beta\alpha) \\ \text{Trace}(\alpha + \beta) &= \text{Trace}(\alpha) + \text{Trace}(\beta) \end{aligned} \tag{11-51}$$

"Direct Product" of Matrices

This is a "product" in a very different sense since the result is a matrix entirely different from either of its factors. It arises often in compounding two physical systems into a single system. The notation is rather a barrier to the really simple concept. In block-matrix form, the direct product (denoted by $\alpha \times \beta$) is

$$\alpha \times \beta = \begin{Vmatrix} \alpha_{11}\beta, & \alpha_{12}\beta, & \cdots \\ \alpha_{21}\beta, & \alpha_{22}\beta, & \cdots \\ \cdot & \cdot & \\ \cdot & \cdot & \end{Vmatrix} \qquad \beta \times \alpha = \begin{Vmatrix} \beta_{11}\alpha, & \beta_{12}\alpha, & \cdots \\ \beta_{21}\alpha, & \beta_{22}\alpha, & \cdots \\ \cdot & \cdot & \\ \cdot & \cdot & \end{Vmatrix} \tag{11-52}$$

NOTE:

$$\alpha \times \beta \neq \beta \times \alpha \qquad \text{in general}$$

In index notation, if $\gamma = \alpha \times \beta$, we may denote elements of γ by *pairs* of indices; then

$$\gamma_{ij,mn} = \alpha_{im}\beta_{jn} \tag{11-53}$$

Theorems (rather obscured by the notation)

$$(\alpha \times \beta) \cdot (\gamma \times \delta) = (\alpha\gamma) \times (\beta\delta) \tag{11-54}$$

(provided the multiplications indicated are possible)

$$\text{Trace}(\alpha \times \beta) = \text{Trace}(\alpha) \cdot \text{Trace}(\beta) \tag{11-55}$$

$$I \times I = I$$

(where the dimensions of the various I are, of course, different)

If α and β are diagonal, so is $\alpha \times \beta$.

SIGNAL-FLOW GRAPHS

This is a computational device which avoids much of the labor of solving linear equations under certain circumstances—particularly when subsidiary variables are of no interest and may be eliminated. The technique arises naturally in communication networks, where the graph usually appears ab initio and the equations need never be written down. Markov chains can also be fruitfully studied in this way (especially after taking Laplace transforms on the time variable; see W. H. Huggins, *Proc. Inst. Radio Engrs.* **45**, 74, (1955)).

The manipulations are peculiarly difficult to describe but "go" very rapidly once the "picture" is in mind.

To set up the graph: Write the equations to be solved in the form:

$$x_i = \sum_j \alpha_{ij} x_j + b_i \tag{11–56}$$

(where x_i may appear on both sides). Represent each x_i and each non-zero b_i by a labeled dot or "node." Connect the nodes b_i to the respective x_i by an arrow, labeled "1" and directed from b_i to x_i; represent the non-zero α_{ij} by arrows, labeled with the value of α_{ij} and directed from x_j to x_i.

[The resulting graph is conveniently viewed as a set of transmission paths (the arrows) with gain α_{ij} connecting a set of summing and distributing centers (the nodes) which add their inputs and send the sum out along each of their output links.]

Reducing the graph: This step is not vital but can materially shorten later work. It consists in simplifying individual parts of the graph and eliminating uninteresting nodes (x_i) by such transformations as the following. (Short lines indicate possible heads or tails of other arrows in the graph.)

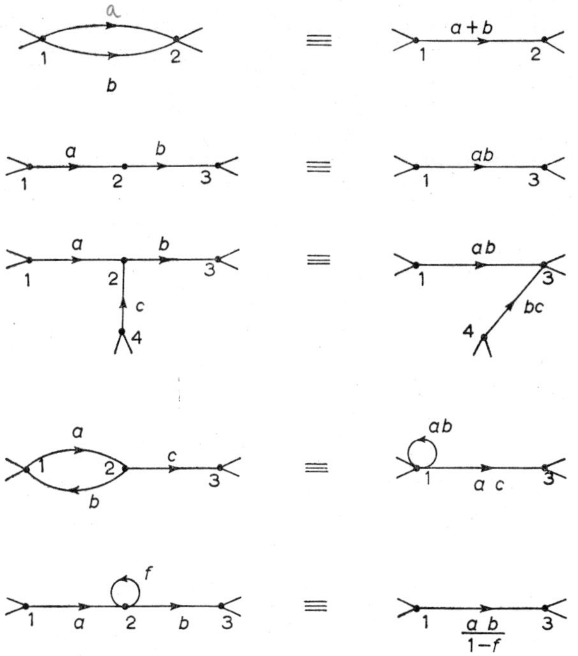

Many variants on these operations become evident as one's familiarity with the technique improves. (In any case of doubt, a reduction can be checked by writing out the equations represented by the two configurations.)

Writing down final solutions. Usually, the desired solution is to give a variable (call it y) in terms of* the b_i. By superposition, this is a sum of expressions, each of

* The notational distinction between b_i and x_j need not be preserved carefully; it is obvious from the graph which nodes are inputs and which are "driven". Since the equations are linear, the response to a sum of inputs is always the sum of the individual responses.

which gives y when all but one of the b_i's vanish (call the exceptional one b). Then:
The "gain" from b to y, that is, $G = y/b$ is given by,

$$G = \frac{\sum D_k G_k}{D} \tag{11-57}$$

where the sum is over all direct paths* from b to y, and

G_k = gain‡ along the kth direct path

$$D = 1 - \sum_m P_m(1) + \sum_m P_m(2) - \cdots$$

$$= 1 + \sum_{n=1}^{(\infty)} (-1)^n \sum_m P_m(n)$$

where $P_m(n)$ = *product* of the gains† around any n mutually non-touching‡ loops§; m denotes the mth way of selecting n such loops.

$D_k = D$ for that part of the graph not touching‡ the kth direct path.

An *alternative definition* of the D's

$$D = \Pi^* (1 - L_i) \tag{11-58}$$

where the L_i are (all) the loop gains and the asterisk indicates that, in expanded form, any product $(L_i L_j \cdots L_k)$ is to be omitted if it contains any pair of loops which touch each other.

$$D_k = D^{*k} \tag{11-59}$$

where "$*k$" indicates that (in addition) any terms which involve any loops touching G_k are to be omitted. ("Touch" always denotes "having any common node with"; a "loop" is any "circle" (which does not cross itself and) all of whose arrows touch tip-to-tail).

While the labor and care required to set up this expression increases rapidly with the complexity of the graph, it must be remembered that alternative algebraic manipulations also rapidly become prohibitively complex (especially if the α_{ij} are functions rather than mere numbers). To repeat, the description is, unhappily, far more confusing than the actual process itself.

"Normalization" is a process for simplifying the expressions by factoring out inessential parameters:

(a) If each link in the graph is part of some loop: Select any "tree" (a subgraph interconnecting all nodes but containing no loops¶); the gains of the links on the tree may then be altered arbitrarily (e.g. set = 1) provided other gains are simultaneously altered in such a way as to leave all (directed-) *loop* gains unchanged.

(b) If the graph does not have the property postulated in (a): Temporarily introduce additional links to give it that property—each labelled $1/G(\alpha)$. where $G(\alpha)$ stands for the gain from tip to tail before the arrow α was added. Apply (a), note the effects on $G(\alpha)$, and then remove the added links.

---

* A path following the directions of the arrows and not passing through any node more than once.

† Product of the labels on the arrows.

‡ Having no common nodes or arrows.

§ Any closed circuit all of whose arrows point in the same sense, the circuit not crossing itself.

¶ Even when the direction of the arrows is ignored.

CHAPTER 12

FUNCTIONS OF A COMPLEX VARIABLE

Elementary Notation

"Complex numbers" are sums of the form $a + ib$ where a and b are ordinary ("real") numbers and i is defined only by the property, $i^2 = -1$. This rule suffices to define all algebraic operations with complex numbers. Equality of two complex numbers indicates two arithmetic equalities—for the real and imaginary parts separately.

$$\text{If} \qquad z = x + iy \qquad (x \text{ and } y \text{ real})$$

$$\left.\begin{aligned} z^* &= x - iy && (\text{"conjugate" of } z) \\ |z| &= \sqrt{x^2 + y^2} = \sqrt{zz^*} \\ \text{Re}\,(z) &= x = \tfrac{1}{2}(z + z^*) && (\text{real part}) \\ \text{Im}\,(z) &= y = \left(\frac{z - z^*}{2i}\right) && (\text{imaginary part}) \\ \text{Arg}\,(z) &= \tan^{-1}(y/x) && (\text{in radians}) \end{aligned}\right\} \tag{12–1}$$

$z = x + iy$ may be represented as a point with coordinates (x, y) in a plane; $|z|$ is then the distance from this point to the origin and Arg $(z) = \phi$ is the angle with the x-axis.

$$z = x + iy = |z| \cos \phi + i\,|z| \sin \phi = |z|\, e^{i\phi}$$

Generally, $|z_1 - z_2|$ is the distance between the points z_1 and z_2.

$\int_C f\,dz$ is defined in terms of the four real integrals which result from expanding z and f in real and imaginary parts; "C" specifies the curve along which z travels. The symbol $\oint_C$ is often used for emphasis when C is closed on itself and the integral is to be taken once all around C (in a counter-clockwise direction).

$f(z) = O(g(z))$ ("order of g") means that, for some constant, M: $|f(z)| \leqslant M|g(z)|$ for values of z implied by the context.

$f(z) = o(g(z))$ means $(f/g) \to 0$ as z approaches some value specified by the context.

$f(z) \sim g(z)$ means $(f/g) \to 1$ as z approaches some value specified by the context.

Differentiable† Functions:

If $\lim\limits_{\delta \to 0} \left\{\frac{1}{\delta}[f(z + \delta) - f(z)]\right\} = \frac{df}{dz}$ exists and is independent of the manner in which $\delta = \epsilon + i\eta \to 0$, then $f(z)$ is said to be differentiable at the point, z.

Analytic† Functions

If $f(z)$ is both *differentiable* at all points in some region, R, of the z-plane and also *single-valued* WITHIN R then $f(z)$ is said to be analytic in the region, R.

† The terminology is not completely standard. Some authors use "analytic" as synonymous with "differentiable throughout the region in question"; the terms "regular" or "holomorphic" are then used to describe functions which are both differentiable and single-valued. The terminology used above, however, is becoming standard.

("Single-valued in R" means that no matter how z may be varied through the region, R, the function always resumes a given value when z returns to a given point. Thus, in later terminology, a branch of a multiple-valued function can be analytic in a region which excludes the branch points.)

Points where $f(z)$ is not analytic† are called "*singularities*" of $f(z)$. Note that, for a multiple-valued function, a point may be a singularity of one branch but not of another (example: $f(z) = (a + \sqrt{z})^{-1}$).

Note, finally, that, although the function, $f(z) = z^* = x - iy$, is analytic *nowhere*, nevertheless (since the introduction of a symbol, i, defined only by $i^2 = -1$ is a purely formal step) the sign of i may be changed *throughout* the entire theory without altering any of the final arithmetic results.

General Properties of Analytic Functions

1. $\dfrac{d^n f}{dz^n}$ (for any n) exists and is analytic wherever f is analytic.

2. $\displaystyle\int_a^z f(u)\,du$ is analytic if the path of integration does not cross any singularity of f.

3. A *uniformly*‡ convergent infinite series of analytic functions converges to a function analytic in the same region (where all terms are analytic and the uniformity of convergence is valid). Derivatives and integrals of all orders can be calculated by differentiating or integrating the series term by term. Note the application to power series in particular.

4. The zeros of an analytic function are isolated points.

5. If $F(z, w)$ is a continuous function of its two complex variables and if, for every value of w lying on some contour, C, the function F is analytic over some region, R, in the z-plane, then

$$g(z) = \int_C F(z, w)\,dw$$

is an analytic function of z in R and the derivatives of g (of all orders) may be obtained by differentiation under the integral sign.

6. *Power series:* If $f(z)$ is analytic at $z = b$, then Taylor's series,

$$f(z) = \sum_{n=0}^{\infty} \frac{1}{n!} f^{(n)}(b)(z - b)^n \qquad (12\text{–}3)$$

converges uniformly inside any circle, $|z - b| \leqslant R$, within and on which $f(z)$ is analytic. As R is increased, the series first fails to converge when the circle $|z - b| = R$ crosses a singularity of f. This value of R is called the "radius of convergence" of the series and always signals the presence of the singularity of f nearest to $z = b$. Outside this radius of convergence, the series always diverges (even though f may be analytic in large parts of that region).

---

† That is, points which destroy either differentiability or single-valuedness when adjoined to the region, R. The function, $f(z) = z^{3/2}$, for example, is differentiable at $z = 0$ but is not analytic there.

‡ That is, given any $\epsilon > 0$, then $\left|\sum_N^{\infty} u_n(z)\right| < \epsilon$ whenever $N \geqslant N_0(\epsilon)$, where N_0 is *independent of z*—at least within the specified region.

7. *Cauchy–Riemann equations:* If $f = \phi + i\psi$, then

$$\frac{\partial \phi}{\partial x} = \frac{\partial \psi}{\partial y} \quad \text{and} \quad \frac{\partial \psi}{\partial x} = -\frac{\partial \phi}{\partial y} \tag{12–4}$$

and conversely if these derivatives exist in a finite region and satisfy (12–4) then f is analytic in that region.

From (12–4), $\nabla^2\phi = 0$ and $\nabla^2\psi = 0$ (where $\nabla^2 = \partial^2/\partial x^2 + \partial^2/\partial y^2$), so that analytic functions yield solutions to Laplace's equation in two variables.

Conversely, if $\nabla^2\phi = 0$ then ϕ determines (to an additive constant) an analytic function $f(z)$ by:

$$\frac{\partial f}{\partial x} = \frac{\partial \phi}{\partial x} - i\frac{\partial \phi}{\partial y} \quad \left(\text{or } \frac{\partial f}{\partial y} = \frac{\partial \phi}{\partial y} + i\frac{\partial \phi}{\partial x}\right)$$

whence

$$f(z) = \int_{g(y)}^{x} \left(\frac{\partial \phi}{\partial x} - i\frac{\partial \phi}{\partial y}\right) \mathrm{d}x \tag{12–5}$$

where $g(y)$ is chosen to make $\mathrm{Re}\,(f) = \phi$.

8. *Liouville's theorem:* The only function analytic for all z (including $z = \infty$) is $f =$ constant.

Also if $f(z)$ is analytic merely for all finite values of z and if $|f(z)| \leqslant M|z|^k$ as $|z| \to \infty$ (where M is some constant) then $f(z)$ is a polynomial of degree at most k.

9. *Schwarz reflection principle:* If $f(x + i0)$ is real then $f(z^*) = f^*(z)$. By obvious changes of variable, an analogue is true whenever f follows some straight line as z follows another straight line.

10. Two analytic functions which have the same values at an infinite number of points† in a finite region (where both are analytic) are actually identical at all points.

11. *Cauchy's formula:* If $f(z)$ is analytic inside a (simple) closed curve, C, and continuous inside *and on* C, then for all positive integers, n

$$\frac{\mathrm{d}^n f}{\mathrm{d}z^n} = \frac{n!}{2\pi i}\oint_C \frac{f(\zeta)\,\mathrm{d}\zeta}{(\zeta - z)^{n+1}} \tag{12–6}$$

where z lies inside C. Also

$$\oint_C f(\zeta)\,\mathrm{d}\zeta = 0 \tag{12–7}$$

12. *Analytic continuation:* The definition of any particular function (by a series or an integral, etc.) may fail outside certain regions. However, it may be shown that if the definition can‡ be extended in any manner consistent with the original definition (e.g. power series development about a point near the boundary), then the function so obtained is unique (though not necessarily single-valued). This is essentially an application of #10 and shows that the original definition need apply only to a small region.

Classification of Singularities

1. *Poles*: If $f(z)$ has an *isolated* singularity at $z = p$ but if, for some integer, n, $(z - p)^n f(z)$ is analytic at (and hence near) $z = p$, then p is called a "pole" of f; the (smallest such) n is called the "order" of the pole.

---

† These points must have a limit-point inside the region (and therefore not (only) at a singularity of one function).

‡ A few functions have "unbreachable" boundaries beyond which analytic continuation is impossible.

"Residue" at a pole; This is the coefficient of $(z-p)^{n-1}$ in the Taylor's series of $(z-p)^n f(z)$. It may also be defined as

$$\text{Residue} = \frac{1}{2\pi i}\oint_C f(z)\,dz = \frac{1}{(n-1)!}\left[\left(\frac{d}{dz}\right)^{n-1}(z-p)^n f(z)\right]_{z=p} \tag{12–8}$$

where C encircles p. $\left[\text{Note that } \frac{1}{2\pi i}\oint \frac{dz}{(z-c)^n} = 0 \text{ unless } n = +1.\right]$

2. *Branch points:* If, upon circling about the point $z = b$, the function $f(z)$ changes value (example: $f = \sqrt{z}$), then $z = b$ is called a branch point of f.

If, after a finite number*, k, of such circuits, f returns to its original value, then k is called the "order" of the branch point and $f(b + w^k)$ is single-valued near $w = 0$—although not necessarily analytic.

3. All other† singularities are (usually) called "*essential singularities*" (because they cannot be "removed" by rational changes of variable). (Warning: This term is not always given quite the same meaning by different authors.)

The very complex nature of essential singularities is shown by:

Weierstrass' theorem: If $f(z)$ has an isolated essential singularity at $z = a$, then, given any positive numbers ρ, ϵ, and any assigned complex value c, there is a point in the circle: $|z - a| < \rho$, where $|f(z) - c| < \epsilon$.

(Roughly: Within any circle about $z = a$, however small its radius, f essentially assumes *all* complex values. Example: $e^{1/z}$ near $z = 0$.)

Conformal Mapping

If $f(z) = u + iv$ is plotted in Cartesian (u, v) coordinates as $z = x + iy$ varies, one obtains a *mapping* of the (x, y) plane (or z-plane) onto the (u, v) plane (or f-plane). The mapping may "cover" some regions more than once.

This mapping is "conformal" in the sense that angles between short curve-segments are preserved—and hence, locally, lengths are uniformly magnified. In fact, $|f'(z)|$ is the local magnification and Arg (f') is the local rotation.

Riemann mapping theorem: Every simply connected region with at least two points on its boundary can be mapped conformally, by means of an analytic function, onto the unit circle; $|z| \leqslant 1$, and hence onto any other such region.

Conformal mapping is also a way of transforming certain physical problems involving Laplace's equation in two variables into simpler problems. In this way, a number of problems in electrostatics, etc., have been solved and compilations of useful transformations have been assembled. One rather general case is:

Schwarz–Christoffel transformations: To map a polygon (convex or concave but not crossing itself), in the z-plane and with interior angles θ_i, onto the real axis of the w-plane with the corners going to $w = a_i$, determine $w(z)$ from:

$$\frac{dz}{dw} = (\text{constant}) \prod_i (w - a_i)^{(\theta_i - \pi)/\pi} \tag{12–9}$$

If one a_i is to be infinite, omit the corresponding factor in (12–9).

---

* An example where no such k exists is $f = \log z$.

† We ignore "removable singularities" where (owing to inept definition initially) $f(z)$ can be *made* analytic by re-defining f as $[\lim_{z\to a} f(z)]$.

Contour Integration

This subject is more of an art than a systematic theory. It is based on: (a) Cauchy's formula (12–7), from which follows the fact that an integration path can be moved about over the z-plane with impunity so long as it never passes over a singularity of the integrand; provided the end-points (if any) are held fixed, the value of the integral is unchanged. (b) The "residue" concept (12–8) from which it follows that if $f(z)$ is analytic on and inside a (simple) closed curve, C, except at poles, $z = p_1, p_2, \cdots, p_k$, located inside C then if $r_1, r_2, \cdots, r_k$ are the respective residues of f at these poles,

$$\frac{1}{2\pi i}\oint_C f(z)\,dz = \sum_1^k r_i \tag{12–10}$$

(c) If $f(z)$ is suitably bounded in appropriate regions, part of a closed-curve integral can be made to approach zero by displacing the curve of integration sufficiently far (usually toward $|z| = \infty$).

Locating the Zeros of an Analytic Function

If $f(z)$ is analytic on and inside C, than as z runs around C the values of $f(z)$ encircle the origin ($f = 0$) a number of times equal to the number of zeros inside C (a zero of order m being counted m times).

This theorem (which follows from (12–10), using f'/f as the integrand) is useful for locating roughly the complex zeros of very complicated functions. One need only plot the complex values of f itself around various contours and note the changes in the number of times f encircles $f = 0$.

Schwarz's Lemma

If $f(z)$ is analytic in $|z| < R$ and continuous in $|z| \leqslant R$ and if $|f(z)| \leqslant M$ on $|z| = R$ and if $f(0) = 0$, then either

$$|f(re^{i\theta})| < Mr/R, \quad \text{for} \quad 0 \leqslant r < R \tag{12–11}$$

or else

$$f(z) = (M/R)ze^{ia}$$

This is a consequence (let $g = f/z$) of:

Maximum-Modulus Theorem

If $|f(z)| \leqslant M$ on the closed (simple) curve, C, and if f is analytic inside C and continuous *on* and inside C, then

$$\text{either } |f(z)| < M \text{ inside } C \text{ or } |f(z)| = M \text{ for all } z. \tag{12–12}$$

Further Limitations

If $f(z)$ is analytic in $|z| < 1$ and $|f| < 1$ there, then:

1. $$|f(z)| \leqslant \frac{|z| + |f(0)|}{1 + |z| \cdot |f(0)|} \quad (\text{in } |z| < 1) \tag{12–13}$$

2. If $|z_1| < r$ and $|z_2| < r$ where $r < 1$ then

$$\left|\frac{f(z_1) - f(z_2)}{z_1 - z_2}\right| \leqslant \frac{1}{1 - r^2} \tag{12–14}$$

3. If $f(z) \neq h$ $(0 < h < 1)$ anywhere in $|z| < 1$ and if $f(0) = 0$ then in $|z| < r < 1$,

$$|f(z) - h| > (1 - h)\exp\left(\frac{1 + r}{1 - r}\ln h\right) \tag{12–15}$$

4. (Julia's theorem) If $\lim_{z\to 1} f(z) = 1$ (even merely for a single sequence of $z_n \to 1$) and if

$$\alpha = \lim_{z\to 1} \frac{1 - |f(z)|}{1 - |z|}$$

then

$$\frac{|1 - f(z)|^2}{1 - |f(z)|^2} \leqslant \alpha \frac{|1 - z|^2}{1 - |z|^2} \qquad [\text{in } |z| < 1] \tag{12-16}$$

Functions With Positive Real-Part in a Half-Plane

Such functions arise in the theory of (driving-point) impedances or scattering functions of physical systems. Specifically, let $\text{Re}\,(f(z)) \geqslant 0$ in $x \geqslant 0$. Then by means of the transformation:

$$w = \frac{1 - z}{1 + z} \qquad g(w) = \frac{f(1) - f(z)}{f(1) + f(z)} \tag{12-17}$$

we obtain a function, $g(w)$, with $|g| < 1$ in $|w| < 1$ and thereby can apply standard results such as (12–11)–(12–16) to such physical impedance or scattering functions. [For examples, see (3–138)–(3–141).]

Pragmén–Lindeloef Theorems

There is a whole class of results of which the following are typical:

1. If $f(z) \to a$ as $z \to \infty$ along a straight line and if $f(z) \to b$ as $z \to \infty$ along another straight line and if $f(z)$ is analytic and bounded in the angle between these lines, then (actually) $a = b$ and $f(z) \to a$ uniformly in the angle.

2. If, in $\text{Re}\,(z) \geqslant 0$, $f(z)$ is analytic and $|f| \leqslant Me^{k|z|}$ and if on the imaginary axis $|f| \leqslant Ne^{-a|z|}$ (where $a > 0$) then (actually) $f(z) \equiv 0$ everywhere.

Special Types of Analytic Functions

1. If an analytic function has no singularities other than poles (including the "point" $z = \infty$), then it is necessarily a *rational* function (ratio of two polynomials). In particular, all "transcendental" functions have at least one singularity which is not a pole.

2. "*Entire*" (*or* "*integral*") *functions* are functions which have no singularities except at $z = \infty$. (Examples.*) For entire functions,

(a) Taylor's power series for f then converges for any finite z (and uniformly in any finite circle).

(b) Conversely, if the power series converges for all finite z, f is an entire function.

(c) Any entire function which is not a polynomial assumes every complex value, with at most one exception, infinitely often. (Picard's theorem.)

(d) Every entire function can be expanded as an infinite product. (If $f(0) = 0$, divide by z—or z^k—before applying the theorem.)

$$f(z) = f(0)e^{g(z)}\Pi(z) \tag{12-18}$$

where $g(z)$ is an entire function and $\Pi(z)$ is an infinite product of factors of the form:

$$\left(1 - \frac{z}{a_i}\right) \exp\left[\frac{z}{a_i} + \frac{1}{2}\left(\frac{z}{a_i}\right)^2 + \cdots + \frac{1}{n}\left(\frac{z}{a_i}\right)^n\right]$$

Here a_i are the zeros of $f(z)$. This factorization is not unique but holds even for such functions as $\exp\,(e^z)$.

---

* Important examples: e^{az}, $\sin z$, $1/\Gamma(z)$, $\left[\zeta(z) - \frac{1}{z - 1}\right]$, $J_\nu(z)/z^\nu$, ${}_1F_1(a;\, b;\, z)$.

(e) If $|f(z)| \leqslant M \exp(|z|^\rho)$ as $|z| \to \infty$ then in (12–18) we may take $g(z)$ to be a polynomial; its degree and n (in the second line) need not exeed ρ. The lower bound of such ρ is called the "order" of f. The function df/dz has the same order as f.

Examples: For the trigonometric functions, cos z and (sin $z)/z$, and the Bessel functions, $J_\nu(z)/z^\nu$, we can take $\rho = 1$ in (e) and hence (12–18) becomes

$$f(z) = f(0)\left[\exp\left(z\frac{f'(0)}{f(0)}\right)\right]\prod^{\infty}\left(1 - \frac{z}{a_n}\right)e^{z/a_n}$$

Or, since the above functions are all even $[f(z) = f(-z)]$ this becomes

$$f(z) = f(0)\prod^{\infty}\left(1 - \frac{z^2}{a_n{}^2}\right) \tag{12–19}$$

(where now only one of the roots $\pm a_i$ is counted).

3. "*Meromorphic*" *functions* are functions whose only singularities for finite $|z|$ are poles so arranged that every finite circle, $|z| = R$, contains only a finite number of such poles. (Examples: tan z, $\Gamma(z)$, ratio of any two entire functions.)

(a) If $f(z)$ is such that, on contours C_n which contain n poles of f and whose length* is $O(R_n)$, we have $f = o(R_n{}^{k+1})$ where k is a positive integer. Then (if all poles of f are of first order),

$$f(z) = f(0) + zf'(0) + \cdots + \frac{z^k}{k!}f^{(k)}(0) + \sum_{n=0}^{\infty}\frac{b_n z^{k+1}}{a_n{}^{k+1}(z - a_n)} \tag{12–20}$$

(where b_n are the residues of f at the poles, a_n). The series converges uniformly inside any finite region which contains none of the a_n.

(b) The "order" of a meromorphic function can also be defined in a manner too complex to reproduce here. Its significance is that a function of order m can be expressed as the ratio of two entire functions also of order m and hence the original function can be expanded as the ratio of two infinite products of the type (12–18) with $g(z)$ a polynomial of degree at most m. Example:

$$\cot z = \frac{1}{z} + 2z\sum_{1}^{\infty}\frac{1}{z^2 - n^2\pi^2}$$

$$= \frac{\prod_{1}^{\infty}\left(1 - \frac{z^2}{(n - \frac{1}{2})^2\pi^2}\right)}{z\prod_{1}^{\infty}\left(1 - \frac{z^2}{n^2\pi^2}\right)}$$

---

* R_n is the minimum distance of C_n from $z = 0$. For the notation, "$O(\cdots)$", see following (12–1).

CHAPTER 13

INTEGRAL TRANSFORMS

INTEGRAL transforms are used to change a problem (often drastically) to another type which may be easier to solve; if so, the solution may then be inverted ("transformed back") to yield the desired answer, often with far less labor than any other method.

More specifically, an integral transform generates (by integration) from a given function, $F(t)$, an entirely *new* function, $f(p)$, of a completely different variable, p. Nevertheless, $f(p)$ is uniquely correlated with $F(t)$ and the inversion formula always regenerates $F(t)$ and no other function. In addition, the more useful integral transforms have other simplifying properties such as transforming many transcendental functions to algebraic functions, differential operators to algebraic factors, discontinuous functions (of a real variable) to analytic functions of a complex variable —to name a few.

LAPLACE TRANSFORMS

Laplace transforms ("ordinary" or "one-sided") are defined by,

$$\mathscr{L}[F(t)] = \int_0^\infty e^{-pt} F(t)\, dt = f(p) \tag{13–1}$$

where $F(t)$ is the "original function" and $f(p)$ is its Laplace transform. The relation is often abbreviated,

$$F(t) \leftrightarrow f(p) \tag{13–2}$$

Inversion Formulas

$$\mathscr{L}^{-1}[f(p)] = \frac{1}{2\pi i} \int_{c-i\infty}^{c+i\infty} e^{pt} f(p)\, dp = F(t) \tag{13–3}$$

(where c is to be chosen positive and such that (13–1) converges in $\mathrm{Re}(p) \geqslant c$; that is, such that $f(p)$ is analytic on and to the right of $\mathrm{Re}(p) = c$, except possibly at $p = \infty$).

$$\int_0^t F(t)\, dt = \lim_{s\to\infty} \sum_1^\infty \frac{(-1)^{n+1}}{n!} e^{nst} f(ns) \tag{13–4}$$

$$\mathscr{L}^{-1}[f(p)] = \lim_{\epsilon\to 0} \frac{1}{2\pi i} [h(-t - i\epsilon) - h(-t + i\epsilon)] \tag{13–5}$$

where

$$h(s) = \mathscr{L}\mathscr{L}[F(t)] = \int_0^\infty e^{-sp} f(p)\, dp$$

Thus the operation $\mathscr{L}^{-1}$ can (if h exists) be accomplished by "going the wrong way" and applying $\mathscr{L}$ instead.

(Many other inversion formulas are known but the above plus indirect methods using (13–7)–(13–10) seem the most generally useful. The inversion is unique in the sense that two functions can have the same Laplace transform only if they differ by a null-function [one whose integral is identically zero].)

All inversion formulas give the result:

$$\mathscr{L}^{-1}[f(p)] = F(t) = 0, \quad \text{when} \quad t < 0 \tag{13–6}$$

In a sense, this is "assumed" in the definition, (13–1). The convention (13–6) must therefore be adopted whenever (ordinary) Laplace transforms are employed. It is implicit in the entire theory. This property makes the Laplace transform especially appropriate for treating initial-value problems.

General Properties of Laplace Transforms

$$\left.\begin{aligned}
F(t/a) &\leftrightarrow af(pa) \\
\frac{\mathrm{d}F}{\mathrm{d}t} &\leftrightarrow pf(p) - F(0^+), \text{note*} \\
\int_0^t F(\tau)\,\mathrm{d}\tau &\leftrightarrow \frac{1}{p} f(p) \\
t^n F(t) &\leftrightarrow \left(-\frac{\mathrm{d}}{\mathrm{d}p}\right)^n f(p) \\
\frac{1}{t} F(t) &\leftrightarrow \int_p^\infty f(s)\,\mathrm{d}s \\
e^{at} F(t) &\leftrightarrow f(p - a) \\
F(t + |a|) &\leftrightarrow e^{|a|p}\left[f(p) - \int_0^{|a|} e^{-p\tau} F(\tau)\,\mathrm{d}\tau\right] \\
F(t - |a|) &\leftrightarrow e^{-|a|p} f(p), \text{note}\dagger \\
\int_0^t F_1(\tau) F_2(t - \tau)\,\mathrm{d}\tau &\leftrightarrow f_1(p) f_2(p) \\
F_1(t) F_2(t) &\leftrightarrow \frac{1}{2\pi i} \int_{c-i\infty}^{c+i\infty} f_1(z) f_2(p - z)\,\mathrm{d}z, \text{note}\ddagger
\end{aligned}\right\} \tag{13–7}$$

The integrals in the last two relations are known as "convolution integrals" (real and complex, respectively).

$$\int_0^\infty G(x) H(x)\,\mathrm{d}x = \int_0^\infty \mathscr{L}[G] \mathscr{L}^{-1}[H] \text{ “d}y\text{”} \tag{13–8}$$

Some general consequences of (13–7) are:

$$\left.\begin{aligned}
\frac{\mathrm{d}^n}{\mathrm{d}t^n} F(t) &\leftrightarrow p^n f(p) - \sum_{k=0}^{n-1} p^k F^{(n-k-1)}(0^+) \\
\int_t^\infty F(\tau) \frac{\mathrm{d}\tau}{\tau} &\leftrightarrow \frac{1}{p} \int_0^p f(s)\,\mathrm{d}s \\
e^{-at} \int_0^t e^{ax} F(x)\,\mathrm{d}x &\leftrightarrow \frac{f(p)}{p + a}
\end{aligned}\right\} \tag{13–9}$$

---

* Provided $F(t)$ is *continuous*; if F has a jump of magnitude J at $t = T$, then $\mathscr{L}[\mathrm{d}F/\mathrm{d}t] = pf(p) - F(0^+) - Je^{-pT}$.

† Under the convention, (13–6); otherwise, an additional (integral) term appears on the right.

‡ The integration path must pass between the singularities of the two factors in the integrand.

Some consequences of (13–8):

$$\left.\begin{aligned} & F_1(t)F_2(t) \leftrightarrow \int_0^\infty f_1(p+s)\mathscr{L}^{-1}[F_2]\,ds \\ & \text{If } F(t) = 0 \text{ for } t < 1 \text{ then} \\ & F(e^{at}) \leftrightarrow \frac{1}{a\Gamma\left(\dfrac{p}{a}+1\right)}\int_0^\infty s^{p/a}f(s)\,ds \\ & \mathscr{L}\mathscr{L}[F(t)] = \int_0^\infty \frac{F(t)}{t+s}\,dt \\ & \left.\begin{aligned} & \int_0^\infty \psi(\tau,t)F(\tau)\,d\tau \\ & \psi(\tau,t) = \mathscr{L}^{-1}[e^{-\tau\phi(p)}/\theta(p)] \end{aligned}\right\} \leftrightarrow f[\phi(p)]/\theta(p) \\ & \text{In particular:} \\ & \int_0^t J_0(a\sqrt{t^2-u^2})F(u)\,du \leftrightarrow \frac{f(\sqrt{p^2+a^2})}{\sqrt{p^2+a^2}} \end{aligned}\right\} \tag{13–10}$$

Some basic Laplace transform pairs are given in the table on p. 325; since very extensive tables have recently been compiled, we list only those which are "almost worth memorizing". [The notation for Bessel functions is that of Watson—which is used in virtually all modern works; L_n is defined in (13–47); $U(x)$ is the unit jump-function: $U = 0$ for $x < 0$ and $U = 1$ for $x > 0$.]

Periodic Functions

If $F(t + nT) = F(t)$ then

$$\mathscr{L}[F(t)] = \sum_0^\infty e^{-npT}\int_0^T e^{-pt}F(t)\,dt = \frac{\displaystyle\int_0^T e^{-pt}F(t)\,dt}{1 - e^{-pT}} \tag{13–11}$$

Positive Functions

$F(t)$ is non-negative for all $t \geqslant 0$ if and only if

$$(-1)^k f^{(k)}(p) \geqslant 0$$

for all real positive p and all integers $k \geqslant 0$; hence:

Bounded Functions

$m \leqslant F(t) \leqslant M$ for all t if and only if

$$\frac{m}{p^{k+1}} \leqslant \frac{(-1)^k f^{(k)}(p)}{k!} \leqslant \frac{M}{p^{k+1}}$$

"Delayed" Functions

$F(t) = 0$ for $t < a$ if and only if

$$\frac{e^{ap}f(p)}{p} \to 0 \quad \text{as} \quad p \to \infty \quad \text{(along the real axis).}$$

TABLE 13.1

Basic Laplace Transform Pairs

$F(t)$	$f(p) = \int_0^\infty e^{-pt} F(t)\, dt$	
$\frac{t^a}{a!} = \frac{t^a}{\Gamma(a+1)}$	$\frac{1}{p^{a+1}}$	
e^{at} (hence: $\sin at$, $\cos at$, $\sinh at$, $\cosh at$)	$\frac{1}{p-a}$	
$\frac{e^{-bt} - e^{-at}}{t}$	$\ln \frac{p+a}{p+b}$	
$J_0(at)$	$\frac{1}{\sqrt{p^2 + a^2}}$	
$\frac{1}{t} J_\nu(at)$	$\frac{a^\nu}{\nu(p + \sqrt{p^2 + a^2})^\nu} = \frac{(\sqrt{p^2 + a^2} - p)^\nu}{\nu a^\nu}$	
$\operatorname{erfc}\left(\frac{a}{\sqrt{t}}\right) = \frac{2}{\sqrt{\pi}} \int_{a/\sqrt{t}}^\infty e^{-u^2}\, du$	$\frac{1}{p} e^{-2a\sqrt{p}}$	
$\frac{a^\nu e^{-a^2/4t}}{(2t)^{\nu+1}}$	$p^{\nu/2} K_\nu(a\sqrt{p})$	
$e^{-t} L_n(t)$	$\frac{p^n}{(p+1)^{n+1}}$	
$J_0(a\sqrt{t^2 - b^2})$ (zero for $t < b$)	$\frac{e^{-b\sqrt{p^2+a^2}}}{\sqrt{p^2 + a^2}}$	
$\delta(t)$	1	note*
$U(t)F'(t) + \delta(t)F(0)$	$pf(p)$	note*
$U(t)F''(t) + \delta(t)F'(0) + \delta'(t)F(0)$	$p^2 f(p)$	note*
$\frac{d^n}{dt^n} \delta(t)$	p^n	note*

Asymptotic Relations

Roughly, if $F \sim G(t)$ as $t \to 0$ or ∞, then $\mathscr{L}[F] = f \sim g(p) = \mathscr{L}[G]$ as $1/p \to 0$ or ∞ (respectively). However, certain precautions must be observed; basic results of this type are,

If $$\lim_{t\to\infty} t^{-\alpha} F(t) = A \quad \text{then} \quad \lim_{p\to 0} \frac{p^{\alpha+1}}{\alpha!} f(p) = A \tag{13–12}$$

* Corresponding to the fact that the δ-function does not strictly exist, these functions, $f(p)$, violate some of the general properties listed below, but such transform pairs are of great heuristic value nevertheless.

If $$\lim_{t\to 0} t^{-\alpha}F(t) = B \quad \text{then} \quad \lim_{p\to\infty} \frac{p^{\alpha+1}}{\alpha!} f(p) = B \tag{13-13}$$

See also (8–25).

The *converses* of these statements are not true in general, but one can say, for example, that if $F(t)$ *does* approach a limit as $t \to \infty$ then this limit must equal the limit of $pf(p)$ as $p \to 0$.

By repeated application of (13–12) or (13–13) (subtracting off earlier terms in F and f), one can often obtain asymptotic (or even convergent) series for f or F respectively near 0 or ∞.

Analytic Properties

If the Laplace transform (integral) converges for $p =$ some p_0, then it converges throughout the half-plane, Re $(p) >$ Re $(p_0) \equiv \beta$, and it converges *uniformly* in any *finite* region within this half-plane and also converges uniformly in any wedge. $|\text{Arg}\,(p - p_0)| \leqslant \theta < \frac{1}{2}\pi$. The function, $f(p)$, is analytic in the half-plane Re $(p) > \beta$. (except possibly *at* $p = \infty$). In the wedge $|\text{Arg}\,(p - p_0)| \leqslant \theta \leqslant \frac{1}{2}\pi$, $f(p)$ *approaches zero* uniformly *as* $p \to \infty$. Usually, $f(p)$ has a singularity somewhere on the line, Re $(p) = \beta$ (when β is chosen so that the defining integral diverges when Re $(p) < \beta$) but this is not invariably true.

FOURIER AND BILATERAL LAPLACE TRANSFORMS

Bilateral Laplace Transform

$$\mathscr{L}_{\text{II}}[F(t)] = \int_{-\infty}^{\infty} e^{-pt} F(t)\, dt = g(p) \tag{13-14}$$

$$= \mathscr{L}[F(t)] + \mathscr{L}[F(-t)]_{p\to -p}$$

Fourier (Exponential) Transform

$$\mathscr{F}_e[F(t)] = \mathscr{L}_{\text{II}}[F(t)]_{p=i\omega} = \int_{-\infty}^{\infty} e^{-i\omega t} F(t)\, dt = G(\omega) \tag{13-15}$$

The $\mathscr{L}_{\text{II}}$ transform is essentially identical with the Fourier transform but has the added advantage that it may exist when the latter does not (*Example*: $F(t) = e^{at}(1 + t^2)^{-1}$). These two transforms are most useful when the independent variable covers the full range, $(-\infty, \infty)$. A common generalization of (13–15) is the three-dimensional Fourier transform,

$$\mathscr{F}_e[F(\mathbf{r})] = \iiint_{-\infty}^{\infty} e^{-i\mathbf{k}\cdot\mathbf{r}}\, F(\mathbf{r})\, dV = H(\mathbf{k}) \tag{13-16}$$

which is essentially a three-fold application of $\mathscr{F}_e$ to each coordinate variable in turn.

Inversion Formulas

Three-dimensional Fourier:

$$\mathscr{F}_e^{-1}[H(\mathbf{k})] = \frac{1}{(2\pi)^3} \iiint_{-\infty}^{\infty} e^{i\mathbf{k}\cdot\mathbf{r}} H(\mathbf{k})\, dV_k = F(\mathbf{r}) \tag{13-17}$$

Fourier:

$$\mathscr{F}_e^{-1}[G(\omega)] = \frac{1}{2\pi}\int_{-\infty}^{\infty} e^{i\omega t}G(\omega)\,\mathrm{d}\omega = F(t) \tag{13–18}$$

Bilateral Laplace:

$$\mathscr{L}_{II}^{-1}[g(p)] = \frac{1}{2\pi i}\int_{x-i\infty}^{x+i\infty} e^{pt}g(p)\,\mathrm{d}p = F(t) \tag{13–19}$$

(where x is to be chosen so that the line of integration, Re $(p) = x$, lies in the region where (13–14) converges.) In these formulas, the integrals are to be interpreted as Cauchy principle-values where necessary. If $F(t)$ is discontinuous, the inversion yields $\frac{1}{2}[F(t+0) + F(t-0)]$.

General Properties of $\mathscr{L}_{II}$ (and hence $\mathscr{F}_e$)

$$\left.\begin{aligned}
F(at) &\leftrightarrow \frac{1}{a}\,g\left(\frac{p}{a}\right)\\
e^{-at}F(t) &\leftrightarrow g(p+a)\\
F(t+a) &\leftrightarrow e^{ap}g(p)\\
\frac{\mathrm{d}^nF}{\mathrm{d}t^n} &\leftrightarrow p^n g(p)\\
t^nF(t) &\leftrightarrow \left(-\frac{\mathrm{d}}{\mathrm{d}p}\right)^n g(p)\\
\int_{-\infty}^{t} F(x)\,\mathrm{d}x &\leftrightarrow \frac{1}{p}\,g(p)\\
\int_{-\infty}^{\infty} F_1(t-x)F_2(x)\,\mathrm{d}x &\leftrightarrow g_1(p)g_2(p)\\
F_1(t)F_2(t) &\leftrightarrow \frac{1}{2\pi i}\int_{c-i\infty}^{c+i\infty} g_1(p-s)g_2(s)\,\mathrm{d}s
\end{aligned}\right\} \tag{13–20}$$

For any $G(x)$, $H(x)$,

$$\int_{-\infty}^{\infty} G(y)H(y)\,\mathrm{d}y = \int_{-\infty}^{\infty} \mathscr{L}_{\mathrm{II}}[G]\,\mathscr{L}_{\mathrm{II}}^{-1}[H]\,\text{“dz”} \tag{13–21}$$

(where the independent variable of both of the latter functions is written, “z”).

Analytic Properties

In accord with (13–14), the analytic properties of $\mathscr{L}_{\mathrm{II}}$ and $\mathscr{F}_e$ transforms are a consequence of those for the ordinary Laplace transform. The conspicuous feature is that $g(p)$ is in general analytic only in a strip, $\beta_1 \leqslant \mathrm{Re}\,(p) \leqslant \beta_2$, which represents the intersection of the two half-planes of convergence of $\mathscr{L}[F(t)]$ and $\mathscr{L}[F(-t)]_{p\to -p}$ respectively.

Uniqueness of Inversion for $\mathscr{L}_{II}$ and $\mathscr{F}_e$

For the bilateral Laplace (and hence for the Fourier) transform, the inversion formula leads “back” to a unique original function, $F(t)$, only in a rather technical sense: The original function, $F(t)$, is uniquely specified when both $g(p) = \mathscr{L}_{\mathrm{II}}[F]$ *and the region of convergence* (of the defining integral, (13–14)) are given.

EXAMPLE: The functions,

$$F_1(t) = U(t) = \begin{cases} 0, t < 0 \\ 1, t > 0 \end{cases} \quad \text{and} \quad F_2(t) = -U(-t)$$

have the $\mathscr{L}_{II}$ transforms,

$$g_1(p) = \frac{1}{p} \, [\text{in Re}\,(p) > 0] \quad \text{and} \quad g_2(p) = \frac{1}{p} \, [\text{in Re}\,(p) < 0]$$

That is, given $g(p) = 1/p$ one could obtain for its "original" either the function, $U(t)$, or the function, $-U(-t)$, and no decision between these would be possible without some criterion equivalent to specifying the region of convergence of the defining integrals.

Correlation Functions

If
$$\phi_{fg}(\tau) = \int_{-\infty}^{\infty} f(t)g(t+\tau)\,dt = \int_{-\infty}^{\infty} f[-(\tau - u)]g(u)\,du$$
then
$$\Phi(p) = \mathscr{L}_{\text{II}}[\phi_{fg}] = \mathscr{L}_{\text{II}}(f; -p)\,\mathscr{L}_{\text{II}}(g; p) = F(-p)G(p)$$

(convergence strip including Re $(p) = 0$ for most functions). Similarly, if f and g are drawn from statistical ensembles of functions ("$\langle \cdots \rangle$" means "average of $\cdots$"),

$$\mathscr{L}_{\text{II}}[\langle \phi_{fg} \rangle] = \langle F(-p)G(p) \rangle \tag{13–22}$$

This relation can be a powerful aid in computing or studying asymptotic properties of correlation functions.

OTHER USEFUL INTEGRAL TRANSFORMS

1. Stieltjes Transform

$$\mathscr{S}[F(t)] = s(y) = \int_0^{\infty} \frac{F(t)\,dt}{t+y} = \mathscr{L}[\mathscr{L}[F(t)]] \tag{13–23}$$

Inverse:

$$F(t) = \lim_{\epsilon \to 0} \frac{1}{2\pi i}[s(-t - i\epsilon) - s(-t + i\epsilon)] \tag{13–24}$$

which is sometimes useful for evaluating $\mathscr{L}^{-1}[f(p)]$.

$$\int_0^{\infty} G(x)H(x)\,dx = \int_0^{\infty} \mathscr{S}[G]\,\mathscr{S}^{-1}[H]\,d\text{“}z\text{”} \tag{13–25}$$

2. Hankel Transforms

$$\mathscr{H}_\nu[F(r)] = \int_0^{\infty} \sqrt{xr}\,J_\nu(xr)F(r)\,dr \tag{13–26}$$

(J_ν is a Bessel function of the first kind.) These transforms are their own inverses:

$$\mathscr{H}_\nu[\mathscr{H}_\nu[F(r)]] = F(r) \tag{13–27}$$

The special case $\nu = 0$ is especially useful for treating the ∇^2 operator in cylindrical coordinates:

$$\mathscr{H}_0\left[\frac{1}{\sqrt{r}}\frac{\partial}{\partial r}r\frac{\partial\psi}{\partial r}\right] = -x^2\,\mathscr{H}_0\,[\sqrt{r}\,\psi] \tag{13–28}$$

(Provided $\sqrt{r}\,\psi \to 0$ as $r \to \infty$.) More generally,

$$\mathscr{H}_\nu\left[\frac{1}{\sqrt{r}}\frac{\partial}{\partial r}r\frac{\partial\psi}{\partial r}\right] = -x^2\mathscr{H}_\nu[\sqrt{r}\,\psi] + \nu^2\mathscr{H}_\nu[r^{-3/2}\,\psi] \tag{13–29}$$

$$\text{if } \sqrt{r}\,\psi \to 0 \quad \text{as} \quad r \to \infty$$

For $\nu = \frac{1}{2}, -\frac{1}{2}$ the $\mathscr{H}_\nu$ operator becomes $\sqrt{\pi/2}$ times the Fourier sine and cosine transforms respectively. The former has a similar property relative to ∇^2 in spherical coordinates:

$$\mathscr{F}_s\left[\frac{1}{r}\frac{\partial}{\partial r}r^2\frac{\partial\psi}{\partial r}\right] = -x^2\,\mathscr{F}_s[r\psi] \tag{13–30}$$

(where $\mathscr{F}_s[F(r)] = \int_0^\infty \sin(xr)F(r)\,dr$ and provided that $r\psi \to 0$ as $r \to \infty$.)

$$\int_0^\infty f(r)g(r)\,dr = \int_0^\infty \mathscr{H}_\nu[f]\,\mathscr{H}_\nu^{-1}[g]\,d\text{“}x\text{”} \tag{13–31}$$

Connection with Laplace transforms: If we explicitly display the independent variable of the transformed function: $f(p) = \mathscr{L}[F(t);\ p]$, etc., then

$$\left.\begin{aligned} &\mathscr{L}[(2t)^{\frac{1}{2}\nu-\frac{1}{4}}\,F(\sqrt{2t});\ p] = p^{-\nu-1}\mathscr{L}\left[(2t)^{\frac{1}{2}\nu-\frac{1}{4}}\,h(\sqrt{2t});\ \frac{1}{p}\right] \\ &\text{where} \\ &h(t) = \mathscr{H}_\nu[F(r);\ t] \end{aligned}\right\} \tag{13–32}$$

For $\mathscr{H}_0$ there is a more directly useful relation:

$$\left.\begin{aligned} &\mathscr{H}_0\left[\sqrt{r}\,\frac{g(\sqrt{p^2+r^2})}{\sqrt{p^2+r^2}}\ ;\ x\right] = \sqrt{x}\,\mathscr{L}\left[\frac{f(\sqrt{t^2-x^2})}{\sqrt{t^2-x^2}}\ ;\ p\right] \\ &\text{where} \\ &g(p) = \mathscr{L}[f(t);\ p] \end{aligned}\right\} \tag{13–33}$$

and it is understood that $f(\sqrt{t^2-x^2}) = 0$ for $t < x$. Another relation of this type:

$$\left.\begin{aligned} \mathscr{H}_0[\sqrt{r}\,g(\sqrt{p^2+r^2});\ x] &= \sqrt{x}\int_p^\infty s\mathscr{L}[f(\sqrt{t^2-x^2});\ s]\,ds \\ &= \sqrt{x}p\mathscr{L}\left[\frac{1}{t}f(\sqrt{t^2-x^2});\ p\right] + \sqrt{x}\,\mathscr{L}\left[\frac{1}{t^2}f(\sqrt{t^2-x^2});\ p\right] \\ &= \sqrt{x}\,\mathscr{L}\left[\frac{f'(\sqrt{t^2-x^2})}{\sqrt{t^2-x^2}}\ ;\ p\right] \end{aligned}\right\} \tag{13–34}$$

where $f(\sqrt{t^2-x^2}) = 0$ for $t < x$ and $g(p) = \mathscr{L}[f(t);\ p]$

Asymptotic Behavior of $\mathscr{H}_0$ Transform

No theorems for $\mathscr{H}_\nu$ transforms of generality comparable to those for Laplace transforms are known, but for $\mathscr{H}_0$ transforms, the following can be applied in special cases.

Use the relation [where $H_0^{(1)}(z)$ is the Hankel function of the first kind and $H_0^{(1)}(-z)$ is more precisely $H_0^{(1)}(e^{i\pi}z)$],

$$J_0(x) = \tfrac{1}{2}[H_0^{(1)}(x) - H_0^{(1)}(-x)]$$

to convert the desired expression to the form,

$$\int_{-\infty}^{\infty} H_0^{(1)}(rx)\phi(x)\,dx$$

The asymptotic behavior of this integral as $r \to \infty$ can now be obtained by deforming the integration path into the *upper* half-plane [using the fact that $|H_0^{(1)}(z)| \sim \sqrt{2/\pi z}\exp[-\mathrm{Im}(z)]$ there, and taking due account of any poles of $\phi(x)$] and then applying the "Saddle Point" method, Chapter 8.

3. Mellin Transform

$$\mathscr{M}[F(t)] = \int_0^{\infty} t^{z-1}F(t)\,dt = \phi(z) = \mathscr{L}_{\mathrm{II}}[F(e^{-t})] \tag{13-35}$$

Inversion:

$$F(t) = \frac{1}{2\pi i}\int_{C-i\infty}^{C+i\infty} t^{-z}\phi(z)\,dz \tag{13-36}$$

This transform is a generalization of the "moments" of a function, F; see (9–24)–(9–34). Some general properties:

$$\left.\begin{aligned} t^{\beta}F(at^{h}) &\leftrightarrow \frac{1}{|h|}\,a^{-(z+\beta)/h}\phi\left(\frac{z+\beta}{h}\right) \\ \frac{d}{dt}F(t) &\leftrightarrow -(z-1)\phi(z-1) \\ \int_0^{\infty} F_1(\tau)F_2\left(\frac{t}{\tau}\right)\frac{d\tau}{\tau} &\leftrightarrow \phi_1(z)\phi_2(z) \\ \int_0^{\infty} F_1(\tau t)F_2(\tau)\,d\tau &\leftrightarrow \phi_1(z)\phi_2(1-z) \end{aligned}\right\} \tag{13-37}$$

4. Hilbert Transform

$$\mathrm{Hi}[f(x)] = \frac{1}{\pi}\int_{-\infty}^{\infty}\frac{f(x)\,dx}{x-z} = g(z) \tag{13-38}$$

(principal-values of the integral are understood if x and z are both real). The transformed function, $g(z)$, is analytic both in Im $(z) > 0$ and also in Im $(z) < 0$. However, $g(z^*)$ is not the analytic continuation of $g(z)$. In fact, if $f(x)$ is analytic in Im $(x) \geqslant 0$ and is such that $\oint f(x)(x-z)^{-1}\,dx$ over the semicircle, $|x| = R$ and Im $(x) \geqslant 0$, approaches zero as $R \to \infty$, then

$$g(z) = \begin{cases} 2if(z), & \text{for Im } (z) > 0 \\ if(z), & \text{if } z \text{ is real} \\ 0, & \text{for Im } (z) < 0 \end{cases}$$

as follows from Cauchy's theorem (12–6). (Taking real or imaginary parts of this relation will yield many Hilbert transform pairs.)

Inversion:

$$f(z) = -\mathrm{Hi}[g(x)] \tag{13–39}$$

also

$$\int_{t_1}^{t_2} f(u)\,\mathrm{d}u = \lim_{\epsilon\to 0} \frac{1}{2i} \int_{t_1}^{t_2} [g(t+i\epsilon) - g(t-i\epsilon)]\,\mathrm{d}t \tag{13–40}$$

Properties:

$$\left.\begin{aligned} \mathrm{Hi}[xf(x)] &= z\mathrm{Hi}[f(x)] + \frac{1}{\pi}\int_{-\infty}^{\infty} f(x)\,\mathrm{d}x \\ \mathrm{Hi}[\mathrm{d}f/\mathrm{d}x] &= \frac{\mathrm{d}}{\mathrm{d}z}\,\mathrm{Hi}[f(x)] \end{aligned}\right\} \tag{13–41}$$

APPROXIMATE INVERSION OF INTEGRAL TRANSFORMS

1. The "moments" of a function, $f(x)$, namely,

$$\mu_n = \int_a^{\infty} x^n f(x)\,\mathrm{d}x \tag{13–42}$$

are intimately connected with its various integral transforms. If the integral transform of an unknown function is given, the moments, μ_n, of that function (or a closely related one) can be determined by *differentiation* alone, using the relations below. These numbers, μ_n, can then be used to determine the function approximately, even though only a finite set of μ_n are known; see (9–24)–(9–34).

If $a = 0$ in (13–42)

$$\left.\begin{aligned} \mu_n &= \left[\left(-\frac{\mathrm{d}}{\mathrm{d}p}\right)^n \mathscr{L}[f]\right]_{p=0} \\ \mu_n &= \mathscr{M}[f(x)]_{z=n+1} \end{aligned}\right\} \tag{13–43}$$

If $a = -\infty$ in (13–42)

$$\left.\begin{aligned} \mu_n &= \left[\left(-\frac{\mathrm{d}}{\mathrm{d}p}\right)^n \mathscr{L}_{\mathrm{II}}[f]\right]_{p=0} \\ \mu_n &= \left[\left(i\frac{\mathrm{d}}{\mathrm{d}\omega}\right)^n \mathscr{F}_e[f]\right]_{\omega=0} \end{aligned}\right\} \tag{13–44}$$

If $f(x) = f(-x)$, this is a relation for the Fourier cosine transform.

If $a = 0$ in (13–42) there is also a relation of this type for $\mathscr{H}_0$ transforms as follows from (13–28). This is conveniently written,

$$\sum_0^{\infty} \frac{(-1)^n}{(n!)^2} z^n \mu_n = \int_0^{\infty} f(x) J_0(2\sqrt{xz})\,\mathrm{d}x \tag{13–45}$$

and similarly for Fourier sine transforms,

$$\mathscr{F}_s\left(\frac{f(x)}{x}\right) = \sum_0^{\infty} \frac{(-1)^n}{(2n+1)!} \mu_{2n}\omega^{2n+1} \tag{13–46}$$

A special result for (ordinary) Laplace transforms is, if $f(p) = \int_0^\infty e^{-pt} F(t)\, dt$

$$\left.\begin{aligned} F(t) &= \sum_0^\infty c_k e^{-t} L_k(t) \\ \text{with} \qquad c_k &= \sum_0^k \binom{k}{j} a_j \quad \text{where} \quad f(p) = \sum_0^\infty a_i p^i \end{aligned}\right\} \tag{13–47}$$

$$\left[L_k(t) = \sum_0^k \binom{k}{j} \frac{(-t)^j}{j!} = \text{Laguerre polynomial.} \right]$$

2. A rather general method of approximately inverting Laplace transforms is to expand the unknown $F(t)$ in a series of the form,

$$F(t) = \sum c_k G_k(e^{-at}) \tag{13–48}$$

where a is any constant and the G_k are some "suitable" set of functions. Then, with $f(p(= \mathscr{L}[F(t)]$,

$$af[(b+1)a] = \sum c_k \int_0^1 x^b G_k(x)\, dx$$

which is a set of simultaneous equations for determining the c_k from the given function, $f(p)$. More generally, if $P_n(x)$ is a polynomial let $\mathscr{P}_n f$ denote the result of substituting $f[(i+1)a]$ for x^i in P_n (including $f(a)$ for x^0 in the constant term). Then

$$a\mathscr{P}_n f = \sum c_k \int_0^1 P_n(x) G_k(x)\, dx \tag{13–49}$$

In particular, it may be expedient to choose the polynomials P_n to be orthonormal to the functions G_k (see (18–38) ff.), for then (13–49) reduces to $c_n = a\mathscr{P}_n f$ and the computation reduces to mere substitution.

INTEGRAL TRANSFORMS OF CONVOLUTION TYPE

Consider an integral transform of the type,

$$f(x) = \int_{-\infty}^{\infty} G(x-y)\phi(y)\, dy \tag{13–50}$$

(where the "kernel" function, G, is regarded as fixed while f and ϕ assume various forms). This has the general (formal) inverse:

$$E\left(\frac{d}{dx}\right) f(x) = \phi(x) \tag{13–51}$$

where $1/E$ is the bilateral Laplace transform of G:

$$\frac{1}{E(p)} = \mathscr{L}_{II}[G(t)] \tag{13–52}$$

Symbolic proof:

$$\frac{1}{E\left(\frac{\mathrm{d}}{\mathrm{d}x}\right)}\phi(x) = \left[\int_{-\infty}^{\infty} G(t)\exp\left(-t\frac{\mathrm{d}}{\mathrm{d}x}\right)\mathrm{d}t\right]\phi(x)$$

$$= \int_{-\infty}^{\infty} G(t)[e^{-t(\mathrm{d}/\mathrm{d}x)}\phi(x)]\,\mathrm{d}t$$

$$= \int_{-\infty}^{\infty} G(t)\phi(x-t)\,\mathrm{d}t \quad \text{(Taylor's series)}$$

$$= \int_{-\infty}^{\infty} G(x-\tau)\phi(\tau)\,\mathrm{d}\tau = f(x)$$

Similarly, in three dimensions,

$$\left.\begin{aligned} &\text{If} && f(\mathbf{r}) = \iiint_{-\infty}^{\infty} G(\mathbf{r}-\mathbf{R})\phi(\mathbf{R})\,\mathrm{d}V_R \\ &\text{and if} && \frac{1}{E(\mathbf{s})} = \iiint_{-\infty}^{\infty} e^{-\boldsymbol{\rho}\cdot\mathbf{s}} G(\boldsymbol{\rho})\,\mathrm{d}V_\rho \\ &\text{then} && \phi(\mathbf{r}) = E(\boldsymbol{\nabla})f(\mathbf{r}) \end{aligned}\right\} \quad (13\text{–}53)$$

In particular, if G is a "displacement kernel", namely

$$G(\mathbf{r}-\mathbf{R}) = G(|\mathbf{r}-\mathbf{R}|)$$

then the inversion operator becomes

$$\frac{1}{E(\mathbf{s})} = \frac{4\pi}{s}\int_0^{\infty} tG(t)\sinh st\,\mathrm{d}t = 4\pi\sum_0^{\infty}\frac{(s^2)^n}{(2n+1)!}\int_0^{\infty} t^{2n+2}G(t)\,\mathrm{d}t = \frac{1}{\mathscr{E}(s^2)} \quad \text{(say)}$$

and

$$\phi(\mathbf{r}) = \mathscr{E}(\boldsymbol{\nabla}^2)f(\mathbf{r}) \qquad (13\text{–}54)$$

The one-dimensional inversion (13–51) can also be cast as a contour integral. Let

$$K(z) = \mathscr{L}[E(s)] = \mathscr{L}\left[\frac{1}{\mathscr{L}_{\mathrm{II}}[G]}\right]$$

Then one can show formally,

$$\phi(t) = \frac{1}{2\pi i}\oint_{C_\rho} K(z)f(t+z)\,\mathrm{d}z \qquad (13\text{–}55)$$

where C_ρ is a "suitable" contour. One result of this type which can be rigorously proved is:

If $$E(s) = \prod_1^{\infty}\left(1-\frac{s^2}{a_n{}^2}\right) \quad \text{where} \quad \lim_{n\to\infty}(n/a_n) = \Omega$$

then if C_ρ encircles $\pm i\pi\Omega$ and lies inside $|\mathrm{Im}\, z| < \pi\Omega/\rho$ then (13–55) is valid if one takes its limit $\rho \to 1$ (from below).

Application, Effect of Finite Instrument Resolution

If a spectrum or distribution is measured with an instrument whose response to a single, concentrated line-source is $G(t)$ then the true spectrum, $\phi(t)$, is related to the measured spectrum, $f(t)$, by

$$f(t) = \int_{-\infty}^{\infty} G(t-u)\phi(u)\,du$$

This can be inverted by employing the $\mathscr{L}_{II}$ transform, but the practical case (where $f(t) \doteqdot \phi(t)$) can be treated more expediently by the formalism (13–52). Thus if $G(t)$ is a narrow Gaussian function, $G(t) = \exp(-t^2/\sigma^2)$, then by (13–52)

$$E(s) = \frac{1}{\sigma\sqrt{\pi}} \exp(-s^2\sigma^2/4)$$

and by (13–51)

$$\phi(t) = \frac{1}{\sigma\sqrt{\pi}}\left[f(t) - \frac{\sigma^2}{4}\frac{d^2f}{dt^2} + \cdots\right]. \tag{13–56}$$

Connection With Laplace, Fourier and Hankel Transforms

Consider transforms of the type,

$$g(s) = \int_0^{\infty} H(st)f(t)\,dt \tag{13–57}$$

If we set $s = e^{-x}$ and $t = e^{y}$, this is changed to the convolution form, (13–50), and the symbolic results, (13–51), (13–52) can be written as follows in terms of s and t.

If

$$\frac{1}{E(p)} = \mathscr{M}[H(z)] = \int_0^{\infty} z^{p-1}H(z)\,dz$$

then

$$wf(w) = E\left(w\frac{d}{dw}\right) g\left(\frac{1}{w}\right) \tag{13–58}$$

is the inversion of (13–57). For the Laplace transform, where $H(x) = e^{-x}$, the function $E(p) = 1/\Gamma(p)$.

Another form of this inversion is:

$$u^{\alpha}f\left(\frac{1}{u}\right) = E_{\alpha}\left(-u\frac{d}{du}\right)[u^{\alpha+1}g(u)] \tag{13–59}$$

where, for any constant α,

$$E_{\alpha}(p) = E(p + 1 + \alpha)$$

CHAPTER 14

ORDINARY DIFFERENTIAL EQUATIONS

THE theory of differential equations, like that of integration, is to a great extent a series of "tricks", with relatively less unification than other mathematical fields.

Above all, reference should be made to:

E. Kamke, "*Differentialgleichengungen, Loesungsmethoden und Loesungen*", Chelsea Pub. Co., New York (1948)

This contains an extensive catalogue of ordinary differential equations and their known solutions; it is the analogue of an ordinary table of integrals.

Terminology

1. An *ordinary* differential equation contains only ordinary (total) derivatives—as opposed to partial derivatives. (It therefore contains only two variables.)

2. The *order* of a differential equation is the order of the highest derivative occurring therein.

3. A *linear* differential equation is linear in all derivatives and in the dependent variable. The independent variable can occur in arbitrary form. The general linear differential equation of order n is thus,

$$\sum_{i=0}^{n} f_i(x) \frac{\mathrm{d}^i y}{\mathrm{d}x^i} = g(x) \tag{14-1}$$

4. A *homogeneous*, linear differential equation has the form (14–1) with $g(x) = 0$. (The term "homogeneous" is seldom applied to non-linear differential equations.)

METHODS APPLICABLE TO ALL ORDINARY DIFFERENTIAL EQUATIONS

1. **Independent variable missing:**

$$F(y, y', y'', \cdots, y^{(n)}) = 0$$

Letting,

$$\left.\begin{aligned} y' = p = p(y); \qquad y'' = p\frac{\mathrm{d}p}{\mathrm{d}y}; \cdots \end{aligned}\right\} \tag{14-2}$$

will lower the order by one degree.

2. **Dependent variable missing:**

$$F(x, y', y'', \cdots, y^{(n)}) = 0$$

Letting,

$$\left.\begin{aligned} y' = p = p(x); \qquad y'' = \mathrm{d}p/\mathrm{d}x; \cdots \end{aligned}\right\} \tag{14-3}$$

lowers the order by one.

3. **"Equi-dimensional" equations:** (In many physical problems, this property necessarily arises.)

(a) If the differential equation is unaffected by a scale-change in y:

then set
$$\left.\begin{aligned} \bar{y} &= ay \\ y &= e^{z(x)} \end{aligned}\right\} \tag{14–4}$$

and all terms involving z itself will cancel out, so that (14–3) may be applied. Alternatively, set

$$u(x) = y'/y$$

to obtain immediately an equation of lower order.

(b) If the differential equation is unaffected by some simultaneous scale-change of both x and y:

then set
$$\left.\begin{aligned} \bar{x} &= ax, \qquad \bar{y} = a^{\alpha}y \\ x &= e^{\theta}, \qquad y = e^{\alpha\theta}z(\theta) \end{aligned}\right\} \tag{14–5}$$

and all factors, e^{θ}, will cancel out so that (14–2) may be applied. Alternatively, the order is immediately reduced by unity if one sets

$$\left.\begin{aligned} &y = x^{\alpha}z, \qquad \mathrm{d}y/\mathrm{d}x = x^{\alpha-1}p \\ &\left(\text{thus:}\quad x\frac{\mathrm{d}}{\mathrm{d}x} = (p - \alpha z)\frac{\mathrm{d}}{\mathrm{d}z}\right) \end{aligned}\right\} \tag{14–6}$$

and x will disappear completely, leaving an equation (of lower degree) in p and z alone.

4. **Interchange of variables:** Take y as independent and x as dependent. This may convert a non-linear equation to a linear one or otherwise simplify the problem. The order of the equation, however, will not be affected. Formulas useful for this "inversion":

$$\left.\begin{aligned} &\frac{\mathrm{d}y}{\mathrm{d}x} = \frac{1}{(\mathrm{d}x/\mathrm{d}y)}; \qquad \frac{\mathrm{d}^2y}{\mathrm{d}x^2} = \frac{-\mathrm{d}^2x/\mathrm{d}y^2}{(\mathrm{d}x/\mathrm{d}y)^3} \\ &\frac{\mathrm{d}^3y}{\mathrm{d}x^3} = \frac{3(\mathrm{d}^2x/\mathrm{d}y^2)^2 - (\mathrm{d}x/\mathrm{d}y)(\mathrm{d}^3x/\mathrm{d}y^3)}{(\mathrm{d}x/\mathrm{d}y)^5} \end{aligned}\right\} \tag{14–7}$$

5. **Substitutions:** Sometimes, the equation, $F(x, y, y', y'', \cdots, y^{(n)}) = 0$, can be written $F\left(u, v, \frac{\mathrm{d}v}{\mathrm{d}u}, \cdots, \frac{\mathrm{d}^{(n-1)}v}{\mathrm{d}u^{n-1}}\right) = 0$ where $u = u(x, y)$ and $v = v(x, y, y')$. This latter form, of course, is of order $n - 1$. The rules (14–2)–(14–6) all are special cases of this observation [in (14–5) $u = y/x^{\alpha}$ and $v = y'x^{1-\alpha}$]. Others of this type are:

$$\left.\begin{aligned} F(x, xy' - y, y'', \cdots) &= 0 \\ F(ax + by, y', y'', \cdots) &= 0 \end{aligned}\right\} \tag{14–8}$$

In general, the difficulty, of course, lies in recognizing that such a reduction is possible (see para. 7 below, however).

Another "obvious" case is where the equation can be written

$$G(x, y, y', \cdots)H(x, y, y', \cdots) = 0;$$

here a solution of either factor is a solution of the original equation.

6. **The Legendre transformation:** This will alter drastically the form of the equation and is therefore *sometimes* useful when an equation resists the methods above. One defines new variables z, p by setting,

$$\left.\begin{aligned} &x = \frac{dz}{dp}; \qquad y = p\frac{dz}{dp} - z \\ &\text{whence it follows} \\ &\frac{dy}{dx} = p; \qquad \frac{d^2y}{dx^2} = \left[\frac{d^2z}{dp^2}\right]^{-1}; \qquad \frac{d}{dx} = \frac{1}{z''}\frac{d}{dp} \end{aligned}\right\} \tag{14–9}$$

If a solution of the transformed equation can be found, say $z = f(p)$, then (14–9) with $z = f$ is a solution of the original equation, expressed in parametric form. That is,

$$\left.\begin{aligned} y &= pf'(p) - f(p) \\ x &= f'(p) \end{aligned}\right\} \text{ eliminate } p \tag{14–10}$$

7. **Equations with invariance properties:** If the differential equation is unchanged by a (one-parameter) group of transformations of which the infinitesimal operator [see (22–1)–(22–4)] is

$$\xi(x, y)\frac{\partial}{\partial x} + \eta(x, y)\frac{\partial}{\partial y}$$

then the order of the original equation can be reduced as follows. Let

$$\zeta(x, y, y') = \frac{d\eta}{dx} - y'\frac{d\xi}{dx}$$

and solve the set (see (15–2) for conventions):

$$\frac{dx}{\xi} = \frac{dy}{\eta} = \frac{dp}{\zeta(x, y, p)} \tag{14–11}$$

in the form,

$$u(x, y) = \text{constant}; \qquad v(x, y, p) = \text{constant}$$

Taking u and $v(x, y, y')$ as new variables will then reduce the order of the original equation.

8. **"Last-resort" methods:** If a differential equation resists all other attempts at solution, a few special solutions can often be obtained by "splitting" it. For example, given such forms as

$$f(x, y, y', \cdots) + g(x, y, y', \cdots) = 0$$

or

$$\frac{f(x, y, y', \cdots)}{g(x, y, y', \cdots)} = C$$

we may write $f = -h(x) = -g$ [or, respectively $f = Ch$, $g = h$] where $h(x)$ is chosen arbitrarily. Then any *common* solution of the resulting pair is a solution of the original equation.

Occasionally, this method can succeed spectacularly, but usually only a few decidedly non-general results can be obtained in this way.

9. **Perturbation methods** (*approximate*): In many problems, especially in physics, one knows or has reason to suspect that the desired solution is "close to" a known solution of a simpler problem. The complex problem may be a slight perturbation of the simpler one. Thus:

If certain terms of an equation are known or suspected to be small* compared to others, then, schematically,

$$f(x, y, y', y'', \cdots) = \epsilon g(x, y, y', y'', \cdots) \tag{14–12}$$

where ϵ indicates small terms. If now the solution of

$$f(x, y, y', y'', \cdots) = F(x) \tag{14–13}$$

is known for arbitrary $F(x)$, then an approximate solution of (14–12) may be found by substituting the initial estimate, $y = y_0(x)$, into g (*only*). The result is an equation of the form (14–13) and its solution yields an improved approximation, say $y_1(x)$. In principle, the process may be repeated indefinitely by substituting each improved function, $y_n(x)$, into the right side of (14–12) and solving for the next approximation, $y_{n+1}(x)$.

In practice, it is often difficult to go beyond the first improvement, $y_1(x)$. Indeed, the process may fail to converge, but this circumstance (seldom critically examined) need not vitiate its usefulness, inasmuch as sound physical reasoning will often yield an *asymptotic* sequence of functions. That is, $y_1(x)$ can be a great improvement over $y_0(x)$ even though $y_{100}(x)$, for example, might be an even poorer approximation than y_0.

10. **Graphical methods**: A method applicable to an equation of any order is set forth in Kamke, *op. cit.*, p. 174.

11. **Reduction to a *system* of first-order equations**: This is merely a formal change but sometimes a useful one. The reduction can be made in an infinity of ways, but a common one is to set,

$$(y_0 = y) \qquad y_i = \frac{d}{dx} y_{i-1} \tag{14–14}$$

These defining equations plus the original equation then form a first-order system.

12. **Numerical solution**: An especially flexible, efficient method is "analytic continuation" by *successive* expansions in Taylor's series about each integration point: If at any point, x_k, values of y and its first $n - 1$ derivatives are given, then the differential equation determines all higher derivatives and hence the Taylor's series about $x = x_k$. If the (truncated) series is used to compute values of y (and its first $n - 1$ derivatives) *both* at the previous x_{k-1} and at the new x_{k+1}, then a continuous check on accuracy can be maintained and the interval, Δx, or the number of series-terms can be changed from time to time as required by the accuracy desired. (Also blunders can be detected quickly.)

If the boundary conditions do not specify values of y and its first $n - 1$ derivatives at some initial point, x_0, it is possible to assume values and to integrate repeatedly until the desired solution is found. If the equation is linear it has only n independent solutions and at most n trial-integrations will (usually) give a set of functions, linear combinations of which will satisfy any boundary conditions.

---

* This property may depend on those of the *particular* solution desired—and not be true for all solutions.

LINEAR EQUATIONS OF GENERAL ORDER

The general linear ordinary differential equation has the form,

$$\sum_{i=0}^{n} f_i(x) \frac{d^i y}{dx^i} = g(x) \tag{14–15}$$

The distinguishing feature of this form is that the discovery of a solution can be broken down into a series of simpler (but not necessarily solvable) problems. (If all f_i are constant, see (14–25)–(14–26) below.)

1. **The general solution:** Consider the homogeneous ($g = 0$) version of (14–15),

$$\sum_{i=0}^{n} f_i(x) \frac{d^i y}{dx^i} = 0 \tag{14–16}$$

If *any* solution, $\phi(x)$, of this equation has been found, the order may be reduced with the substitution,

$$y = z(x)\phi(x) \tag{14–17}$$

In particular, if $n - 1$ solutions have been found, the remaining solution of (14–16) may be found by a quadrature (evaluating an ordinary integral).

When a "complete set" of solutions, $\phi_i(x)$, $i = 1, 2, \cdots, n$ of the homogeneous form (14–16) has been found, then consider the matrix,

$$M_{ij}(x) = \frac{d^{n-i}}{dx^{n-i}} \phi_j(x) \tag{14–18}$$

The functions, ϕ_i, are linearly independent *if and only if* their "Wronskian" does not vanish:

$$|M(x)| = \text{Det}\,(M_{ij}(x)) \neq 0 \tag{14–19}$$

(proof: this is equivalent to the condition that the equation, $\sum_i c_i\phi_i(x) = 0$, and its first $n - 1$ derivatives have as their only solution, $c_i = 0$). Incidentally, if the ϕ_i are solutions of (14–16), then, as is easily proved,

$$|M(x)| = |M(a)| \exp\left[-\int_a^x \frac{f_{n-1}(x)}{f_n(x)}\, dx\right] \tag{14–20}$$

Let $\mu_{ij}(x)$ be the matrix inverse of $M_{ij}(x)$; then the *general solution* of (14–15) is

$$y = \sum_{r=1}^{n} \phi_r(x)\left[C_r + \int_a^x [g(t)\mu_{r1}(t)/f_n(t)]\, dt\right] \tag{14–21}$$

where the C_r and a are arbitrary constants.

Note also that if all $\phi_i(x)$ are known and if, in addition, *any* solution of (14–15) is known, say $h(x)$, then these matrix manipulations can be avoided since the *general solution* of (14–15) is then

$$y = h(x) + \sum_{r=1}^{n} C_r\phi_r(x) \tag{14–22}$$

as follows from the form of (14–21).

2. **Green's function:** Another approach is to seek a solution of (14–15) for a "point source"—that is, a solution of (14–15) with $g(x) = 0$ except in a small region.

If such solutions can be found (say $y(x) = G(x, a)$ when the point source lies at $x = a$), then a solution of (14–15) will be [note the similarity to (14–21)]

$$y(x) = \int_{(-\infty)}^{(\infty)} g(u)G(x, u)\, \mathrm{d}u \tag{14–23}$$

A rigorous foundation for these ideas must avoid the (strictly non-existent) delta-function (which corresponds to a *point* source of finite strength), but, in applications, the main point is the discovery of $G(x, a)$ and this can be done in any expedient way. Generally, G has a discontinuous $(n - 1)^{\text{th}}$ derivative (with respect to x) at $x = a$ and satisfies any other *boundary conditions* of the problem.

Thus, when new boundary conditions are introduced, the whole problem must be solved anew. This is the only disadvantage of the method as contrasted with the general method sketched above, but it will often yield solutions for simple boundary conditions when the general problem is insoluble.

3. **Integral transforms:** If the $f_i(x)$ in (14–15) are *polynomials* (of low degree) the Laplace or other integral transform may be helpful, but these methods are not usually applicable to (14–15).

4. **Reduction of order:** The order of (14–15) can always be reduced, but the result is a *non*-linear equation, which often represents no gain. The reduction is accomplished by setting $y = \exp(\int u(x))$.

5. **Elimination of the $y^{(n-1)}$ term** in (14–15) can always be achieved by setting,

$$y = v(x) \exp\left[\frac{-1}{n}\int_a^x \frac{f_{n-1}(x)}{f_n(x)}\, \mathrm{d}x\right] \tag{14–24}$$

6. **Reduction to first-order (linear) system:** When (14–14) is applied to (14–15), the result is a *linear* system of first-order equations. The solution for arbitrary initial values, $y^{(k)}(x_0) = a_k$ can then be obtained in series form by using (14–44)–(14–46).

Linear Differential Equations with *Constant Coefficients*

If the equation reads,

$$\sum_{j=0}^{n} A_j \frac{\mathrm{d}^j y}{\mathrm{d}x^j} = V(x) \tag{14–25}$$

with the A_j = constants, the solution can always be expressed as a convolution integral:

$$y(x) = \int_{x_0}^{x} h(x - t)V(t)\, \mathrm{d}t + \sum_i C_i\phi_i(x)$$

This solution is usually obtained most conveniently by taking the *Laplace transform* of (14–25)—especially if the initial conditions, $y^{(i)}(x_0)$ for $i = 0, 1, \cdots, n - 1$, are stipulated by the particular problem at hand.

Another procedure is to enter the homogeneous equation ($V = 0$) with the assumption, $y = e^{ax}$; this leads to the "characteristic equation",

$$\sum_{j=0}^{n} A_j a^j = 0 \tag{14–26}$$

whose distinct algebraic roots, $a = \alpha_j$, yield the solutions, $\phi_j(x) = e^{\alpha_j x}$. [If α_j has multiplicity m the corresponding different ϕ_i are $e^{\alpha_j x}$, $xe^{\alpha_j x}$, $\cdots$, $x^{m-1}e^{\alpha_j x}$.] The "impulse-response function", $h(x - t)$ above, can then be determined by (14–18), (14–21).

Stability: If it is desired only to know whether all α_j have negative real part, (7–6) may be applied directly to (14–26) without solving the equation.

FIRST-ORDER DIFFERENTIAL EQUATIONS

1. **Singular solutions** are particularly troublesome for non-linear first-order* equations; an apparently general solution (that is, one involving an arbitrary constant) may not include all possible solutions. In particular, the envelope of any set of solutions is again a solution.

A singular solution (whether an envelope or not) of the equation, $\phi(x, y, \mathrm{d}y/\mathrm{d}x) = 0$ must satisfy *also* the relations (where $p = \mathrm{d}y/\mathrm{d}x$),

$$\frac{\partial\phi}{\partial p} = 0; \qquad \frac{\partial\phi}{\partial x} + p\,\frac{\partial\phi}{\partial y} = 0 \tag{14–27}$$

and this fact can usually be used to determine whether any singular solutions exist.

2. **Simple forms:**

Separable:

$$\left.\begin{aligned} &f(y)\,\mathrm{d}y = g(x)\,\mathrm{d}x \\ &\text{solution:} \\ &\int_\alpha^y f(y)\,\mathrm{d}y = \int_\beta^x g(x)\,\mathrm{d}x + C \end{aligned}\right\} \tag{14–28}$$

Linear:

$$\left.\begin{aligned} &\frac{\mathrm{d}y}{\mathrm{d}x} + f(x)y + g(x) = 0 \\ &\text{solution:} \\ &y = \left[C - \int_\beta^x g(x)\exp\left(\int_\alpha^x f\,\mathrm{d}x\right)\mathrm{d}x\right]\cdot\exp\left(-\int_\alpha^x f\,\mathrm{d}x\right) \end{aligned}\right\} \tag{14–29}$$

Linear (in x):

$$\left.\begin{aligned} &\left(\frac{\mathrm{d}y}{\mathrm{d}x}\right)^{-1} + f(y)x + g(y) = 0 \\ &\text{solution:} \\ &x = \left[C - \int_\beta^y g(y)\exp\left(\int_\alpha^y f\,\mathrm{d}y\right)\mathrm{d}y\right]\cdot\exp\left(-\int_\alpha^y f\,\mathrm{d}y\right) \end{aligned}\right\} \tag{14–30}$$

Note that in all of these, α and β are not truly "extra" constants. Changing their values is equivalent, at most, to a change in C.

3. **Special forms:**

In addition to the important cases already listed in (14–2)–(14–8), the following forms can be reduced to one of the simple forms above. (Note: *Always try interchanging "x" and "y".*)

---

* Singular solutions can also occur with higher-order equations. Thus, $(y'')^2 + (y')^2 = 1$ has the "general" solution $y = \sin(x + B) + C$ but also the singular solutions, $y = x + D$.

Bernoulli equation:

$$\left.\begin{aligned} &\frac{dy}{dx} + yF(x) + y^a G(x) = 0 \\ &\text{set:} \quad \bar{y} = u^{1/(1-a)} \end{aligned}\right\} \tag{14–13}$$

Clairaut equation:

$$\left.\begin{aligned} &y = x\frac{dy}{dx} + f\left(\frac{dy}{dx}\right) \\ &\text{differentiate to find} \quad y'' = 0 \quad or \quad x = -f'\left(\frac{dy}{dx}\right) \\ &\text{thus} \quad y = Cx + f(C) \quad \text{or the envelope of such curves.} \end{aligned}\right\} \tag{14–32}$$

$$\left.\begin{aligned} &\frac{dy}{dx} = F(ax + by); && \text{set} \quad \bar{y} = ax + by \\ &x\frac{dy}{dx} + \alpha y = y^\rho \phi(x) F(yx^\alpha); && \text{set} \quad \bar{y} = yx^\alpha \\ &x\frac{dy}{dx} + \alpha y = x^\rho \psi(y) G(yx^\alpha)\frac{dy}{dx}; && \text{set} \quad \bar{x} = yx^\alpha \end{aligned}\right\} \tag{14–33}$$

$$P(x, y)\, dy + Q(x, y)\, dx = 0, \quad \text{with} \quad \frac{\partial P}{\partial x} = \frac{\partial Q}{\partial y} \tag{14–34}$$

This is "exact"; that is, there is a function, $F(x, y)$, with $P = \partial F/\partial y$ and $Q = \partial F/\partial x$ and the equation is simply $dF = 0$.

Equations invariant under a group of transformations: If

$$P(x, y)\, dx = Q(x, y)\, dy \tag{14–35}$$

is invariant under the group of (one-parameter) transformations whose infinitesimal operator (see Chapter 22) is

$$\xi(x, y)\frac{\partial}{\partial x} + \eta(x, y)\frac{\partial}{\partial y}$$

then

$$\frac{P\,dx - Q\,dy}{P\xi - Q\eta} = d[F(x, y)] \tag{14–36}$$

and the general solution of (14–35) is F = constant.

Riccati equation:

$$\frac{dy}{dx} = P(x) + yQ(x) + y^2 R(x) \tag{14–37}$$

This is equivalent to the most general linear, second-order differential equation, and transformation to that form may facilitate solution. To transform, set

$$u = \exp\left[-\int^x y(x)R(x)\, dx\right]$$

to find:

$$u'' - \left(Q + \frac{R'}{R}\right)u' + RPu = 0 \tag{14–38}$$

By (14–59) and (14–60) below, this can be further transformed to make $Q = 0$ and $R = 1$.

4. Special methods (*especially applicable to first-order equations*):

(a) Always try *interchanging* x and y—that is, considering y as the independent variable.

(b) A non-linear equation may *factor algebraically* into simpler equations; a solution of either factor is a solution of the original.

(c) *Differentiate* to obtain an equation of higher order but (perhaps by using the original equation) of simpler type. In particular:

1. Solve for y in the form $f(x, p)$ where $p = \mathrm{d}y/\mathrm{d}x$, and regard p as a third variable by adjoining the equation, $dy = p\,\mathrm{d}x$.
2. Differentiate: $\mathrm{d}y = f_1\,\mathrm{d}x + f_2\,\mathrm{d}p = p\,\mathrm{d}x$, which is an equation in p and x *only*. If the latter can be solved, then its solution, $p = g(x) = \mathrm{d}y/\mathrm{d}x$ is a *separated* equation for y.

(d) *Convert to a Partial Equation*: Write the given equation as $P(x, y)\,\mathrm{d}x + Q(x, y)\,\mathrm{d}y = 0$ and determine an "integrating factor", $M(x, y)$ from

$$\frac{\partial(MP)}{\partial y} = \frac{\partial(MQ)}{\partial x}$$

If such an M can be found, multiplication of the original equation by M will make it "exact"—(14–34).

(e) *Legendre Transformation*: Given $F(x, y, \mathrm{d}y/\mathrm{d}x) = 0$, try to solve,

$$F\left(\mathrm{d}Y/\mathrm{d}X, \frac{\mathrm{d}Y}{\mathrm{d}X}X - Y, X\right) = 0$$

If this can be solved, a solution of the original equation (in parametric form) is,

$$x = Y'(X), \quad y = XY'(X) - Y(X)$$

5. Numerical and graphical methods:

(a) $\mathrm{d}y/\mathrm{d}x = F(x, y)$ establishes a "vector field" in the (x, y)-plane and solutions are the curves traced by these vectors. This is often a good way to derive general features concerning solutions before undertaking any more arduous calculation.

(b) For a rapid graphical method—given the condition, $y(x_0) = a$—see Kamke, *op. cit.* The method is essentially equivalent to solving by a finite difference approximation.

(c) Iteration: Take any $\phi_0(x)$ (the better the initial choice, the faster the convergence, however) and compute successively better approximations by:

$$\phi_{n+1}(x) = \int_\beta^x f(t, \phi_n(t))\,\mathrm{d}t$$

where the differential equation is $\mathrm{d}y/\mathrm{d}x = f(x, y)$ and β is chosen to match the required boundary conditions. An error formula, when the boundary condition is $y(x_0) = \alpha$: If

$$|f(x, d) - f(x, c)| \leqslant M\,|d - c| \quad \text{and} \quad |f| \leqslant A$$

whenever $\quad |x - x_0| < a \quad \text{and} \quad |y - \alpha| < b$

and if $\phi_0(x) \equiv \alpha$ *then*

$$|\phi_n(x) - y(x)| \leqslant \frac{A}{M} \sum_{n+1}^{\infty} \frac{M^i |x - x_0|^i}{i!}$$

at least for $|x - x_0| <$ Smaller of $(a, b/A)$. Moreover, if in addition to the above we have

$$f(x, \alpha) \neq 0, \qquad D = [f(x, d) - f(x, c)]/(d - c) < 0$$

throughout the range of integration, then the true solution $y(x)$ lies *between* any two successive iterates, $\phi_n(x)$; if $D > 0$, the iterates increase or decrease steadily to $y(x)$.

(d) Numerical analytic continuation: See the material following (14–14).

SYSTEMS OF DIFFERENTIAL EQUATIONS (MATRIX OR VECTOR DIFFERENTIAL EQUATIONS)

Any system of differential equations (with a single independent variable) can be reduced to the following form by using (14–14).

$$\frac{dy_i}{dx} = f_i(x, y_1, y_2, \cdots, y_n); \quad i = 1, 2, \cdots, n$$

or, in vector notation,

$$\frac{d\mathbf{y}}{dx} = \mathbf{f}(x, \mathbf{y}) \tag{14–39}$$

1. *Iteration*: Set $\mathbf{y} \equiv \boldsymbol{\phi}_0(x)$ (arbitrary, but a close first approximation will improve convergence) and compute the successively better approximations,

$$\boldsymbol{\phi}_{k+1}(x) = \int^x \mathbf{f}(x, \boldsymbol{\phi}_k(x))\, dx + \mathbf{C} \tag{14–40}$$

where $\mathbf{C}$ is chosen to satisfy the required boundary conditions. An error formula: If the boundary condition is $\mathbf{y}(c) = \mathbf{B}$ and we choose $\boldsymbol{\phi}_0(x) \equiv \mathbf{B}$ then provided that

$$|f_i(x, \mathbf{Y}) - f_i(x, \mathbf{y})| \leqslant M \sum_1^n |Y_j - y_j| \quad \text{and} \quad |f_i| \leqslant A$$

whenever

$$|x - c| < a \quad \text{and} \quad |y_i - B_i| < b$$

we have

$$|\phi_{k,i}(x) - y_i(x)| \leqslant (A/nM) \sum_{k+1}^{\infty} (nM|x - c|)^p/p!$$

at least when $|x - c| <$ Smaller of $(a, b/A)$.

2. If $\mathbf{f}$ is independent of x:

$$\frac{d\mathbf{y}}{dx} = \mathbf{g}(\mathbf{y}) \tag{14–41}$$

then the solution satisfying $\mathbf{y}(0) = \mathbf{a}$ can be expanded in the form,

$$\mathbf{y} = e^{xU}\mathbf{a}$$

where

$$U = \mathbf{g}(\mathbf{a}) \cdot \boldsymbol{\nabla}_a = \sum_{i=0}^{n} g_i(\mathbf{a}) \frac{\partial}{\partial a_i} \tag{14–42}$$

and

$$e^{xU} = \sum_{j=0}^{\infty} \frac{1}{j!} (xU)^j$$

3. *Linear* sets with *constant* coefficients:

$$\frac{d\mathbf{y}}{dx} = \mathfrak{A} \cdot \mathbf{y} + \mathbf{h}(x) \tag{14–43}$$

The discussion under (14–25) applies mutatis mutandis: The Laplace transform is usually the most expedient method. Alternatively, first assume $\mathbf{y} = \mathbf{a}e^{\lambda x}$ as a solution of the homogeneous ($\mathbf{h} = 0$) equation to obtain $\lambda\mathbf{a} = \mathfrak{A} \cdot \mathbf{a}$. This requires $|\mathfrak{A} - \lambda\mathfrak{I}| = 0$ which specifies n values for λ (eigenvalues of $\mathfrak{A}$) and the corresponding $\mathbf{a}$ are the eigenvectors of $\mathfrak{A}$. [If a root, λ_i, occurs repeated r times, the corresponding solutions are of the form $e^{\lambda_i x}, xe^{\lambda_i x}, \cdots, x^{r-1}e^{\lambda_i x}$.] Then any solution of the inhomogeneous equation is added to obtain the general solution of (14–43). Compare also:

4. *The Matrizant*: If the equations are (merely) *linear*,

$$\frac{d\mathbf{y}}{dx} = \mathfrak{M}(x) \cdot \mathbf{y} + \mathbf{h}(x) \tag{14–44}$$

then the solution with $\mathbf{y}(x_0) = \mathbf{a}$ may be expressed as:

$$\mathbf{y} = \Omega(x) \cdot \mathbf{a} + \Omega \cdot \int_{x_0}^{x} \Omega^{-1} \cdot \mathbf{h}\, dx \tag{14–45}$$

where the matrix, $\Omega(x)$, is called the "matrizant" and is that solution of the homogeneous equation, $d\Omega/dx = \mathfrak{M} \cdot \Omega$, with the boundary condition, $\Omega(x_0) = \mathfrak{I}$ (the unit matrix). It may be expressed as the series,*

$$\left.\begin{aligned} \Omega_{x_0}{}^{x}(\mathfrak{M}) = \mathfrak{I} &+ \int_{x_0}^{x} \mathfrak{M}(u)\, du + \int_{x_0}^{x} \mathfrak{M}(u_1)\, du_1 \int_{x_0}^{u_1} \mathfrak{M}(u_2)\, du_2 \\ &+ \int_{x_0}^{x} \mathfrak{M}(u_1)\, du_1 \int_{x_0}^{u_1} \mathfrak{M}(u_2)\, du_2 \int_{x_0}^{u_2} \mathfrak{M}(u_3)\, du_3 + \cdots \end{aligned}\right\} \tag{14–46}$$

(Note that the products involved are matrix products.) Symbolically, if $\mathcal{J}$ is the integral operator, $\int_{x_0}^{x} \cdots du$, then

$$\Omega_{x_0}{}^{x}(\mathfrak{M}) = \sum_{n=0}^{\infty} (\mathcal{J}\mathfrak{M})^n \tag{14–47}$$

Properties of the matrizant:

$$\left.\begin{aligned} &\frac{d}{dx}[\Omega_{x_0}{}^{x}(\mathfrak{M})] = \mathfrak{M}(x) \cdot \Omega_{x_0}{}^{x}; \quad \Omega_{x_0}{}^{x_0} = \mathfrak{I} \\ &\ln |\Omega| = \int_{x_0}^{x} \text{Trace}\, \mathfrak{M}\, dx \\ &[\Omega_{x_0}{}^{x}]^{-1} = \Omega_{x}{}^{x_0} \\ &\Omega_{x_0}{}^{x_2} = \Omega_{x_1}{}^{x_2} \cdot \Omega_{x_0}{}^{x_1} \end{aligned}\right\} \tag{14–48}$$

—If $\mathfrak{M}$ is anti-Hermitian ($\mathfrak{M}^\dagger = -\mathfrak{M}$) then Ω is unitary ($\Omega^{-1} = \Omega^\dagger$). (Proof: let $\mathfrak{Z} = \Omega \cdot \Omega^\dagger$ and derive $d\mathfrak{Z}/dx = \mathfrak{M}\mathfrak{Z} - \mathfrak{Z}\mathfrak{M}$; $\mathfrak{Z}(0) = \mathfrak{I}$ of which the (unique) solution is $\mathfrak{Z} = \mathfrak{I}$.)

$$\left.\begin{aligned} &\Omega(\mathfrak{M} + \mathfrak{N}) = \Omega(\mathfrak{M}) \cdot \Omega(\mathfrak{T}) \\ \text{where} \quad &\mathfrak{T} = [\Omega(\mathfrak{M})]^{-1} \cdot \mathfrak{N} \cdot \Omega(\mathfrak{M}) \end{aligned}\right\} \tag{14–49}$$

---

* If the elements, $M_{ij}(x)$, are bounded for all x, the series converges at least as rapidly as an exponential series for all x. Often $\Omega = \exp(\int \mathfrak{M}\, dx)$ but this is not true in general. For example,

$$\mathfrak{M} = \begin{Vmatrix} 1 & x \\ 0 & 0 \end{Vmatrix} \qquad \text{Note also } \Omega^{-1}(\mathfrak{M}) \neq \Omega(-\mathfrak{M}).$$

This is a formula for "change of representation" in Quantum mechanics. [Proof: evaluate $(\mathrm{d}/\mathrm{d}x)\Omega(\mathfrak{M}) \cdot \Omega(\mathfrak{T})$.]

5. *Further forms*: A system is sometimes more easily or naturally treated in matrix (rather than vector) form:

$$\frac{\mathrm{d}}{\mathrm{d}x}\mathfrak{y} = \mathfrak{M}(x) \cdot \mathfrak{y} - \mathfrak{y} \cdot \mathfrak{N}(x) + \mathfrak{C}(x) \tag{14–50}$$

The solution is:

$$\mathfrak{y}(x) = \Omega(\mathfrak{M}) \cdot \left[\mathfrak{y}(x_0) + \int_{x_0}^{x} \mathrm{d}x\, \Omega^{-1}(\mathfrak{M})\mathfrak{C}\Omega(\mathfrak{N})\right] \cdot \Omega^{-1}(\mathfrak{N}) \tag{14–51}$$

In particular, the solution of

$$\frac{\hbar}{i}\frac{\mathrm{d}\rho}{\mathrm{d}t} = H\rho - \rho H$$

is

$$\rho(t) = \Omega\left(\frac{i}{\hbar}H\right)\rho(0)\Omega^{-1}\left(\frac{i}{\hbar}H\right) \tag{14–52}$$

SECOND-ORDER LINEAR EQUATIONS

The general form* is

$$\boxed{\frac{\mathrm{d}^2y}{\mathrm{d}x^2} + X_1(x)\frac{\mathrm{d}y}{\mathrm{d}x} + X_2(x)y = V(x)} \tag{14–53}$$

A. Exact Techniques

If one solution of (14–53) is known for $V = 0$, then the general solution can be expressed in integral form (as follows from (14–16)–(14–21)):

First, if $y_1(x)$ satisfies (14–53) with $V = 0$, "the" other independent solution of the homogeneous equation is

$$y_2(x) = Gy_1(x)\int_{\alpha}^{x} \frac{\exp\left[-\int_{\beta}^{x'} X_1(x'')\,\mathrm{d}x''\right]}{[y_1(x')]^2}\,\mathrm{d}x' \tag{14–54}$$

where α, β, G are arbitrary constants.

The general solution of (14–53) itself may then be expressed in several ways:

$$y(x) = y_1(x)\left[C_1 - \int_{\alpha}^{x}\frac{V(\xi)y_2(\xi)}{W(\xi)}\,\mathrm{d}\xi\right] + y_2(x)\left[C_2 + \int_{\beta}^{x}\frac{V(\xi)y_1(\xi)}{W(\xi)}\,\mathrm{d}\xi\right] \tag{14–55}$$

where C_1, C_2, α, β are arbitrary and where

$$W(x) = y_1\frac{\mathrm{d}y_2}{\mathrm{d}x} - y_2\frac{\mathrm{d}y_1}{\mathrm{d}x} = C_3\exp\left[-\int_{\gamma}^{x} X_1(x')\,\mathrm{d}x'\right] \tag{14–56}$$

---

* A rather common special form is

$$\frac{\mathrm{d}}{\mathrm{d}x}f(y') = g(y)$$

which may be integrated by multiplying through with $\mathrm{d}y$:

$$g(y)\,\mathrm{d}y = \mathrm{d}[y'f(y')] - f(y')\,\mathrm{d}(y')$$

(Note that C_3 is not arbitrary; for any γ, it is determined by the choice of independent y_1 and y_2 functions.)

Again: Let

$$\left.\begin{aligned} g(x) &= \frac{V(x)}{X_2(x)} \\ \text{then} \quad y(x) &= g(x) + y_1(x)\left[C_1 - \int_\alpha^x \frac{g'(\xi)y_2'(\xi)}{W(\xi)}\,d\xi\right] \\ &\quad + y_2(x)\left[C_2 + \int_\beta^x \frac{g'(\xi)y_1'(\xi)}{W(\xi)}\,d\xi\right] \end{aligned}\right\} \tag{14-57}$$

where α, β, C_1, C_2 are arbitrary and $W(x)$ is defined by (14–56).

Again: Let

$$W_0(x) = \exp\left[-\int_\alpha^x X_1(v)\,dv\right]$$

then

$$y(x) = C_1 y_1(x) + C_2 y_1(x)\int_\gamma^x \frac{W_0}{(y_1)^2}\,du + y_1(x)\int_\gamma^x \frac{W_0}{(y_1)^2}\left[\int_\delta^u \frac{Vy_1}{W_0}\,du'\right]du \tag{14-58}$$

which involves a double integration but requires knowledge of only one solution of the homogeneous equation.

Rigorous solution of (14–53) *therefore reduces to finding* **any** *solution of the homogeneous equation* ($V = 0$).

If any of the methods, (14–2)–(14–11), are applicable, they will usually save considerable labor. The following formalism is helpful in determining whether any of the standard functions of analysis can be used to construct a solution.

In (14–53), set

$$\boxed{y(x) = u(x)\exp\left[-\frac{1}{2}\int_\alpha^x X_1(t)\,dt\right] = \sqrt{W_0}\,u} \tag{14-59}$$

The homogeneous equation then becomes,

$$\boxed{\begin{aligned} &\frac{d^2u}{dx^2} + uI(x) = 0 \\ \text{where} \quad &I(x) = X_2(x) - \tfrac{1}{4}[X_1(x)]^2 - \frac{1}{2}\frac{dX_1}{dx} \end{aligned}} \tag{14-60}$$

The function, $I(x)$, is known as the "invariant" of (14–53) because: Any substitution of the form, $y = wf(x) + g(x)$, will (upon going to the homogeneous form and eliminating the term in w' as above) again yield exactly the same equation (14–60) with the same function, $I(x)$.

By contrast, however, transformation of the *independent* variable will change the function, I. Specifically, for any $f(x)$,

$$\bar{I}(z) = I(x)f^2(x) + \tfrac{1}{2}f\frac{d^2f}{dx^2} - \frac{1}{4}\left(\frac{df}{dx}\right)^2 \tag{14-61}$$

is the new invariant function appearing in

$$\left.\begin{aligned} &\frac{d^2\bar{u}}{dz^2} + \bar{I}(z)\bar{u}(z) = 0 \\ \text{where} \qquad & \\ &z = \int^x \frac{dx}{f(x)}\,; \quad \bar{u}(z) = u(x)/\sqrt{f(x)} \end{aligned}\right\} \tag{14–62}$$

Some examples are given as $R1$–$R4$ in Table 14.1.

Table 14.1 lists solutions for various functions, $I(x)$. (With this table, at least 180 out of the first 220 second-order linear equations listed by Kamke, *op. cit.*, can be solved immediately.)

Reduction to First-order, Non-linear Form

This reduction is seldom of help in finding rigorous solutions but is useful in obtaining asymptotic or approximate results. There are many possibilities:

(a) Set $u = \exp\left(\int \phi \, dx\right)$ in (14–60) to get the Riccati equation:

$$\frac{d\phi}{dx} + \phi^2 + I = 0 \tag{14–63}$$

If ϕ_0 is any solution of this equation, the general solution of (14–60) is then

$$u = \left[C_1 + C_2 \int^x \exp\left(-2\int \phi_0\right) dx\right] \exp\left(\int \phi_0\right) \tag{14–64}$$

(b) In (14–63) further set $\phi \equiv \sqrt{I}w$ *and* $z = \int^x \sqrt{I}\, dx$

$$\left.\begin{aligned} &\frac{dw}{dz} + w^2 + 1 + wr(z) = 0 \\ \text{where} \qquad & \\ &r(z) = \frac{1}{2}\frac{d}{dz}\ln\{I[x(z)]\} = \frac{1}{I}\frac{d\sqrt{I}}{dx} \end{aligned}\right\} \tag{14–65}$$

which has the advantage that the coefficient, $r(z)$, usually varies more slowly than I.

(c) In (14–60) set

$$\left.\begin{aligned} u\sqrt{I} &= \rho(x) \sin[\theta(x)] \\ \frac{du}{dx} &= \rho(x)\cos[\theta(x)] \end{aligned}\right\} \tag{14–66}$$

Then one finds

$$\frac{d\theta}{dx} = \sqrt{I} + \tfrac{1}{4}(\sin 2\theta)\frac{d}{dx}\ln I \tag{14–67}$$

A solution of (14–60) is then

$$u = \frac{\sin\theta}{\sqrt{I}} \exp\left[\frac{1}{2}\int^x \frac{I'}{I}\sin^2\theta \, dx\right] \tag{14–68}$$

This is useful mainly for obtaining rigorous asymptotic results.

TABLE 14.1

Solutions of $\dfrac{d^2u}{dx^2} + I(x)u = 0$

	$I(x)$	A solution of $\dfrac{d^2u}{dx^2} + I(x)u = 0$	
$R1$	$a^2 I_0(ax+b)$	$u_0\,(ax+b)$	
$R2$	$\dfrac{\beta^2}{x^2}\left[x^{2\beta} I_0(x^\beta) - \dfrac{\beta^2-1}{4\beta^2}\right]$	$\dfrac{\sqrt{x}}{x^{\beta/2}}\,u_0(x^\beta)$	
$R3$	$\dfrac{(\alpha\delta-\beta\gamma)^2}{(\alpha+\gamma x)^4}\,I_0\left(\dfrac{\beta+\delta x}{\alpha+\gamma x}\right)$	$(\alpha+\gamma x)u_0\left(\dfrac{\beta+\delta x}{\alpha+\gamma x}\right)$	where $u_0(z)$ is a solution of $\dfrac{d^2u_0}{dz^2} + I_0(z)u_0 = 0$
$R4$	$a^2 e^{2ax} I_0(e^{ax}) - \dfrac{a^2}{4}$	$e^{-ax/2}u_0(e^{ax})$	
$R5$	$\frac{1}{4}(\cos\frac{1}{2}x)^{-4} I_0(\tan\frac{1}{2}x) + \frac{1}{4}$	$(\cos\frac{1}{2}x)u_0(\tan\frac{1}{2}x)$	
1.	$(ax+b)^\alpha$	(Use $R1$ to obtain Ax^α; set $b=0$ in 7)	
2.	$\dfrac{ax+b}{Ax+B}$	(Use $R1$ to obtain $(\alpha+\beta x)/x$; set $c=1$ in 8)	
3.	$\dfrac{a}{x^2}$	x^c with $c = \frac{1}{2}(1 \pm \sqrt{1-4a})$	
4.	ax^2+bx+c	(Use $R1$ to obtain Ax^2+B; set $c=2$ in 8)	
5.	$\dfrac{A}{ax^2+bx+c}$	(Use $R1$ to obtain $\alpha/(\beta x^2+\gamma)$ and again to obtain 16 with $\mu=1$.)	
6.	$\dfrac{a+bx^2}{(d^2-x^2)^2}$	(Use $R1$ to obtain 16)	
7.	$\dfrac{ax^\mu+b}{x^2}$	$\sqrt{x}Z_\nu[(2\sqrt{a}/\mu)x^{\mu/2}]$; $\nu = \dfrac{1}{\mu}\sqrt{1-4b}$ where Z_ν is any Bessel function of order ν	
8.	$\dfrac{ax^c - b^2x^{2c}}{x^2}$	$x^{(1-c)/2}W_{k,m}(2bx^c/c)$; $k = \dfrac{a}{2bc}$; $m = \dfrac{1}{2c}$ (Whittaker function; confluent hypergeometric function)	
9.	$\dfrac{ax^2+bx+c}{x^3}$	Set $x = \sqrt{c/a}e^{iz}$ and use (14–61) to obtain 19.	
10.	$\dfrac{-a^2x^2+4kax+(1-4m^2)}{4x^2}$	$W_{k,m}(ax)$ (Whittaker function or confluent hypergeometric function)	
11.	$(ax^{2\alpha}+bx^\alpha+c)/x^2$	(Use $R2$ with $\beta=\alpha$ to obtain 10.)	
12.	$(ax^{2\gamma}+bx^\gamma+c)/x^{2\gamma+2}$	(Use $R2$ with $\beta=-\gamma$ to obtain 10.)	

TABLE 14-1—(*continued*)

	$I(x)$	A solution of $\frac{d^2u}{dx^2} + I(x)u = 0$
13.	$\frac{Ax^2 + Bx + C}{[(x+a)(x+b)]^2}$	(See 17)
14.	$\frac{Ax^2 + Bx + C}{[(x+a)(x+b)(x+c)]^2}$	(See 18)
15.	$\frac{c}{(x-a)^2(x-b)^2}$	$\lvert x-a\rvert^{(1+\lambda)/2}\cdot\lvert x-b\rvert^{(1-\lambda)/2}$; $\lambda^2 = 1 + \frac{4c}{(a-b)^2}$
16.	$\frac{\nu(\nu+1)}{1-x^2} + \frac{1-\mu^2}{(1-x^2)^2}$	$\sqrt{1-x^2}P_\nu{}^\mu(x)$ or $\sqrt{1-x^2}Q_\nu{}^\mu(x)$ (Legendre functions)
17.	$\frac{1-\lambda^2}{4x^2} + \frac{1-\mu^2}{4(1-x)^2} + \frac{1+\nu^2-\mu^2-\lambda^2}{4x(1-x)}$	$\lvert x\rvert^{\frac{1}{2}(\lambda+1)}\cdot\lvert 1-x\rvert^{\frac{1}{2}(\mu+1)}\cdot{}_2F_1[\frac{1}{2}(\mu+\lambda+\nu+1), \frac{1}{2}(\mu+\lambda-\nu+1);\ \lambda+1;\ x]$ (Hypergeometric function)
18.	$\frac{(\alpha\delta-\beta\gamma)^2}{4(\alpha+\gamma x)^2}\left[\frac{1-\lambda^2}{(\beta+\delta x)^2} + \frac{1-\mu^2}{[\alpha-\beta+(\gamma-\delta)x]^2} + \frac{1+\nu^2-\mu^2-\lambda^2}{(\beta+\delta x)[\alpha-\beta+(\gamma-\delta)x]}\right]$ (Riemann "P-equation")	$\left(\frac{\delta x+\beta}{\alpha+\gamma x}\right)^{\frac{1}{2}(\lambda+1)}\left(\frac{\alpha-\beta+(\gamma-\delta)x}{\alpha+\gamma x}\right)^{\frac{1}{2}(\mu+1)}\cdot(\alpha+\gamma x)\cdot{}_2F_1\left(\frac{1}{2}(\mu+\nu+\lambda+1), \frac{1}{2}(\mu-\nu+\lambda+1);\ \lambda+1;\ \frac{\beta+\delta x}{\alpha+\gamma x}\right)$ (Hypergeometric function)
19.	$a\cos bx + c$	Mathieu functions
20.	$be^x + c$	$Z_\nu(2\sqrt{b}e^{x/2})$; $\nu = \sqrt{-4c}$ (Bessel function)
21.	$a^2e^{2x} + be^x + c^2$	$e^{-x/2}W_{k,c}(2ae^x)$; $k = -b/2a$ (Whittaker function; confluent hypergeometric function)
22.	$-f''(x)/f(x)$	$f(x)$
23.	$-[f(x)]^2 \pm f'(x)$	$\exp\left[\mp\int_c^x f(u)\,du\right]$ ("*Reduction to first order*")
24.	$f(x) + g(x)$	Any *common* solution of: $\left\{\begin{array}{l} u'' + \frac{f}{h}u = 0 \\ u'' + \frac{g}{1-h}u = 0 \end{array}\right\}$ for any $h(x)$

B. Approximate Methods

Numerical Calculation

This may be based on a reduction of (14–53) to a pair of first-order equations such as,

$$\frac{dz}{dx} = V(x) - X_2 y - X_1 z; \quad \frac{dy}{dx} = z \tag{14–69}$$

The method of numerical analytic continuation [described following (14–14)] is particularly useful for linear, second-order equations.

Integral Series

According to (14–46)–(14–48), the normal form, (14–60), has solutions,*

$$\left.\begin{aligned} u_1(x) &= 1 - Q^2I + Q^2IQ^2I - Q^2IQ^2IQ^2I + \cdots \\ u_2(x) &= x - Q^2xI + Q^2IQ^2xI - Q^2IQ^2IQ^2xI + \cdots \end{aligned}\right\} \tag{14–70}$$

where $Qg(x) = \int_0^x g(t)\,dt$ and the operator, Q, always acts on all that follows it (in any one term).

Iteration

Choose any $y_0(x)$—though the convergence is faster the better y_0 approximates the desired solution of (14–53). Then compute the successively better approximations,

$$y_{k+1}(x) = \int_a^x \int_b^x (V - X_2 y_k - X_1 y_k')\,dx\,dx$$

where a and b are chosen to match the boundary conditions.

Continued Fractions

Write (14–53)—or (14–60)—in the form,

$$y = Q_0 y' + P_1 y''$$

and define successively

$$P_{i+1} = \frac{P_i}{1 - Q_{i-1}'}; \quad Q_i = \frac{Q_{i-1} + P_i'}{1 - Q_{i-1}'}$$

then

$$\frac{y}{y'} = Q_0 + \frac{P_1|}{|Q_1} + \frac{P_2|}{|Q_2} + \cdots \tag{14–71}$$

Asymptotic Approximations

This method is an improved form of the so-called "WKB" method of quantum mechanics.†

If in (14–65) we assume $r(z) \doteq$ constant, then (singular) solutions are $w =$ constant and we find that the corresponding approximate solutions of (14–60) are

$$u_{\pm}(x) = \exp\left\{-\int^x \frac{I'}{4I}\left[1 \pm \sqrt{1 - [16I^3/(I')^2]}\right] dx\right\} \tag{14–72}$$

* To prove this, write (14–60) in the form, $v' = -Iu$, $u' = v$.

† See V. A. Bailey, *Phys. Rev.* **96,** 865 (1954).

Of these, the one with the *lower sign*, u_-, *remains finite* at zeros of I (even though the assumption, $r \doteqdot$ constant, is grossly violated at such zeros). Thus u_- represents a realistic approximate solution and another can be found from (14–54), namely $u_2 = u_- \int^x (u_-)^{-2}\,dx$. These expressions are usually asymptotic to rigorous solutions of (14–60).

Power Series

Power series are a classic but less generally practical method of solution (though they can more readily be made rigorous in favorable cases). By expanding (if necessary) X_1, X_2, V of (14–53) in power series and substituting the assumption $y = \sum \alpha_i x^i$, one gets, by setting the resulting coefficient of each x^n equal to zero, a set of equations which can be successively solved if (say) α_0 and α_1 are given arbitrarily assigned values (corresponding to the two arbitrary constants available in the general solution of (14–53)). If the given functions in (14–53) are singular at $x = 0$, the expansions can be performed about another value of x or such assumptions as $y = x^r \sum \alpha_i x^i$ or $y = x^r (\ln x) \sum \alpha_i x^i$ can be used, where now the negative powers of x, arising from the singularities of X_1, X_2, or V, determine r. (Indicial equation.)

TOTAL DIFFERENTIAL EQUATIONS (PFAFF EQUATIONS)

Total differential equations are equations with *several independent variables* such as

$$P\,dx + Q\,dy + R\,dz = 0 = \mathbf{S} \cdot d\mathbf{r} \tag{14–73}$$

where P, Q, R are functions of x, y, z.

The equation (14–73) does not in general specify a relation between x, y and z. Specifically, a relation of the form

$$\Phi(x, y, z) = C \tag{14–74}$$

is specified by (14–73) if and only if*

$$\mathbf{S} \cdot \nabla \times \mathbf{S} = 0 \tag{14–75}$$

In this case, (14–73) is equivalent to $d\Phi = 0$.

(a) When condition (14–75) holds, to find the "unique" solution of (14–73), first set $y = ax$ and solve (with a = constant),

$$\frac{dz}{dx} = \left(\frac{P}{R} + a\,\frac{Q}{R}\right)_{y=ax} \tag{14–76}$$

Let the solution be $\phi(x, z, a)$ = constant. Then the solution of (14–73) is

$$\phi(x, z, y/x) = \phi(0, z_0, y/x) \tag{14–77}$$

where z_0 is an arbitrary constant.

(b) When the condition (14–75) is not satisfied, there are an infinity of solutions of (14–73). (Usually, in physical problems, added conditions are implied by other considerations.) One may then *add an arbitrary requirement*,

$$\psi(x, y, z) = 0 \tag{14–78}$$

This condition and its corollary, $(\nabla\psi) \cdot d\mathbf{r} = 0$ may then be algebraically solved for z and dz as functions of x, y, dx and dy. When these are substituted into (14–73), there results an ordinary first-order differential equation, $M\,dx + N\,dy = 0$. The

* For unfortunate historical reasons, this condition is often referred to by the misnomer, "integrability condition".

solution of this, combined with (14–78), then represents a family of space-curves satisfying (14–73).

Geometric Meaning

When condition (14–75) is satisfied, (14–73) defines a family of surfaces; otherwise (14–73) merely picks out certain curves on any arbitrarily assigned surface. In the second case, by following along pieces of such curves on suitably chosen surfaces, it is possible to reach any point (x, y, z) from any other; whereas when (14–75) does hold, it is not possible to follow (even pieces of) curves satisfying (14–75) and thereby reach any point from any other.

These considerations can be easily extended to any number of dimensions. In particular, for $\sum F_i\,dx_i = 0$ to define a hyper-surface, $\phi(x_1, x_2, x_3, \cdots, x_n) = C$, it is necessary and sufficient that for all $i \neq j \neq k \neq i$,

$$0 = F_i\left(\frac{\partial F_j}{\partial x_k} - \frac{\partial F_k}{\partial x_j}\right) + F_j\left(\frac{\partial F_k}{\partial x_i} - \frac{\partial F_i}{\partial x_k}\right) + F_k\left(\frac{\partial F_i}{\partial x_j} - \frac{\partial F_j}{\partial x_i}\right) \tag{14–79}$$

DIFFERENCE EQUATIONS

1. If $F(t) = \mathscr{L}^{-1}[f(p)]$, then $\mathscr{L}^{-1}[f(p + a)] = e^{-at}F(t)$. (Note that this is *not* true for the direct Laplace transform.) Thus, taking Laplace *inverse* transforms will often remove the differencing features and yield a solution. This technique is also useful for differential-difference equations, etc., but it fails for homogeneous difference equations.

2. **Z**-transforms: Let

$$\mathbf{Z}[f(n)] = \sum_{-\infty}^{\infty} z^n f(n) = F(z) \tag{14–80}$$

If the series converges in some open annulus, $a < |z| < b$, an inversion formula is

$$f(n) = \frac{1}{2\pi i}\oint \frac{F(z)}{z^{n+1}}\,dz \tag{14–81}$$

The following theorems indicate the value of this transform in solving difference equations.

$$\left.\begin{aligned} &\mathbf{Z}[f(n - N)] = z^N F(z) && \mathbf{Z}[f(-n)] = F(1/z) \\ &\mathbf{Z}\left[\sum_{-\infty}^{n} f(j)\right] = F(z)/(1 - z) && \mathbf{Z}[nf(n)] = z\,dF/dz \\ &\mathbf{Z}[f + g] = F + G && \mathbf{Z}\left[\sum_{-\infty}^{\infty} g(n - k)f(k)\right] = F(z)G(z) \\ &\mathbf{Z}[(1/n)f(n)] = \int_0^z z^{-1}F(z)\,dz, \quad \text{if} \quad f(0) = 0 \end{aligned}\right\} \tag{14–82}$$

These transforms arise naturally in the theory of sampled-data systems, the inputs of which may be regarded as time functions of the form, $f(t) = \sum f(n)\,\delta(t - nT)$, where T is the time-interval between samplings. The Laplace transform of $f(t)$ with z written for $\exp(-pT)$ is then precisely $F(z)$. If the system operates linearly on its input, the **Z**-transform of its output may be written $H(z)F(z)$. For physically realizable systems, $h(n) = \mathbf{Z}^{-1}[H(z)]$ vanishes for negative n; that is, $H(z)$ is analytic at the origin. If the input is a stationary random time-series, its correlation function is $r(n - k) = \langle f(n)f(k)\rangle$ (where "$\langle\ \rangle$" denotes a statistical average) and the **Z**-transform of the correlation function of the output of the system is easily seen to be

$$H(z)\,H(1/z)\,R(z).$$

CHAPTER 15

PARTIAL DIFFERENTIAL EQUATIONS

FIRST-ORDER PARTIAL EQUATIONS

ONLY for first-order equations is there a general theory of solution. Such equations can be reduced to an equivalent *system* of *ordinary* differential equations (of the first order).

(The now infrequently used Hamilton–Jacobi theory of mechanics essentially employed this relation in reverse, solving systems of ordinary equations by first solving the equivalent partial differential equation.)

Quasi-Linear First-Order Partial Equations

Such an equation is linear in the partial derivatives but not necessarily in the independent variable, u:

$$f_0(u, x_1, x_2, \cdots, x_N) = \sum_{i=1}^{N} f_i(u, x_1, \cdots, x_N) \frac{\partial u}{\partial x_i} \tag{15–1}$$

The equivalent ("characteristic") system of ordinary differential equations is

$$\frac{\mathrm{d}u}{f_0} = \frac{\mathrm{d}x_1}{f_1} = \frac{\mathrm{d}x_2}{f_2} = \cdots = \frac{\mathrm{d}x_N}{f_N} \tag{15–2}$$

If any* N (independent) solutions of (15–2) are solved for the integration constants C_k,

$$C_k = \phi_k(u, x_1, x_2, \cdots, x_N) \tag{15–3}$$

("characteristic curves" of (15–1)) then the general solution of (15–1) is

$$H(\phi_1, \phi_2, \cdots, \phi_N) = 0 \tag{15–4}$$

where H is an arbitrary function of its arguments. (Equally well, one can set $\phi_1 = G(\phi_2, \cdots, \phi_N)$ etc.)

All *singular solutions* (those not obtainable as special cases of (15–4)), if there exist any, must cause one of the $N + 1$ coefficient functions to vanish:

$$f_i(u, x_1, \cdots, x_N) = 0 \tag{15–5}$$

The technique of specializing these general solutions to specific boundary conditions can be described in general terms, but it is usually far simpler to proceed directly, using any special properties of the problem at hand to simplify the procedure.

(It should be noted that some boundary conditions cannot be satisfied and that others can be satisfied by an infinity of solutions; the general theory of these matters is omitted here since, when the situation arises in applications, the physics of the problem will usually suggest a method of handling it. Note also the analogy to eigenvalue problems where similar situations arise.)

---

* In particular, a solution of any part of (15–2)—for example, $x_i = C$ if $f_i = 0$—can be used to simplify other parts of (15–2) without loss of final generality.

Non-Linear First-Order Partial Equations

The general form is,

$$F(x_1, x_2, \cdots, x_N, u, p_1, p_2, \cdots, p_N) = 0 \tag{15–6}$$

where*

$$p_i = \frac{\partial u}{\partial x_i}$$

Singular solutions are usually a minor class and none need exist, but their determination is simple: Algebraically eliminate all p_i from (15–6) and the N relations,

$$\frac{\partial F}{\partial p_i} = 0 \tag{15–7}$$

The result will contain all singular solutions.

The equivalent ("characteristic") system of ordinary differential equations is (wherein the p_i are momentarily to be regarded as variables on an equal footing with u and the x_i):

$$\left.\begin{aligned} &\frac{dx_1}{\partial F/\partial p_1} = \frac{dx_2}{\partial F/\partial p_2} = \cdots = \frac{dx_N}{\partial F/\partial p_N} \\ &= \frac{-dp_1}{\dfrac{\partial F}{\partial x_1} + p_1 \dfrac{\partial F}{\partial u}} = \cdots = \frac{-dp_N}{\dfrac{\partial F}{\partial x_N} + p_N \dfrac{\partial F}{\partial u}} = \frac{du}{\sum_1^N p_i \dfrac{\partial F}{\partial p_i}} \end{aligned}\right\} \tag{15–8}$$

These, however, are $2N$ equations in $2N + 1$ variables and it is seldom expedient to solve them *completely*. A more practical scheme is based on the concept of:

A "*complete integral*" of (15–6) is any (!) solution of (15–6) which contains at least N arbitrary (independent) constants:

$$u = \phi(x_1, x_2, \cdots, x_N;\quad a_1, a_2, \cdots, a_N) \tag{15–9}$$

Although a specific, non-arbitrary function such as (15–9) cannot *itself* be the most general solution of (15–6), the name, "complete integral", is almost justified because (usually†) all solutions of (15–6) can be *generated* from it by methods discussed below.

A "complete integral" (15–9) may, of course, be discovered by any means whatever, including trial and error, but in any case it can in principle be found by only partly solving the characteristic system (15–8):

Finding a "Complete Integral"

1. If N solutions of (15–8) have been found (including N arbitrary constants) then the p_i can be eliminated between these solutions and (15–6) to obtain a "complete integral", (15–9).

---

* The notation in (15–6) is intended to imply the meaning of later symbols; for example, in $\partial F/\partial x_1$ all $2N$ quantities $x_2, \cdots, x_N, u, p_1, \cdots, p_N$ are held constant during differentiation.

† The exceptions are rather artificial cases, such as $F = GH$ in (15–6). Then (15–9) might be a solution only of $H = 0$.

2. In fact, if only $N - 1$ solutions of (15–8) have been found, these may be adjoined to (15–6) and the set algebraically solved to obtain $p_i = \psi_i(x_1, x_2, \cdots, x_N)$. Then (15–9) is the integral of

$$du = \psi_1\, dx_1 + \psi_2\, dx_2 + \cdots + \psi_N\, dx_N \tag{15–10}$$

(To solve, see (14–73)–(14–79); in the present instance, the solution is always "determined".)

3. Also in the *special case when F does not involve u explicitly* ($\partial F/\partial u = 0$) then if an integral of (15–6) is known which involves only $N - 1$ constants:

$$u = \Phi(x_1, \cdots, x_N;\ \ a_1, a_2, \cdots, a_{N-1}) \tag{15–11}$$

then the following is a complete integral (provided it is distinct from Φ itself—that is provided Φ does not contain any a_i additively).

$$u = \Phi(x_1, \cdots, x_N;\ \ a_1, \cdots, a_{N-1}) + a_N \tag{15–12}$$

Constructing the General Solution

Having found a "complete" integral of (15–6) such as (15–9), the *general* solutions of (15–6) (except in the artificial cases noted above) consist of "envelopes" of arbitrarily chosen families of the surfaces, (15–9). Thus, for example, set

$$a_1 = w(a_2, a_3, \cdots, a_N) \tag{15–13}$$

where w has been arbitrarily chosen. If from this equation and the $N - 1$ equations,

$$\frac{\partial \phi}{\partial a_i} + \frac{\partial \phi}{\partial a_1}\frac{\partial w}{\partial a_i} = 0 \quad (i = 2, 3, \cdots, N) \tag{15–14}$$

one solves algebraically for the a_i as *functions** (!) of $x_1, x_2, \cdots, x_N$ and substitutes the results for the a_i in (15–9), the final result is a solution of (15–6).

Usually, one wishes to pick out a specific solution satisfying given boundary conditions. To this end, set up equations (15–9), (15–13) and (15–14) with an unspecified w function and regard $a_2, \cdots, a_N$ as "parametric variables". Seek to determine w so that (15–9), (15–13) and (15–14) then represent (for appropriate values of x_i) the given boundary conditions in parametric form. (In doing so, it is usually convenient to convert to parameters other than the a_i.) When this has been accomplished, the set (15–9), (15–13) and (15–14) also represent (for general x_i) the final solution in parametric form from which, at least in principle, the parameters may be eliminated.

Simple Example

(Equation numbering corresponds to the foregoing.)

$$\frac{\partial u}{\partial x}\frac{\partial u}{\partial y} - 1 = 0 \tag{6}$$

Among the "characteristic system" (15–8) there occurs the term, $dp_x/0$, whose solution

---

* Alternatively: The a_j can be replaced by any functions, $a_j(x_1, \cdots, x_N)$ provided these satisfy (15–13) and (15–14), for then $\partial u/\partial x_i = \partial \phi/\partial x_i$ (even though the a_j are no longer constants) and the function, $u = \phi$, must therefore still be a solution.

is (by convention) $p_x = C$, a constant. From (6) we then have $p_y = 1/C$ and (15–10) becomes

$$du = C\,dx + (1/C)\,dy \tag{10}$$

with the obvious solution ("complete integral" of (6)),

$$u = Cx + (y/C) + b \tag{9}$$

which indeed is a solution of (6) involving two independent arbitrary constants. In accord with (15–13) now let

$$b = w(C) \tag{13}$$

Then (15–14) becomes

$$0 = x - (y/C^2) + w'(C) \tag{14}$$

while now (9) reads

$$u = Cx + (y/C) + w(C) \tag{9'}$$

With any arbitrary function, w, the result of eliminating C between these last two equations will be a solution of (6). (There are no singular solutions.)

Consider, for example, the boundary condition, $u(0, t) = f(t)$. (We use t to distinguish this special relation where $x = 0$ from the general values of x and y.) Then, from the last two equations, we require

$$\left.\begin{aligned} f(t) &= (t/C) + w(C) \\ 0 &= (-t/C^2) + w'(C) \end{aligned}\right\} \tag{I}$$

These determine both the function, w, and the relation between the parameters t and C. Thus, differentiating the first and using the second,

$$C = 1/f'(t) \tag{II}$$

then from the first,

$$w(C) = f(t) - tf'(t) \tag{III}$$

which indeed satisfies the second of (I) if (II) holds. Thus the final solution for these boundary conditions is

$$\left\{\begin{aligned} u &= \frac{x}{f'(t)} + yf'(t) + f(t) - tf'(t) \\ 0 &= x - [f'(t)]^2 y + t[f'(t)]^2 \end{aligned}\right.$$

or

$$\left\{\begin{aligned} u &= \frac{2x}{f'(t)} + f(t) \\ y &= t + \frac{x}{[f'(t)]^2} \end{aligned}\right.$$

wherein t may in principle be eliminated to obtain $u = u(x, y)$.

Systems of First-order Partial Equations

Such systems are in general equivalent to partial differential equations of higher order, and there is no very useful systematic theory for the general case. Some special instances are:

(a) Systems of the form:

$$\sum_{i=1}^{N} f_i \frac{\partial u_j}{\partial x_i} = g_j \quad (j = 1, \cdots, M) \tag{15–15}$$

(the f's and g's are functions of all $N + M$ variables, x_i, u_j) where it will be noted that

24

the f's are the same in all M equations. This system is equivalent to the single first-order equation,

$$\sum_{i=1}^{N} f_i \frac{\partial \phi}{\partial x_i} + \sum_{j=1}^{M} g_j \frac{\partial \phi}{\partial u_j} = 0 \tag{15–16}$$

Namely, if M distinct solutions, $\phi_1, \cdots, \phi_M$ of (15–16) are known then the M equations, $\phi_k(x_i, u_j) = C_k$ (constants), together represent a solution of (15–15) and conversely.

(b) Systems of the form:

$$\frac{\partial u_i}{\partial x_k} = g_{ik}(u_1, u_2, \cdots, u_M) \tag{15–17}$$

may *often* be solved by setting $x_k = a_k y$ where $\sum a_k^2 = 1$ and the a_k are momentarily regarded as constants. The system is thus converted to a set of ordinary equations.

(c) Two-dimensional systems of the form:

$$\left.\begin{aligned} f_1(u, v)\frac{\partial u}{\partial x} + f_2(u, v)\frac{\partial u}{\partial y} + f_3(u, v)\frac{\partial v}{\partial x} + f_4(u, v)\frac{\partial v}{\partial y} = 0 \\ g_1(u, v)\frac{\partial u}{\partial x} + g_2(u, v)\frac{\partial u}{\partial y} + g_3(u, v)\frac{\partial v}{\partial x} + g_4(u, v)\frac{\partial v}{\partial y} = 0 \end{aligned}\right\} \tag{15–18}$$

If u and v are taken as independent variables, then since $\partial(u, v)/\partial(x, y)$ and $\partial(x, y)/\partial(u, v)$ are inverse matrices,

$$\left.\begin{aligned} f_1(u, v)\frac{\partial y}{\partial v} - f_2\frac{\partial x}{\partial v} - f_3\frac{\partial y}{\partial u} + f_4\frac{\partial x}{\partial u} = 0 \\ g_1\frac{\partial y}{\partial v} - g_2\frac{\partial x}{\partial v} - g_3\frac{\partial y}{\partial u} + g_4\frac{\partial x}{\partial u} = 0 \end{aligned}\right\} \tag{15–19}$$

which are *linear* so that solutions can be superposed. "Singular" solutions satisfying $\frac{\partial u}{\partial x}\frac{\partial v}{\partial y} = \frac{\partial u}{\partial y}\frac{\partial v}{\partial x}$ must be separately investigated.

(d) Characteristics: (Useful in certain two-dimensional initial-value problems.) Given the two-dimensional system,

$$\left.\begin{aligned} \mathbf{f}\cdot\nabla u + \mathbf{g}\cdot\nabla v + F = 0 \\ \mathbf{h}\cdot\nabla u + \mathbf{k}\cdot\nabla v + G = 0 \end{aligned}\right\} \tag{15–20}$$

(where the coefficients may be functions of all four variables: x, y, u, v), define λ_1 and λ_2 as the roots of (vector product)

$$(\mathbf{f} + \lambda\mathbf{h}) \times (\mathbf{g} + \lambda\mathbf{k}) = 0 \tag{15–21}$$

If the roots $\lambda_i(x, y, u, v)$ are real and distinct, the system is called "hyperbolic" and if we define

$$\boldsymbol{\alpha}_i = \mathbf{f} + \lambda_i\mathbf{h}; \quad H_i\boldsymbol{\alpha}_i = \mathbf{g} + \lambda_i\mathbf{k}; \quad J_i = F + \lambda_i G \tag{15–22}$$

[H_i exists because of (15–21)] then $\boldsymbol{\alpha}_1$ and $\boldsymbol{\alpha}_2$ point in what are called the "characteristic directions" for the system (15–20), and a system equivalent to (15–20) is:

$$\boldsymbol{\alpha}_i\cdot\nabla u + H_i\boldsymbol{\alpha}_i\cdot\nabla v + J_i = 0 \quad (i = 1, 2) \tag{15–23}$$

(It may be verified that the $\boldsymbol{\alpha}_i$ form a "light cone" in the sense that values of u and v at a given point, P, are influenced only by values at points lying between curves with tangent vectors $\boldsymbol{\alpha}_1$, $\boldsymbol{\alpha}_2$ and passing through P.)

In the special case where $H_i = H_i(u, v)$, then if integrating factors, $\mu_i(u, v)$, can be found such that $\mu_i(du + H_i\, dv) = d\phi_i(u, v)$ then (15–23) becomes

$$\boldsymbol{\alpha}_i \cdot \nabla\phi_i + \mu_i J_i = 0 \quad (i = 1, 2) \tag{15–24}$$

which is especially convenient for numerical integration (proceeding along the directions, $\boldsymbol{\alpha}_i$, in each step). An important example of this fortunate situation is the isentropic two-dimensional ("x, t" or "x, y") flow of a non-viscous fluid. See (1–111).

THE SECOND-ORDER "WAVE-DIFFUSION" EQUATION

$$\boxed{\nabla \cdot [v(\mathbf{r})\nabla\phi] + \rho(\mathbf{r})\phi - u(\mathbf{r})\frac{\partial\phi}{\partial t} - w(\mathbf{r})\frac{\partial^2\phi}{\partial t^2} = q(\mathbf{r}, t)} \tag{15–25}$$

where $\phi(\mathbf{r}, t)$ is the unknown function.

Equation (15–25) occurs in electromagnetics, gravitation, sound, heat-conduction, elasticity, diffusion, quantum mechanics, etc. (though not usually in the general form shown). A common treatment applies to many general results.

The discussion below applies in an arbitrary number of dimensions (with "∇" and "$\mathbf{r}$" interpreted according to the analogy presented at the end of Chapter 10).

Reduction to:

$$\boxed{\nabla \cdot [v(\mathbf{r})\nabla\psi] + P(\mathbf{r})\psi = Q(\mathbf{r})} \tag{15–26}$$

may be achieved by taking the Laplace transform of (15–25) with respect to t, provided that values of ϕ and $\partial\phi/\partial t$ (if $w \neq 0$) at $t = 0$ are given.* Note that the boundary conditions must also be transformed.

If initial values of ϕ are not given, the appropriate integral transform for reducing (15–25) to (15–26) is the bilateral Laplace transform (or exponential Fourier transform). In this case, the coefficients of (15–26) are sometimes allowed to be frequency-dependent.†

Finally, if q has harmonic time-dependence, (15–25) is reduced to (15–26) by assuming the same dependence (steady-state solution) for ϕ, that is, $\phi = \psi(\mathbf{r}, \omega)e^{i\omega t}$. In particular, if q is independent of t, static solutions are obtained by setting $\partial/\partial t = 0$ in (15–25).

---

* If p is the transform variable (a mere parameter in (15–26)) then

$$\psi(\mathbf{r}, p) = \mathscr{L}[\phi(\mathbf{r}, t)]$$

$$P(\mathbf{r}, p) = \rho(\mathbf{r}) - pu(\mathbf{r}) - p^2 w(\mathbf{r})$$

$$Q(\mathbf{r}, p) = \mathscr{L}[q(\mathbf{r}, t)] - [u(\mathbf{r}) + pw(\mathbf{r})]\phi(\mathbf{r}, 0) - w(\mathbf{r})\left.\frac{\partial\phi}{\partial t}\right|_{t=0}$$

Although the problem of later inverting the Laplace transform can lead to difficulties, it should be noted that the convolution theorem (next-to-last line in (13-7)) will always yield an answer in *physical* variables, albeit still in integral form. Compare (15–59). The physical reason for this is the principle of superposition.

† Strictly speaking, such a situation cannot follow from (15–25) but is rather an extra postulate, equivalent to introducing convolution integrals in place of the corresponding products in (15–25).

Methods of Solving (15–26)

1. **Separation of variables** is a classic method leading to solutions of great generality, but the method works only in certain coordinate systems and with only certain forms of $v(\mathbf{r}), \cdots, Q(\mathbf{r})$.

One substitutes into (15–26) (or (15–25)) the assumption,

$$\psi(\mathbf{r}) = \prod_i f_i(x_i) \tag{15–27}$$

The resulting equation is then algebraically separated into a term depending only on (say) x_1 and another depending only on $(x_2, x_3, \cdots, x_n)$. Each of these terms must then equal an (undetermined) constant. The separation is then continued to isolate a term in x_2, etc. The final result is a set of (independent) *ordinary* differential equations for the f_i in (15–27).

When the latter have been solved, one has a solution of (15–25) or (15–26) involving $2n$ integration constants and $n - 1$ separation constants. The latter usually allow such generality that a *complete* set of functions is obtained, so that in principle any boundary conditions can be satisfied* by using "Fourier" type series expansions.

Nevertheless, these results are of practical use primarily when the coordinate system "fits" the natural physical symmetry of the problem, as expressed in the boundary conditions and the coefficient functions in (15–25).

2. **Other special assumptions.** Solutions (seldom of much generality) may also be obtained by assuming other special forms for ϕ. For example, one may choose specific functions, $f(\mathbf{r}, t)$ and $g(\mathbf{r}, t)$, and assume that $\phi = gF(f)$. Through appropriate choice of f and g, this assumption may reduce (15–25) or (15–26) to an ordinary differential equation in F. This method can also be applied to non-linear equations. Useful choices for f and g are often suggested by invariance properties of the equation to be solved or by dimensional analysis.

3. **Superposition: linear operations.** The principle of superposition is the "obvious" fact that, to any solution of (15–25) [or (15–26)] we may add any solution satisfying the same equation with $q = 0$ [or $Q = 0$]. More generally, if ϕ_1 is a solution of (15–25) [or (15–26)] with $q = q_1$ [or $Q = Q_1$] and ϕ_2 is a solution with $q = q_2$ [or $Q = Q_2$] then $\phi_1 + \phi_2$ is a solution with $q = q_1 + q_2$ [or $Q = Q_1 + Q_2$].

This simple consequence of the linearity of (15–25) and (15–26) expresses the fundamental "linearity" of many physical systems, whose response to two stimuli is the sum of the separate responses.

Full and imaginative use of this simple principle will often enable one to split a problem into two or more simpler sub-problems (examples: sections 6 and 8 below). This basic idea also underlies the use of Fourier or Laplace transforms and is the physical picture behind the method of Green's functions (point-source solutions).

Further, if $q = 0$ or $Q = 0$ then any arbitrary sum or integral of any solution, using arbitrary "weights", is again a solution, as also is the result of applying any linear operation to any arbitrary parameter or variable. Thus if $\phi = f(\mathbf{r}, t, \alpha)$ is a solution of (15–25) with $q = 0$ then so are, for example,

$$\frac{\partial f}{\partial \alpha} \quad \text{and} \quad \int_{-\infty}^{\infty} h(\alpha) f(\mathbf{r}, t, \alpha)\, d\alpha$$

---

* The fact that solutions obtained in one coordinate system *must* then be expressible in terms of those obtained in other coordinate systems originally suggested (especially in the case of the equation, $\nabla^2\phi + k^2\phi = 0$) many abstruse mathematical results concerning the standard functions of analysis.

for arbitrary $h(\alpha)$. The latter, when applied to solutions found by separation of variables is especially powerful.*

4. **Green's functions (Point-source solutions);** *Reduction of* (15–26) *to*:

$$\nabla \cdot [v(\mathbf{r})\nabla G] + P(\mathbf{r})G = 0 \tag{15–28}$$

with the *same boundary conditions* as are required for ψ (in special cases, these can be relaxed, however; see below).

The physical idea behind the method of Green's function is that, by the principle of superposition, the solution of (15–26) for an arbitrary "source", $Q(\mathbf{r})$, should be merely the "Q-weighted" *sum of* corresponding (same boundary conditions) solutions for *point sources* at arbitrary locations. Thus:

Seek a solution, $G(\mathbf{r}, \mathbf{A})$ of (15–28) which represents a point source located at $\mathbf{A}$. That is, besides satisfying (15–28) and the given boundary conditions (in both cases regarding $\mathbf{A}$ as a parameter), G is also singular near $\mathbf{r} = \mathbf{A}$ in such a manner that, if S_ϵ is a sphere of radius ϵ about $\mathbf{A}$, then

$$\lim_{\epsilon \to 0} \iint_{S_\epsilon} d\mathbf{S} \cdot (\nabla G)v(\mathbf{r}) = 1 \tag{15–29}$$

(which implies that G behaves like $|\mathbf{r} - \mathbf{A}|^{2-n}$ near $\mathbf{A}$ if n is the number of dimensions in the space; for $n = 2$, $G \sim \ln |\mathbf{r} - \mathbf{A}|$).

Then the solution of (15–26) itself is†

$$\psi(\mathbf{r}) = \iiint G(\mathbf{R}, \mathbf{r})Q(\mathbf{R})\, dV_R \tag{15–30}$$

In particular, consider the case where Q itself corresponds to a "point" source; this shows ("reciprocity theorem"):

$$G(\mathbf{R}, \mathbf{r}) = G(\mathbf{r}, \mathbf{R}) \tag{15–31}$$

so that (15–30) can in general be interpreted as a simple superposition of point sources distributed according to $Q(\mathbf{r})$.

5. **Green's functions with special boundary conditions.** If it is desired to solve (15–26) in a region, V_0, whose boundary surface is S and if it is required that‡

$$\text{on } S: \qquad a\frac{\partial \psi}{\partial n} + b\psi = f(\mathbf{r}) \tag{15–32}$$

---

* Example:

$$\int_0^\infty J_0(\rho\sqrt{k^2 + \alpha^2})e^{\pm \alpha z}h(\alpha)\, d\alpha$$

(cylindrical coordinates) satisfies $\nabla^2\phi + k^2\phi = 0$ and, by using Laplace or Hankel transforms, can be assigned arbitrary values for $\rho = 0$ or for $z = 0$.

† Proof: Multiply (15–28) by $\psi(\mathbf{r})$ and (15–26) by $G(\mathbf{r}, \mathbf{A})$, subtract and integrate over the region of space involved in the problem but excluding a sphere S_ϵ about $\mathbf{A}$. The result, (15–30), follows by Gauss' theorem and (15–29).

‡ Here, $\frac{\partial}{\partial n} = \hat{n} \cdot \nabla$ where $\hat{n}$ is an (outward) unit vector perpendicular to S.

Then solve (15–28) as before, but with the simpler boundary condition:

$$\text{on } S: \qquad a\frac{\partial G}{\partial n} + bG = 0 \tag{15–33}$$

The solution of (15–26) satisfying (15–32) is then (proof as for (15–30)),

$$\left.\begin{aligned}\psi(\mathbf{r}) &= \iiint_{V_0} G(\mathbf{R}, \mathbf{r})Q(\mathbf{R})\,\mathrm{d}V_R - \frac{1}{a}\iint_S G(\mathbf{R}, \mathbf{r})v(\mathbf{R})f(\mathbf{R})\,\mathrm{d}S_R \\ &= \iiint_{V_0} G(\mathbf{R}, \mathbf{r})Q(\mathbf{R})\,\mathrm{d}V_R + \frac{1}{b}\iint_S v(\mathbf{R})f(\mathbf{R})\frac{\partial}{\partial n}G(\mathbf{R},\mathbf{r})\,\mathrm{d}S_R\end{aligned}\right\} \tag{15–34}$$

(where the first form must be used when $b = 0$ and the second when $a = 0$; otherwise, either may be used). Again, if $Q(\mathbf{R})$ itself represents a point source and if $f \equiv 0$, (15–34) shows that the reciprocity theorem, (15–31), holds also for the boundary conditions (15–33).

6. **Some techniques for finding Green's functions.** *Infinite region*: A point-source solution can occasionally be found from a still simpler problem. For example, in an infinite homogeneous medium, a uniform, plane, distributed source in the (x, y)-plane generates the solution,

$$g(z) = \int_0^\infty G(\sqrt{\rho^2 + z^2}, 0)2\pi\rho\,\mathrm{d}\rho = 2\pi\int_z^\infty G(u, 0)u\,\mathrm{d}u$$

whence, conversely,

$$G(u, 0) = \frac{-1}{2\pi u}\frac{\mathrm{d}}{\mathrm{d}u}g(u) \tag{15–35}$$

so that G can be simply obtained from g which itself is easier to find.

The general guide in discovering such relations lies in physical considerations guided by the principle of superposition.

Finite regions: To find the point-source solution for finite regions, it is usually simplest to *set* $G = G_\infty + g$, where G_∞ is the infinite-region Green's function and g is a solution of (15–28) which is smooth everywhere and will be chosen so that $g + G_\infty$ satisfies the boundary conditions.

This method essentially "splits" the requirements for G and enables one to treat separately the two problems of establishing the proper singularity at $\mathbf{r} = \mathbf{A}$ and satisfying the boundary conditions. When working with integral transforms, the method also helps to avoid highly singular (improper) functions.

7. **Normal modes (eigenfunctions) for finite regions**; *Reduction to*:

$$\nabla \cdot [v(\mathbf{r})\nabla\Phi] + \lambda P(\mathbf{r})\Phi = 0 \tag{15–36}$$

where λ is an undetermined constant. Again, the boundary conditions on Φ are the same as those on ϕ or ψ. The discussion below applies when the space-region in which (15–26) is to be solved is *finite*. Extension to unbounded regions is sometimes possible (see Chapter 19) but seldom of great practical utility for boundary-value problems.

In general, for arbitrary λ, (15–36) will *not* have a solution which is both smoothly varying (in contrast to the Green's functions) and also satisfies the boundary conditions. However, for *certain* values of λ, denoted by λ_n, such a smooth solution, $\Phi_n(r)$, will exist:*

$$\nabla \cdot [v(\mathbf{r})\nabla\Phi_n] + \lambda_n P(\mathbf{r})\Phi_n = 0 \tag{15–37}$$

If V is the (finite) space-region of the problem, these "modes" or eigenfunctions can be chosen orthonormal:

$$\iiint_V \Phi_n\Phi_m P\,\mathrm{d}V = \delta_{nm} = \begin{cases} 0 \text{ if } n \neq m \\ 1 \text{ if } n = m \end{cases} \tag{15–38}$$

For methods of computing Φ_n, λ_n see Chapter 19.

Subject to very general restrictions, the Φ_n are "complete" and the solution of (15–26) itself is† (as is easily checked formally),

$$\left.\begin{aligned} \psi(\mathbf{r}) &= \sum_{n=1}^{\infty} \frac{a_n}{1-\lambda_n}\Phi_n(\mathbf{r}) \\ \text{where}\qquad a_n &= \iiint_V \Phi_n Q\,\mathrm{d}V \end{aligned}\right\} \tag{15–39}$$

(That is, $Q/P = \sum a_n\Phi_n$; the a_n are the "degrees of excitation" of mode, Φ_n.)

It is thus seen that, *for any (finite) region and any boundary conditions there are certain* $Q(\mathbf{r})$ *for which* (15–26) *has especially simple solutions,* namely when $Q(\mathbf{r}) = P(\mathbf{r})\Phi_k(r)$ for some k. This fact is often helpful in choosing "model problems" to explore the general nature of a physical system.

For a general theorem on the number of modes Φ_i with $\lambda_i \leqslant \lambda$ (i.e. the number of "resonances" with frequency below any given frequency) see (19–5).

8. **Use of integral transforms.** In addition to reducing (15–25) to (15–26), integral transforms will often further simplify a problem, provided that it possesses convenient symmetries. In particular:

- If v and P are independent of r (spherical coordinates) then application of the Fourier sine transform ($\mathscr{H}_{1/2}$) to (15–26), after multiplication by r, will eliminate derivatives with respect to r.
- If v and P are independent of ρ (cylindrical coordinates) then application of the Hankel transform ($\mathscr{H}_0$) to (15–26), after multiplication by $\sqrt{\rho}$, will eliminate ρ derivatives.
- If v and P are independent of z, application of the (one- or two-sided) Laplace transform will eliminate z derivatives.

In all cases, the boundary conditions should be subjected to the same transformation.

These techniques are useful not so much for discovering general solutions but rather for fitting particular boundary-value problems. If point sources are involved, it is frequently helpful to separate out explicitly a term like G_∞ before carrying out the transformation. This will have the effect of displaying singularities explicitly and making the whole problem more straightforward.

---

* In most physical problems, the Φ_n represent free natural vibrations of the system; however, note that the method is equally useful, for example, in heat-flow problems (where one "mode" rapidly dominates).

† If $\lambda = 1$ is an eigenvalue of (15–36), then (15–26) has no solution unless (Q/P) is orthogonal to ($a_n = 0$) all those Φ_n whose $\lambda_n = 1$.

SOME SPECIAL CASES OF THE "WAVE-DIFFUSION" EQUATION

1. **Poisson's equation.** (The potential equation)

$$\nabla^2\phi = -4\pi\rho(\mathbf{r}) \tag{15-40}$$

The point-source solution (Green's function) in an *infinite* region is,

$$\left.\begin{aligned} G_\infty(\mathbf{r}, \mathbf{A}) &= \frac{1}{2\pi}\ln|\mathbf{r}-\mathbf{A}|, \text{ in 2 dimensions} \\ G_\infty(\mathbf{r}, \mathbf{A}) &= \frac{-\Gamma(n/2)}{2(n-2)\pi^{n/2}}|\mathbf{r}-\mathbf{A}|^{2-n}, \text{ in } n \neq 2 \text{ dimensions} \end{aligned}\right\} \tag{15-41}$$

and the solution of (15–40) in an infinite region is given immediately by (15–30).

Green's functions for a half-space (say $z \geqslant 0$), a sphere, and certain other regions may be obtained by:

The *method of images* whereby "fictitious", extra, point sources are located *outside* the region of interest in such a manner that the sum total of contributions, G_∞, satisfies the boundary conditions—usually of the form (15–33). The name of the method expresses the fact that such external sources are usually located at those optical images of the actual point source which would arise if the boundary were a mirror. (For a sphere of radius, a, about $\mathbf{r} = 0$, the image of $\mathbf{r} = \mathbf{A}$ lies at radius $A' = a^2/A$.)

The final results, (15–34), for special problems are known as "Poisson integrals". Thus if $\rho(\mathbf{r}) \equiv 0$ and we require $\phi \equiv f(x_2, \cdots, x_n)$ on the plane $x_1 = 0$, then in $x_1 > 0$,

$$\phi(x_1, x_2, \cdots, x_n) = \frac{x_1\Gamma\left(\frac{n}{2}\right)}{\pi^{n/2}}\int_{-\infty}^{\infty}\cdots\int\frac{f(\xi_2, \cdots, \xi_n)\,\mathrm{d}\xi_2\cdots\mathrm{d}\xi_n}{[x_1{}^2 + (x_2-\xi_2)^2 + \cdots + (x_n-\xi_n)^2]^{n/2}} \tag{15-42}$$

while if we are given $\phi(\mathbf{r}) = f(\mathbf{r})$ on the sphere, $|\mathbf{r}| = R$, then in $|\mathbf{r}| \leqslant R$,

$$\phi(\mathbf{r}) = \frac{\Gamma\left(\frac{n}{2}\right)}{2\pi^{n/2}}R^{n-2}(R^2 - r^2)\int\cdots\int_{|\boldsymbol{\zeta}|=R}\frac{f(\boldsymbol{\zeta})\,\mathrm{d}\boldsymbol{\zeta}}{[r^2 - 2rR\cos(\mathbf{r}, \boldsymbol{\zeta}) + R^2]^{n/2}} \tag{15-43}$$

Solutions of (15–40) obtainable by separation of variables are special cases of those for the wave equation.

2. **Laplace's equation in 2 dimensions.**

$$\frac{\partial^2\phi}{\partial x^2} + \frac{\partial^2\phi}{\partial y^2} = 0 \tag{15-44}$$

This equation has among its solutions the real (or the imaginary) part of any *analytic* function of the complex variable, $z = x + iy$.

$$\phi = \mathrm{Re}\,[f(z)] \tag{15-45}$$

(and conversely any solution of (15–44) leads to an analytic function through (15–45)).

This connection with the theory of functions of a complex variable can be given a geometric interpretation which is often helpful in finding solutions. The interpretation is based on the concept of *conformal mapping*. If a function, $w = w(z)$ can be found which maps the given problem onto one (whose solution is known) in the w-plane, $x' = \text{Re}\,(w(z))$ and $y' = \text{Im}\,(w(z))$, then the solution (15–45) can easily be found. In particular, if the simpler problem in the w-plane is just that where ϕ must take constant values on $x' = a$ and $x' = b$ then $w(z)$ itself is the function required in (15–45).

Since the Green's function of (15–44) is $\ln |\mathbf{r}| = \text{Re}\,(\ln z)$, functions related to the logarithm are frequently of use. The other main tools are (1) the "projective transformations", $w = (az + b)/(cz + d)$ which can take circles into half-planes and lunes into wedges;* (2) multi-valued transformations such as $z^{1/2}$, $z^{1/3}$, $\sqrt{1 - z^2}$ etc., which can map corners on straight lines; (3) the Schwarz–Christoffel transformation (12–9) which maps the interior of polygons (including open ones, "with one vertex at ∞") onto a half-plane.

Specific examples are as numerous as analytic functions and any complete listing, even of once-used functions, would be inordinately long. Some few simple examples are given below. [The description is couched in three-dimensional language where the "$x + iy = z$" plane is regarded as a cross section of the full, three-dimensional problem.] Other results can be found in works on electrostatics (electron optics; vacuum tubes) and (linearized) hydrodynamic theory.

$w = \text{ctnh}^{-1}\,(z/a)$	—parallel wires at different potentials
$w = \ln\,(\sin z/a) + ibz$	—infinite grid of wires in a uniform external field
$w = \cos^{-1} z$	—charged elliptic cylinder (or flat strip)
	—pair of charged hyperbolic cylinders
	—co-planar half-infinite plates separated by a slit
$w = \ln \dfrac{\sin\,(z/a)}{\sin\,(b + z/a)}$	—infinite grid of wires with charges alternating in sign
	—charged wire between grounded planes
(inverse of:) $z = w + e^w$	—edge of parallel-plate condenser

3. Extension of 2-dimensional results to 3 dimensions: By the principle of superposition, solutions, $\phi_1(x, y)$, $\phi_2(y, z)$, $\phi_3(x, z)$ can be added, for example, to obtain a solution:

$$\phi(x, y, z) = \phi_1(x, y) + \phi_2(y, z) + \phi_3(x, z) \tag{15–46}$$

Thus, the potential, $\phi_1 = \text{Re}\left(\ln \sin \dfrac{x + iy}{a}\right)$ for a "grating" of wires can be used to obtain the potential of a mesh ("screen"),

$$\phi = \text{Re}\left[\ln \sin \frac{x + iy}{a} + \ln \sin \frac{x + iz}{a}\right]$$

4. The wave equation:

$$\nabla^2\phi - \frac{1}{c^2}\frac{\partial^2\phi}{\partial t^2} = -q(\mathbf{r}, t) \tag{15–47}$$

---

* If we generalize "circle" to include lines ("circles through $z = \infty$") then the projective transformations always take "circles" into "circles".

This is reduced by the Laplace transform (with respect to t) to the form:

$$\nabla^2\psi - \frac{p^2}{c^2}\psi = -\frac{1}{c^2}\frac{\partial\phi}{\partial t}\bigg|_{t=0} - \frac{p}{c^2}\phi(\mathbf{r}, 0) - \mathscr{L}[q] \tag{15–48}$$

The point-source solution for an infinite three-dimensional* region of space is

$$G_\infty(\mathbf{r}, \mathbf{A}) = -\frac{\exp\left[\frac{-p}{c}|\mathbf{r} - \mathbf{A}|\right]}{4\pi|\mathbf{r} - \mathbf{A}|} \tag{15–49}$$

Again, the *method of images* is useful for constructing Green's functions for certain other regions with simple boundaries.

Some useful special cases of (15–30) are:

(a) If
$$\nabla^2\phi - k^2\phi = -4\pi w(r) \tag{15–50}$$

(three dimensions; ϕ to vanish at $r = \infty$) then the solution found from (15–30) and (15–49) is

$$\phi(r) = \frac{2\pi}{kr}\int_0^\infty [e^{-k|r-\rho|} - e^{-k(r+\rho)}]\,\rho w(\rho)\,d\rho \tag{15–51}$$

(b) If:
$$\nabla^2\mathbf{A} - k^2\mathbf{A} = -4\pi\frac{\mathbf{r}}{r}f(r) \tag{15–52}$$

(three dimensions; $|\mathbf{A}|$ to vanish at $r = \infty$) then:

$$\mathbf{A} = \frac{2\pi\mathbf{r}}{(kr)^3}\int_0^\infty [(k^2r\rho + k(r + \rho) + 1)e^{-k(r+\rho)} + (k^2r\rho - k|r - \rho| - 1)e^{-k|r-\rho|}]f(\rho)\,d\rho \tag{15–53}$$

These results are most easily derived in spherical coordinates; note that if $\mathbf{r}$ is taken as the polar axis during the integration, then

$$\frac{\sin\theta'\,d\theta'}{|\mathbf{r} - \mathbf{r}'|} = \frac{1}{rr'}\,d(|\mathbf{r} - \mathbf{r}'|) \qquad (r' \text{ fixed}) \tag{15–54}$$

and the integration limits, $\theta' = 0, \pi$ become $|\mathbf{r} - \mathbf{r}'| = r + r'$ and $|\mathbf{r} - \mathbf{r}'| = |r - r'|$.

The infinite-region solution (15–30) when applied to (15–48) leads to a result whose Laplace inverse can be explicitly evaluated, leading to the following *infinite-region solution for the wave equation* (15–47):

$$\phi(\mathbf{r}; t) = \iiint \frac{q(\mathbf{R}; t - |\mathbf{r} - \mathbf{R}|/c)}{4\pi|\mathbf{r} - \mathbf{R}|}\,dV_R + \frac{t}{4\pi}\iint_{S_t}\frac{\partial\phi}{\partial t}\bigg|_{t=0} d\Omega + \frac{1}{4\pi}\frac{\partial}{\partial t}\,t\iint_{S_t}\phi(\mathbf{R}, 0)\,d\Omega \tag{15–55}$$

where S_t is the spherical surface $|\mathbf{r} - \mathbf{R}| = ct$ and $d\Omega$ is an element of solid angle centered at $\mathbf{r}$.

The first term of (15–55) is known as "Helmholtz's integral" and is often the only non-vanishing term.

---

* In n dimensions (with $\mathbf{A} = 0$)

$$G_\infty(\mathbf{r}, 0) = (\text{constant})r^{1-\frac{1}{2}n}K_{\frac{1}{2}n-1}\left(\frac{pr}{c}\right)$$

where K_ν is a Hankel function with imaginary argument.

If $q \equiv 0$, (15–55) expresses "Huygens' principle": that disturbances propagate as (the envelopes of) spherical wavelets arising from all points where disturbances ("at $t = 0$") previously existed.

Separation of variables, when applied to (15–48), leads to the classical functions of analysis (Legendre, Bessel, etc.) and the results are tabulated in many standard references. From these, the "normal modes" for volumes of many simple shapes can be determined.

For a cavity of any shape and containing volume, V, if we require $a\phi + b\partial\phi/\partial n = 0$ on the walls, then the number, $N(\omega)$, of modes with eigenvalues ω_i below ω ($p = i\omega$ in (15–48)) satisfies

$$\lim_{\omega\to\infty} \frac{N(\omega)}{\omega^3} = V/(6\pi^2c^3) \tag{15–56}$$

(special case of (19–5)).

5. **The diffusion equation.** With absorption, this reads,*

$$\nabla^2\phi = \frac{\partial\phi}{\partial t} + \frac{\phi}{T} - q(\mathbf{r}, t) \tag{15–57}$$

The Laplace transform with respect to t leads to,

$$\nabla^2\psi - \left(p + \frac{1}{T}\right)\psi = -\mathscr{L}[q] - \phi(\mathbf{r}, 0) \tag{15–58}$$

which is the same form as (15–48). Consequently, the results listed for (15–48) apply to (15–58) as well.

If $q \equiv 0$ *for* $t > 0$, the general solution (15–39) leads to a useful result: Explicit Laplace inversion shows that *the lowest mode always becomes dominant*, usually very rapidly. This fact is often a useful guide in transient-heating problems.

The *infinite-region result* analogous to (15–55) is, in the present case:

$$\phi(\mathbf{r}, t) = (4\pi t)^{-3/2}e^{-t/T}\iiint \phi(\mathbf{R}, 0) \exp\left[-|\mathbf{r} - \mathbf{R}|^2/4t\right] \mathrm{d}V_R$$
$$+ \int_0^t e^{-u/T}(4\pi u)^{-3/2}\iiint q(\mathbf{R}, t - u) \exp\left[-|\mathbf{r} - \mathbf{R}|^2/4u\right] \mathrm{d}V_R \tag{15–59}$$

Solution of (15–57) under rather general boundary conditions can be reduced to the solution of several much simpler problems.† Essentially, the technique is to use superposition (convolution integrals). Consider:

$$\left.\begin{aligned} \frac{\partial\phi}{\partial t} + \frac{\phi}{T} &= D\nabla^2\phi + S(\mathbf{r}, t) \\ \mathbf{a}\cdot\nabla\phi + b\phi &= g(\mathbf{r}, t), \quad \text{on } \mathscr{S} \\ \phi(\mathbf{r}, 0) &= F(\mathbf{r}) \end{aligned}\right\} \tag{15–60}$$

with the conditions, (15–60)

(where $\mathbf{a}$, b are constants and $\mathscr{S}$ is some boundary surface). The solution is,

$$\phi(\mathbf{r}, t) = F(\mathbf{r}) + \int_0^t e^{(\lambda - t)/T}\left[\theta(\mathbf{r}, \lambda, t - \lambda) + \frac{\partial}{\partial t}\eta(\mathbf{r}, \lambda, t - \lambda)\right] \mathrm{d}\lambda \tag{15–61}$$

---

* A constant "diffusivity", D, appearing as $D\nabla^2\phi$ in (15–57) can be absorbed by changing the units of length or of time.

† D. G. O'Sullivan, *J. Chem. Phys.* **25**, 270 (1956).

where θ and η are both solutions of problems involving no arbitrary functions of time. Namely, θ and η satisfy

$$\left.\begin{aligned} \left(\frac{\partial}{\partial t} - \nabla^2\right) f(\mathbf{r}, \lambda, t) &= 0 \\ (\mathbf{a} \cdot \nabla + b) f &= 0 \quad \text{on } \mathscr{S} \\ \text{with} \qquad \theta(\mathbf{r}, \lambda, 0) &= S(\mathbf{r}, \lambda) - \frac{1}{T} F(\mathbf{r}) \\ \eta(\mathbf{r}, \lambda, 0) &= F(\mathbf{r}) - u(\mathbf{r}, \lambda) \end{aligned}\right\} \tag{15–62}$$

wherein $u(\mathbf{r}, \lambda)$ is the solution of:

$$\left.\begin{aligned} \nabla^2 u &= 0 \\ \mathbf{a} \cdot \nabla u + bu &= g(\mathbf{r}, \lambda) \quad \text{on } \mathscr{S} \end{aligned}\right\} \tag{15–63}$$

[That (15–61) satisfies the first and last lines of (15–60) is readily verified; to show that (15–61) also satisfies the second line, the following more complicated form is useful

$$\phi = \frac{\partial}{\partial t} \int_0^t \left\{ u(\mathbf{r}, \lambda) + e^{(\lambda - t)/T} \eta(\mathbf{r}, \lambda, t - \lambda) + \int_0^{t-\lambda} e^{-\mu/T} I(\mathbf{r}, \lambda, \mu)\, d\mu \right\} d\lambda$$

where $I = \theta + \dfrac{1}{T}\eta$.]

LINEAR PARTIAL DIFFERENTIAL EQUATIONS OF ORDER $\geqslant 2$

There is no general theory even approaching the completeness of that for first-order partial equations. The most useful results are extensions of those for the "wave-diffusion" equation.

Linearity

A differential operator, L, is said to be linear if for arbitrary functions, ϕ, ψ,

$$L(a\phi + b\psi) = aL(\phi) + bL(\psi) \tag{15–64}$$

The discussion below concerns mainly equations of the type,

$$L(\phi) = q(\mathbf{r}, t) \tag{15–65}$$

Superposition is valid for equations of this type, by definition of "linearity", (15–64).

Green's Functions; Adjoint Equations

In order to introduce Green's functions in the treatment of (15–65), it is necessary to introduce the concept of the operator "adjoint" to L. Namely, to be able to apply Gauss' theorem, we define the (usually unique) operator, M, adjoint to L to be any operator with the property,

$$\phi M(\psi) - \psi L(\phi) = \nabla \cdot \mathbf{F}(\phi, \psi) \tag{15–66}$$

where $\mathbf{F}$ is some (vector) expression involving ϕ, ψ and their gradients—and higher derivatives if necessary. (The "wave-diffusion" operator was *self* adjoint.)

In particular, if L is of second order:

$$L(\phi) = \sum_i \sum_k f_{ik} \frac{\partial^2 \phi}{\partial x_i \partial x_k} + \sum_j H_j \frac{\partial \phi}{\partial x_j} + h\phi \tag{15–67}$$

(the coefficients are functions of $\mathbf{r}$ and t in general) then the adjoint of L is

$$M(\psi) = \sum_i \sum_k \frac{\partial^2}{\partial x_i \partial x_k} (f_{ik}\psi) - \sum_j \frac{\partial}{\partial x_j} (H_j \psi) + h\psi \tag{15–68}$$

and the vector, $\mathbf{F}$, of (15–66) in this case is

$$(\mathbf{F})_i = \sum_j \left[\phi \frac{\partial}{\partial x_j} (f_{ji}\psi) - \psi f_{ij} \frac{\partial \phi}{\partial x_j} \right] - H_i \phi \psi$$

The *Green's function* of (15–65) (and its boundary conditions!) may now be defined as a "point-source" solution of

$$M(G) = 0 \tag{15–69}$$

with *boundary conditions* related to those of (15–65) in such a way that $\mathbf{F} \cdot d\mathbf{S} = 0$ on the boundary surface, where $\mathbf{F}$ is defined in (15–66). Likewise, the definition of "point-source solution" depends on $\mathbf{F}$: the generalization of (15–29) is that, for all $g(\mathbf{r})$,

$$\lim_{\epsilon \to 0} \iint_{S_\epsilon} d\mathbf{S} \cdot \mathbf{F}(g, G) = g(\mathbf{A})$$

The solution of (15–65) for arbitrary $q(\mathbf{r}, t)$ is then given by (15–30):

$$\phi(\mathbf{r}, t) = \iiint G(\mathbf{R}, \mathbf{r}) q(\mathbf{R}, t)\, dV_R$$

Note, however, that now $G(\mathbf{R}, \mathbf{r}) \neq G(\mathbf{r}, \mathbf{R})$ in general.

Normal Modes

If the operator L is not only linear but also *self-adjoint*,* then the formalism of (15–36)–(15–39) *may be taken over directly*. In particular, *any linear, second-order operator can always be made self-adjoint:*

If L is linear and of second-order, it has the form (15–67); let the matrix $(f^{-1})_{ik}$ (whose elements are functions of $\mathbf{r}$) be the inverse of the matrix $f_{ik}(\mathbf{r})$. Then if u satisfies the following system of equations,

$$\frac{\partial u}{\partial x_i} = \sum_k (f^{-1})_{ik} \left[\sum_l \frac{\partial}{\partial x_l} f_{kl} - H_k \right] \tag{15–70}$$

(which can be integrated immediately), it follows that

$$e^{-\frac{1}{2}u} L[\psi e^{\frac{1}{2}u}] = \psi \left[h - \tfrac{1}{2} \sum_i \frac{\partial H_i}{\partial x_i} \right] + \sum_k \sum_i \left[\frac{\partial}{\partial x_k} f_{ki} \frac{\partial \psi}{\partial x_i} + \tfrac{1}{2}\psi \frac{\partial^2 f_{ki}}{\partial x_k\, \partial x_i} \right] \tag{15–71}$$

* That is, $uL(v) - vL(u) = \nabla \cdot \mathbf{Z}(u, v)$. This is needed to obtain orthogonal normal modes (eigenfunctions).

Thus the substitution, $\phi = \psi e^{\frac{1}{2}u}$, will convert any linear, second-order equation of the form,

$$L(\phi) + \rho(\mathbf{r})\phi = q(\mathbf{r}, t) \tag{15–72}$$

to a similar form where L is self-adjoint.

Perturbation (Iteration) Techniques

Specific details of these powerful methods of approximate solution are difficult to give without presenting too narrow a view of the possibilities. Generally speaking, the guiding principles are usually physical arguments which enable one to predict that the final solution will cause certain terms of an equation to be very small compared to others. Roughly:

If one can isolate terms which will be small on the right side of an equation:

$$L_0(\phi) = \epsilon N(\phi) \tag{15–73}$$

then, if the solutions of $L_0(\phi) = f(\mathbf{r})$ are known for any f, and if the solution of (15–73) is expected to be "close to" some *known* function, $\phi_0(\mathbf{r})$, an approximate solution of (15–73) may be expected to be found by substituting ϕ_0 in the small terms:

$$L_0(\phi) = \epsilon N(\phi_0) = F(\mathbf{r}) \tag{15–74}$$

When this is solved for ϕ, the result should be a first-order correction to ϕ_0. In principle, this approximation could be improved by again substituting it into the small terms of (15–73) and solving for a better approximation (iteration). In practice, it is often difficult to proceed very far* in this manner. Consequently, it is a practical necessity to obtain a fairly good approximation to start with; that is, ϕ_0 should be *known* to be close to the desired final answer, and it is here that physical arguments and the ingenuity of the investigator are most important for obtaining useful results.

Some Special Equations

$$(\nabla^4 - k^2)\phi = q \tag{15–75}$$

Here, one notes that $(\nabla^4 - k^2)\phi = (\nabla^2 - k)(\nabla^2 + k)\phi$ and the remaining theory then follows from that of the "wave-diffusion" equation. The general solution of the homogeneous equation is a sum of solutions of the individual factors.

$$(a\nabla^4 + b\nabla^2 + c)\phi = q \tag{15–76}$$

Again the operator can be factored and the results for the "wave-diffusion" equation become available. More generally, if $P(x)$ is a polynomial whose roots are known, the equation,

$$P(\nabla^2)\phi = q$$

can be factored.

$$\left(\nabla^2 - \frac{1}{c_1^2}\frac{\partial^2}{\partial t^2}\right)\left(\nabla^2 - \frac{1}{c_2^2}\frac{\partial^2}{\partial t^2}\right)\phi = 0 \tag{15–77}$$

The general solution is again a sum of solutions of the individual factors. The inhomogeneous equation ($F(\mathbf{r})$ on the right) can be solved by duplication of (15–55).

$$\nabla^2\mathbf{u} + a\nabla(\nabla \cdot \mathbf{u}) = b\nabla f \tag{15–78}$$

that is,

$$(a + 1)\nabla(\nabla \cdot \mathbf{u}) - \nabla \times (\nabla \times \mathbf{u}) = b\nabla f$$

---

* Indeed, the sequence of approximations may be asymptotic (rather than convergent) so that it could be unwise to proceed too far.

Any solution can be written in the form,

$$\left.\begin{aligned} \mathbf{u} &= \nabla(\phi + \mathbf{r}\cdot\boldsymbol{\omega}) - 2(1 + a^{-1})\boldsymbol{\omega} \\ \nabla^2\boldsymbol{\omega} &= 0; \qquad \nabla^2\phi = \frac{b}{a+1}f \end{aligned}\right\} \tag{15–79}$$

where

More generally, any solution of

$$\nabla^2\mathbf{u} + \frac{1}{1-2\nu}\nabla(\nabla\cdot\mathbf{u}) - \frac{\rho}{\mu}\frac{\partial^2 u}{\partial t^2} + \frac{1}{\mu}\mathbf{F} = 0 \tag{15–80}$$

(μ, ν, ρ constants) may be written,

$$2\mu\mathbf{u} = 2(1-\nu)\left(\nabla^2 - \frac{1}{c_1^{\,2}}\frac{\partial^2}{\partial t^2}\right)\mathbf{G} - \nabla(\nabla\cdot\mathbf{G}) \tag{15–81}$$

where $\mathbf{G}$ is a solution of

$$\left.\begin{aligned} &\left(\nabla^2 - \frac{1}{c_1^{\,2}}\frac{\partial^2}{\partial t^2}\right)\left(\nabla^2 - \frac{1}{c_2^{\,2}}\frac{\partial^2}{\partial t^2}\right)\mathbf{G} = \frac{-\mathbf{F}}{1-\nu} \\ &c_1^{\,2} = (\mu/\rho)\frac{2(1-\nu)}{1-2\nu}; \qquad c_2^{\,2} = \mu/\rho \end{aligned}\right\} \tag{15–82}$$

with

(Sternberg and Eubanks, *Quart. Appl. Math.* **15,** 149 (1957).)

Numerical Solution; Stability

Numerical treatments usually replace the partial differential equation (and the boundary conditions) by a set of algebraic equations. Each continuous function $u(\mathbf{r})$ is replaced by a set of values $u_\alpha = u(\mathbf{r}_\alpha)$ at a set of lattice points $\mathbf{r}_\alpha$ and derivatives are replaced by finite differences, such as (schematically),

$$\left.\frac{\partial u}{\partial x}\right|_{x=x_i} = \frac{u(x_i + \Delta x) - u(x_i - \Delta x)}{2(\Delta x)}$$

$$\left.\frac{\partial^2 u}{\partial x^2}\right|_{x=x_i} = \frac{u(x_i + \Delta x) - 2u(x_i) + u(x_i - \Delta x)}{(\Delta x)^2}$$

The resulting algebraic equations will be linear in the unknowns, u_α, if the original partial differential equation was linear.

Stability: Formal resemblance of the algebraic and differential equations is no guarantee that even approximately correct results will be obtained. Initial-value problems are particularly likely to diverge when treated numerically and this divergence can even persist for (certain) arbitrarily fine subdivisions of the coordinates. The physical reason for such behavior lies in limitations inadvertently imposed on wave propagation: The simpler algebraic schemes usually allow a wavelet to move at most a distance Δx during each time interval Δt. (Here Δx and Δt are the differences between successive lattice points x_i and t_j respectively.) If Δt is taken too large *relative* to Δx, wavelets cannot propagate over the correct distances and the final results will be completely false. Accordingly, in treating the wave equation, $\partial^2 u/\partial x^2 = (1/c^2)(\partial^2 u/\partial t^2)$, it is necessary that Δt be less than $\Delta x/c$, and for the diffusion equation, $\partial u/\partial t = D(\partial^2 u/\partial x^2)$, the condition, $\Delta t < (\Delta x)^2/2D$ is necessary. (The accuracy will usually be poor unless Δt is taken somewhat smaller than these limits.)

If the algebraic approximation is so constructed that all space points are mutually adjusted during each time interval (so that there is no limitation on the distance to which a disturbance can propagate during Δt) then such restrictions disappear. The interval Δt can then be made large, but a compensating price is paid through more complicated calculations. For example, the diffusion approximation,

$$(\Delta t)^{-1}[u(x, t) - u(x, t - \Delta t)] = (\Delta x)^{-2}[u(x + \Delta x, t) - 2u(x, t) + u(x - \Delta x, t)]$$

is stable for all values of Δt but computation of $u(x, t)$ [given $u(x, t - \Delta t)$] requires solving simultaneously the full set of equations for all values of x.

SOME NON-LINEAR EQUATIONS AND TECHNIQUES

$$a^2\nabla^2\phi + |\nabla\phi|^2 = 0 \tag{15–83}$$

Any solution can be written, $\phi = a^2 \ln \psi$ where $\nabla^2\psi = 0$.

$$\frac{\partial^2 z}{\partial x^2}\frac{\partial^2 z}{\partial y^2} = \left[\frac{\partial^2 z}{\partial x \partial y}\right]^2 \tag{15–84}$$

This equation has as solutions "developable" or "non-warped" surfaces (and only such surfaces); these may be defined as any envelope of the family of planes: $z = ax + w(a)y + u(a)$, where w and u are arbitrary functions of the parameter, a.

The continuity equation: If ρ represents the density per unit volume of a "material" (mass, charge, etc.) which cannot be created or destroyed and if $\mathbf{v}$ is the (local) velocity of such "material", then*

$$\frac{\partial \rho}{\partial t} + \nabla \cdot (\rho \mathbf{v}) = 0 \tag{15–85}$$

If ρ is considered given, then one solution for $\mathbf{v}$ (that for which $\nabla \times \rho\mathbf{v} = 0$) is

$$\mathbf{v} = \frac{1}{4\pi\rho(\mathbf{r})}\nabla \iiint \frac{\partial\rho/\partial t}{|\mathbf{r} - \mathbf{r}'|}\, dV' \tag{15–86}$$

The continuity equation can also be satisfied by setting, for arbitrary $\mathbf{F}(\mathbf{r})$,

$$\rho = \nabla \cdot \mathbf{F}; \qquad \rho\mathbf{v} = -\frac{\partial \mathbf{F}}{\partial t} \tag{15–87}$$

It is then often convenient to convert (in the remainder of the physical problem) to variables, $\mathbf{F}$, instead of $\mathbf{r}$ ("von Mises transformation"). The relations are:

$$\left.\begin{aligned} \left.\frac{\partial}{\partial t}\right|_{\mathbf{r}} &= \left.\frac{\partial}{\partial t}\right|_{\mathbf{F}} + \frac{\partial \mathbf{F}}{\partial t} \cdot \nabla_{\mathbf{F}} \\ \nabla_{\mathbf{r}} &= (\nabla \mathbf{F}) \cdot \nabla_{\mathbf{F}} \end{aligned}\right\} \tag{15–88}$$

The final solution will then generally emerge in parametric form (compare the Legendre transformation below).

Techniques

Assuming unknown functions to depend on the variables in special ways will frequently yield some special results. Such assumptions can sometimes be guided

---

* $\frac{\partial}{\partial t}[\rho \Delta V]$ = (rate of increase of "mass" in ΔV) = (total current flowing through the boundary of ΔV) = $-[\nabla \cdot (\rho\mathbf{v})]\Delta V$ by Gauss' theorem.

by physical considerations, dimensional analysis, etc. In shock-wave theory, such solutions are known as "similarity" solutions.

Legendre transformation. This is especially useful if the independent variables do not appear explicitly in the equation. Define a new function, W, of new independent variables, $\boldsymbol{\omega}$, by setting

$$\left.\begin{aligned} \phi(\mathbf{r}) &= \boldsymbol{\omega} \cdot \nabla_{\omega} W - W(\boldsymbol{\omega}) \\ \nabla_r \phi &= \boldsymbol{\omega}; \qquad \mathbf{r} = \nabla_{\omega} W \end{aligned}\right\} \tag{15–89}$$

It then follows that the matrices, $\partial^2\phi/\partial x_i \partial x_j$ and $\partial^2 W/\partial\omega_k \partial\omega_l$, are each others inverse: $[\nabla\nabla\phi : \nabla\nabla W] = \mathfrak{J}$ so that a (first or) second-order equation in $\phi(\mathbf{r})$ can be transformed to a (very different) equation in W and $\boldsymbol{\omega}$. If a solution of the latter can be found, $W = H(\boldsymbol{\omega})$, then a solution of the original is, in parametric form*

$$\left.\begin{aligned} \phi &= \boldsymbol{\omega} \cdot \nabla_{\omega} H - H(\boldsymbol{\omega}) \\ \mathbf{r} &= \nabla_{\omega} H \end{aligned}\right\} \tag{15–90}$$

A special case is the "hodograph transformation" of aerodynamics. The equation for the velocity potential, ϕ, in the steady, two dimensional motion of a compressible fluid is of the form,

$$\left.\begin{aligned} &\left[f^2 - \left(\frac{\partial\phi}{\partial x}\right)^2\right]\frac{\partial^2\phi}{\partial x^2} - 2\frac{\partial\phi}{\partial x}\frac{\partial\phi}{\partial y}\frac{\partial^2\phi}{\partial x\partial y} + \left[f^2 - \left(\frac{\partial\phi}{\partial y}\right)^2\right]\frac{\partial^2\phi}{\partial y^2} = 0 \\ &\text{where} \\ &f^2 = a\left[\left(\frac{\partial\phi}{\partial x}\right)^2 + \left(\frac{\partial\phi}{\partial y}\right)^2\right] + b \end{aligned}\right\} \tag{15–91}$$

By means of the Legendre transformation which takes $u = \partial\phi/\partial x$, $v = \partial\phi/\partial y$ as new independent variables and as dependent variable:

$$\left.\begin{aligned} H &= ux + vy - \phi \\ &\text{whence} \\ \phi &= u\frac{\partial H}{\partial u} + v\frac{\partial H}{\partial v} - H \end{aligned}\right\} \tag{15–92}$$

(15–91) is transformed to a *linear* equation,

$$\left.\begin{aligned} &(f^2 - u^2)\frac{\partial^2 H}{\partial v^2} + 2uv\frac{\partial^2 H}{\partial u\partial v} + (f^2 - v^2)\frac{\partial^2 H}{\partial u^2} = 0 \\ &\text{where} \\ &f^2 = a(u^2 + v^2) + b \end{aligned}\right\} \tag{15–93}$$

Not only do solutions of this equation lead to solutions, ϕ, of (15–91) but, more important, various solutions of (15–93) may be *superposed* to generate many more solutions, H, and hence many solutions, ϕ.

"Simple waves". If the independent variables do not appear explicitly in the equation, the assumption,

$$\frac{\partial\phi}{\partial x} = f\left(\frac{\partial\phi}{\partial y}\right) \qquad \left\{\text{whence } \frac{\partial^2\phi}{\partial x^2} = \left[f'\left(\frac{\partial\phi}{\partial y}\right)\right]^2\frac{\partial^2\phi}{\partial y^2}\right\} \tag{15–94}$$

may convert the equation to a simpler form. These solutions, of course, are of very special type and are known in hydrodynamics as "simple waves".

---

* A developable surface, viz. $|\nabla\nabla\phi| = 0$ cannot be so expressed; such solutions (if any) must be found by other means.

THE TRANSPORT EQUATION; AN INTEGRO-PARTIAL-DIFFERENTIAL EQUATION

Integro-differential equations have been little more than christened. Only recently have rigorous solutions of the simplest problems in transport theory been obtained.

The one type of equation which has yielded even numerical rigorous results to date is that for scattering by fixed "centers". Its form* is ($N = N(\mathbf{r}, \mathbf{v}, t) = N(\mathbf{r}, \mathbf{v}/v, E, t)$ where $\mathbf{v}$ is velocity and E is energy; N has the dimensions of a flux)

$$\left.\begin{aligned} &\frac{1}{v}\frac{\partial N}{\partial t} + \frac{\mathbf{v}}{v}\cdot\nabla N + \mu_t(\mathbf{r}, E)N \\ &\quad = \int \mathrm{d}E' \oint\!\!\oint \mathrm{d}\left(\frac{\mathbf{v}'}{v'}\right)\mu_s(\mathbf{r}, E' \to E)N(\mathbf{r}, \mathbf{v}', E')f\left(E', E, \frac{\mathbf{v}\cdot\mathbf{v}'}{vv'}\right) \\ &\qquad + \text{Source Terms} \end{aligned}\right\} \tag{15–95}$$

It is important to note that the problem involves seven independent variables and that, in particular, $\mathbf{v}$ and $\mathbf{r}$ are independent. The notation, ∇N, then *means* $(\nabla N)_{\mathbf{v}=\text{constant}}$ and (unlike the situation in fluid mechanics, where other conventions hold) $\mathbf{v}\cdot\nabla N = \nabla\cdot\mathbf{v}N$ *always*.

It is often convenient to replace the unit vector, $\mathbf{v}/v$, by other variables, Ω_1, Ω_2, which may be such that their values change as $\mathbf{v}$ is moved parallel to itself from one position in space to another. (Example, $\mathbf{v}/v$ can be specified by its angles relative to $\mathbf{r}$ and $\hat{z}$.) In that case,

$$(\nabla N)_{\mathbf{v}=\text{const}} = (\nabla N)_{\Omega_i=\text{const}} + \sum_i (\nabla\Omega_i)_{\mathbf{v}=\text{const}}\frac{\partial N}{\partial\Omega_i} \tag{15–96}$$

and it is this whole quantity which belongs in (15–95).

Entire books have been written on single problems involving these equations. Some general comments:

1. The time-dependent case can be formally reduced† to that for the steady-state ($\partial N/\partial t = 0$) by taking the Laplace transform. Lumping the term, $N(\mathbf{r}, \mathbf{v}/v, E, 0)$ with the source terms, the result is that $\mathscr{L}(N)$ satisfies an equation identical to (15–95) with $\partial N/\partial t = 0$ except that the coefficient, $\mu_t(\mathbf{r}, E)$, is replaced by

$$\bar{\mu}_t(\mathbf{r}, E, p) = \mu_t(\mathbf{r}, E) + p/v.$$

Note, however, that this simpler equation must be solved for an infinity of values of the transform-variable, p.

2. An equivalent integral equation can be derived by considering the flux at a given point as generated by "simultaneously" scattered‡ flux from other points (plus "direct beams" from sources). A characteristic feature of these integral forms is the appearance of the function, $\alpha(\mathbf{r}, \mathbf{r}', E)$, the "optical depth" between $\mathbf{r}$ and $\mathbf{r}'$:

$$\alpha(\mathbf{r}, \mathbf{r}', E) = \int_{s=0}^{|\mathbf{r}-\mathbf{r}'|} \mu_t\left(\mathbf{r} + s\frac{\mathbf{r}'-\mathbf{r}}{|\mathbf{r}'-\mathbf{r}|}, E\right)\mathrm{d}s = \alpha(\mathbf{r}', \mathbf{r}, E) \tag{15–97}$$

* The more general Boltzmann equation will be found in (6–169).

† Provided the cross-sections, μ_t, μ_s, f, are independent of t.

‡ Propagation delays can, of course, be ignored in *steady-state* problems and are usually neglected in light-scattering problems.

Its physical interpretation is that, if a beam of particles of energy E is directed from $\mathbf{r}$ toward $\mathbf{r}'$ (or vice versa), then a fraction, $e^{-\alpha}$, of the particles will survive the journey without being either scattered or absorbed.

The integral form of (15–95) is then

$$\left.\begin{aligned} N(\mathbf{r}, \mathbf{\Omega}, E) &= N_d(\mathbf{r}, \mathbf{\Omega}, E) \\ &\quad + \int_0^\infty \exp\left[-\alpha(\mathbf{r}, \mathbf{r} - s\mathbf{\Omega}, E)\right] ds \int_{(0)}^{(\infty)} \mu_s(\mathbf{r} - s\mathbf{\Omega}; E' \to E)\, dE' \\ &\quad \cdot \oint\!\!\oint f(E', E, \mathbf{\Omega}\cdot\mathbf{\Omega}') N(\mathbf{r} - s\mathbf{\Omega}, \mathbf{\Omega}', E')\, d\mathbf{\Omega}' \end{aligned}\right\} \quad (15\text{–}98)$$

where N_d is the unscattered ("direct") flux and $\mathbf{\Omega} = \mathbf{v}/v$.

3. For numerical solution, the best techniques to date have been based *not* on an approximation of the desired function, N, directly, but rather on successively deriving numerical values for certain of its characteristic quantities. These have generally been space-moments of the form (for one dimension)

$$N_n = \frac{1}{n!}\int_0^\infty x^n N(x)\, dx \qquad (15\text{–}99)$$

It happens that, for some problems, quantities of this nature can be evaluated systematically to arbitrary accuracy. The "reconstruction" of $N(x)$ from a finite number of values of the N_n turns out to yield rather surprising accuracy when additional information concerning asymptotic behavior, etc., is taken into account.* (See also (9–24)–(9–34).)

4. In problems involving sources which emit at a single energy, it is generally expedient for analytic work and necessary for numerical work to remove the unscattered beams from the function, N, so that it represents only beams which have been scattered at least once. This removes delta-functions in both the energy and angle variables. Physically, this manipulation is equivalent to replacing the actual sources by virtual, distributed sources located according to the first-scatter points.

5. An exact expression for the flux generated by a steady point source, situated in an infinite medium which scatters isotropically and without velocity-change, is given in the section on continuous random-walks, following (20–54) in Chapter 20.

Usually, however, an analogous calculation by "successive scatterings" converges too slowly for practical computation unless the (true) absorption probability, $(\mu_t - \mu_s)/\mu_t$, is fairly large.

6. *Approximations:*

(a) Transport approximation: The theory presented in (6–169)–(6–189) indicates that (at least when the absorption is slight) the results on a "macroscopic" scale (distances $\gg 1/\mu_t$) will be almost unaffected if the actual angular distribution, f, is replaced by an isotropic distribution, $1/4\pi$, and the cross sections reduced:

$$\mu_s' = \langle 1 - \cos\theta \rangle \mu_s; \qquad \mu_t' = \langle 1 - \cos\theta \rangle \mu_t \qquad (15\text{–}100)$$

where θ is the (center-of-mass) scattering angle and "$\langle\ \rangle$" denotes an average over the actual angular distribution, f.

---

* Originally pointed out by L. V. Spencer and U. Fano. For recent developments see P. I. Richards, *Jour. Optical Soc. Am.* **49**, 245 (1959) and references therein.

(b) For isotropic scattering:* With $f \equiv 1/4\pi$, it follows from (15–98) that the total flux,

$$\rho(\mathbf{r}, E) = \oint\oint N(\mathbf{r}, \mathbf{\Omega}, E)\, \mathrm{d}\mathbf{\Omega} \tag{15–101}$$

for all $\mathbf{r}$, E completely determines N itself. Further, if $\lambda(E) \equiv 1/\mu_t$ is independent of position, integration of (15–98) shows

$$\rho(\mathbf{r}, E) = \rho_d(\mathbf{r}, E) + \int \mathrm{d}E' \oint\oint\oint \mu_s(\mathbf{R}, E' \to E)\rho(\mathbf{R}, E') \frac{\exp[-|\mathbf{r} - \mathbf{R}|/\lambda(E)]}{4\pi|\mathbf{r} - \mathbf{R}|^2}\, \mathrm{d}V_R \tag{15–102}$$

where ρ_d is the total unscattered flux. By (13–53) and (13–54), this can be written,

$$\rho(\mathbf{r}, E) = \rho_d(\mathbf{r}, E) + \sum_{n=0}^{\infty} \frac{[\lambda(E)]^{2n+1}}{2n+1} \nabla^{2n}\left[\int \mu_s(\mathbf{r}, E' \to E)\rho(\mathbf{r}, E')\, \mathrm{d}E'\right] \tag{15–103}$$

To obtain more rapid convergence,† operate on this equation with $\lambda^2\nabla^2 - 1$:

$$(\lambda^2\nabla^2 - 1)(\rho - \rho_d) = \lambda(\tfrac{2}{3}\lambda^2\nabla^2 - 1) \int \mu_s\rho\, \mathrm{d}E' + 2\sum_{u=2}^{\infty} \frac{\lambda^{2n+1}}{4n^2 - 1} \nabla^{2n} \int \mu_s\rho\, \mathrm{d}E' \tag{15–104}$$

By neglecting higher terms (e.g. the final sum) in this equation, various approximate schemes can be developed. In particular, for the one-velocity problem, where

$$\mu_s(\mathbf{r}, E' \to E) = [\omega(\mathbf{r})/\lambda(E)]\delta(E' - E),$$

neglecting the final sum in (15–104) gives:

$$\left.\begin{aligned} &\rho = \frac{3}{3 - 2\omega(\mathbf{r})}[P(\mathbf{r}) + \rho_d(\mathbf{r})] \\ \text{where}\quad &\lambda^2\nabla^2 P(\mathbf{r}) - K^2 P(\mathbf{r}) = -(1 - K^2)\rho_d(\mathbf{r}) \\ \text{with}\quad &K(\mathbf{r}) = \sqrt{\frac{3[1 - \omega(\mathbf{r})]}{3 - 2\omega(\mathbf{r})}} \end{aligned}\right\} \tag{15–105}$$

and it can then be shown that the *net* vector flux (or "current") is, with no further approximations,

$$\mathbf{J} = \mathbf{J}_d - \lambda v \nabla P \tag{15–106}$$

where $\mathbf{J}_d$ is the net unscattered vector flux.

(c) Fermi's "age theory": If each scattering is accompanied, on the average, by an energy degradation of the form, $\ln(E'/E) = \xi$ (a constant), then it is convenient to replace the particle energy by a new variable, the "lethargy", defined by $u = \ln(E_0/E)$ where E_0 is the source (or other reference) energy. The approximation $\mu_s(\mathbf{r}, E' \to E) = \mu_s(E')\delta(u' - u + \xi)$ is then appropriate and if $\phi(\mathbf{r}, u) = E\rho(\mathbf{r}, E)$ is the flux per unit lethargy interval, $\mathrm{d}u$, the first few terms of (15–103) yield (with $\mu = \mu_t = 1/\lambda$ and after replacing u by $u + \xi$),

$$\begin{Bmatrix}\text{source}\\ \text{terms}\end{Bmatrix} + \frac{1}{3\mu^2}\nabla^2(\mu_s\phi) = \mu\phi(\mathbf{r}, u + \xi) - \mu_s\phi(\mathbf{r}, u) \doteq \left[\frac{\mu}{\mu_s} - 1\right]\mu_s\phi + \xi\frac{\mu}{\mu_s}\frac{\partial(\mu_s\phi)}{\partial u}$$

* Provided that any correlation between energy-change and deflection angle is neglected.
† P. I. Richards, *Phys. Rev.* **100**, 517 (1955).

If we let

$$\xi\mu_s(u)\phi(\mathbf{r}, u) = q_0 \exp\left[\frac{-1}{\xi}\int_0^u \frac{\mu - \mu_s}{\mu}\,du\right]$$

$$= q_0(\mathbf{r}, \tau) \exp\left[\frac{-1}{\xi}\int_E^{E_0} \frac{\mu_a}{\mu}\frac{dE}{E}\right]$$

and

$$\tau = \int_0^u \frac{\mu_s}{3\xi\mu^3}\,du = \frac{1}{3\xi}\int_E^{E_0} \frac{\mu_s}{\mu^3}\frac{dE}{E}$$

then we obtain Fermi's "age equation",

$$\frac{\partial q_0}{\partial \tau} = \nabla^2 q_0 + \text{source terms}$$

The variable, τ, is called the "age" but has the dimensions of a length squared and represents the mean square distance over which the particles diffuse as their energy is degraded from E_0 to E. The quantity $\xi\mu_s\phi$ is called the "slowing down density" and the exponential factor is called the "resonance escape probability" (because the absorption cross section, μ_a, for neutrons is usually associated with resonant peaks in the total cross section). For neutrons, isotropically scattered by fixed nuclei of atomic mass A,

$$\xi = 1 - \frac{(A-1)^2}{2A}\ln\frac{A+1}{A-1} \doteq \frac{2}{A + \frac{2}{3}}$$

[see footnote under (5–89)]. The cross sections in the definition of τ should be interpreted as "transport" cross sections, (15–100); for neutrons $\langle\cos\theta\rangle = 2/3A$.

CHAPTER 16

INTEGRAL EQUATIONS

SOME SPECIAL EQUATIONS

$$\left.\begin{aligned} \tfrac{1}{2}\pi f(x) &= \int_0^{\pi/2} \phi(x \sin\theta)\, d\theta \\ \text{solution:} \qquad & \\ \phi(x) &= f(0) + x\int_0^{\pi/2} f'(x\sin\theta)\, d\theta \end{aligned}\right\} \tag{16–1}$$

$$\left.\begin{aligned} g(x) &= \int_0^{\infty} h(x\cosh u)\, du \\ \text{solution:} \qquad & \\ h(x) &= -(2x/\pi)\int_0^{\infty} g'(x\cosh u)\, du \end{aligned}\right\} \tag{16–2}$$

(These two pairs are equivalent, as may be seen by setting $\sin\theta = 1/\cosh u$ and $\phi(x) = g(1/x) + f(0)$ in (16–1).)

$$\left.\begin{aligned} g(x) &= \int_1^{\infty} \frac{h(xv)\, dv}{\sqrt{v^2-1}} \\ \text{solution:} \qquad & \\ h(x) &= -\frac{2x}{\pi}\int_1^{\infty} \frac{g'(xw)\, dw}{\sqrt{w^2-1}} \end{aligned}\right\} \tag{16–3}$$

(This is also equivalent to the previous pairs.)

$$\left.\begin{aligned} f(x) &= \phi(x) - \lambda\int_0^{\infty} \cos(2xs)\phi(s)\, ds \\ \text{solution:} \qquad & \\ \left(1-\lambda^2\frac{\pi}{4}\right)\phi(x) &= f(x) + \lambda\int_0^{\infty} f(s)\cos(2xs)\, ds \end{aligned}\right\} \tag{16–4}$$

(In the limit, $\lambda \to \infty$, this is the Fourier cosine-integral theorem.) Unlike the foregoing, the next pair reads very differently when the order of the equations is reversed:

$$\left.\begin{aligned} \phi(t) &= \frac{(1-t^2)^{\frac{1}{2}(n-1)}}{2\pi}\int_0^{\pi} h(t + i\sqrt{1-t^2}\cos\alpha)\sin^{n-1}\alpha\, d\alpha \\ h(s) &= \int_{-1}^{+1} \frac{n(1-s^2)\phi(t)\, dt}{(1-2ts+s^2)^{1+\frac{1}{2}n}} \end{aligned}\right\} \tag{16–5}$$

Hilbert's formulas: If $f(\pi) = f(-\pi)$ [or $\phi(\pi) = \phi(-\pi)$] then

$$\left.\begin{aligned} f(x) &= \frac{1}{2\pi}\int_{-\pi}^{\pi}[1+\cot\tfrac{1}{2}(x-y)]\phi(y)\,dy \\ \phi(y) &= \frac{1}{2\pi}\int_{-\pi}^{\pi}[1+\cot\tfrac{1}{2}(x-y)]f(x)\,dx \end{aligned}\right\} \tag{16–6}$$

(where the integrals are Cauchy principal-values).

$$f(x) = \phi(x) - \lambda F_1(x)\int_a^b F_2(y)\phi(y)\,dy$$

solution:

$$\phi(x) = f(x) + \frac{\lambda F_1(x)}{1-A\lambda}\int_a^b F_2(y)f(y)\,dy \tag{16–7}$$

where $$A = \int_a^b F_1(x)F_2(x)\,dx$$

Similarly, when $F_1(x)F_2(x)$ is replaced by a finite sum of such terms, the theory of (16–18)–(16–25) can be carried through analytically to yield a solution in finite terms.

$$g(x) = \int_{-1}^{+1} f(y)\ln|x-y|\,dy$$

solution:

$$\pi^2\sqrt{1-x^2}\,f(x) = \int_{-1}^{1}\frac{\sqrt{1-s^2}}{s-x}g'(s)\,ds - \frac{1}{\ln 2}\int_{-1}^{1}\frac{g(s)\,ds}{\sqrt{1-s^2}} \tag{16–8}$$

(Cauchy principal-value in the first integral.) For (16–8) with $\ln|x-y|$ replaced by

$$P(x-y)\ln|x-y| + Q(x-y)$$

where P and Q are (or may be approximated by) polynomials [see C. E. Pearson, *Quart. Appl. Math.* **15**, 203 (1957)]. In particular, if $P \equiv 1$, the main effect in the second line of (16–8) is to add on the right a polynomial of the same degree as Q. Compare also (13–38)–(13–41).

Abel's equation:

$$\left.\begin{aligned} G(x) &= \int_0^x (x-y)^{-a}\phi(y)\,dy; \qquad (0 < a < 1) \\ \phi(y) &= \frac{\sin\pi a}{\pi}\left[\int_0^y (y-x)^{a-1}G'(x)\,dx + G(0)y^{a-1}\right] \end{aligned}\right\} \tag{16–9}$$

This is readily proved by taking Laplace transforms. Similarly, given:

$$G(x) = \int_0^x \Phi(y)F(x-y)\,dy = \int_0^x F(y)\Phi(x-y)\,dy \tag{16–10}$$

take Laplace transforms to obtain,

$$\phi(p) = \frac{g(p)}{f(p)} \tag{16–11}$$

Often, as in (16–9), the inversion can be performed in general terms. Thus, even though $\mathscr{L}^{-1}[1/f(p)]$ will not exist in general, F may be such that, for some n,

$$\mathscr{L}^{-1}[1/p^n f(p)] = K(t), \quad \text{say}$$

exists. Then it follows that

$$\Phi(t) = \left(\frac{\mathrm{d}}{\mathrm{d}t}\right)^n \int_0^t K(t-y)G(y)\,\mathrm{d}y = \left(\frac{\mathrm{d}}{\mathrm{d}t}\right)^n \int_0^t G(t-y)K(y)\,\mathrm{d}y \tag{16–12}$$

is the solution for "arbitrary" G. (This final result can often be proved—once the form of K is known—for a much wider class of functions than might appear rigorous in view of this derivation.)

Infinite convolutions:

$$F(x) = \int_{-\infty}^{\infty} G(x-y)\phi(y)\,\mathrm{d}y = \int_{-\infty}^{\infty} G(u)\phi(x-u)\,\mathrm{d}u \tag{16–13}$$

Formally, (16–13) can be solved by taking Fourier or bilateral-Laplace transforms. The formalism given in (13–50)–(13–52) is also often useful, especially for obtaining approximate results.

Wiener–Hopf equations (half-infinite convolution):

$$\left.\begin{array}{c} g_0(x) = \displaystyle\int_0^{\infty} f(x-y)\phi_0(y)\,\mathrm{d}y \\ \text{(required for } x \geqslant 0 \text{ only)} \end{array}\right\} \tag{16–14}$$

The method of solution is, in essence, to introduce another function representing the "analytic continuation" of g_0 for $x < 0$ and then to eliminate the latter by an appeal to Liouville's theorem. Thus:

First complete the definitions of ϕ and g:

$$g(x) = J(x)g_0(x); \qquad \phi(x) = J(x)\phi_0(x)$$

where

$$J(x) = \begin{cases} 0, & \text{if } x < 0 \\ 1, & \text{if } x > 0 \end{cases}$$

Then define

$$h(x) = J(-x)\int_0^{\infty} f(x-y)\phi(y)\,\mathrm{d}y \tag{16–15}$$

Thus

$$g(x) + h(x) = \int_{-\infty}^{\infty} f(x-y)\phi(y)\,\mathrm{d}y, \quad \text{for all } x.$$

Taking two-sided Laplace transforms and denoting $\mathscr{L}_{\mathrm{II}}[g(t)] = G(p)$, etc., this equation is equivalent to $G + H = \Phi F$. Now because of the definitions of ϕ and h the function $\Phi(p)$ will be analytic in Re $(p) > \alpha$ (for some α) and H will be analytic in Re $(p) < \beta$. The method is now to factor F in the form,

$$L_1(p)L_2(p) = F(p) = \mathscr{L}_{\mathrm{II}}[f]$$

in such a way that, in the equation,

$$\frac{G(p) + H(p)}{L_1(p)} = \Phi(p)L_2(p) \tag{16–16}$$

one side is (known to be) analytic and bounded in Re $(p) > \alpha$ *and* the other side is (known to be) analytic and bounded in Re $(p) < \beta$. Then if $\alpha \leqslant \beta$, the principles of analytic continuation plus an appeal to Liouville's theorem show that

$$\Phi(p)L_2(p) = \text{constant}$$

so that $\phi(x)$ is determined. The success of the method, of course, hinges on the investigator's success in achieving the necessary form, (16–16).

"Transform type":

$$F(x) = \int_0^\infty H(xy)G(y)\,dy \qquad (16\text{–}17)$$

These can be solved, at least formally, by taking Mellin transforms. As discussed in connection with (13–57), a change of variable will also make available the techniques applicable to (16–14).

For certain H functions, the solution of (16–17) is given by classical "inversion" formulas for integral transforms:

$H(t) = e^{-t}$: Laplace transform

$H(t) = J_\nu(t)$: Hankel transform

FREDHOLM AND VOLTERRA EQUATIONS

$$\boxed{f(x) = \phi(x) - \lambda \int_a^b K(x, y)\phi(y)\,dy} \qquad (16\text{–}18)$$

(where K and f are given and ϕ is sought).

For simplicity, the theory will be stated for one-dimensional problems, but **all the following results remain valid in an arbitrary number of dimensions** with only such changes as are obviously necessary to make the formulas meaningful. In particular the region of integration may be any *finite* volume.

This equation turns out to have properties very similar to those of linear, second-order differential equations (or eigenvalue problems). While the latter can always be cast into integral form, (16–18), (Green's function), the integral equation is more general in the sense that the reverse transformation is not always possible.

$K(x, y)$ essentially "characterizes" the equation, as does the differential operator of a differential equation; $f(x)$ plays the role of a "driving" (inhomogeneous) term.

Other forms reducible to (16–18) are:

$$f(x) = \phi(x) - \lambda \int_a^x K(x, y)\phi(y)\,dy \qquad (16\text{–}19)$$

If we define $K = 0$ when $y > x$ then this may be written in the form (16–18). [This will not violate the conditions on K needed for the theorems quoted below.]

$$f(x) = \lambda \int_a^x K(x, y)\phi(y)\,dy \qquad (16\text{–}20)$$

Differentiation yields an equation of the form (16–19). Conversely, any solution of this resulting equation is a solution of (16–20)—as follows from re-integrating and noting that $f(a) = 0$.

$$f(x) = \int_a^b K(x, y)\phi(y)\,dy \qquad (16\text{–}21)$$

This equation itself cannot be directly reduced to (16–18), but its solutions can be determined from the same theory; see (16–40)–(16–47).

Restrictions

The theorems below are true under the following restrictions.

1. In (16–18), a and b are finite and $a \leqslant x \leqslant b$.

2. $f(x)$ is continuous and $\int_a^b [f(x)]^2\, dx$ exists.

3. $\int_a^b \int_a^b [K(s, t)]^2\, ds\, dt$ exists and *either*

   (a) $K(x, y)$ is piecewise* continuous in the rectangle, $a \leqslant x \leqslant b;\ a \leqslant y \leqslant b$

   or

   (b) $\int_a^b [K(x, t)]^2\, dt$ and $\int_a^b [K(t, x)]^2\, dt$ are bounded functions of x and $K(x, y)$ has, for $x =$ constant and for $y =$ constant, at most a "countably" infinite number of discontinuities.

The Character of the Solutions

The situation is reminiscent of that for ordinary linear algebraic (matrix) equations. Given a value of λ:

Either (16–18) has a unique solution for any continuous function, $f(x)$, or else the "homogeneous" equation,

$$0 = \phi(x) - \lambda \int_a^b K(x, y)\phi(y)\, dy \tag{16–22}$$

has at least one non-trivial solution ($\phi \not\equiv 0$).

In any case, the number of linearly independent solutions of (16–22) for given λ is finite. In particular, if $K(x, y) = K(y, x)$, this number is at most $\lambda^2 \iint K^2(u, v)\, du\, dv$.

Finally, when (16–22) is solvable, (16–18) has no solution unless $f(x)$ is such that

$$\int_a^b \tilde{\phi}_j(x) f(x)\, dx = 0$$

where the $\tilde{\phi}_j$ are all independent solutions of the "transposed homogeneous" equation,

$$0 = \tilde{\phi}(x) - \lambda \int_a^b \tilde{\phi}(y) K(y, x)\, dy \tag{16–23}$$

which has the same number of independent solutions as (16–22). The general solution of (16–18) in this case is *any* solution of (16–18) plus any linear combination of solutions of (16–22).

Methods of Solution (Unsymmetric Kernel, K)

1. *Fredholm series:* The unique solution of (16–18) (when (16–22) has none) is given by

$$\phi(x) = f(x) + \frac{1}{D(\lambda)} \int_a^b D(x, y;\ \lambda) f(y)\, dy \tag{16–24}$$

---

* That is, the region can be divided into a finite number of subregions within each of which K is continuous and on whose boundaries K assumes (approaches) finite values (which can be different when approaching from different sides).

where $D(\lambda)$ and $D(x, y;\ \lambda)$ are integral ("entire") functions of λ and are defined by series which are most conveniently expressed as follows. If

$$\left.\begin{aligned} K_0(x, y) &= 0; \qquad K_n(x, y) = \int_a^b K(x, t)K_{n-1}(t, y)\,dt + \kappa_{n-1}K(x, y) \\ \kappa_0 &= 1; \qquad \kappa_n = (-1/n)\int_a^b K_n(t, t)\,dt \end{aligned}\right.$$

then

$$D(\lambda) = \sum_0^\infty \kappa_n\lambda^n; \qquad D(x, y;\ \lambda) = \sum_0^\infty \lambda^n K_n(x, y) \tag{16–25}$$

In these series, we have the following convergence criterion:

If
$$|K(x, y)| \leqslant M \quad (\text{in} \quad a \leqslant x, y \leqslant b)$$
then
$$|K_n(x, y)| \leqslant \frac{n^{n/2}}{n!}\, n\, M^n(b-a)^{n-1} \tag{16–26}$$

In particular, the series converge for all values of λ.

Remark: If $K(x, y) = \sum_{i=1}^{N} f_i(x)g_i(y)$ then the series break off after the Nth term and $D(\lambda)$ and $D(x, y;\ \lambda)$ are polynomials of degree N in λ. For low values of N, the explicit solutions are easily written out.

2. *Iteration:* Choose any arbitrary, bounded, continuous function, $\phi_0(x)$. (However, the convergence will be the more rapid the better ϕ_0 approximates the true solution.) Then successively compute

$$\phi_n(x) = f(x) + \lambda\int_a^b K(x, y)\phi_{n-1}(y)\,dy \tag{16–27}$$

which will converge uniformly to the solution, ϕ, at least under the convergence conditions given for (16–28) below. (With a "good" choice for ϕ_0, the sequence may converge even when these conditions are violated.)

If, in particular, $\phi_0(x)$ is taken to be $f(x)$ we obtain:

3. *Neumann's series:*

$$\phi(x) = f(x) + \sum_{n=1}^{\infty}\lambda^n\int_a^b K^{(n)}(x, u)f(u)\,du$$

where

$$K^{(n+1)}(s, t) = \int_a^b K(s, v)K^{(n)}(v, t)\,dv; \qquad K^{(1)} = K \tag{16–28}$$

This converges uniformly to the solution, ϕ, of (16–18) either

(a) for all values of λ if $K(x, y) = 0$ when $y > x$ or

(b) if
$$\lambda^2\int_a^b\int_a^b [K(x, y)]^2\,dx\,dy < 1$$

When these conditions are not satisfied, the following artifice is useful.

4. Improving the convergence of (16–25), (16–27) or (16–28): Approximate $K(x, y)$ by an expression $\sum g_i(x)h_i(y)$; that is,

$$K(x, y) = R(x, y) + \sum_{i=1}^{n} g_i(x)h_i(y) \tag{16–29}$$

where the approximation is at least good enough to give

$$\lambda^2 \int_a^b \int_a^b [R(x, y)]^2 \, dx \, dy < 1$$

and preferably as small as is convenient. Then we can use the series (16–25), (16–27) or (16–28) to solve the $(n + 1)$ equations,

$$\begin{aligned} g_i(x) &= G_i(x) - \lambda \int_a^b R(x, y) G_i(y) \, dy \\ f(x) &= F(x) - \lambda \int_a^b R(x, y) F(y) \, dy \end{aligned} \tag{16–30}$$

The solution of (16–18) then satisfies the following equation, whose solution can be obtained in finite terms (see "Remark" following (16–26)).

$$F(x) = \phi(x) - \lambda \sum_{i=1}^{n} G_i(x) \int_a^b h_i(y)\phi(y) \, dy \tag{16–31}$$

5. Reduction to the symmetric case: The preceding are about the only practical methods* for solving (16–18) *directly* when $K(x, y) \neq K(y, x)$. However, (16–18) can always be converted to an equation with $\bar{K}(x, y) = \bar{K}(y, x)$ as follows. Let

$$\left.\begin{aligned} \bar{K}(x, y) &= K(x, y) + K(y, x) - \lambda \int_a^b K(t, x) K(t, y) \, dt \\ &\text{and} \\ \bar{f}(x) &= f(x) - \lambda \int_a^b K(t, x) f(t) \, dt \end{aligned}\right\} \tag{16–32}$$

Then the equation,

$$\bar{f}(x) = \phi(x) - \lambda \int_a^b \bar{K}(x, t)\phi(t) \, dt \tag{16–33}$$

has the same solutions as (16–18).

THE SYMMETRIC CASE, $K(x, y) = K(y, x)$; NORMAL MODES

1. *Normal modes* (*eigenfunctions*) are solutions of the *homogeneous* equation, (16–22). With a symmetric kernel, $K(x, y)$, there is always at least one value of λ for which (16–22) has a solution and there are at most a countable infinity† of such "eigenvalues", λ_n. If K is real, all eigenvalues are real and (ordering them according to increasing magnitude),

$$\lambda_n^2 \geqslant \frac{n}{W}; \qquad \text{where} \qquad W = \int_a^b \int_a^b [K(x, y)]^2 \, dx \, dy \tag{16–34}$$

Associated with each eigenvalue, λ_n, are at most $\lambda_n^2 W$ linearly independent solutions ϕ_{ni}, of (16–22). Those "eigenfunctions" belonging to different λ_n are necessarily

* Aside from straightforward *numerical* integration—whereupon K becomes a matrix of numbers and the solution can be carried out by algebraic operations, (11–24)–(11–28).

† This statement becomes false if the integration range becomes infinite. A countably infinite set is an infinite set whose members can be numbered (or, as commonly phrased, put in one-to-one correspondence with the set of all positive integers). "Denumerably infinite" is an equivalent term.

orthogonal and (because of the linearity of (16–22)) those associated with the same λ_n may be *chosen* to be orthogonal. Finally, all ϕ_{ni} may be normalized so that, in all

$$\int_a^b \phi_{ni}(x)\phi_{mj}(x)\,dx = \delta_{nm}\delta_{ij} \tag{16–35}$$

(for further details on these "geometric" concepts, see Chapters 18 and 19).

Provided that a function, F, can be expressed* in the form,

$$F(x) = \int_a^a K(x, t)g(t)\,dt \qquad \text{(for some } g(t))$$

then it can also be expanded in a (uniformly and absolutely) convergent series of eigenfunctions:

$$F(x) = \sum_{n,j} a_{nj}\phi_{nj}(x); \qquad \text{where} \qquad a_{nj} = \int_a^b F(x)\phi_{nj}(x)\,dx \tag{16–36}$$

2. *Finding the normal modes:* The eigenvalues λ_n can be characterized as the roots of $D(\lambda) = 0$ where D is defined in (16–25). There are in general an infinite number; the number is finite when and only when

$$K(x, y) = \sum_1^N h_i(x)h_i(y)$$

in which case the eigenfunctions are linear combinations of the $h_i(x)$ themselves.

An iteration theorem: If we select an arbitrary normalized function, $q_0(x)$ and recursively define,

$$q_n(x) = l_n \int_a^b K(x, t)q_{n-1}(t)\,dt$$

where l_n is chosen to normalize q_n, then l_n converges toward some eigenvalue λ_n and $q_n(x)$ converges toward a corresponding eigenfunction.

Some variational methods are given in Chapter 19. (Note that the λ_n used here are the reciprocals of those used in the general formalism of Chapter 19.)

In general, however, "ingenious devices" and a certain amount of luck are needed to obtain a full infinite set of eigenfunctions in explicit analytic form.

3. *Using normal modes to solve* (16–18): If the complete set of normal modes, or eigenfunctions, ϕ_{ni}, adjusted to satisfy (16–35), are known, then whenever (16–18) has a solution, it is given by,

$$\phi(x) = f(x) + \lambda \sum_{n,i} \frac{\phi_{ni}(x)}{\lambda_n - \lambda} b_{ni} \tag{16–37}$$

where

$$b_{ni} = \int_a^b f(t)\phi_{ni}(t)\,dt$$

In particular, if $\lambda =$ some λ_N, then all b_{N_i} must vanish if (16–18) is to be soluble. The series converges uniformly and absolutely in x.

Note that there are certain $f(x)$, namely simple combinations of a few $\phi_{ni}(x)$, for which (16–18) has especially simple solutions. This is sometimes helpful in choosing simple "model problems" to approximate a physical situation.

---

* This restriction is important [although it is virtually vacuous for some $K(x, y)$] because there exist kernels with only one eigenfunction; $K = h(x)h(y)$, for example.

4. *Further properties:* To bring out the analogy between the normal modes of a (symmetric) kernel, $K(x, y)$, and the eigenvectors of a matrix, it is interesting to note that the "operator function", $K(x, y)$, can be expanded as a series of "projection operators", each of which "projects" an arbitrary function "along" a normal mode:

$$K(x, y) = \sum_{n,i} \frac{\phi_{ni}(x)\phi_{ni}(y)}{\lambda_n} \tag{16–38}$$

provided the series converges uniformly in x and y. [Compare (18–29) and (18–40)–(18–41).]

Moreover, the "squared operator", $K \cdot K = \int K(x, z)K(z, y)\, dz = K^{(2)}(x, y)$ in the notation of (16–28), has eigenvalues $(\lambda_n)^2$ and the *same* eigenfunctions. In general for the nth iterate,

$$K^{(n)}(x, y) = \sum_{m,i} \frac{\phi_{mi}(x)\phi_{mi}(y)}{(\lambda_m)^n} \tag{16–39}$$

where, for $n \geqslant 2$, the series *necessarily* converges uniformly and absolutely.

THE EQUATION OF THE "FIRST KIND"

$$f(x) = \int_a^b K(x, t)\phi(t)\, dt \tag{16–40}$$

(with the same restrictions as before on $K(x, y)$).

1. If $K(x, y) = K(y, x)$ then the "normal modes" of (16–22) may be used to solve (16–40); namely, if (16–40) has any solution, then $f(x)$ must be expressible in the form,

$$f(x) = \sum_{n,i} a_{ni}\phi_{ni}(x); \qquad \text{where} \qquad a_{ni} = \int_a^b f(x)\phi_{ni}(x)\, dx \tag{16–41}$$

The series then necessarily converges uniformly and absolutely and the solution of (16–40) is

$$\phi(x) = \sum_{n,i} a_{ni}\lambda_n\phi_{ni}(x) \tag{16–42}$$

2. The unsymmetric case: When $K(x, y) \neq K(y, x)$, there need be no solutions of (16–22) for any value of λ whatever; that is, there may be no normal modes. However, the two symmetric kernels,

$$\left.\begin{aligned} K_1(x, y) &= \int_a^b K(x, t)K(y, t)\, dt \\ K_2(x, y) &= \int_a^b K(t, x)K(t, y)\, dt \end{aligned}\right\} \tag{16–43}$$

have normal modes and equal positive eigenvalues, say $\lambda_n^{\,2}$. These modes ϕ, ψ, which can be chosen individually orthonormal, have the property with respect to K itself that:

$$\left.\begin{aligned} \lambda_n \int_a^b K(x, t)\phi_{ni}(t)\, dt &= \psi_{ni}(x) \\ \lambda_n \int_a^b \psi_{ni}(t)K(t, y)\, dt &= \phi_{ni}(y) \end{aligned}\right\} \tag{16–44}$$

These functions may be used to solve (16–40); namely if (16–40) has any solution, then $f(x)$ must be expressible as a uniformly and absolutely convergent series,

$$f(x) = \sum_{n,i} \alpha_{ni}\psi_{ni}(x); \qquad \text{where} \qquad \alpha_{ni} = \int_a^b f(x)\psi_{ni}(x)\,dx \tag{16–45}$$

(we assume that the two sets, ψ_{ni} and ϕ_{ni} have been made orthonormal—adjusted to satisfy (16–35)), and the solution of (16–40) is

$$\phi(x) = \sum_{n,i} \lambda_n \alpha_{ni}\phi_{ni}(x) \tag{16–46}$$

Similarly, the solution of

$$f(x) = \int_a^b \phi(t)K(t, x)\,dt$$

is

$$\phi(t) = \sum_{ni} \lambda_n \psi_{ni}(t) \int_a^b f(u)\phi_{ni}(u)\,du \tag{16–47}$$

CHAPTER 17

VARIATIONAL PROBLEMS; LINEAR PROGRAMMING

A VARIATIONAL problem is a problem in which one must choose, from all functions of some given (infinite) class, that one which makes some integral expression a minimum (or maximum). Naturally, the integral must be of a rather special type before this requirement will suffice to specify a unique function, and it is easy to formulate "problems" which have no solution or which have an infinity of solutions.*

Nevertheless, a large class of physical problems can be formulated as variational problems and this formulation has several advantages:

(a) The expressions involved are virtually independent of the coordinate system used and hence share many of the advantages of vector notation.

(b) Variational formulations can be used as the basis of straightforward approximate calculations (numerical or otherwise).

(c) If several formulations can be made for the same physical problem, one can sometimes "box in" the quantity desired by obtaining two expressions, one always greater and one always less than the desired quantity. Such bounds themselves represent information which may be entirely sufficient for the problem at hand.

As a general guide in physical problems, the quantity to be maximized or minimized usually turns out to be the energy or entropy. Frequently the kinetic and potential energies are individually stationary.

Notation

Expressions such as

$$\delta\int\cdots\int F\left[f(\mathbf{r}), \frac{\partial f}{\partial x}, \cdots\right] \mathrm{d}V = 0; \qquad \delta\int\int|\nabla f|^2 \,\mathrm{d}V = 0 \tag{17-1}$$

indicate that the problem at hand is to minimize or maximize (or make "stationary"; see below) the expression which follows the symbol, δ.

The function which is free to be chosen ("varied") must be made clear from the context. (In (17–1), f is intended to indicate the arbitrary or variable function.)

Sketch of Basic Concepts and Techniques

With but few exceptions, problems do not initially arise in variational form. Usually, one derives an integral expression and then tests it to determine whether setting its "variation" equal to zero is equivalent to the original problem. This test employs techniques which also serve to convert a variational problem to other forms; namely:

Set $f(\mathbf{r}) = f_0(\mathbf{r}) + \epsilon h(\mathbf{r})$ where f_0 is the (unknown) solution† of the variational

---

* For example, in the notation below, $\delta\int_a^b f(x)\,\mathrm{d}x = 0$ has no solution, even if we also require $f > 0$. (It does have a solution if the requirement is $f \geqslant 0$.)

† Note that this step *assumes that there* IS *a solution.* False results can be obtained unless this is independently verified—possibly by physical arguments.

problem and $h(\mathbf{r})$ is so chosen that the sum, $f_0 + \epsilon h$ is an admissible function (satisfies the boundary or other conditions defining the class of functions from which the solution is to be drawn). Otherwise, h is arbitrary.

After making the substitution $f = f_0 + \epsilon h$, in the integral expression to be maximized or minimized, pick out terms of the first order in ϵ. Employing integration-by-parts,* those terms of the form, $\epsilon \partial h/\partial x$ etc., can be converted to the form ϵh. The final result is an integral expression whose integrand contains h only as a factor:

$$\int \cdots \int \epsilon h(\mathbf{r}) \left\{ G\left[f_0(\mathbf{r}), \frac{\partial f_0}{\partial x}, \cdots \right] \right\} \mathrm{d}V \tag{17–2}$$

(The function, G, is often called the "variational derivative" of the integrand in (17–1).)

For the original expression, (17–1), to be a maximum or minimum (or "stationary"; see below), the expression (17–2) must vanish. But $h(\mathbf{r})$ is arbitrary except for boundary conditions and hence we must have,

$$G\left[f_0(\mathbf{r}), \frac{\partial f_0}{\partial x}, \cdots \right] = 0 \tag{17–3}$$

which is the condition on the solution $f_0(\mathbf{r})$, equivalent to the original problem, (17–1).

"Stationary values": Strictly speaking, the vanishing of (17–2) need not lead to a maximum (or minimum) of (17–1). To ascertain this, it would be necessary to evaluate terms in ϵ^2 and show that these are necessarily negative (or positive).† However, the integral (17–1) will be "stationary" when (17–3) holds; that is, the function, f_0, satisfying (17–3) has in any case the property that the value of (17–1) is *changed only to the second order* in ϵ when f_0 is replaced by $f_0 + \epsilon h$, even though the change may take either sign. For many applications, this property alone suffices.

Hence we speak of the f_0 which satisfies (17–3) as the "solution" of (17–1), but refer to the resulting value of (the integral in) (17–1) as a "stationary" value to indicate that it need not be a maximum or a minimum.

Lagrange's Problem

Lagrange's equations for a mechanical system in arbitrary coordinates are most easily obtained from a variational principle. Its form is

$$\delta \int_{t_1}^{t_2} L[x, y, \cdots; \dot{x}, \dot{y}, \cdots; t] \, \mathrm{d}t = 0 \tag{17–4}$$

where $x = x(t)$, $\dot{x} = \mathrm{d}x/\mathrm{d}t, \cdots$ and the end-values, $x(t_1)$, $x(t_2), \cdots$, are assumed to have certain fixed (but unspecified) values.

The basic techniques above‡ lead to Lagrange's equations, which are equivalent to (17–4),

$$\frac{\mathrm{d}}{\mathrm{d}t}\frac{\partial L}{\partial \dot{x}} = \frac{\partial L}{\partial x}; \qquad \frac{\mathrm{d}}{\mathrm{d}t}\frac{\partial L}{\partial \dot{y}} = \frac{\partial L}{\partial y}; \cdots \tag{17–5}$$

* The "integrated" terms will vanish by virtue of the boundary conditions on f and hence on h. If this does not happen, it is an indication that the problem has no solution, without introducing further restrictions on f.

† This step is therefore needed to show that some desired quantity lies between two integral expressions for arbitrary f.

‡ Here, since there are several functions, x, y, $\cdots$, one makes, simultaneously, the several substitutions, $x(t) = x_0(t) + \epsilon\xi(t)$; $y(t) = y_0(t) + \epsilon\eta(t)$; $\cdots$.

(Observe that the notation implies that $x, \dot{x}, \cdots$ are all to be treated as *independent* variables in taking the partial derivatives, but that this convention is then dropped in applying the operator, d/dt.)

Auxiliary Conditions

A convenient technique for including additional conditions is that of "Lagrange multipliers": Given,

$$\delta \int \cdots \int L \, ds \cdots dt = 0 \tag{17-6}$$

with the conditions*

$$\int \cdots \int G \, ds \cdots dt = 0; \qquad \int \cdots \int H \, ds \cdots dt = 0; \cdots \tag{17-7}$$

or the conditions,

$$G = 0; \qquad H = 0; \cdots \tag{17-8}$$

Multiply each equation in (17–7) or (17–8) by a constant, $\lambda, \mu, \cdots$—as yet unspecified. Then add (17–7) to (17–6) or integrate (17–8) and add to (17–6) to obtain

$$\delta \int \cdots \int [L + \lambda G + \mu H + \cdots] \, ds \cdots dt = 0 \tag{17-9}$$

Solve the problem (17–9) and, finally, determine $\lambda, \mu, \cdots$ (which will occur as parameters in the final functions, $f_0, \cdots$) by substitution of the solutions, $f_0 \cdots$, into (17–7) or (17–8).

General Forms

1. Consider the problem,

"First solve $K\phi = f$ and then evaluate $\int gL\phi$" where K and L are symmetric, linear operators.† This problem can be converted to a variational problem if two (symmetric, linear) operators, L', K', can be found such that $L'K = K'L$. Namely, the problem,

$$\delta\left[\int \psi L'f + \int gL\phi - \int \psi K'L\phi\right] = 0 \tag{17-10}$$

(ψ and ϕ "variable" functions‡) has the solution,

$$K\phi = f, \qquad K'\psi = g$$

and the stationary value of the integral in (17–10) is $\int gL\phi$.

2. If L is a linear, symmetric operator, then the equation, $L\phi = 0$, is equivalent to $\delta \int \phi L \phi = 0$. More generally,

$$L\phi_i = 0 \quad \text{are equivalent to:} \quad \delta \int \phi_i L \phi_j = 0 \tag{17-11}$$

Further consider the problems,

$$L\phi_i = f_i \tag{17-12}$$

---

* The functions, $G, H, \cdots$, depend on the unknown functions, $f(s, \cdots, t), \cdots$ in a manner similar to that of L in (17–4) or (17–6); the unknown functions are not shown explicitly.

† That is, $\int \phi L \psi = \int \psi L \phi$ for all (admissable) functions and also $L(a\phi + b\psi) = aL\phi + bL\psi$.

‡ The class of admissable functions is defined by the boundary conditions etc. initially given with the equation, $K\phi = f$. The range of all integrations likewise corresponds to that in the original problem.

If L has an inverse, then equivalent problems are

$$\delta\int(\phi_j L\phi_i - \phi_j f_i - \phi_i f_j) = 0 \tag{17–13}$$

(proof: set $\phi_i' = \phi_i - L^{-1}f_i$ in (17–11)). The stationary value of the integral is $-\int\phi_i f_j$.

Numerical Solution

The basic technique is to choose a "trial" function with adjustable constants. Substitution into the expression to be minimized (or made stationary), followed by differentiation with respect to the adjustable parameters, then leads to conditions determining the "best choice" of these parameters.

About the only direct way to estimate the remaining error is to repeat the process either with a different function or with one containing more parameters. Comparison of the final results then indicates (but does not rigorously prove) the magnitude of the remaining error.

Care must be taken to ensure that the trial function is admissible (satisfies boundary conditions, etc.) for all values of the parameters.

A common type of trial function is

$$f(t) = \sum_n c_n F_n(t) \tag{17–14}$$

where the $F_n(t)$ satisfy the boundary conditions. If these are stated for $t = 0$ and $t = \infty$, it may be possible to use,

$$f(t) = \sum_n c_n F_n(b_n t) \tag{17–15}$$

The c_n and b_n are then adjusted to minimize the desired integral (and to satisfy other equations, if necessary).

In general, the final results are the more accurate the more the "form" of f has been chosen to have features which are shared by the solution. This process of forcing in the "proper" behavior can often be guided by physical considerations.

LINEAR PROGRAMMING

This name (of historical origin) is given to any problem of the following form. To maximize (by varying the numbers, $x_1, x_2, \cdots, x_n$) the linear expression,

$$f = \sum_{i=1}^{n} p_i x_i$$

subject to the restrictions, (17–16)

$$\sum_{i=1}^{n} a_{1i}x_i \geqslant b_1; \qquad \sum_{i=1}^{n} a_{2i}x_i \geqslant b_2; \qquad \cdots; \qquad \sum_{i=1}^{n} a_{ki}x_i \geqslant b_k$$

Remark: This form includes several apparently different types of problem:

(1) If, say, $\sum_1^n a_{3i}x_i \leqslant b_3$ is required, reverse the signs of b_3 and the a_{3j}.

(2) If f is to be minimized, reverse the signs of the p_j.

(3) If, say, $\sum_1^n a_{Ii}x_i = b_I$ is required, either replace this by the two restrictions, $\sum a_{Ii}x_i \geqslant b_I$ and $\sum [-a_{Ii}]x_i \geqslant [-b_I]$, or else use the equation to eliminate one variable say x_n.

Geometric Interpretation; Method of Solution

In vector notation, with $\mathbf{r} = (x_1, x_2, \cdots, x_n)$ etc., the problem (17–16) may be written,

$$f(\mathbf{r}) = \mathbf{p} \cdot \mathbf{r} = \max; \qquad \mathbf{a}_j \cdot \mathbf{r} \geqslant b_j \qquad (j = 1, \cdots, k) \tag{17–17}$$

Here, each inequality restricts $\mathbf{r}$ to one side of a plane (whose normal vector is $\mathbf{a}_j$ and whose distance from $\mathbf{r} = 0$ is b_j). The totality of inequalities restricts $\mathbf{r}$ to a *convex* region bounded by planes. Now the gradient of $f(\mathbf{r})$ is the constant vector, $\mathbf{p}$, and hence $f(\mathbf{r})$ will usually assume its maximum in a corner of this region.

At such a corner, we have

$$-\mathbf{p} = \sum_{j=1}^{n} c_j \mathbf{a}_j, \qquad \text{where} \qquad c_j \geqslant 0 \tag{17–18}$$

(where only those planes which define the corner have $c_j > 0$). If the vector, $(-\mathbf{p})$, cannot be expressed in the form (17–18), the problem has no solution; if it can be so expressed with fewer than n coefficients which do not vanish, the problem has an infinity of solutions (for then $\nabla f = \mathbf{p}$ is normal to a "face" or "edge" of the allowed region).

Conversely, one may choose all sets of n independent vectors from the $\mathbf{a}_j$ and seek an equation, (17–18), expressing $(-\mathbf{p})$ as a "positive" combination of such as set. The value of $f(\mathbf{r})$ in such a corner (17–18) is

$$f = \mathbf{p} \cdot \mathbf{r} = -\sum b_j c_j \tag{17–19}$$

and this will be a solution provided that $\mathbf{r}$ as determined from $\mathbf{a}_j \cdot \mathbf{r} = b_j$ (for those j whose $c_j \neq 0$) is in the region, $\mathbf{a}_l \cdot \mathbf{r} \geqslant b_l$ for *all* l and provided that no other corner yields a larger value of f. Thus a systematic, finite (though tedious) procedure can locate the solution.

CHAPTER 18

UNITARY SPACES

THE CONCEPT of an n-dimensional "space", mentioned at the end of Chapter 10, can be further generalized, and the result provides essentially the formal mathematical machinery to which much of quantum mechanics is welded. Important concepts and relations in the theory of Fourier-type series and of differential equations can also be summarized in easily recalled form by a further generalization.

It should be reiterated that *the geometric terminology is merely an analogy*, used for its brevity and suggestiveness; there is *no* implication that the "space" can be visualized.

Definitions

The "*points*" or "*vectors*", ϕ, of an n-dimensional unitary space are columns of n complex numbers, $\phi_1, \phi_2, \cdots, \phi_n$, called the "*components*" of ϕ. A vector is thus a column matrix. Its Hermitian conjugate, $\phi^\dagger$, is a row matrix with complex-conjugate components, ϕ_i^*.

Addition and subtraction of such vectors and multiplication by an ordinary number are defined in the usual way:

$$(\phi \pm \psi)_i = \phi_i \pm \psi_i; \qquad (a\phi)_i = a\phi_i \tag{18-1}$$

The "*scalar product*" of two vectors, ϕ and ψ, is defined (*ad hoc*) as the complex number,

$$(\phi, \psi) = \phi^\dagger \psi = \sum_{i=1}^{n} \phi_i^* \psi_i \tag{18-2}$$

(* denotes complex conjugate). The "*length*" (or "norm") of ϕ then denotes (of course)

$$\begin{aligned}(\text{length})^2 \equiv \|\phi\|^2 &= (\phi, \phi) = \phi^\dagger \phi \\ &= \sum_{i=1}^{n} \phi_i^* \phi_i = \sum_{i=1}^{n} |\phi_i|^2\end{aligned} \tag{18-3}$$

which is real and non-negative.

Fundamental Theorems

$$\left.\begin{aligned}(\eta, a\phi + b\psi) &= a(\eta, \phi) + b(\eta, \psi) \\ (\phi, \psi) &= (\psi, \phi)^* \\ \|\phi\|^2 \equiv (\phi, \phi) &> 0, \text{ unless } \phi = 0 \\ \text{then } \|\phi\|^2 &= 0\end{aligned}\right\} \tag{18-4}$$

(These three properties are taken as *axioms* in abstract generalizations of "unitary space". In addition, of course, it must be assumed that $\phi + \psi$ and $a\phi$ always also belong to the space and that there is a null vector, 0, such that $\phi + 0 = \phi$ for all ϕ.)

Note that

$$(a\phi, \psi) = a^*(\phi, \psi) \tag{18–5}$$

—Schwarz inequality:

$$|(\phi, \psi)| \leqslant \|\phi\| \cdot \|\psi\| \qquad (\text{that is, "}|\cos\theta| \leqslant 1\text{"}) \tag{18–6}$$

(proof: use $0 \leqslant \|\phi + x\psi\|^2$ for all complex x.)
—Triangle inequality:

$$\|\phi + \psi\| \leqslant \|\phi\| + \|\psi\| \tag{18–7}$$

(proof: evaluate $\|\phi + \psi\|^2$ and use (18–6).)

A Convention

To avoid confusion with the components, ϕ_i, of a vector, we shall denote *sets of vectors* by a subscript preceded by a *dot*: $\phi_{\cdot i}$. The component of a vector of the set is then indicated by replacing the dot by an index: ϕ_{ki} represents the kth component of the ith vector. (The advantages of this notation will emerge later.)

Sub-spaces

A "sub-space" (or "linear manifold") is any set of vectors which are "closed" under the operations of addition and multiplication by a constant—that is, such operations on vectors in the set yield only vectors which also belong to the set. Thus adding or "extending" vectors of a sub-space does not yield vectors outside the sub-space. The concept is the analogue of a plane or line in ordinary space.

It follows immediately that, given any set of N vectors, $\phi_{\cdot k}$, the set of all vectors of the form $\sum a_k \phi_{\cdot k}$ is a sub-space—said to be the sub-space "spanned by the $\phi_{\cdot k}$." In a sense, the $\phi_{\cdot k}$ form a (possibly redundant and in general "askew") coordinate system, or set of basis vectors, for the sub-space.

A general vector of the whole space cannot (usually) be expressed in this form. It "projects into other dimensions somewhat".

Coordinates (Basis-vectors)

The vectors introduced in the original definitions are said to be expressed in the "coordinates", $\epsilon_{\cdot i}$, where

$$\epsilon_{ij} \equiv (\epsilon_{\cdot j})_i = \delta_{ij} = \begin{cases} 0 & \text{if} \quad i \neq j \\ 1 & \text{if} \quad i = j \end{cases} \tag{18–8}$$

Indeed,

$$\left.\begin{aligned} \phi_i &= (\epsilon_{\cdot i}, \phi) \\ \phi &= \sum \phi_i \epsilon_{\cdot i} = \sum (\epsilon_{\cdot i}, \phi)\epsilon_{\cdot i} \end{aligned}\right\} \tag{18–9}$$

(In the generalizations mentioned later, the $\epsilon_{\cdot i}$ are essentially postulated to exist and ϕ_i is defined as $(\epsilon_{\cdot i}, \phi)$.)

N vectors $\phi_{\cdot k}$ are said to be *orthonormal* if

$$(\phi_{\cdot k}, \phi_{\cdot j}) = \delta_{kj} \tag{18–10}$$

(that is, they are mutually perpendicular and have unit lengths). N vectors are said to be *independent* if

$$\sum_{k=1}^{N} c_k \phi_{\cdot k} = 0 \qquad \text{only when} \qquad c_k = 0 \qquad (\text{all } k)$$

(that is, no vector of the set can be expressed in terms of the others). The $\phi_{\cdot k}$ are said to be "complete" if their number, N, equals n, the dimension of the "space" and if they are independent (for then any vector can be expressed in terms of them).

It follows immediately from the theory of sets of linear equations that (if n is the number of dimensions),

1. n vectors $\phi_{\cdot k}$ are independent if and only if $\mathrm{Det}(\phi_{ik}) \neq 0$.
2. N vectors are always *de*pendent if $N > n$.
3. If $N < n$, the N vectors $\phi_{\cdot k}$ are independent if and only if the determinant of some N-by-N submatrix of ϕ_{ik} does not vanish.
4. Mutually orthogonal vectors are always independent [for $0 = (\phi_{\cdot i}, \sum c_k \phi_{\cdot k}) = c_i$].
5. If $\phi_{\cdot i}$ are orthonormal, the matrix ϕ_{ki} is unitary and conversely.

Bessel Inequality

If $\eta_{\cdot i}$ are orthonormal (but not necessarily complete)

$$\sum_i |(\eta_{\cdot i}, \phi)|^2 \leqslant \|\phi\|^2 \tag{18–11}$$

and more generally,

$$\sum_i |(\eta_{\cdot i}, \phi)(\psi, \eta_{\cdot i})| \leqslant \tfrac{1}{2}\|\phi\|^2 + \tfrac{1}{2}\|\psi\|^2 \tag{18–12}$$

[The following proof applies for $n = \infty$. Since $\phi = \phi' + \sum (\eta_{\cdot i}, \phi)\eta_{\cdot i}$ where $(\phi', \eta_{\cdot i}) = 0$, evaluation of (ϕ, ϕ) proves the first statement, (18–11). Secondly, for any two complex numbers $2\,|ab| \leqslant |a|^2 + |b|^2$ and (18–12) follows from (18–11).]

Schmidt's Orthogonalizing Process

Given N vectors, $\phi_{\cdot\alpha}$, we can obtain from them an orthonormal set ("Cartesian coordinates") by the following procedure. Denote the new set by $\theta_{\cdot i}$ and define them inductively:

1. $\theta_{\cdot 1} = \phi_{\cdot 1}/\|\phi_{\cdot 1}\|$
2. For $\theta_{\cdot k}$, subtract from $\phi_{\cdot k}$ all its projections along previous $\theta_{\cdot i}$; thus define

$$\psi_{\cdot k} = \phi_{\cdot k} - \sum_{j<k} (\theta_{\cdot j}, \phi_{\cdot k})\theta_{\cdot j}$$

and if $\psi_{\cdot k} = 0$, omit $\phi_{\cdot k}$ and proceed to $\phi_{\cdot k+1}$; otherwise normalize:

$$\theta_{\cdot k} = \psi_{\cdot k}/\|\psi_{\cdot k}\|$$

If the vectors $\phi_{\cdot\alpha}$ are independent, then (by definition) no $\psi_{\cdot k}$ can vanish and the final set $\theta_{\cdot i}$ also contains N members (now orthonormal).

Dimension of a Sub-space

Given any set of vectors, the "dimension "of the (sub)space which they span may be defined as the (maximum) number of *independent* vectors, $\phi_{\cdot k}$, which can be chosen from the set (and hence as the rank of the matrix, ϕ_{ik}). By the Schmidt process, any set of vectors can be replaced by an orthonormal set—automatically independent and of the correct number—if desired. Thus every (sub)space can be expressed as a set of all vectors of the form, $\sum a_k \phi_{\cdot k}$; the concept of such sets is identical with that of a sub-space.

Decomposition into Sub-spaces

If the dimension, m, of a given sub-space, S, is less than n, then by definition there exist vectors not in S (that is, independent of the $\phi_{\cdot k}$ defining the sub-space S).

By the Schmidt process, we can find $(n - m)$ vectors $\psi_{\cdot i}$ which are *orthogonal* to the $\phi_{\cdot k}$ and hence to the entire sub-space S. These then span a sub-space, S', defined as all vectors of the form $\sum b_i \psi_{\cdot i}$ and all such vectors are all the vectors orthogonal to S. Then S and S' are said to be orthogonal sub-spaces.

The entire space is thereby decomposed into the "vector sum" of the orthogonal sub-spaces, S and S', in the sense that, while a general vector may lie in neither, it can be expressed as a sum of two vectors (its "projections") lying in S and S' respectively. (Compare the analogue: $S = (x, y)$-plane and $S' = z$-axis in ordinary space.)

Matrices and Operators

Any n-by-n matrix, M, can be multiplied into a (column) vector, ϕ; the result is again a vector, $M\phi$, whose i^{th} component is

$$(M\phi)_i = \sum M_{ik}\phi_k \tag{18–13}$$

Thus, matrices may be regarded as (linear) *operators*, acting on vectors of the "space" in such a way as to map them onto other vectors of the "space".

Conversely, if a linear operator, Q, has been specified by its "geometric" properties (that is, $Q\phi = \psi$ given for all ϕ), then its matrix elements can be deduced by its action on the "basis vectors, $\epsilon_{\cdot i}$, whose components are $\epsilon_{ji} = \delta_{ji}$,

$$Q_{ki} = (Q\epsilon_{\cdot i})_k = (\epsilon_{\cdot k}, Q\epsilon_{\cdot i}) \tag{18–14}$$

The operator "adjoint" to Q is defined by the property that

$$(Q^\dagger\psi, \phi) = (\psi, Q\phi)$$

for all ψ and ϕ. From (18–14) it follows that $(Q^\dagger)_{ij} = Q_{ji}^*$, and the corresponding matrix is indeed the Hermitian conjugate of Q_{ij}.

Projection Operators

For any sub-space, S, an operator, P, may be defined which "projects" an arbitrary vector onto the sub-space—that is, it first decomposes the vector into a sum of two vectors, one orthogonal to the sub-space and one lying in the sub-space, and then yields the latter alone as the final result of the operation; P selects the part of ϕ lying in S.

If we select (Schmidt process) an orthonormal basis, $\eta_{\cdot i}$, for S then P may be defined in the intuitively obvious fashion,

$$P\phi = \sum_i (\eta_{\cdot i}, \phi)\eta_{\cdot i} \tag{18–15}$$

or, in matrix form,

$$P_{ke} = \sum_i \eta_{ki}\eta_{ei}^*$$

(the sum here is *not* itself a matrix product; there are fewer than n vectors, $\eta_{\cdot i}$, but each has n components and P is n-by-n).

Transformation of Coordinates

Basis vectors other than $\epsilon_{\cdot i}$ can, of course, be used provided they "span" the full space. Let $\eta_{\cdot k}$ be any set of n independent vectors; express them in terms of the $\epsilon_{\cdot i}$,

$$\eta_{\cdot k} = \sum_k \eta_{ik}\epsilon_{\cdot k} \tag{18–16}$$

(In matrix notation: $\eta = \eta I$.) If (and only if) the $\eta_{\cdot k}$ are independent, the matrix

η_{ik} has an inverse, T say, and the ϵ's can be expressed inversely in terms of the η's; using the *summation convention* (see preceding (11–2)),

$$\epsilon_{\cdot k} = \eta_{\cdot j} T_{jk} \tag{18–17}$$

Then, indeed, any vector ϕ can be expressed in terms of the new basis $\eta_{\cdot k}$ thus

$$\phi = \epsilon_{\cdot k}\phi_k = \eta_{\cdot j} T_{jk}\phi_k \tag{18–18}$$

The coefficients of the η's are now said to be the components of ϕ relative to the new coordinate system,

$$\phi_j' = T_{jk}\phi_k \tag{18–19}$$

(Contrast the order here with that in the transformation equation, (18–17).) These manipulations remain valid whether or not the ϵ's have the special form $\epsilon_{ik} = \delta_{ik}$.

An Ambiguity

A particular case of (18–19) is $\eta_{je}' = T_{jk}\eta_{ke} = \delta_{je}$ (by definition of T).

However, if we now regard *all* vectors as represented by their primed components arranged in columns, we obtain an "n-dimensional unitary space", abstractly indistinguishable from the original unitary space with but one exception:

The scalar product was originally defined in terms of the old components, ϕ_i. The corresponding "new" quantity,

$$[\psi, \phi] = \sum_i \phi_i'(\psi_i')^* \tag{18–20}$$

will not in general have the same value. In particular, $[\eta_{\cdot i}, \eta_{\cdot k}] = \delta_{ik}$ whatever the original η's. Since the "space" is completely abstract, there is no way of deciding which definition is "correct".

About the only tenable convention is to define the scalar product always in terms of the components "at hand" and to regard any changes in the scalar products as due to a "mapping onto another space".

Scalar-product-preserving Transformations

Those transformations which do *not* give a different space (in the sense of the above convention) are characterized by $[\phi, \psi] = (T\phi, T\psi) = (T^\dagger T\phi, \psi) = (\phi, \psi)$ for arbitrary ϕ and ψ. Thus, such transformations are those with the property,

$$T^\dagger = T^{-1} \tag{18–21}$$

that is, (the matrix) T is *unitary*. Equivalently, recalling that $T^{-1} = \eta$:

The new basis vectors, $\eta_{\cdot k}$, must be *orthonormal.*

Mappings (Linear)

For any matrix, M, we can regard the relation,

$$\phi = M\psi \quad \text{or} \quad \psi \rightarrow M\psi$$

as a mapping of the space onto itself. By the general conventions of matrix algebra, this type of mapping is necessarily linear; that is,

$$M(a\psi + b\psi) = aM\psi + bM\phi \tag{18–22}$$

Under the (general) coordinate transformation, T, (or further mapping onto another space), this mapping M may be expressed in the new coordinates as a mapping, M', as follows.

$$\phi' = T\phi = TM\psi = TMT^{-1}\psi'$$

or

$$M \to TMT^{-1} = M' \tag{18–23}$$

The matrix transformation (18–23) is therefore of especial interest. It is easily shown that any algebraic relation between matrices is invariant under such transformations (that is, the new relation in primed quantities is the same as the old in unprimed quantities).

The determinant and diagonal sum ("trace") of M are also unchanged by transformations of the type (18–23) and, indeed, the characteristic polynomial, Det $(M - xI)$, is invariant under (18–23).

However, only if T is unitary do Hermitian and unitary matrices retain their properties under (18–23). [Example: $(H')^\dagger = (THT^{-1})^\dagger = (THT^\dagger)^\dagger = TH^\dagger T^\dagger = THT^\dagger = H'$.] Also only if T is unitary do we have

$$M_{jl}' = (\eta_{\cdot j}, M\eta_{\cdot l})$$

$$\{\text{in general: } M_{jl}' = [\eta_{\cdot j}, M\eta_{\cdot l}]\}$$

Eigenvectors and Eigenvalues

Certain vectors have especially simple behavior under a mapping:

$$M\xi = \lambda\xi \qquad (\lambda \text{ a number}) \tag{18–24}$$

In particular, *if* there exist n independent vectors of this type, a coordinate (or space) transformation will reduce M to diagonal form (the "operator" M then becomes a non-uniform magnification).

The values of λ for which (18–24) has a non-null solution ξ are called *eigenvalues* of M and the solutions ξ are called‡ *eigenvectors* of M.

We have:

1. If M is Hermitian, all eigenvalues are real. [Proof: $\lambda(\xi, \xi) = (\xi, M\xi) = (M\xi, \xi) = \lambda^*(\xi, \xi)$.]

2. If M is unitary, all eigenvalues have unit magnitude. [Proof: $|\lambda|^2(\xi, \xi) = (M\xi, M\xi) = (M^\dagger M\xi, \xi) = (\xi, \xi)$.]

3. If M is Hermitian or unitary, eigenvectors associated with distinct eigenvalues are necessarily orthogonal. [Proof: Given $M\eta = \mu\eta$ as well as $M\xi = \lambda\xi$ then

(a) If $M = M^\dagger$: $\lambda(\eta, \xi) = (\eta, M\xi) = (M\eta, \xi) = \mu^*(\eta, \xi) = \mu(\eta, \xi)$

(b) If $M^{-1} = M^\dagger$: $\lambda(\eta, \xi) = (\eta, M\xi) = (M^{-1}\eta, \xi) = \dfrac{1}{\mu^*}(\eta, \xi) = \mu(\eta, \xi)$.]

Equation (18–24) is a set of homogeneous equations in the components ξ_i. These equations will have a non-null solution if and only if

$$\text{Det}\,(M - \lambda I) = 0 \tag{18–25}$$

Thus, the *eigenvalues of M are the roots* (in general complex) *of the characteristic*

‡ This nomenclature is virtually universal in modern physics literature; the corresponding English term was originally "characteristic" vectors and values.

polynomial. By the fundamental theorem of algebra, there will by n roots, λ_k, some of which may be repeated. These eigenvalues are unchanged under arbitrary coordinate transformations.

For each root (eigenvalue), λ_k, there exists at least one solution of (18–24) which we denote by $\xi_{\cdot k}$; by definition, $M\xi_{\cdot J} = \lambda_J \xi_{\cdot J}$ (not summed). Define a diagonal matrix Λ by:

$$\Lambda_{Ij} = \lambda_I \delta_{Ij} \quad \text{(not summed)} \tag{18–26}$$

Then

$$\boxed{M\xi = \xi\Lambda} \tag{18–27}$$

(where the matrix ξ is understood to be ξ_{ik}). Note the similarity to (11–10).

The result (18–27) is true for arbitrary matrices. In general, there is no assurance that the $\xi_{\cdot k}$ are independent‡, but this is true for unitary or Hermitian matrices (see later); then ξ^{-1} exists, so that

$$M = \xi\Lambda\xi^{-1}, \qquad \Lambda = \xi^{-1}M\xi \tag{18–28}$$

Thus M is diagonalized by transforming to basis vectors $\xi_{\cdot k}$. This coordinate transformation is not in general unitary (scalar-product-preserving) for this requires $\xi\xi^\dagger = I$ or $(\xi_{\cdot k}, \xi_{\cdot j}) = \delta_{kj}$; that is, the eigenvectors must form an orthonormal set. For unitary and for Hermitian matrices, the eigenvectors may always be chosen orthonormal:

Eigenvalues and Eigenvectors of Hermitian and Unitary Matrices

The special properties of these two types of matrices are best established indirectly: Given any such matrix, choose any eigenvalue, λ_1, and an associated eigenvector, $\xi_{\cdot 1}$; the latter may be normalized, $\|\xi_{\cdot 1}\| = 1$, without affecting (18–24). Choose (Schmidt process) any other $n - 1$ vectors, $\theta_{\cdot i}$, forming an orthonormal set with $\xi_{\cdot 1}$ and transform to the basis, $\{\xi_{\cdot 1}, \theta_{\cdot i}\}$. (The transformation is thus unitary and preserves the Hermitian or unitary character of M.) In this basis, the first equation of the set (18–24) must read:

$$(M')_{1i}\, \delta_{ij} = \lambda_1 \delta_{ij} = M_{1j}'.$$

Thus $(M')_{11}$ is the only non-zero element of the first row. Then: (a) for M Hermitian, the condition $M_{ji}' = (M_{ij}')^*$ and (b) for M unitary, the condition, $\sum_k |M_{k1}'|^2 = 1$ (from $MM^\dagger = I$) show in both cases that M_{11}' is also the only non-zero element in the first column. The process may now be repeated with the submatrix, M_{ij}' where $i \geqslant 2, j \geqslant 2$ (which is also Hermitian or unitary, respectively, under the conditions just proved). Thus:

The eigenvectors of a Hermitian, or of a unitary matrix can be chosen to be a complete, orthonormal basis.

Alternatively: A Hermitian or a unitary matrix can be diagonalized by a unitary coordinate transformation.

For Hermitian and unitary matrices, the equation, (18–28) where the $\xi_{\cdot k}$ are orthonormal can be cast into the (intuitively suggested) form,

$$M = \sum_I \lambda_I P_I \tag{18–29}$$

‡ One necessary and sufficient condition is that M satisfy some polynomial equation with n distinct roots. Thus if the λ_k are distinct, the Cayley–Hamilton theorem shows that the $\xi_{\cdot k}$ must be independent.

where $(P_I)_{lk} = \xi_{lI}\xi_{kI}^*$ (not summed) are projection operators:

$$P_I\phi = (\xi_{\cdot I}, \phi)\xi. \tag{18–30}$$

They have the properties,

$$P_IP_J = \begin{cases} 0 \text{ if } I \neq J \\ \\ P_I \text{ if } I = J \end{cases}; \qquad \sum_J P_J = I; \qquad P_I{}^\dagger = P_I \tag{18–31}$$

The expansion (18–30) is convenient for expressing functions of matrices in closed, explicit form. By $P_IP_J = \delta_{IJ}P_I$, we have $M^n = \sum \lambda_I{}^nP_I$ and thus a general definition of a function of a Hermitian or unitary matrix (which agrees with the power-series definition whenever both are applicable) is

$$F(M) = \sum_I F(\lambda_I)P_I \tag{18–32}$$

An important special case is $F(M) = (M - xI)^{-1} = \sum_J \dfrac{P_J}{\lambda_J - x}$

The expansion, (18–29), also shows that if a Hermitian or unitary matrix maps a subspace on itself, it also maps the remaining, orthogonal subspace onto itself. (This can also be proved directly and can then be used to prove diagonalizability. Thus diagonalizable and only diagonalizable matrices have this property.)

The General Transformation

The polar-decomposition theorem [following (11–44)] now acquires a significant geometric interpretation: *Any arbitrary matrix (operator) is equivalent to a rigid rotation (unitary transformation) either followed or preceded by non-uniform "magnifications" along mutually perpendicular directions*, as in (18–29) with $\lambda_I \geqslant 0$.

Alternative Eigenvalue Problem

By (18–29)–(18–32), the eigenvalue problem can be cast into the form:

To find a set of numbers, λ_I, and a set of n projection operators, P_J, such that

$$\sum_J P_J = I, \qquad M = \sum_I \lambda_I P_I \tag{18–33}$$

If M is unitary or Hermitian, this problem is equivalent to the original formulation, (18–24), and $P_IP_J = \delta_{IJ}P_J$ can also be satisfied.

The new form (18–33) is used in the theory of generalized unitary space (Hilbert space), with the modifications that the sums may be replaced by integrals over continuous ranges of λ and the second condition in (18–33) may be replaced by the weaker requirement: $(\psi, M\phi) = \sum \lambda_I(\psi, P_I\phi)$ for all ϕ and ψ.

In such spaces, this formulation is not equivalent to (18–24) but is in some ways more suited to applications in quantum mechanics.

Characterization of Projection Operators

Any linear operator, P, with the properties,

$$P^2 = P = P^\dagger$$

is a projection operator.

[Proof: Let S be the set of all vectors expressible as $P\phi$. Since P is linear, S is a subspace (linear manifold). Let $\eta_{\cdot i}$ be an orthonormal basis spanning S; by definition, $\eta_{\cdot i} = P\xi_{\cdot i}$ for some $\xi_{\cdot i}$ (not necessarily orthonormal) and thus $P\eta_{\cdot i} = \eta_{\cdot i}$. Let

$P\phi = \sum a_i \eta_{\cdot i}$ (any ϕ); then $a_j = (\eta_{\cdot j}, P\phi) = (P\eta_{\cdot j}, \phi) = (\eta_{\cdot j}, \phi)$ and thus indeed $P\phi = \sum (\eta_{\cdot i}, \phi)\eta_{\cdot i}$ where $\eta_{\cdot i}$ span S and ϕ is any vector.]

Another useful relation is,

$$(\phi, R\phi) = \text{Trace}\,\{P_{[\phi]}\, R\} \tag{18–34}$$

Simultaneous Diagonalization of Matrices

1. Two matrices (of any type) can both assume diagonal form in the same coordinate system only if they "commute", $MN = NM$. (For if both are diagonal this is true and must then be generally true.)

2. If two Hermitian or unitary (more generally, two diagonalizable) matrices commute, there exists a coordinate system in which both are diagonal. (For diagonalize one; if its λ_i are distinct, the relation $HU = UH$ shows immediately that the other is already diagonal; if not, the sub-spaces $\sum_{\lambda_i=\lambda_1} P_i$ etc. can be transformed independently to diagonalize the second without affecting the first.)

3. The above principles apply (by reiteration) to any number of matrices, all pairs of which commute.

Definite Operators

If the (linear) operator, R, has the property that for all ϕ, $(\phi, R\phi)$ is real and non-negative, then R is Hermitian and

$$|(\psi, R\phi)|^2 \leqslant (\phi, R\phi)(\psi, R\psi) \tag{18–35}$$

(Proof: If $(\phi, R\phi)$ is real, then $(R\phi, \phi) = (\phi, R\phi)$ and hence $R^\dagger = R$; the inequality follows from $(a\phi + \psi, R[a\phi + \psi]) \geqslant 0$ for all complex a.)

Alternatively, (18–35) can be regarded as the Schwarz inequality expressed in the "metric", R—in the sense of (18–39) below.

Non-Orthogonal Coordinates

As in ordinary space, one can also work with n independent vectors, $\rho_{\cdot i}$, which are not orthogonal. Again, define another set, $\eta_{\cdot j}$, such‡ that

$$(\rho_{\cdot i}, \eta_{\cdot j}) = \delta_{ij} \tag{18–36}$$

Then

$$\phi = \sum \phi_k^{(\rho)} \rho_{\cdot k} = \sum \phi_i^{(\eta)}\, \eta_{\cdot i}$$

where

$$\phi_k^{(\rho)} = (\eta_{\cdot k}, \phi) \quad \text{and} \quad \phi_k^{(\eta)} = (\rho_{\cdot k}, \phi) \tag{18–37}$$

Also

$$(\psi, \phi) = \sum_k (\psi_k^{(\eta)})^* \phi_k^{(\rho)} = \sum_k (\psi_k^{(\rho)})^*\, \phi_k^{(\eta)} \tag{18–38}$$

Such sets, $\rho_{\cdot i}$ and $\eta_{\cdot j}$, are often called "biorthonormal".

Algorithm for Biorthonormalization

Given a set of "vectors" $\mathbf{u}_i$, to find a set $\mathbf{v}_j$ such that $(\mathbf{u}_i, \mathbf{v}_j) = \delta_{ij}$ [using an obvious adaptation of the notation defined in (18–2)]. Choose an initial estimate, $\mathbf{v}_j^0$, [the choice $\mathbf{v}_j^0 = \mathbf{u}_j$ is always safe; it can fail only if the $\mathbf{u}_i$ are not independent]. Then recursively compute new sets, $\mathbf{v}_j^k$, by the rules:

$$\mathbf{v}_k^k = \frac{\mathbf{v}_k^{k-1}}{(\mathbf{u}_k, \mathbf{v}_k^{k-1})} \qquad \mathbf{v}_j^k = \mathbf{v}_j^{k-1} - (\mathbf{u}_k, \mathbf{v}_j^{k-1})\mathbf{v}_k^k$$

‡ Thus the matrix, $(\eta_{ik})^\dagger$, is the inverse of ρ_{jl} and exists if the $\rho_{\cdot i}$ are independent.

wherein j takes all values except k during the kth cycle. If there are m given vectors, $\mathbf{u}_i$, the mth cycle yields a set, $\mathbf{v}_j{}^m$, biorthonormal to the $\mathbf{u}_i$. (Proof: induction on k.)

In numerical work, if the $\mathbf{u}_i$ are ill-conditioned (almost parallel), round-off error may seriously affect the accuracy of the $\mathbf{v}_j{}^m$. If so, the algorithm may be continued for an additional m cycles to yield a set $\mathbf{v}_j{}^{2m}$ with greatly improved accuracy. (Further continuation is allowable, of course, but seems to be seldom necessary.)

GENERALIZATIONS

I. Arbitrary "Metric" (Notion of Length or Distance)

The three fundamental properties, (18–4), of the scalar product remain valid with the more general definition,

$$[\psi, \phi] = (\psi, R\phi) = \psi^\dagger R\phi \tag{18–39}$$

where R is a fixed (linear) operator with the property,

$$\phi^\dagger R\phi = (\phi, R\phi) \text{ real} \geqslant 0$$

for all ϕ, with equality only if $\phi = 0$.

Equivalence of (18–39) to general coordinate transformations: A non-unitary, "coordinate" transformation, $\phi' = T\phi$, produces precisely (18–39) with $T^\dagger T = R$—see (18–20). Conversely, since R is Hermitian, it can be diagonalized by a (unitary) coordinate transformation and its diagonal form, $\lambda_I \delta_{Ij}$, will have positive, non-zero diagonal elements. If we divide the ith component of all vectors by $\sqrt{\lambda_i}$ (that is, set $T_{Ij} = \lambda_I^{-1/2}\delta_{Ij}$) this (non-unitary) transformation produces precisely the "space" defined by (18–39).

This alternative of regarding a transformation either as a mapping of one space on another or, again, as the introduction of a new metric (i.e. as a "stretching") or, finally, as a non-uniform mapping is, of course, an ever-present choice in one's point of view. Formally, there is no distinction.

II. Infinite-Dimensional Spaces

The dimension of the space, n, can be allowed to approach infinity; vectors or points then become infinite *sequences* of complex numbers. The manifold questions of convergence which then arise naturally introduce essential complications on a rigorous mathematical level. However, for most applications in physics (principally quantum mechanics), these do not lead to especially important consequences in the final results. In any case, the finite-dimensional theory is a useful mnemonic device for organizing the results of more sophisticated theories.

III. Function-Spaces

We obtain a formally equivalent system ("space") if we call any *function*, $f(\mathbf{r})$, a "vector" or "point" and define the scalar product as

$$(f, g) = \iiint f^*(\mathbf{r})g(\mathbf{r})\, d\mathbf{r} \tag{18–40}$$

(It is often convenient to include under the integral also a fixed function, $\rho(\mathbf{r})$, the "metric" of the space—the same for all f and g, of course.) Usually, the class of "vectors", $f(\mathbf{r})$, is restricted by some such condition as $(f, f) \neq \infty$ and "vectors" may also be required to satisfy (as functions) certain boundary conditions in the region of the integration in (18–40).

The remarks on questions of convergence etc., given under (II) apply here as well. The two types of "space" are, in fact, essentially equivalent (see Remark 2 below).

Remarks

1. *Operators*: Although the matrix-operator concept is easily extended in (II) above, the more general concept of an abstract linear operator is virtually necessary in the function-spaces, (III). Such an operator (for example, a differential or integral operator) is any "mapping" of the space onto itself, $\phi' = M\phi$ with the linearity property: $M(a\phi + b\psi) = aM\phi + bM\psi$. [Matrix elements may then be *defined* as $M_{ij} = (\phi_i, M\phi_j)$, when the basis vectors are ϕ_i.]

The analogue of the Hermitian conjugate of an operator, M, is often called its "adjoint" operator, $M^\dagger$ (*not* the same concept as the adjoint in ordinary matrix and determinant theory). It is *defined* by

$$(\phi, M\psi) = (M^\dagger\phi, \psi) \tag{18–41}$$

Then, as before, "Hermitian" denotes $M = M^\dagger$ (also called "symmetric" or "self-adjoint") and "unitary" denotes $M^\dagger = M^{-1}$. Some further discussion is given in (19–25)–(19–62).

2. The infinite-dimensional and function spaces, (II) and (III), are essentially equivalent. Namely, if in (III), we choose as "basis vectors", $\phi_i(\mathbf{r})$, an (infinite) set of functions suitable for a Fourier-type of series expansion of an arbitrary function (strictly, a set of functions "complete" for the allowable functions, f) and if these are orthonormalized, then $f(\mathbf{r}) = \sum_n a_n\phi_n(\mathbf{r})$ where $a_n = (\phi_n, f)$. Now, consider the infinite sequence, $\{a_n\}$ to be a "vector" in type (II) space. This mapping of (II) and (III) above is easily seen to be one-to-one and to preserve all "geometric" (scalar-product) relations. Thus the two spaces are abstractly identical.

(Thus the matrix and wave-mechanics forms of quantum mechanics are equivalent.)

3. Questions of convergence and mathematical rigor glossed over above will be found in the literature on *Hilbert Space.* A classic treatment, especially concerned with applications to quantum mechanics, is J. von Neumann, "*Mathematische Grundlagen der Quantenmechanik*" (Springer, Berlin, 1932—also published in 1955 English translation by Princeton University Press).

An important qualitative feature which arises when $n = \infty$ is that the eigenvalues of a Hermitian operator need not form an infinite sequence but can* also assume *continuous ranges* of (real) values. The expansions in projection operators, (18–29)–(18–33), then require both summations and integrations (which can be conveniently combined under Stieltjes-integral notation).

COMPUTATION OF EIGENVALUES AND EIGENVECTORS OF MATRICES

For a matrix M of small order (n less than 4 or 5) it may be practical to set up the characteristic polynomial, Det $(M - \lambda I)$, and determine, numerically or otherwise, the roots, λ_J. The corresponding eigenvectors may then be computed by (setting,

* When the integration range in (18–40) is infinite.

say, $x_1 = 1$) solving the simultaneous system, $\sum M_{ik}x_k - \lambda_J x_i = 0$ by elimination (or by other means; note (11-10) wherein one may set $\alpha = M - \lambda_J I$).

When the size of the matrix is large, such direct numerical methods are impractical. This subject is currently undergoing rapid development owing to a need for general, effective methods for use on automatic computing machines.

Many apparently general methods turn out in practice to be either wasteful of machine capacity or numerically unstable. That is, formulas can be mathematically correct but so sensitive to very small changes that round-off errors quickly vitiate calculations employing a finite number of significant figures. (For example, when a difference of almost exactly equal numbers is required, there is no way to restore the lost accuracy, short of increasing the number of significant figures throughout all prior calculations.) Such difficulties seem to be particularly severe in eigenvalue computations.

Bounds for Eigenvalues

In the theorems below, the terms "region" and "point" refer to the ordinary complex plane, on which the eigenvalues, λ_i, of the matrix M_{ik} may be plotted.

1. All eigenvalues lie in the region covered by all complex numbers of the form,

$$z = \sum_{i,k} x_i{}^* M_{ik} x_k \quad \text{where} \quad \sum_k |x_k|^2 = 1 \tag{18–42}$$

(For every eigenvalue can be expressed in this form.)

2. All eigenvalues lie in the region covered by the n circles,

$$|z - M_{ii}| \leqslant \sum_{m \neq i} |M_{im}| \qquad (i = 1, 2, \cdots, n) \tag{18–43}$$

and if this compound region is actually composed of several non-overlapping sub-regions, each sub-region contains a number of eigenvalues equal to the number of circles which it includes. Since M and its transpose have the same eigenvalues, these results also apply if the sums in (18–43) are taken by columns instead of by rows.

This theorem is a simplification of the following stronger but less readily applied theorem.

3. All eigenvalues lie in the region covered by the following $\frac{1}{2}n(n-1)$ regions:

$$|z - M_{ii}| \cdot |z - M_{kk}| \leqslant P_{ki} \qquad (k \neq i) \tag{18–44}$$

where, if P_i is defined by the sum in (18–43),

$$P_{ki} = |M_{ki}|\, P_i + |M_{ik}|\,(P_k - |M_{ki}|) + \sum_{\nu \neq k,i} \{|M_{k\nu} M_{i\nu}| + \tfrac{1}{2} \sum_{\mu \neq k,i} |M_{k\nu} M_{i\mu} + M_{k\mu} M_{i\nu}|\} \tag{18–45}$$

Moreover, if the entire compound region is actually composed of non-overlapping sub-regions, then each sub-region contains a number of eigenvalues equal to the number of points, $z = M_{ii}$, which it covers. Again the theorem applies equally well if M_{ij} is replaced by M_{ji} throughout.

One proof employs the relation $(\lambda - M_{ii})x_i = \sum_{m \neq i} M_{im} x_m$ where λ is an eigenvalue and $\mathbf{x} \neq 0$ is its eigenvector. If all but one of the x_j vanish, $\lambda =$ some M_{jj}; otherwise $(\lambda - M_{rr})(\lambda - M_{ss})x_r x_s = (\sum_{j \neq r} M_{rj} x_j)(\sum_{m \neq s} M_{sm} x_m)$ where x_r and x_s have larger magnitudes than any other components x_j, and (18–44) follows by elementary manipulations after dividing by $x_r x_s$. The statement concerning non-overlapping sub-regions is a consequence of the fact that the roots of an algebraic equation change continuously as the coefficients of the equation are changed.

4. Further information can often be obtained by evaluating Det $(M - zI) = D(z)$ for judiciously chosen values of z [using, for example, the method (11–26)–(11–28)].

In particular, if M is positive definite (all $\lambda_i > 0$), a straight line through $D(0)$ and $D(-\epsilon)$ cannot intersect the graph of $D(z)$ a third time so that $\epsilon D(0)/[D(-\epsilon) - D(0)]$ is less than any eigenvalue.

For any matrix,

$$\sum (\lambda_i)^n = \sum (M^n)_{ii} = \text{Trace } (M^n) \tag{18–46}$$

which is also sometimes helpful.

The "Power Method"

Let $\mathbf{x}^0$ be an arbitrary vector and define recursively:

$$\mathbf{x}^m = a_m M \mathbf{x}^{m-1} \tag{18–47}$$

where a_m is chosen to normalize $\mathbf{x}^m$. If M has a single eigenvalue, λ_1, with magnitude greater than all others, the a_m will approach λ_1 and the $\mathbf{x}^m$ will approach the corresponding eigenvector (provided that $\mathbf{x}^0$ has not inadvertently been chosen orthogonal to this eigenvector). A proof may be based on (11–47)–(11–48) or, for Hermitian matrices, on (18–32). If there are k eigenvalues with a common magnitude larger than the others, methods can be developed from (11–47) for determining these eigenvalues and eigenvectors from the limiting forms of any $k + 1$ successive $\mathbf{x}^m$. The main practical use of such methods occurs with a dominant conjugate-complex pair, $\lambda_{1,2} = a \pm ib$ in which case, for any j and sufficiently large m,

$$(a^2 + b^2)(\mathbf{x}^{m-1})_j - 2a(\mathbf{x}^m)_j + (\mathbf{x}^{m+1})_j = 0 \tag{18–48}$$

and the eigenvector belonging to λ_1 is $(\lambda_2 \mathbf{x}^m - \mathbf{x}^{m+1})$.

The method is most effective when preceded by judiciously chosen *spectral transformations*: The matrix $M' = M + aI$ has eigenvalues $\lambda_k' = \lambda_k + a$ and this fact may be used to increase the ratios $|\lambda_1'/\lambda_i'|$ (or to make some eigenvalue other than λ_1 dominant). More generally, polynomial transformations may be employed to rearrange the λ_i. The kernel polynomials mentioned under (9–7.5) can be helpful in this regard. [For any matrix M, the matrix M^m has eigenvalues $\lambda_i{}^m$.]

The eigenvalues with smaller magnitudes can be found either by using a spectral transformation which causes them to dominate or by the following procedure (here illustrated for an Hermitian matrix and for the eigenvalue with next-to-largest magnitude; $\mathbf{e}_1$ is the previously computed, normalized eigenvector for the dominant λ_1).

$$\mathbf{y}^n = a_n H \mathbf{x}^{n-1}, \qquad \mathbf{x}^n = \mathbf{y}^n - \mathbf{e}_1(\mathbf{e}_1, \mathbf{y}^n) \tag{18–49}$$

(Orthogonalizing $\mathbf{x}^n$ and $\mathbf{e}_1$ in principle need be done only once, but repeated orthogonalization avoids numerical instability from round-off errors.)

Ramifications and refinements of these basic methods are extensively discussed in the current literature.

L–R Transformation

[See the article by H. Rutishauser in the (U.S.) National Bureau of Standards, Applied Mathematics Series No. 49 (January 1958).]

A class of methods which are applicable to most of the matrices occurring in practice (in particular all Hermitian, positive definite matrices and many others) and which appears to have remarkable numerical stability may be based on *triangular decomposition*, $M = LR$ with $L_{ii} = 1$. [See the footnote preceding (11–24) but apply it to the transpose of M.] If the product RL is then computed and the result again decomposed and the process is continued:

$$M^{(1)} = M, \quad L^{(n)}R^{(n)} = M^{(n)} \quad \text{with} \quad (L^{(n)})_{ii} = 1, \quad M^{(n+1)} = R^{(n)}L^{(n)}$$

then all $M^{(n)}$ have the same set of eigenvalues and for sufficiently large n the $M^{(n)}$ (usually) approach triangular form. Hence the diagonal elements of $M^{(n)}$ are themselves the eigenvalues of M. The method succeeds even when some eigenvalues are equal.

If, further, the product of all $L^{(n-k)}$ has been carried along by defining

$$\Lambda^{(n)} = \Lambda^{(n-1)}L^{(n)}, \qquad \Lambda^{(0)} = I$$

then $M = \Lambda^{(n)}M^{(n+1)}(\Lambda^{(n)})^{-1}$ so that the eigenvectors of M are $\mathbf{x} = \Lambda^{(n-1)}\mathbf{y} \doteqdot \Lambda^{(n)}\mathbf{y}$ where the $\mathbf{y}$ are the eigenvectors of $M^{(n)}$ and can be easily computed because $M^{(n)}$ is triangular.

Modifications are necessary if M has pairs of conjugate complex roots, and various special steps for accelerating the convergence are often advisable. In particular, the method can be adapted to yield successively the steps with $n = 2^p$, completely avoiding all intermediate computations. Another advantage of the method (which, however, is not retained in the last-mentioned modification) is that if M is a "striped matrix" (that is, $M_{ij} = 0$ when $|i - j| > m_0$; such matrices arise frequently in approximating partial differential equations), then this property is maintained in all $L^{(n)}$, $R^{(n)}$, $M^{(n)}$ with consequent saving of computer storage requirements. Details are given in Rutishauser, *op. cit.*, and further modifications are apparently being developed.

CHAPTER 19

EIGENVALUE PROBLEMS PERTURBATION THEORY

AN "EIGENVALUE* PROBLEM" is a problem involving an arbitrary parameter, λ, and in which a function, ϕ, is to be found (by solving a differential or integral equation, etc.). Usually, an "acceptable" solution ϕ exists only for certain values of λ. These values, λ_i, are known as the *eigenvalues* of the problem and the corresponding solutions, ϕ_i, as the *eigenfunctions*.

Despite the generality of this concept, little is known about eigenvalue problems which are not *linear* and *homogeneous*. That is, if ϕ is a solution, $k\phi$ is also a solution and if ϕ_1 and ϕ_2 are two solutions for the *same* λ then $(\phi_1 + \phi_2)$ is also a solution for that λ.

SECOND-ORDER DIFFERENTIAL EIGENVALUE PROBLEMS

Consider the equation (in any number of dimensions),

$$\nabla \cdot [p(\mathbf{r})\nabla u] - q(\mathbf{r})u + \lambda\rho(\mathbf{r})u = 0 \tag{19–1}$$

where u is the unknown function and λ the arbitrary parameter. For the theorems below, the (given) coefficient-functions in (19–1) are assumed to be real and continuous (including the boundaries) and ∇p is assumed to be continuous; also we assume

$$p(\mathbf{r}) > 0; \qquad \rho(\mathbf{r}) > 0 \tag{19–2}$$

Equation (19–1) is to be solved in a *finite region*, Ω, and on its boundary†, Γ, the conditions, on u must be either of the form

$$u(\mathbf{r}) = 0 \qquad \text{on } \Gamma \tag{19–3}$$

or of the form,

$$\frac{\partial u}{\partial n} + \sigma(\mathbf{r})u = 0 \qquad \text{on } \Gamma \tag{19–4}$$

where $\sigma(\mathbf{r})$ is piecewise continuous (on Γ); in one dimension, σ reduces to two constants.

Under these conditions, the following results can be proved:

(1) There are a countably infinite number of eigenvalues, λ_i, all of which are real. Only a finite number of the λ_i can be negative‡ and $\lambda_n \to \infty$ as $n \to \infty$. (The λ_n have no finite limit point§.) More precisely;

---

* German "eigen" means, roughly, "self". The original English term, "characteristic value problem" is seldom used in modern literature.

† The boundary cannot be "infinitely wrinkled"—e.g. its normal vector must be piecewise continuous.

‡ All $\lambda_i \geqslant 0$ when $q(\mathbf{r}) \geqslant 0$ and $\sigma(\mathbf{r}) \geqslant 0$.

§ This is almost always violated when Ω is infinite.

(2) If $N(\lambda)$ denotes the number of eigenvalues, λ_n, less than λ, then if the number of dimensions (of Ω) is D,

$$\lim_{\lambda\to\infty} \frac{N(\lambda)}{\lambda^{D/2}} = \frac{1}{2^D \pi^{D/2}(D/2)!} \int \cdots \int_{\Omega} \left[\frac{\rho(\mathbf{r})}{p(\mathbf{r})}\right]^{D/2} dx_1 \cdots dx_D \tag{19–5}$$

In one dimension, we have the sharper result,

$$\lim_{n\to\infty} \frac{n^2}{\lambda_n} = \frac{1}{\pi^2}\left[\int_a^b \sqrt{\rho/p}\, dx\right]^2 \tag{19–6}$$

(3) The λ_n change *continuously* with any changes in the functions, p, q, ρ, σ.

(4) If $q(\mathbf{r}) \geqslant 0$ and $\sigma(\mathbf{r}) \geqslant 0$ and if we arrange the λ_n (all $\geqslant 0$) according to increasing magnitude ($\lambda_1 \leqslant \lambda_2 \leqslant \lambda_3 \leqslant \cdots$) then:

(a) Contraction of Ω raises (or at least does not lower) each λ_n.

(b) The eigenvalues, λ_n^0, for the condition (19–3) are at least as great as the corresponding λ_n for any condition of the form (19–4).

(c) If $\bar{\sigma}(\mathbf{r}) \geqslant \sigma(\mathbf{r})$ (everywhere on Γ) then $\bar{\lambda}_n \geqslant \lambda_n$.

(d) If $\bar{\rho}(\mathbf{r}) \geqslant \rho(\mathbf{r})$ (everywhere in Ω) then $\bar{\lambda}_n \leqslant \lambda_n$.

(e) If $\bar{p}(\mathbf{r}) \geqslant p(\mathbf{r})$ and/or $\bar{q}(\mathbf{r}) \geqslant q(\mathbf{r})$ (everywhere in Ω) then $\bar{\lambda}_n \geqslant \lambda_n$.

In (1)–(4), sets of successive eigenvalues may be equal; that is, if, for example, some value, $\lambda = l$, has several independent solutions, $u_1, \cdots, u_k$, then $\lambda_1 = \lambda_2 = \cdots = \lambda_k = l$ is the convention adopted. In particular (1) implies,

(5) For no value of λ does the problem (19–1)–(19–4) have more than a finite number of independent solutions, $u_i(\mathbf{r})$. In one dimension, all λ_n have but a single eigenfunction, u_i.

Properties of Eigenfunctions

If several independent $u_i(\mathbf{r})$ are associated with the same value of λ then, by taking appropriate linear combinations of these u_i, we may always replace them by a set with the orthonormal property:

$$\int \cdots \int_{\Omega} \rho(\mathbf{r}) u_i(\mathbf{r}) u_k(\mathbf{r})\, dV = \delta_{ik} \tag{19–7}$$

(See Schmidt's procedure, following (18–12).) Moreover, if u_i and u_k belong to different values λ_i and λ_k, then they are automatically orthogonal (see discussion leading to (19–36) below) and may be multiplied by appropriate constants to satisfy (19–7) in all respects.

Thus, finally, *all eigenfunctions of the problem may be chosen orthonormal*, (19–7).

Under the conditions of the problem (19–1)–(19–4) we have:

If $f(\mathbf{r})$ is any continuous function (in Ω) then if

$$c_n = \int \cdots \int_{\Omega} \rho(\mathbf{r}) f(\mathbf{r}) u_n(\mathbf{r})\, dV$$

we have

$$\sum_{n=1}^{\infty} c_n^2 = \int \cdots \int_{\Omega} \rho(\mathbf{r}) f^2(\mathbf{r})\, dV \tag{19–8}$$

In this sense the sum, $\sum c_n u_n(\mathbf{r})$, approximates $f(\mathbf{r})$. [The conventional term is "converges in mean to $f(\mathbf{r})$".]

In one dimension, there is a much more powerful result (the region Ω is here $a \leqslant x \leqslant b$):

If $f(x)$ is any piecewise continuous function with a finite value of $\int_a^b [f'(x)]^2 \, dx$ (the integral means the sum of the integrals over all regions in which f is continuous), then

$$f(x) = \sum_{n=1}^{\infty} c_n u_n(x); \qquad c_n = \int_a^b \rho f u_n \, dx \tag{19–9}$$

where the series converges absolutely and uniformly in any region throughout which $f(x)$ is continuous. Where $f(x)$ has a jump, we have

$$\tfrac{1}{2}[f(x+0) + f(x-0)] = \sum_{n=1}^{\infty} c_n u_n(x) \tag{19–10}$$

(with "mere" convergence of the series).

Near such points of discontinuity *finite* sums of the form (19–10) tend to oscillate (with increasing amplitude but over smaller regions as the number of terms is increased). This behavior is called "Gibbs' phenomenon" and can be avoided by employing "Cesàro sums" (also called "Fejér means"):

$$(1/N) \sum_{n=1}^{N} (N - n + 1) c_n u_n(x)$$

which approach the same limits but more smoothly.

Linear, Second-order Problems

$$\sum_i \sum_k F_{ik} \frac{\partial^2 u}{\partial x_i \partial x_k} + \sum_i G_i \frac{\partial u}{\partial x_i} + Hu + \lambda \rho u = 0 \tag{19–11}$$

Make the substitution, $u = v e^{\frac{1}{2} g}$ where g satisfies

$$\frac{\partial g}{\partial x_i} = \sum_{k,l} (F^{-1})_{ik} \left(\frac{\partial}{\partial x_l} F_{kl} - G_k \right) \tag{19–12}$$

[where $(F^{-1})_{ik}$ is the (i, k) element in the matrix inverse to $F_{ik}(\mathbf{r})$]. Then (19–11) is transformed to "self-adjoint" form [compare (15–71)]:

$$\sum_i \sum_k \frac{\partial}{\partial x_i} F_{ik} \frac{\partial v}{\partial x_k} + hv + \lambda \rho v = 0 \tag{19–13}$$

and the eigenfunctions of this equation form a complete orthonormal system in the sense that they satisfy (19–8).

Practical Calculations

Aside from directly solving the differential equation (19–1) and determining the λ_n by (19–3) or (19–4) (which usually can be done only in certain by now standard problems), the most practical methods of solution seem to be:

1. *Perturbation theory*, (19–63)–(19–88) below. This is useful mainly when a "nearly identical" problem has already been solved.

2. *Variational methods:* Consider

$$\delta\left[\int \cdots \int_{\Omega} \left(p|\nabla\phi|^2 + q\phi^2\right) dV + \iint_{\Gamma} p\sigma\phi^2 \, dS\right] = 0 \tag{19–14}$$

with the condition,

$$\int \cdots \int_{\Omega} \rho[\phi]^2 \, dV = 1 \tag{19–15}$$

where ϕ is restricted to be continuous in Ω and where $\nabla\phi$ is piecewise continuous.* (If (19–3) is the boundary condition, omit the term in σ and require $\phi = 0$ on Γ.) This problem has the solution,

$$\phi = u_1(\mathbf{r})$$

$$\lambda_1 = \text{Min}\left[\int \cdots \int_{\Omega} \left(p|\nabla\phi|^2 + q\phi^2\right) dV + \iint_{\Gamma} p\sigma\phi^2 \, dS\right] \tag{19–16}$$

where u_1 is the eigenfunction associated with the lowest eigenvalue, λ_1.

Higher u_n and λ_n may in principle be obtained recursively: If we add the conditions,

$$\int \cdots \int \rho\phi u_i \, dV = 0 \qquad (i = 1, 2, \cdots, n) \tag{19–17}$$

then the solution ϕ becomes $u_{n+1}(\mathbf{r})$ and the stationary value of (19–14) is λ_{n+1}.

(This extension to higher λ_n is useful for deriving formal results but is not of much help in calculation since the "earlier" functions, $u_1, u_2, \cdots, u_n$, should be known *exactly* before seeking an approximate u_{n+1}; however, compare (19–21) below.)

If ϕ satisfies the *boundary conditions* (in addition to being continuous and having a piecewise continuous gradient) then

$$\frac{\displaystyle\int \cdots \int_{\Omega} \phi L(\phi) \, dV}{\displaystyle\int \cdots \int_{\Omega} \rho\phi^2 \, dV} \geqslant \lambda_1 \tag{19–18}$$

(Rayleigh's principle). The linear operator is defined in terms of the coefficient-functions of (19–1):

$$L(\phi) = -\nabla \cdot (p\nabla\phi) + q\phi \tag{19–19}$$

Bounds on the higher eigenvalues may be obtained by choosing *any* set of independent functions, $\psi_1(\mathbf{r}), \cdots, \psi_n(\mathbf{r})$ which satisfy the boundary conditions (19–3) or (19–4) and setting

$$\phi = \sum_{i=1}^{n} a_i \, \psi_i(\mathbf{r})$$

Inserting this in (19–18) and minimizing the expression on the left by varying the a_i, one finds as a necessary condition

$$\text{Det}\left\| \int \cdots \int_{\Omega} \psi_j[L(\psi_k) - \mu\rho\psi_k] \, dV \right\| = 0 \tag{19–20}$$

* Note that ϕ need not satisfy the boundary condition, (19–4).

(where μ is a "Lagrange multiplier"). If the roots of this equation are $\mu_1 \leqslant \mu_2 \leqslant \cdots \leqslant \mu_n$ then*

$$\mu_j \geqslant \lambda_j \tag{19–21}$$

These results give no information on *lower* bounds for λ_1. Lower bounds may be obtainable from theorems (3) and (4) [following (19–6)]; see also (19–39). In one dimension, further results are:

If $\phi(x)$ satisfies the boundary conditions and $(1/\rho\phi)L\phi$ is continuous in $a \leqslant x \leqslant b$, then its maximum and minimum values enclose λ_1. (Note that this computation involves only *differentiating* the trial function, ϕ.)

If we set, for any $\phi(x)$ which satisfies the boundary conditions,

$$\left.\begin{aligned} &\alpha = \frac{\int_a^b \phi L(\phi)\, \mathrm{d}x}{\int_a^b \rho\phi^2\, \mathrm{d}x}; \qquad \beta^2 = \frac{\int_a^b \frac{1}{\rho}[L(\phi)]^2\, \mathrm{d}x}{\int_a^b \rho\phi^2\, \mathrm{d}x} \\ &\text{then some } \lambda_i \text{ lies between} \\ &\qquad \alpha \pm \sqrt{\beta^2 - \alpha^2} \end{aligned}\right\} \tag{19–22}$$

(which is always real).

All of these results are most useful if ϕ is a good approximation to the first eigenfunction.

3. *Iteration:* If we know the Green's function, G, for the equation,

$$L(\phi) = 0 = -\nabla \cdot (p\nabla\phi) + q\phi \tag{19–23}$$

with the same boundary conditions, (19–3) or (19–4), then we may choose an arbitrary $\phi_0(\mathbf{r})$ and compute successively,

$$\phi_{n+1}(\mathbf{r}) = \int \cdots \int_\Omega G(\mathbf{r}, \mathbf{R})\phi_n(\mathbf{R})\rho(\mathbf{R})\, \mathrm{d}V_R \tag{19–24}$$

Then

$$\frac{\phi_{n+1}(\mathbf{r})}{\phi_n(\mathbf{r})} \rightarrow \text{some } \lambda_i \text{ (independent of } \mathbf{r})$$

and

$$(\lambda_i)^n\phi_n(\mathbf{r}) \rightarrow u_i(\mathbf{r})$$

Usually, if ϕ_0 is chosen to be positive in Ω then λ_1 and $u_1(\mathbf{r})$ are obtained by this process.

Remark on Non-finite Regions, Ω

Virtually all of the above results depend on the finite size of Ω. In general (although not invariably) if Ω is allowed to be infinite, the λ_i may "pile up" at some finite "series limit", and it usually happens that *all* λ larger than this limit allow non-zero solutions, $u(\mathbf{r})$. All such λ are "eigenvalues" and one speaks of a "*continuous spectrum*".

Such features introduce difficulties in the concepts of ortho-normality of the functions $u_i(\mathbf{r})$ and in the expansion theorems, etc. When such matters are important, a physical problem can generally be "confined to a very large box" and in this way the finite region can be retained without doing violence to any of the physical answers.

---

* The logic of this theorem is: If ϕ is *further* restricted to have the form, $\Sigma\, a_i\psi_i$, then the solutions of the variational problem (19–14)–(19–17) or its equivalent in terms of L must have *higher* minima, μ_n.

GENERAL FORMALISM OF EIGENVALUE PROBLEMS

Preliminary

Eigenvalue problems are greatly unified by using the unitary space (Hilbert space) notation, (9–6).

The "metric" function, $\rho(\mathbf{r})$ *in the definition,*

$$(\phi, \psi) = \int \cdots \int_{\Omega} \phi^*(\mathbf{r})\psi(\mathbf{r})\rho(\mathbf{r})\, dV, \tag{19–25}$$

must be the same $\rho(\mathbf{r})$ *that appears in the eigenvalue problem:*

$$L\phi(\mathbf{r}) = \lambda\rho(\mathbf{r})\phi(\mathbf{r}) \tag{19–26}$$

where L is a linear operator, some examples of which are discussed below. The region, Ω, of $\mathbf{r}$-space in both of these equations must be finite for most of the theorems which follow.

All functions $\phi(\mathbf{r})$ are assumed to have finite "norms" (or "lengths"):

$$\|\phi\|^2 \equiv (\phi, \phi) < \infty \tag{19–27}$$

This condition (plus any boundary conditions which might also be required in some problems) defines the "Hilbert space" of *functions* involved. The functions may take complex values (an asterisk will denote complex conjugation), but the (fixed) metric function, $\rho(\mathbf{r})$, is assumed to be real and >0 everywhere in Ω.

From the restriction (19–27) it can be shown that there exist (many) orthonormal systems of functions, $\psi_i(\mathbf{r})$, that is, $(\psi_i, \psi_j) = \delta_{ij}$, which are "*complete*" in the sense that for *any* function (in the Hilbert space, of course):

$$\phi(\mathbf{r}) = \sum^{\infty} c_j\, \psi_j(\mathbf{r}) \quad \text{with} \quad c_j = (\psi_j, \phi) \tag{19–28}$$

at least in the sense of convergence-in-mean:

$$\lim_{n \to \infty} \|\phi - \sum^{n} c_j \psi_j\|^2 = 0 \tag{19–29}$$

(These results are valid even when Ω is infinite.)

The "*linear operator*", L, in (19–26) is postulated to satisfy $(L\phi, L\phi) < \infty$ and $L(a\phi + b\psi) = aL\phi + bL\psi$ for all (admissible) ϕ and ψ. Examples are:

(a) Differential operators, such as $L'\phi = \nabla^2\phi + q(\mathbf{r})\phi$, etc. (Boundary and differentiability conditions are usually imposed on all functions concerned.)

(b) Integral operators such as $L''\phi(\mathbf{r}) = \int \cdots \int_{\Omega} G(\mathbf{r}, \mathbf{R})\phi(\mathbf{R})\, dV_R$. (Note that G itself need not have finite "norm".)

[In particular if G in (b) is the Green's function of L' in (a) (with the required boundary conditions) then L'' is the inverse of L'. Integral operators, however, need not have inverses; for example, if $G(\mathbf{r}, \mathbf{R}) = \psi_0(\mathbf{r})\psi_0^*(\mathbf{R})\rho(\mathbf{R})$, where $\|\psi_0\| = 1$, then L'' is a projection operator $L''\phi = (\psi_0, \phi)\psi_0$, and has no inverse—all but one of its eigenfunctions are associated with the eigenvalue,* $\lambda = 0$.]

* Note that, in the theory of integral equations, Chapter 16, (since λ was defined as the reciprocal of the present λ), such operators were regarded as having only *one* eigenfunction. The present formalism leads to more generally applicable results, however.

Matrix Form of an Operator

If attention is directed to a specific complete orthonormal basis, $\epsilon_i(\mathbf{r})$, (satisfying (19–28) and (19–29) for any ϕ), then the expansion coefficients, $c_i = (\epsilon_i, \phi)$, appearing in $\phi = \sum c_i\epsilon_i$ may be regarded as "components" of the "vector", $\phi(\mathbf{r})$, and any operator, L, can be described in terms of its effect on these "components". In this way, L can be regarded as a "matrix" whose (infinite set of) component elements in the $\epsilon_i(\mathbf{r})$ coordinates are

$$L_{ij} = (\epsilon_i, L\epsilon_j) \tag{19–30}$$

for then if $c_i = (\epsilon_i, \phi)$ and $d_j = (\epsilon_j, \psi)$, the equation, $\phi = L\psi$, may be expressed in $\epsilon_i(\mathbf{r})$ coordinates as

$$c_i = \sum_j L_{ij} d_j \tag{19–31}$$

This expression for L is especially useful in perturbation theory.

Conversely, L may in principle be recovered from the numbers, L_{ij}, by:

$$Lf = \sum_{i=1}^{\infty} \sum_{j=1}^{\infty} L_{ij}(\epsilon_j, f)\epsilon_i(\mathbf{r}) \tag{19–32}$$

In quantum mechanics (where the subscripts can become rather complicated), L_{ij} is often denoted $\langle i|L|j\rangle$; it is a fortunate coincidence that these quantities are usually correlated with average values, $\langle \cdots \rangle$, of physical "observables".

Eigenvalue Problems with Symmetric ("Hermitian") Operators

We consider:

$$\boxed{H\phi(\mathbf{r}) = \lambda\rho(\mathbf{r})\phi(\mathbf{r})} \tag{19–33}$$

where H is "symmetric" in the sense that, for all ϕ and ψ,

$$\boxed{\int \cdots \int_{\Omega} \psi^*(H\phi)\, dV = \int \cdots \int_{\Omega} (H\psi)^*\phi\, dV} \tag{19–34}$$

That is, in the notation (19–25),

$$\left(\frac{\psi}{\rho}, H\phi\right) = \left(H\psi, \frac{\phi}{\rho}\right) \tag{19–35}$$

A self-adjoint differential operator is symmetric (in the Hilbert space of functions satisfying given boundary conditions). An integral operator with an "Hermitian" kernel, $G(\mathbf{r}, \mathbf{R}) = G^*(\mathbf{R}, \mathbf{r})$, is also symmetric.

Equation (19–33) need have no solution (except $\phi \equiv 0$) for general values of λ. For certain λ, however, denoted by λ_i, there will exist (one or more) solutions with $\|\phi\|^2 \neq 0$. These are the "eigenvalues", λ_i, and "eigenfunctions", $\phi_i(\mathbf{r})$, respectively.

If ϕ_i is associated with λ_i (so that $H\phi_i = \lambda_i\rho\phi_i$) then $\lambda_j(\phi_i, \phi_j) = (\phi_i/\rho, H\phi_j) = (H\phi_i, \phi_j/\rho) = \lambda_i^*(\phi_i, \phi_j)$ whence first setting $i = j$ we have.

(1) *All eigenvalues* λ_i *are real.*

Secondly, we then may write $(\lambda_i - \lambda_j)(\phi_i, \phi_j) = 0$ whence,

(2) *If* $\lambda_i \neq \lambda_j$ *then* $(\phi_i, \phi_j) = 0$.

If, for $\lambda = \lambda_i$, there are several linearly independent* solutions, $\phi_i^{(\nu)}$, then since H is linear there is a freedom of choice: any linear combination of the $\phi_i^{(\nu)}$ is again a solution. This may be exploited (Schmidt process; following (18–12)) to achieve in addition to #2:

(3) *All eigenfunctions may be chosen mutually orthonormal:*

$$(\phi_i, \phi_j) = \delta_{ij} \tag{19–36}$$

It will be assumed in the following that this has been done. Note that (19–36) implies that at most one eigenfunction can be everywhere real and positive.

(4) *Completeness:* It is often (tacitly) assumed that for any $f(\mathbf{r})$:

$$f = \sum_i c_i\phi_i; \quad \text{with} \quad c_j = (\phi_j, f) \tag{19–37}$$

that is, that the eigenfunctions are complete and may be used as a coordinate basis. This is very often true (compare (19–8)–(19–10) and (16–36)), but rigorous results would lead us too far afield. Note that, in many cases, it is merely the series (19–37) for a *particular* $f(\mathbf{r})$ which is needed, and this can sometimes be established independently.

Variational Principle

If H has a "complete" set of eigenfunctions, ϕ_i, and a *lowest* eigenvalue, λ_1 (which may be negative), then for any (admissable) $f(\mathbf{r}) = \sum c_i\phi_i(\mathbf{r})$ say, we have

$$\left(\frac{f}{\rho}, Hf\right) = \sum_{i,j} c_i^* c_j \left(\frac{\phi_i}{\rho}, H\phi_j\right) = \sum_i \lambda_i |c_i|^2$$

and thus, because according to (19–29), $(f, f) = \sum |c_j|^2$ we have the general result,

For any (admissible) $f(\mathbf{r})$,

$$\lambda_1 \leqslant \frac{\left(\dfrac{f}{\rho}, Hf\right)}{(f, f)} = \frac{\displaystyle\int f^*(Hf)\,\mathrm{d}V}{\displaystyle\int f^* f\rho\,\mathrm{d}V} \tag{19–38}$$

and the $f(\mathbf{r})$ which minimizes this expression is $\phi_1(\mathbf{r})$ (or a linear combination of the ϕ_i belonging to λ_1).

Similarly, if $g(\mathbf{r})$ is required to be orthogonal to ϕ_1 (and any other ϕ_i belonging to λ_1), the corresponding expression (19–38) with g for f is an upper bound to λ_2 and the minimizing g is ϕ_2 (or a linear combination of ϕ_j belonging to λ_2) etc.

Conversely, these variational problems lead back to (19–33).

"Enclosing Theorem"

The variational principle (19–38) yields only an upper bound to λ_1. An estimate of the error remaining may sometimes be obtained from:†

---

* $\sum_\nu c_\nu \phi_i^{(\nu)} \equiv 0$ *only* if all $c_\nu = 0$.

† To prove, set $f = \Sigma\, c_i\phi_i$ and evaluate D and E to show that $D - E^2 = \Sigma\, |c_i|^2(\lambda_i - E)^2 > (\lambda_j - E)^2$ for some j, namely such that λ_j is closer to E than any other λ_i.

At least one eigenvalue (not necessarily the lowest) lies in the range:

$$\left.\begin{aligned} & E - \sqrt{D - E^2} \leqslant \lambda_j \leqslant E + \sqrt{D - E^2} \\ \text{where} \\ & E = \frac{\left(\dfrac{f}{\rho}, Hf\right)}{(f, f)}; \qquad D = \frac{\left(\dfrac{Hf}{\rho}, \dfrac{Hf}{\rho}\right)}{(f, f)} \end{aligned}\right\} \tag{19–39}$$

for any (admissible) function $f(\mathbf{r})$.

Solution of Inhomogeneous Equations

Consider

$$H\phi - \bar{\lambda}\rho\phi = \psi(\mathbf{r}) \tag{19–40}$$

(where H is symmetric and ψ is given).

If $\bar{\lambda}$ is not an eigenvalue of H and if the eigenfunctions, ϕ_i, of H are complete,* the solution of (19–40) is

$$\phi = \sum_i \frac{(\phi_i, \psi/\rho)}{\lambda_i - \bar{\lambda}} \phi_i \tag{19–41}$$

(which again shows that if ψ has certain forms—"normal modes"—then the solution ϕ is especially simple).

If $\bar{\lambda}$ = some λ_i, then (19–40) leads to a contradiction (is insoluble) unless $(\psi/\rho, \phi_i) = 0$ for all ϕ_i associated with that λ_i. If so, (19–41) is again the solution.

THE CASE $\rho(\mathbf{r}) \equiv 1$

1. *Simultaneous eigenfunctions:*

If ϕ_i are to be eigenfunctions for both of the problems with $\rho(\mathbf{r}) \equiv 1$,

$$H\phi = \lambda\phi; \qquad M\phi = \mu\phi \tag{19–42}$$

then since $H(M\phi) = \mu H\phi = \mu\lambda\phi = \lambda M\phi = M(H\phi)$, the ϕ_i can be complete only if (for all admissible functions),

$$HM = MH \tag{19–43}$$

2. *Adjoint operators:*

When $\rho \equiv 1$, a symmetric operator is characterized by $(H\psi, \phi) = (\psi, H\phi)$ and $H_{ij} = (H_{ji})^*$—whence the term, "Hermitian", is often used. With a *non*-symmetric operator, L, one may associate another operator, $L^\dagger$, defined by

$$(L^\dagger)_{ij} = (L_{ji})^* \tag{19–44}$$

which, by (19–32), is equivalent to the definition (for all ϕ, ψ),

$$(L^\dagger\phi, \psi) = (\phi, L\psi) \tag{19–45}$$

or to

$$(\phi, L^\dagger\psi) = (L\phi, \psi) \tag{19–46}$$

3. *Unitary operators:*

A special class of non-symmetric operators may be regarded as coordinate-transforming operators; they may be defined by

$$U^\dagger = U^{-1} \tag{19–47}$$

or equivalently by (for all ϕ, ψ),

$$(U\phi, U\psi) = (\phi, \psi) \tag{19–48}$$

* Less restrictively, if ψ/ρ can be expanded in the form, $\Sigma\, c_i\phi_i$.

That is, a unitary operator has no effect on scalar products and hence the "Hilbert space", $U\phi$, is abstractly identical with (isomorphic to) the original "Hilbert space", $\phi(\mathbf{r})$.

The unitary operators also have eigenfunctions,

$$U\psi_i(\mathbf{r}) = \mu_i\psi_i(\mathbf{r}) \tag{19–49}$$

whence, from (19–48), $(\psi_i, \psi_j) = \mu_i^*\mu_j(\psi_i, \psi_j)$ from which, setting $i = j$,

$$\mu_i\mu_i^* = |\mu_i|^2 = 1 \tag{19–50}$$

and for $i \neq j$, $(\psi_i, \psi_j) = 0$ whence we can always choose the ψ_i such that

$$(\psi_i, \psi_j) = \delta_{ij} \tag{19–51}$$

4. *Functions of symmetric or unitary operators:*

If $\rho \equiv 1$ and if the eigenfunctions, ϕ_i, of H are (orthonormalized and) taken as the coordinate basis, ϵ_i in (19–30), it follows that, in this coordinate system, $H_{ij} = \lambda_i\delta_{ij}$ ("diagonal") and from (19–32):

$$H = \sum_i \lambda_i P_{(i)} \tag{19–52}$$

where $P_{(i)}$ is the projection operator, $P_{(i)}\psi = \phi_i(\phi_i, \psi)$. It then further follows* that $H^2 = \sum \lambda_i^2 P_{(i)}$, etc. and quite generally we may therefore *define* for any function, $F(x)$,

$$F(H) = \sum_i F(\lambda_i)P_{(i)} \tag{19–53}$$

or equivalently,

$$[F(H)]_{ij} = F(\lambda_i)\delta_{ij} \tag{19–54}$$

(Equation (19–53) is independent of the coordinate basis, but (19–54) is valid only when the coordinate basis is ϕ_i.)

Because of (19–51), the same arguments apply to unitary operators.

Note that the definition (19–53) coincides with a definition by power-series whenever both are applicable; however, (19–53) remains meaningful even when $F(x)$ has no power series.

5. *Partition function of a symmetric operator:*

Since the eigenvalues of a symmetric operator are all real, we may define the function of a real variable:

$$\left.\begin{aligned} N(\lambda) &= \text{number of eigen}\textit{functions}\text{ whose } \lambda_i < \lambda. \\ &= \sum_{\lambda_i < \lambda} \text{(degeneracy of } \lambda_i) \end{aligned}\right\} \tag{19–55}$$

Consider the bilateral† Laplace transform of N; let

$$\frac{1}{p} Z(p) = \mathscr{L}_{\text{II}}[N(t)] = \frac{1}{p}\sum_{\phi_i} e^{-\lambda_i p} \tag{19–56}$$

(where the sum is over all solutions; that is, each exponential appears as often as its λ_i has independent eigenfunctions).

By (19–54),

$$Z(p) = \sum_i [e^{-pH}]_{ii} \equiv \text{Trace}(e^{-pH}) \tag{19–57}$$

---

* Because $P_{(i)}P_{(j)} = 0$ if $i \neq j$, due to the orthogonality of the ϕ_i.

† If all $\lambda_i > 0$, this reduces to the standard, one-sided Laplace transform.

This expression is independent* of the "coordinate system", $\epsilon_i(\mathbf{r})$, and hence from (19–56):

The λ_i and their degeneracy can in principle be found without knowledge of the eigenfunctions. Namely, we may evaluate the function, $Z(p)$, according to (19–57) using, say, the power series definition of e^{-pH} and any convenient complete basis of *admissible* functions. Inversion of the $\mathscr{L}_{\text{II}}$ transform then yields $N(\lambda)$.

Knowing $N(\lambda)$, any quantity of the form,

$$\sum_{\phi_i} g(\lambda_i) = \int_{-\infty}^{\infty} g(\lambda)\, dN(\lambda) = \int_{-\infty}^{\infty} N(\lambda)\, dg(\lambda) \qquad (19\text{–}58)$$

can also be evaluated without knowledge of the ϕ_i. (This has applications in quantum statistical mechanics.)

6. *Non-symmetric operators:*

If $(L\phi, \psi) \neq (\phi, L\psi)$, then in general $L\phi = \lambda\phi$ need have no solutions for any λ. However, consider the *pair* of coupled problems,

$$L\phi = \lambda\psi; \qquad L^\dagger\psi = \lambda\phi \qquad (19\text{–}59)$$

($L^\dagger$ is defined by (19–45)). These will have solutions, $[\phi_i, \psi_i, \lambda_i]$ where, in fact, the eigenfunctions, ϕ_i and ψ_i, are solutions of the "independent" problems with symmetric operators:

$$L^\dagger L\phi_i = \mu_i\phi_i; \qquad LL^\dagger\psi_i = \mu_i\psi_i \qquad (19\text{–}60)$$

which have identical (real) eigenvalues, $\mu_i = \lambda_i^2$.

The eigenfunctions, ϕ_i and ψ_i, as found either from (19–59) or from (19–60) may be used to solve,†

$$L\phi = f(\mathbf{r}) \qquad \text{or} \qquad L^\dagger\psi = g(\mathbf{r}) \qquad (19\text{–}61)$$

the solutions of which are respectively,

$$\phi(\mathbf{r}) = \sum \frac{1}{\lambda_i}(\psi_i, f)\phi_i(\mathbf{r}); \qquad \psi(\mathbf{r}) = \sum \frac{1}{\lambda_i}(\phi_i, g)\psi_i \qquad (19\text{–}62)$$

Generalizations

1. If Ω (the region of definition of all functions, $\phi(\mathbf{r})$, considered) is allowed to be infinite, then most operators no longer have discrete eigenvalues, λ_i, but rather there exist continuous ranges of permissible λ associated with solutions of (19–33). While heuristic progress can be made by replacing sums [such as in (19–32), (19–37), (19–41), (19–52), (19–56), (19–62) etc.] by analogous integrals, formal difficulties‡ can arise. For such problems it is often advisable to avoid these difficulties whenever possible by forcing Ω to be finite (for example, by enclosing the physical system in a very large "box" whose volume is finite but so large as not to affect the final answer).

2. The quantities, $\phi(\mathbf{r})$, have been envisaged as ordinary functions of the space-point, $\mathbf{r}$. Naturally, the "space" $\mathbf{r}$ can be multi-dimensional (as for example when functions of the positions of several particles are employed).

---

* Compare (11–51); an analogous proof may be constructed from (19–30).

† If f can be expanded in a series, $\Sigma\, c_i\psi_i$, or, respectively, if $g = \Sigma\, d_i\phi_i$.

‡ Associated with the "orthogonality" of functions belonging to different values of λ. This necessitates either working with delta-functions and divergent expressions or else employing very complicated, advanced mathematics and perhaps sacrificing some physically important results.

Moreover, the $\phi(\mathbf{r})$ themselves can be *vector* functions, $\mathbf{\Phi}(\mathbf{r})$, (electromagnetic fields, for example). The operators, L, may then be matrices of operators—the matrix indices referring to the components of $\mathbf{\Phi}$, but the "elements" being operators in the usual sense.

In quantum mechanics, the "spin" of a particle can be introduced by either of these devices. On the one hand, for each particle an extra coordinate, capable of assuming only two values (for "spin $\frac{1}{2}$"), may be introduced; on the other hand, the space $\mathbf{r}$ may be left as is but the "wave functions", $\phi(\mathbf{r})$, generalized to two-component vectors (that is, *pairs* of functions). In the former case, the "spin operators" act on the added discrete coordinates; in the latter, they are matrices which "mix" (couple) the two components of the "vector", $[\phi_1(\mathbf{r}), \phi_2(\mathbf{r})]$.

PERTURBATION THEORY

This generic name may be applied to any process whereby one solves (approximately) a complicated problem by exploiting, in any manner, its similarity to a simpler problem, whose exact solutions are known. In this general sense, perturbation theory covers a host of iteration, repeated substitution and general "correction" schemes.

A specific, rather general procedure, however, is available for eigenvalue problems, and it is this special case which will be described below.

Ordinary ("Time-Independent") Perturbation Theory

Suppose given the eigenvalue problem:

$$(H + V)\psi(\mathbf{r}) = \mu\rho(\mathbf{r})\psi(\mathbf{r}) \tag{19–63}$$

wherein H and V are linear, symmetric operators and where it is expected (physically or otherwise) that the solutions are close to the solutions of (where i denotes the eigen*functions*, ϕ_i; we may have $\lambda_i = \lambda_j$):

$$H\phi_i = \lambda_i\rho\phi_i \tag{19–64}$$

which is assumed to have known solutions (adjusted to be orthonormal, (19–36)).

By setting

$$\psi_i = \phi_i + \sum_k c_{ik}\phi_k; \qquad \mu_i = \lambda_i + \eta_i$$

(where the constants, c_{ik} and η_i are expected to be small), by substituting these forms into (19–63), using (19–64), neglecting terms in η_i^2, $c_{ik}\eta_k$, $V\eta_i$ etc. (as much smaller than η, c, V) and finally by multiplying with $\phi_j^*(\mathbf{r})$ and integrating, using (19–36), one obtains:

With the notation,*

$$V^{ij} = \left(\frac{\phi_i}{\rho}, V\phi_j\right) = \int \cdots \int_\Omega \phi_i^*(\mathbf{r})[V\phi_j(\mathbf{r})]\, d\mathbf{r} \tag{19–65}$$

then to first order in V, *provided* (19–64) has only one solution for $\lambda = \lambda_n$,

$$\left.\begin{aligned} \mu_n &= \lambda_n + V^{nn} \\ \psi_n(\mathbf{r}) &= \phi_n(\mathbf{r}) + \sum_{j \neq n} \frac{V^{jn}}{\lambda_n - \lambda_j}\phi_j(\mathbf{r}) \end{aligned}\right\} \tag{19–66}$$

(ψ_n is not normalized here.)

* If $\rho(\mathbf{r}) \equiv 1$, the numbers $V^{ij} = V_{ij}$, the "matrix elements" (19–30) of V.

Similarly, repeating this type of argument to obtain terms in higher orders, one obtains:

Provided (19–64) has only one solution for $\lambda = \lambda_n$, then to third order in V,

$$\mu_n = \lambda_n + V^{nn} + \sum_{j \neq n} \frac{V^{nj} V^{jn}}{\lambda_n - \lambda_j}$$

$$+ \sum_{l \neq n} \sum_{j \neq n} \frac{V^{nl} V^{lj} V^{jn}}{(\lambda_n - \lambda_l)(\lambda_n - \lambda_j)} - \sum_{l \neq n} \frac{V^{nn} V^{nl} V^{ln}}{(\lambda_n - \lambda_l)^2} + \cdots \quad (19\text{–}67)$$

and to second order in V

$$\psi_n(\mathbf{r}) = \phi_n(\mathbf{r}) + \sum_{j \neq n} \frac{V^{jn}}{\lambda_n - \lambda_j} \phi_j(\mathbf{r})$$

$$+ \sum_{k \neq n} \sum_{j \neq n} \frac{V^{kj} V^{jn}}{(\lambda_n - \lambda_k)(\lambda_n - \lambda_j)} \phi_k - \sum_{k \neq n} \frac{V^{nn} V^{kn}}{(\lambda_n - \lambda_k)^2} \phi_k \quad (19\text{–}68)$$

Despite the approximate nature of (19–65)–(19–68), the summations are usually infinite. In any practical calculation, only a few "dominant" terms in the sums can be included. In such cases, a substantial improvement in accuracy can often be obtained by multiplying all of the terms (actually used) by arbitrary coefficients and applying the variational principle (19–38). (See Young, Biedenharn, and Feenberg, *Phys. Rev.* **106,** 1151, (1957).)

Degenerate Eigenvalues in (19-64)

If the "simple problem", (19–64), has several solutions for $\lambda = \lambda_n$, the above expressions fail due to vanishing of the denominators in (19–66)–(19–68). The procedure in such cases is to (apply (19–66) for non-degenerate λ_n and) assume for $\lambda = \lambda_I$

$$\psi(\mathbf{r}) = \sum_{\alpha} c_\alpha \phi_{I\alpha}(\mathbf{r}); \qquad \mu = \lambda_I + \eta \quad (19\text{–}69)$$

where $\phi_{I\alpha}$ are all eigenfunctions whose $\lambda = \lambda_I$. These assumptions in (19–63) lead by similar manipulations to

$$0 = \sum_{\alpha} c_\alpha \left[\left(\frac{1}{\rho} \phi_{I\beta}, V\phi_{I\alpha} \right) - \eta(\phi_{I\beta}, \phi_{I\alpha}) \right] \quad (19\text{–}70)$$

In order for $c_\alpha \not\equiv 0$, these require that η be a root of the "secular equation",

$$\text{Det} \, \| V^{\beta\alpha} - \eta(\phi_{I\beta}, \phi_{I\alpha}) \| = 0 \quad (19\text{–}71)$$

(and for each such root, the c_α can then be obtained).

Thus, in general V in (19–63) "removes" the degeneracy of (19–64); each root of (19–71) leads to a different value of μ in (19–69). The corresponding eigenfunction of (19–63) is then found from (19–70) (with this η) followed by substitution in (19–69).

Note that (19–70), (19–71) are a (finite dimensional) matrix-eigenvalue problem; the c_α are the eigenvectors of the matrix, $V^{\alpha\beta}$.

In many physical problems, the "perturbation", V, removes a symmetry (rotational, translational, etc.) of H, that is, of (19–64). In this case, the solution of (19–70), (19–71) can often be greatly simplified by using group theory. In geometric terms, this amounts to choosing (as one is free to do) the "unperturbed eigenfunctions",

$\phi_{I\alpha}(\mathbf{r})$ to "fit" the new symmetry of the problem (19–63) rather than merely the (higher) symmetry of the old problem, (19–64). The result is to make large blocks of terms, $V^{\beta\alpha}$, vanish.

A Generalization

The notation (19–65) can be used to provide a more general point of view for the results above. Let

$$\psi(\mathbf{r}) = \sum_j^{\infty} d_j \phi_j(\mathbf{r}) \tag{19–72}$$

and multiply (19–63) by $\phi_i^*(\mathbf{r})$ and integrate to obtain the "matrix" form of the eigenvalue problem,

$$\mu d_i = \sum_j^{\infty} (H^{ij} + V^{ij})\, d_j \tag{19–73}$$

In (19–72) we need not have used eigenfunctions of any particular operator; any complete, orthonormal set, ϕ_i, will give the same result (19–73).

Ordinary perturbation theory, by choosing ϕ_i as eigenfunctions of (19–64) makes $H^{ij} = \lambda_i \delta_{ij}$ and thus places all the "large" terms on the "main diagonal". If, due to symmetries in the physical problem, large blocks of the V^{ij} terms vanish, (19–73)—and hence (19–63)—can be rigorously reduced to sets of finite-dimensional matrix equations; this is the basis of the theory of complex atoms.

Iteration (Born Approximation)

An alternative way of solving

$$(H + V)\psi(\mathbf{r}) = \mu\rho(\mathbf{r})\psi(\mathbf{r}) \tag{19–74}$$

is to assume that $\psi(\mathbf{r}) = \phi_i(\mathbf{r}) + \eta(\mathbf{r})$ where $H\phi_i = \lambda_i \rho \phi_i$ and $\eta(\mathbf{r})$ is expected to be small compared to ϕ_i. Neglecting, as much smaller than other terms, the term in $V\eta$, one obtains,

$$(H - \mu\rho)\eta = -[V\phi_i + (\lambda_i - \mu)\rho\phi_i] \tag{19–75}$$

This equation can often be solved directly* (Green's function). The results will be accurate to the extent that the resulting function, $\eta(\mathbf{r})$, justifies the original neglect of $V\eta$.

In principle, the process can be continued (η = some ϕ_j + small term), but in practice the difficulties mount rapidly.

TIME-DEPENDENT PERTURBATIONS

If the linear, symmetric operator, H, is independent of (has no effect on) some variable, t, then the equation,

$$[H + V(t)]\psi(\mathbf{r}, t) = i\hbar\rho(\mathbf{r}) \frac{\partial}{\partial t} \psi(\mathbf{r}, t) \tag{19–76}$$

may be solved approximately if one knows the (orthonormalized) eigenfunctions of H:

$$H\phi_j(\mathbf{r}) = \lambda_j \rho(\mathbf{r})\phi_j(\mathbf{r}); \qquad (\phi_i, \phi_j) = \delta_{ij} \tag{19–77}$$

If $V = 0$ in (19–76), solutions would be $\psi = e^{t\lambda_j/i\hbar}\phi_j(\mathbf{r})$. Trying in (19–76) the form,

$$\psi(\mathbf{r}, t) = \sum_j \phi_j(\mathbf{r}) g_j(t) e^{-i\lambda_j t/\hbar} \tag{19–78}$$

* If one uses (19–41) to obtain a solution, the result is essentially the same as that of first-order perturbation theory, (19–66).

and taking the "scalar product" with $\phi_k(\mathbf{r})$, one obtains a (rigorous) infinite set of coupled differential equations,

$$\frac{\mathrm{d}}{\mathrm{d}t} g_k(t) = \frac{1}{i\hbar} \sum_j e^{i(\lambda_k - \lambda_j)t/\hbar} V^{kj}(t) g_j(t) \tag{19–79}$$

where V^{kj} is defined by (19–65). This set can be solved (rigorously) in a form convenient for small t, given $g_k(0)$, by means of the matrizant series, (14–46)–(14–49):

$$g_k(t) = \sum_j \Omega_{kj}(t) g_j(0) \tag{19–80}$$

where

$$\Omega_{kj}(t) = \delta_{kj} + \frac{1}{i\hbar} \int_0^t e^{i(\lambda_k - \lambda_j)\tau/\hbar} V^{kj}(\tau)\,\mathrm{d}\tau$$
$$+ \frac{1}{(i\hbar)^2} \sum_l \int_0^t e^{i(\lambda_k - \lambda_l)\tau/\hbar} V^{kl}(\tau) \int_0^\tau e^{i(\lambda_l - \lambda_j)\tau'/\hbar} V^{lj}(\tau')\,\mathrm{d}\tau'\,\mathrm{d}\tau + \cdots \tag{19–81}$$

Usually, a relatively few terms in these series will dominate for small t.

Of frequent interest in quantum mechanics (collision problems) is the special case,

$$g_j(0) = \delta_{jI}; \qquad V = V_0 \text{ independent of } t \tag{19–82}$$

The dominant terms in (19–80) will then be those with $\lambda_k \doteqdot \lambda_I$ (energy conservation). If $V_0^{kI} \neq 0$, the leading term of this type is (for $k \neq I$)

$$g_k(t) = \frac{1 - e^{i(\lambda_k - \lambda_I)t/\hbar}}{\lambda_k - \lambda_I} V_0^{kI} \tag{19–83}$$

If $V_0^{kI} = 0$, then g_k can grow only through the second-order term, which *then* has the form,

$$g_k(t) = \frac{1 - e^{i(\lambda_k - \lambda_I)t/\hbar}}{\lambda_k - \lambda_I} \left\{ \sum_{l \neq I} \frac{V_0^{kl} V_0^{lI}}{\lambda_I - \lambda_l} \right\} + \epsilon \tag{19–84}$$

where "ϵ" denotes a term which (while not negligible as $t \to 0$) soon becomes unimportant (because $\lambda_k \doteqdot \lambda_I$ in the first term).

Another case occurring frequently in quantum mechanics (radiation problems) is

$$g_j(0) = \delta_{jI}; \qquad V(t) = V_0 \cos(\omega t + \phi)$$
$$= V_0 \{\tfrac{1}{2} e^{i\phi} e^{i\omega t} + \tfrac{1}{2} e^{-i\phi} e^{-i\omega t}\} \tag{19–85}$$

where V_0 is independent of t.

Here, leading terms $g_k(t)$ will be those such that $\lambda_k - \lambda_I \doteqdot \pm\omega\hbar$ (absorption or emission of energy). These leading terms in (19–80) and (19–81) are, usually

$$g_k(t) = \tfrac{1}{2} V_0^{kI} e^{\pm i\phi} \left\{ \frac{1 - e^{i(\lambda_k - \lambda_I \pm \omega\hbar)t/\hbar}}{\lambda_k - \lambda_I \pm \omega\hbar} \right\} \tag{19–86}$$

If, however, g_k is not of the type (19–86), it may make an appearance (though much weaker) through the second-order terms of (19–81) in two ways;

1. If $\lambda_k - \lambda_I \doteqdot \pm 2\omega\hbar$ (two-quantum processes) then

$$g_k(t) \doteqdot \left\{ \frac{1}{4} \sum_l \frac{V_0^{kl} V_0^{lI}}{\lambda_l - \lambda_I \pm \hbar\omega} \right\} \frac{e^{i(\lambda_k - \lambda_I \pm 2\omega\hbar)t/\hbar} - 1}{\lambda_k - \lambda_I \pm 2\omega\hbar} e^{\pm 2i\phi} \tag{19–87}$$

2. If for some state, l we have $\lambda_k - \lambda_l \doteqdot \pm\hbar\omega$ and if V_0^{kl}, V_0^{lI} are both large (Raman scattering):

$$g_k(t) \doteqdot \frac{1}{4} \left\{ \frac{V_0^{kl} V_0^{lI}}{\lambda_l - \lambda_I + \omega\hbar} + \frac{V_0^{kl} V_0^{lI}}{\lambda_l - \lambda_I - \omega\hbar} \right\} \cdot \frac{1 - e^{i(\lambda_k - \lambda_l \pm \omega\hbar)t/\hbar}}{\lambda_k - \lambda_l \pm \omega\hbar} \tag{19–88}$$

CHAPTER 20

PROBABILITY AND GAME THEORY

PROBABILITY theory deals with events whose outcomes are unpredictable in any individual instance (any "trial") but whose various alternative outcomes occur with known relative frequencies.

The "*probability*" of an outcome is its relative frequency normalized so that the sum over all possible outcomes is unity. That is, the probability of a given outcome is the fraction of times that it occurs in a very long (strictly, "infinite") sequence of trials.*

The main problems treated by the theory concern the calculation of various averages and the proper combining of such relative-frequency-data for simple events into corresponding information for more complex events compounded from them.

Sample Spaces ("Cross Sections")

A convenient way of displaying the logical relations between events and their probabilities is by means of a diagram (usually of unit area) on which regions are marked out for each possible outcome, with the areas of such regions proportional to the corresponding probability. Compare the "cross-section" concept of particle-physics.

Elementary Combination Rules

Consider two classes, A and B, of possible outcomes; these classes may overlap. We denote by Pr (A) the probability that (at least one outcome in) the class A occurs, etc. Then (see Fig.),

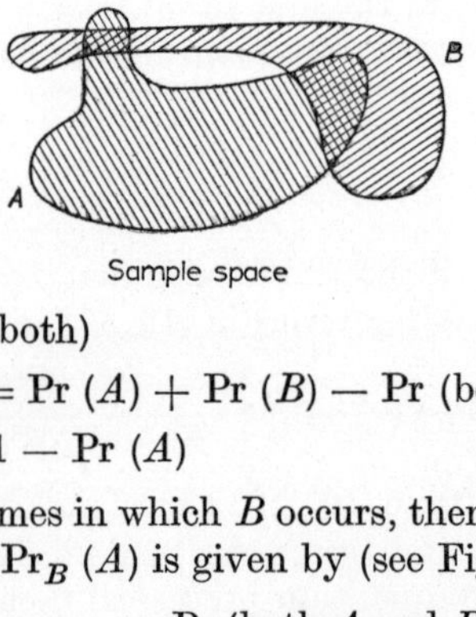

Sample space

$$\left.\begin{aligned} &\Pr(A \text{ or } B \text{ or both}) \\ &\qquad = \Pr(A) + \Pr(B) - \Pr(\text{both } A \text{ and } B) \\ &\Pr(\text{not } A) = 1 - \Pr(A) \end{aligned}\right\} \tag{20–1}$$

If one considers *only* outcomes in which B occurs, then the probability that in such cases A *also* occurs, denoted $\Pr_B(A)$ is given by (see Fig.)

$$\Pr_B(A) = \frac{\Pr(\text{both } A \text{ and } B)}{\Pr(B)} \tag{20–2}$$

Similarly,

$$\Pr_{\text{not } B}(A) = \frac{\Pr(A) - \Pr(\text{both } A \text{ and } B)}{1 - \Pr(B)} \tag{20–3}$$

* In formal mathematical theory, the notion of probability is an undefined term; the "definition" is replaced by a set of postulated properties, essentially (20–1)–(20–3).

Special cases of these results are

1. If A and B are *incompatible* (that is Pr (both A and B) = 0) then

$$\text{Pr}\,(A \text{ or } B) = \text{Pr}\,(A) + \text{Pr}\,(B) \tag{20–4}$$

2. If A and B are *independent* ($\text{Pr}_B\,(A) = \text{Pr}\,(A) = \text{Pr}_{\text{not } B}\,(A)$)

$$\begin{aligned} \text{Pr (both } A \text{ and } B) &= \text{Pr}\,(A) \cdot \text{Pr}\,(B) \\ \text{Pr (neither } A \text{ nor } B) &= \text{Pr (not } A) \cdot \text{Pr (not } B) \end{aligned} \tag{20–5}$$

The general rules (20–1)–(20–3) can obviously be extended to any number of classes $A, B, C, \cdots$ but they become rather unwieldy. The special cases (20–4) and (20–5), however, extend in a simple fashion:

3. If no two A_i can occur simultaneously,

$$\text{Pr}\,(A_1 \text{ or } A_2 \text{ or} \cdots \text{or } A_n) = \sum_i \text{Pr}\,(A_i) \tag{20–6}$$

4. If the A_i are mutually *independent*

$$\left.\begin{aligned} &\text{Pr}\,(A_1 \text{ and } A_2 \text{ and} \cdots \text{and } A_n) = \prod_i \text{Pr}\,(A_i) \\ &\text{Pr (none of } A_i) = \prod_i [1 - \text{Pr}\,(A_i)] \\ &\text{Pr (at least one of } A_i) = 1 - \prod_i [1 - \text{Pr}\,(A_i)] \end{aligned}\right\} \tag{20–7}$$

That is,

The last three relations are especially useful in studying sequences of (independent) trials.

Random ("Stochastic") Variables

Often, "outcomes" are naturally specified by a number. The number may be an integer as in the (actual) number of radioactive nuclei which decayed during a specific time interval; or it may be continuous, as the energy of a neutron after scattering. Such numbers are represented in the theory by variables, n, x, etc. Instead of using words to describe outcomes, the values found for the variables are listed.

Probability (Distribution) Functions

When outcomes can be specified by values of a random variable, it is customary to denote the probabilities as functions of that variable. For a discrete variable, we have merely,

$$\text{Pr (outcome ``}n\text{'')} = P(n)$$

For a continuous variable,

$$\text{Pr}\,(x \leqslant \text{outcome} \leqslant x + \mathrm{d}x) = P(x)\,\mathrm{d}x \tag{20–8}$$

The discrete case can be included in (20–8) if delta-functions are allowed. Then "mixed" cases ($x = a$, precisely, with finite frequency) can also be included. [Delta functions can be avoided by working only with the integral of $P(x)$ and using Stieltjes' (definition of) integrals, but the technique gets cumbersome with more than a single variable and loses some of its physical transparency.]

Of course, in (20–8),

$$\int_{-\infty}^{\infty} P(x)\,\mathrm{d}x = \int_{x\,\text{min}}^{x\,\text{max}} P(x)\,\mathrm{d}x = 1 \tag{20–9}$$

If y is another measure of the same outcome, $y = f(x)$, then it is important to note that $P(y) \neq P(x)$ but rather, by (20–8),

$$P(y)\,|\mathrm{d}y| = P(x)\,|\mathrm{d}x| \tag{20–10}$$

In particular, note that if $\hat{x}$ is the "peak" or most probable value of x, the most probable value of y is *not* $f(\hat{x})$ in general. Similarly, the average values of x and y are *not* related by $\bar{y} = f(\bar{x})$ in general.

If the outcome of a complex trial is specified by several variables, $X_1, X_2, \cdots, X_n$, we define analogously,

$$\Pr(x_1 \leqslant X_1 \leqslant x_1 + \mathrm{d}x_1; \cdots; x_n \leqslant X_n \leqslant x_n + \mathrm{d}x_n) = P(x_1, x_2, \cdots, x_n)\,\mathrm{d}x_1\,\mathrm{d}x_2 \cdots \mathrm{d}x_n \tag{20–11}$$

with relations analogous to (20–9) and (20–10).

If we desire the distribution of $\xi = f(x_1, \cdots, x_n)$, then by integrating P in (20–11) over the hypershell between $f = \xi$ and $f = \xi + \mathrm{d}\xi$, one obtains the useful relation,

$$P(\xi) = \int \cdots \int_{f=\xi} \frac{P(x_1, \cdots, x_n)}{\left|\dfrac{\partial f}{\partial x_n}\right|}\,\mathrm{d}x_1\,\mathrm{d}x_2 \cdots \mathrm{d}x_{n-1} \tag{20–12}$$

(The notation indicates that, in the integral, x_n is replaced by its value obtained by solving, $f(x_1, \cdots, x_n) = \xi$ for x_n.)

Functions of Random Variables; Mean and Variance

If $f(x)$ is a function of the random variable, x, then the "mean" or "expected" value* of $f(x)$ is defined as (in various common notations):

$$\bar{f} = E(f) = \langle f(x) \rangle = \int f(x)P(x)\,\mathrm{d}x \tag{20–13}$$

that is, each value of f is weighted by its frequency of occurrence.

In particular, the mean of x itself is

$$\langle x \rangle = \bar{x} = \int xP(x)\,\mathrm{d}x \tag{20–14}$$

The "*variance*" of x is defined as

$$\mathrm{Var}(x) = \langle (x - \bar{x})^2 \rangle = \langle x^2 \rangle - (\langle x \rangle)^2 \tag{20–15}$$

Its square-root is called the "*standard deviation*",

$$\sigma = \sqrt{\langle (x - \bar{x})^2 \rangle} = \sqrt{\langle x^2 \rangle - \langle x \rangle^2} \tag{20–16}$$

This is a measure of the likely spread of values of x about $\bar{x}$.

With several random variables, an additional concept of "*covariance*" is useful, as a measure of correlation versus independence.

$$\mathrm{Cov}(x, y) = \langle (x - \bar{x})(y - \bar{y}) \rangle = \langle xy \rangle - \bar{x}\bar{y} \tag{20–17}$$

If x and y are independent (so that $P(x, y) = P(x)P(y)$) then $\mathrm{Cov}(x, y) = 0$. The correlation coefficient of x and y is defined as

$$\rho = \frac{\mathrm{Cov}(x, y)}{\sigma_x \sigma_y}$$

---

* The word "average" is not often used with any strict technical meaning; when so used, however, it is generally equivalent to "mean."

Given N random variables, x_i, their sum is a random variable with the directly provable properties,

$$\left.\begin{aligned}\left\langle\sum_1^N x_i\right\rangle &= \sum_1^N \langle x_i\rangle \\ \operatorname{Var}\left(\sum_1^N x_i\right) &= \sum_1^N \operatorname{Var}(x_i) + \sum_{i\neq k} \operatorname{Cov}(x_i, x_k)\end{aligned}\right\} \qquad (20\text{–}18)$$

Some general theorems:

(1) For $x < \bar{x}$,

$$\int_{-\infty}^{x} P(x)\,dx \leqslant \frac{\sigma^2}{\sigma^2 + (x-\bar{x})^2}$$

and for $x > \bar{x}$,

$$\int_{-\infty}^{x} P(x)\,dx \geqslant \frac{(x-\bar{x})^2}{\sigma^2 + (x-\bar{x})^2} \qquad (20\text{–}19)$$

(These are the best limits possible.)

(2) If $g(x) \geqslant 0$ for all x and if $a > 0$, then

$$\Pr[g(x) \geqslant a] \leqslant \frac{1}{a}\langle g\rangle \qquad (20\text{–}20)$$

In particular (Tchebycheff),

$$\Pr[|x-\bar{x}| \geqslant a\sigma] \leqslant 1/a^2 \qquad (20\text{–}21)$$

$$\left[\text{Proof of (20–20): } \Pr(g \geqslant a) = \int_{g\geqslant a} P(x)\,dx \leqslant \int_{g\geqslant a} \frac{g}{a} P\,dx \leqslant \int_{-\infty}^{\infty} \frac{g}{a} P\,dx.\right]$$

(3) By the Schwarz inequality,

$$(\langle|x|^\nu\rangle)^2 \leqslant \langle|x|^{\nu-1}\rangle \cdot \langle|x|^{\nu+1}\rangle \qquad (20\text{–}22)$$

whence by induction,

$$(\langle|x|^n\rangle)^{1/n} \leqslant (\langle|x|^{n+1}\rangle)^{1/(n+1)} \qquad (20\text{–}23)$$

Limit Theorems for Sums of Independent Random Variables

It was long thought that the sum of any N independent random variables would itself have, for very large N, a Gaussian distribution, (20–26). Counter-examples are now known, and a large number of theorems have been proved. Some especially useful ones are given below. Note that in no case below is any assertion made about how rapidly the limits are approached nor as to whether the approach is uniform.

Notation: *Independent* random variables are x_i and

$$x = \sum_1^N x_i; \qquad \bar{x} = \sum_1^N \bar{x}_i; \qquad \sigma^2 = \langle(x-\bar{x})^2\rangle = \sum_1^N \sigma_i^2 \qquad (20\text{–}24)$$

(the last equality is a consequence of the independence of x_i).

1. If either $\sigma/N \to 0$ as $N \to \infty$ or else if all x_i have the same distribution,

$$\lim_{N\to\infty} \Pr\left\{\frac{1}{N}|x-\bar{x}| > \epsilon\right\} = 0 \qquad (20\text{–}25)$$

2. If all x_i have the same distribution and the (common) value of σ_i is finite, then

$$\lim_{N\to\infty} \Pr\{\bar{x} + a\sigma < x < \bar{x} + b\sigma\} = \frac{1}{\sqrt{2\pi}}\int_a^b e^{-t^2/2}\,dt \qquad (20\text{–}26)$$

3. With $\rho_i = \langle |x_i - \bar{x}_i|^3 \rangle$ and $\rho^3 = \sum_1^N \rho_i^3$, the result (20–26) also holds if the x_i do not have the same distribution provided that all σ_i and all ρ_i are finite and that

$$\lim_{N \to \infty} \rho/\sigma = 0.$$

Either (2) or (3) is often called the "Central Limit Theorem".

Experimental data and the Gaussian distribution: Lest these results be taken to support the popular fable that experimental measurements are always distributed according to (20–26), consider an experiment where the desired datum is related to the current, I, flowing in a known, fixed resistor. If one experimenter uses an ammeter (I) and another a wattmeter (I^2), then by (20–10) they can*not* both find their measurements distributed in a Gaussian manner. It is instructive to examine why this is no contradiction to the above theorems.

Generating Functions

Generating functions* have little intuitive meaning, but are a powerful calculational tool. They resemble integral transforms in this respect. The main reason for their usefulness lies in their simple behavior when individual random processes are combined in various common ways. These functions do not explicitly contain the random variable, x, but only a "dummy variable", p.

The generating function for (or "associated with") a random variable, x, with distribution, $P(x)$, is defined as the following function of p

$$g(p) = \langle e^{-px} \rangle = \int_{-\infty}^{\infty} e^{-px} P(x)\, dx \tag{20–27}$$

(i.e., the two-sided Laplace transform of P). For a discrete random variable taking only non-negative integer values, it is often convenient to set $e^{-p} = s$ and define,

$$G(s) = \langle s^n \rangle = \sum_n P(n) s^n \tag{20–28}$$

Formally, it follows immediately that

$$\langle x \rangle = -\left.\frac{dg(p)}{dp}\right|_{p=0} = -g'(0) \tag{20–29}$$

$$\left.\begin{aligned} \langle x^k \rangle &= (-1)^k g^{(k)}(0) \\ \langle (x-a)^k \rangle &= (-1)^k \frac{d^k}{dp^k} e^{ap} g(p) \Big|_{p=0} \end{aligned}\right\} \tag{20–30}$$

Thus

$$\sigma^2 = \text{Var}\,(x) = g''(0) - [g'(0)]^2 \tag{20–31}$$

In principle, $P(x)$ is recoverable as $\mathscr{L}_{\text{II}}^{-1}[g(p)]$.

---

* More generally, this is a generic name for functions, the coefficients of whose Taylor's series are equal to (i.e. "list" or "generate") a desired sequence of numbers, functions, etc. Thus $G(s)$ in (20–28) "generates" the sequence $P(n)$; another example is $(1 - 2xz + x^2)^{-\frac{1}{2}}$, regarded as a function of x, which "generates" the Legendre polynomials, $P_l(z)$.

For the discrete case, these formulas read, in terms of $s = e^{-p}$,

$$\left.\begin{aligned} \bar{n} &= \left.\frac{dG}{ds}\right|_{s=1} = G'(1) \\ \langle (n-\bar{n})^2\rangle &= \mathrm{Var}\,(n) = G''(1) + G'(1) - [G'(1)]^2 \\ \langle (n-\bar{n})^l\rangle &= \left[\frac{1}{s}\left(s\frac{d}{ds}\right)^l \frac{G(s)}{s^{\bar{n}}}\right]_{s=1} \\ \langle n^l\rangle &= \left[\frac{1}{s}\left(s\frac{d}{ds}\right)^l G(s)\right]_{s=1} \end{aligned}\right\} \qquad (20\text{–}32)$$

See also (14–80)–(14–82).

Sums of independent variables: By the convolution theorem for Laplace transforms, if $g_1(p), \cdots, g_n(p)$ are the generating functions for the *independent* random variables, $x_1, \cdots, x_n$, then the generating function for $x = \sum_1^n x_i$ is

$$g(p) = g_1(p)g_2(p)\cdots g_n(p) \qquad (20\text{–}33)$$

from which $\bar{x}$, Var (x), etc., can often be easily computed without explicitly evaluating $P(x) = \mathscr{L}_{\mathrm{II}}^{-1}[g(p)]$.

For discrete independent variables, the same formula, of course, holds when written in terms of $s = e^{-p}$,

$$G(s) = G_1(s)G_2(s)\cdots G_n(s) \qquad (20\text{–}34)$$

Chain reactions: (integer variables). Many processes may be regarded as a succession of "generations" in each of which each previously produced entity (particle, bacterium, etc., etc.) has a probability, $P(n)$, of producing n progeny before dying. If $G(s)$ is the generating function for $P(n)$, then (given one initial particle) the generating function, $G_k(s)$, for the number of entities at the end of the kth generation may be found recursively:

$$\left.\begin{aligned} G_1(s) &= G(s) \\ G_{k+1}(s) &= G[G_k(s)] \end{aligned}\right\} \qquad (20\text{–}35)$$

These successive substitutions are frequently much more easily carried out than direct calculations and again means, variances, etc., can be calculated without explicit knowledge of the actual distributions.

If the production probability, $P(n)$, changes with each generation, so that it is $P_k(n)$ in the kth generation and has a generating function, $H_k(s)$, then

$$\begin{aligned} G_1(s) &= H_1(s) \\ G_2(s) &= H_1[H_2(s)] \\ G_k(s) &= H_1[H_2[\cdots[H_k(s)]\cdots]] \end{aligned} \qquad (20\text{–}36)$$

[The rules, (20–35) and (20–36), may be proved directly from the definition, (20–28).]

Approximations to $P(n)$ in the discrete case: If $G(s)$ is known, then

$$P(n) = \frac{1}{n!}\left.\frac{d^nG}{ds^n}\right|_{s=0} \qquad (20\text{–}37)$$

Alternative formulas which can often lead to good approximations for large n are:

$$P(n) = \frac{1}{2\pi i}\oint_{|z|=a<1} G(z)z^{-n-1}\,dz \qquad (20\text{–}38)$$

and if $G(s)$ is rational with distinct simple poles, $s_1, \cdots, s_k$ so that

$$G(s) = \frac{\rho_1}{s_1 - s} + \frac{\rho_2}{s_2 - s} + \cdots + \frac{\rho_k}{s_k - s} \tag{20–39}$$

then (expand each term in a series about $s = 0$):

$$P(n) = \frac{\rho_1}{s_1^{n+1}} + \frac{\rho_2}{s_2^{n+1}} + \cdots + \frac{\rho_k}{s_k^{n+1}} \tag{20–40}$$

where the first term alone will yield a good approximation if $|s_1|$ is smaller than all other $|s_i|$ and n is large.

Recurrent Composite Events

Given a long string of successive trials with outcomes $\mathcal{O}_1, \mathcal{O}_2, \mathcal{O}_3, \cdots$ (where $P(\mathcal{O}_n)$ may depend on preceding outcomes), consider the occurrence of some specific pattern, $\mathscr{E}$, (such as a run of four heads in coin tossing, or the pattern HXH with X arbitrary). It turns out that the properties of such composite events, $\mathscr{E}$, are simple only when they are required to be *non-overlapping*:

Restriction: We consider only events with the following property. If p_j is the probability that $\mathscr{E}$ occurs at the jth trial (that is, that the jth outcome completes one of the desired patterns, $\mathscr{E}$) and if f_j is the probability that $\mathscr{E}$ occurs for the *first time* at the jth trial, then the probability that it occurs for the first time at the kth trial *and* again at the nth trial is required to be $f_k p_{n-k}$.

With this restriction and with the *convention*, $f_0 = 0$, $p_0 = 1$, then $p_n = \sum_{j=0}^{n} f_j p_{n-j}$ and the generating functions,

$$P(s) = \sum_0^\infty p_n s^n = 1 + \sum_1^\infty p_n s^n; \quad F(s) = \sum_1^\infty f_n s^n \tag{20–41}$$

are related by

$$P(s) = \frac{1}{1 - F(s)} \tag{20–42}$$

If $\mathscr{E}$ happens to be such that f_j vanishes unless $j = n\lambda$, then λ is called the "period" of the event.

The only possible types of (recurrent, non-overlapping) events are:

(a) *Uncertain events:* $P(1)$ is finite (hence $p_n \to 0$ as $n \to \infty$) and the probability that $\mathscr{E}$ *ever* occurs is

$$F(1) = \frac{P(1) - 1}{P(1)} < 1 \tag{20–43}$$

(b) *Certain events:* $F(1) = 1$. Then as $k \to \infty$,

$$p_{k\lambda} \to \frac{\lambda}{\sum n f_n} = \frac{\lambda}{F'(1)} \tag{20–44}$$

while, if $\lambda \neq 1$, then by (20–42) $p_j = 0$ when $j \neq n\lambda$.

In case (b), $\mu \equiv F'(1)$ may be called the "mean recurrence time" of $\mathscr{E}$ and $\sigma^2 \equiv [F''(1) + \mu - \mu^2]$ its variance. The Central Limit Theorem, (20–26), shows:

If M_n is the number of trials, $\mathcal{O}_i$, up to and including the nth occurrence of $\mathscr{E}$, then as $n \to \infty$,

$$\Pr\left\{\frac{M_n - n\mu}{\sigma\sqrt{n}} < \alpha\right\} \to \frac{1}{\sqrt{2\pi}} \int_{-\infty}^{\alpha} e^{-y^2/2}\, dy \tag{20–45}$$

If N_n is the number of occurrences of $\mathscr{E}$ in a string of n trials, then as $n \to \infty$,

$$\Pr\left\{\frac{N_n - \dfrac{n}{\mu}}{\sigma\sqrt{n}}\,\mu^{3/2} < \alpha\right\} \to \frac{1}{\sqrt{2\pi}}\int_{-\alpha}^{\infty} e^{-y^2/2}\,dy \tag{20–46}$$

(The second follows from the first when it is observed that $\Pr(N_r \geqslant k) = \Pr(M_k \leqslant r)$.)

Markoff Chains

1. **Definition:** Consider a physical system capable of assuming "states" S_1, $S_2, \cdots, S_i, \cdots$ (possibly infinite in number). Let the system make transitions from one such state to another at known intervals but in an unpredictable manner such that the probability of the transition, $S_i \to S_j$, is P_{ij} (note the order of the indices). Any process abstractly identical with this is known as a Markoff Chain.* Note that the matrix of *constants*,† P_{ij}, completely characterizes the chain.

Note that almost any system treated in statistical mechanics or in multiple scattering and diffusion can, at least formally, be regarded as a Markoff Chain.

2. **Elementary results:**

$$\sum_j P_{ij} = 1 \quad \left(\text{Note } \sum_i P_{ij} \neq 1, \text{ frequently}\right) \tag{20–47}$$

That is, the row-sums of the matrix, P_{ij} are unity, but the column-sums need not be.

If the system has a distribution of (probability of being in) states S_i given by $(\pi_1, \pi_2, \pi_3, \cdots)$ at a certain time, then after N transitions, the new distribution is given by

$$\pi_k^{(N)} = \sum_j \pi_j P_{jk}{}^N \tag{20–48}$$

where $P_{jk}{}^N$ is an element of the Nth power of the matrix P_{ij}:

$$P_{jk}^{M+1} = \sum_i P_{ji} P_{ik}{}^M; \qquad P_{jk}{}^1 = P_{jk} \tag{20–49}$$

3. **Decomposition:** If the matrix, P, has a form such as

$$P = \begin{Vmatrix} A & 0 & 0 \\ 0 & B & 0 \\ U & V & T \end{Vmatrix} \quad \text{or} \quad P = \begin{Vmatrix} A & 0 \\ U & T \end{Vmatrix} \tag{20–50}$$

---

* The notation implies that the transition $S_i \to S_j$ is not influenced by states preceding S_i. Somewhat more general cases can be reduced to thi-: If the probability of the next state being S_j when the last n states were $S_{i_1}, S_{i_2}, \cdots, S_{i_n}$ is denoted by $f_j(i_1, i_2, \cdots, i_n)$, then define new states $\mathscr{S}_\alpha$ where α is a set of n "old" indices: $\alpha = (i_1, i_2, \cdots, i_n)$. [$\mathscr{S}_\alpha$ is short for: "the last n states were $S_{j_1}, \cdots, S_{i_n}$".] Then set

$$\Pr(\mathscr{S}_\alpha \to \mathscr{S}_\beta) = P_{\alpha\beta} = P_{i_1, i_2, \cdots i_n; j_1, j_2, \cdots j_n}$$

$$= \begin{cases} f_{j_n}(i_1, \cdots, i_n), \text{ if } j_k = i_{k+1} & (\text{for } k = 1, \cdots, n-1) \\ 0, \text{ otherwise} \end{cases}$$

Often, of course, simpler new states, $\mathscr{S}_\alpha$, will also suffice.

† If the P_{ij} are allowed to vary at successive transitions, the model is known as a Markoff *process*. Such general systems have almost none of the simple properties of "chains".

where A, B, T are square (sub-)matrices, then P^N will have a similar form:

$$P^N = \begin{Vmatrix} A^N & 0 & 0 \\ 0 & B^N & 0 \\ W_N & X_N & T^N \end{Vmatrix} \quad \text{or} \quad P^N = \begin{Vmatrix} A^N & 0 \\ Z_N & T^N \end{Vmatrix} \tag{20–51}$$

Here, A and B necessarily have the same property, (20–47), as does P but T does not.

From the definition of P_{ij}, it is seen that A and B (or rather, the states, S_k, which they "cover") each form a "closed set". Once in a state covered by A, the system remains in some state covered by A and similarly for B. On the other hand, T covers "transient" states; eventually, the system will leave such states and become "trapped" in either "A-states" or "B-states".

The location of such "closed sets" (represented by A and B above) is necessary before the results below can be used. Unfortunately, the original ordering or naming of the states, S_i, may obscure the property typified by (20–50). Probably the most practical way of determining whether a given matrix can be decomposed as in (20–50) is to square it (mentally!), observing only whether any vanishing elements of P are also zero in P^2. Those which are zero in both P and P^2 probably connect different "closed sets" and indicate how P may be rearranged to a form like (20–50). Equation (20–51) shows that the sub-matrices corresponding to closed sets can be studied independently of the full matrix. They represent sub-chains.

Indecomposable Markoff chains are defined as chains whose P cannot be written in the form typified by (20–50). That is, any state, S_i, can (eventually) be reached from any other state, S_j, For each pair of indices, (i, j), there is some power, N, such that ${P_{ij}}^N \neq 0$.

4. **Periodic chains:** This concept is necessary to avoid certain pitfalls of the general theory, but is not physically a very interesting case. Certain chains have the property that a system cannot remain in any state when the time comes for a transition but rather it must jump to a new and different state. The matrices for such systems are characterized by* zeros on the diagonal, P_{ii}. Physically, systems of this type would be "cyclic"—showing at least an average tendency to run through cycles of states.

The exact definition is: A chain is called "periodic" if any one of its states, S_i, (or the event: occupancy of S_i) is a periodic recurrent event [in the sense defined following (20–42)]. In fact, if the chain is irreducible, all its states can be shown to have the same period, λ.

Such chains therefore have a "natural period", λ, and if we agree to consider them only at integral multiples of that period: $N = k\lambda + m$ ($m < \lambda$; k an integer), then the theorems below remain true, but different limiting matrices (corresponding to different parts of the natural cycle) are obtained for different values of the "phase", m.

5. **Limit theorem:**

(a) All matrices which satisfy (20–47) (except as noted in #4) have the property,

$$\lim_{N\to\infty} {P_{jk}}^N = \nu_k, \quad \text{independent of } j \tag{20–52}$$

That is, after a great many transitions, the probability of the system being in any state, S_k, settles down to a value, ν_k, independent of the initial conditions. Thereafter, states S_k (within some indecomposable closed set) recur with a definite average frequency.

---

* Precisely: An indecomposable chain cannot be periodic unless all diagonal elements vanish. (Even then, it *need* not be periodic.)

(b) If the chain is *indecomposable*, then all $\nu_k > 0$ and they may be computed from the (unique) solution of

$$\nu_k = \sum_j \nu_j P_{jk}; \qquad \sum_k \nu_k = 1 \tag{20–53}$$

Note that, if $\sum_i P_{ij} = 1$ [in addition to (20–47)] and if the number, N_s, of states is finite, then $\nu_k = 1/N_s$ (all k).

(c) If S_k is a transient state (definition: see (20–50)) then

$$\nu_k = 0$$

6. **Absorption probabilities:** We noted in #3 that if a system starts in a transient state, it may become trapped in any of (in general) many "closed sets". The probability of the system ending in any given closed set, C, may be computed once such a set has been located (that is, once P has been partially decomposed, as in (20–50), into transient states and closed sets).

Consider a starting-state, S_t, which is transient and a (not necessarily indecomposable) closed set of states, C. If Π_t is the probability of ending in C after starting in S_t, then Π_t can be calculated by solving,

$$\sum_{k \text{ in } C} P_{tk} = \Pi_t - \sum_{i \text{ in } T} P_{ti}\Pi_i \tag{20–54}$$

where T is the set of ("known") transient states.

7. Application to **arbitrary matrices with positive elements:** The theorems above may be applied to any* matrix with non-negative elements, $M_{ik} \geqslant 0$, by the following devices.

Let s_i be the row-sums, $s_i = \sum_k M_{ik}$. If any row-sum is greater than unity, first divide the entire matrix by a constant such that the new row-sums are at most unity. Then "border" the matrix at the top and left by a new row and column (numbered "zero"), defined by

$$M_{0j} = \delta_{0j}$$

$$M_{j0} = 1 - s_j \quad (\text{for } j > 0)$$

The final result is a matrix satisfying (20–47) and the theorems above may be applied. The powers of the original matrix, $M_{ik}{}^N$, are simply the submatrix obtained by deleting the added row and column from the corresponding power of the altered matrix.

Continuous Random Walks (Diffusion, Brownian Motion)

If a particle undergoes successive random displacements, $\mathbf{r}_j$, let $p_j(\mathbf{r})\, d\mathbf{r}$ be the probability that the jth displacement vector, $\mathbf{r}_j$, lies in $d\mathbf{r}$, centered on $\mathbf{r}$. By (20–27) and (20–33) if we define the generating functions,

$$g_N(\mathbf{w}) = \prod_{j=1}^{N} \left\{ \int_{-\infty}^{\infty} p_j(\mathbf{r}_j) \exp (i\mathbf{w} \cdot \mathbf{r}_j)\, d\mathbf{r}_j \right\}$$

then the probability distribution, $P_N(\mathbf{R})\, d\mathbf{R}$, for the total displacement, $\mathbf{R} = \Sigma\, \mathbf{r}_j$, after N steps is given by

$$P_N(\mathbf{R}) = (2\pi)^{-3} \int_{-\infty}^{\infty} g_N(\mathbf{w}) \exp (-i\mathbf{w} \cdot \mathbf{R})\, d\mathbf{w}$$

---

* If the matrix is infinite, its row-sums must be bounded.

For ("almost") any form of the individual displacement probabilities, the Central Limit Theorem (20–26) indicates that for large N

$$P_N(\mathbf{R}) \sim AN^{-3/2} \exp\,[-|\mathbf{R} - N\mathbf{B}|^2/NC]$$

where A, $\mathbf{B}$, C are independent of N and $\mathbf{R}$. Compare (15–59).

If $p_j(\mathbf{r}) = (1/4\pi L_j^2)\delta(r - L_j)$ so that only the directions of the steps are random, it is easily shown that

$$P_N(\mathbf{R}) = (1/2\pi^2 R)\int_0^\infty \left\{\prod_1^N (\sin wL_j)/wL_j\right\} (\sin wR)w\,dw$$

which can be expressed in terms of Bessel functions if all L_j have a common value.

Isotropic Scattering

If $p_j(\mathbf{r}) = ce^{-r}/4\pi r^2$, corresponding to isotropic scattering (in a homogeneous, infinite medium) with attenuation by a factor c at each scatter, then

$$g_N(\mathbf{w}) = (1/c)[(c/w)\tan^{-1} w]^N$$

where the factor, $1/c$, accounts for the fact that $p_1(\mathbf{r}) = e^{-r}/4\pi r^2$ if the particles emerge from a point source of unit strength. To obtain a convergent expression, consider the density of *scattered* particles,

$$\sum_2^\infty P_N(\mathbf{R}) = (2\pi)^{-3}\int_{-\infty}^{\infty} \exp\,(-i\mathbf{w}\cdot\mathbf{R}) \sum_2^\infty g_N(\mathbf{w})\,d\mathbf{w}$$

The second series is easily summed and, after adding in the direct beam, one obtains for the total density of particles:

$$\phi(\mathbf{R}) = \frac{e^{-R}}{4\pi R^2} + \frac{c}{2\pi^2 R}\int_0^\infty \frac{(\tan^{-1} w)^2}{w - c\tan^{-1} w}(\sin wR)\,dw$$

Fokker–Planck Equations

Many distribution functions, P, satisfy an equation of the form,

$$P(\mathbf{r}, \mathbf{u}, t) = \iint P(\mathbf{r}', \mathbf{v}', t')G(\mathbf{r}', \mathbf{v}', t';\ \mathbf{r}, \mathbf{v}, t)\,d\mathbf{v}'\,d\mathbf{r}'$$

where G is essentially a transition probability. If (as is usually only approximately true)

$$G(\mathbf{r} - \Delta\mathbf{r}, \mathbf{v} - \Delta\mathbf{v}, t - \Delta t;\ \mathbf{r}, \mathbf{v}, t) = g(\mathbf{r}, \mathbf{v}, \Delta\mathbf{v}, \Delta t)\delta(\Delta\mathbf{r} - \mathbf{v}\Delta t)$$

then one may write:

$$P(\mathbf{r} + \mathbf{v}\Delta t, \mathbf{v}, t + \Delta t) = \int P(\mathbf{r}, \mathbf{v} - \mathbf{u}, t)g(\mathbf{r}, \mathbf{v}, \mathbf{u}, \Delta t)\,d\mathbf{u}$$

Expand P in a Taylor's series in Δt and $\mathbf{u} = \Delta\mathbf{v}$,

$$\left(\frac{\partial P}{\partial t} + \mathbf{v}\cdot\nabla P\right)\Delta t + \cdots = -\sum_i \frac{\partial}{\partial v_i}(P\langle\Delta v_i\rangle) + \tfrac{1}{2}\sum_{i,j}\frac{\partial^2}{\partial v_i \partial v_j}(P\langle\Delta v_i \Delta v_j\rangle) + \cdots$$

where

$$\langle\Delta v_i\rangle = \int u_i g(\mathbf{r}, \mathbf{v}, \mathbf{u}, \Delta t)\,d\mathbf{u}$$

and similarly for $\langle \Delta v_i \Delta v_j \rangle$. Finally, expand these functions in Taylor's series:

$$\langle \Delta v_i \rangle = (\Delta t) F_i(\mathbf{r}, \mathbf{v}) + \cdots$$

$$\langle \Delta v_j \Delta v_i \rangle = (\Delta t) H_{ij}(\mathbf{r}, \mathbf{v}) + \cdots$$

Often the functions F_i and H_{ij} can be computed or estimated directly, without retracing the above derivation. Then taking the limit as Δt approaches zero, one obtains the Fokker–Planck differential equation,

$$\frac{\partial P}{\partial t} + \mathbf{v} \cdot \nabla P + \nabla_{\mathbf{v}} \cdot (P\mathbf{F}) = \tfrac{1}{2}(\nabla_{\mathbf{v}} \nabla_{\mathbf{v}}) : (P\mathfrak{H})$$

Note that this result is not exact for transport problems; it corresponds to a diffusion approximation.

GAME THEORY

We shall consider only two-person (or two-team) games wherein the loser pays the winner ("zero sum"). In outline, the basic ideas are:

1. If each player adopts a complete "*pure strategy*" which inflexibly dictates his response to every conceivable situation, then, even if the game involves chance elements, the payoffs are at least statistically determined.

2. Hence, if *all* such possible strategies for each player are numbered (in any order), the game is completely characterized by a "payoff *matrix*", whose elements, v_{ij}, give the payoff (statistical average) to player 1 when he adopts his i^{th} pure strategy and player 2 adopts his j^{th} pure strategy. (Player 2 then receives $-v_{ij}$.)

3. If both players have complete knowledge of the matrix, v_{ij}, then player 1 expects player 2 to minimize v_{ij} (by varying j) for each fixed i; thus player 1 strives to maximize this minimum by varying i. He can thus choose an i which will *assure* his receiving at least as much as

$$v_1 = \max_i \left\{ \min_j v_{ij} \right\} \tag{20-55}$$

Similarly, player 2 can ensure that player 1 receives no more than

$$v_2 = \min_j \left\{ \max_i v_{ij} \right\} \tag{20-56}$$

It is not difficult to show that $v_1 \leqslant v_2$.

4. *Determined games:* If $v_1 = v_2$, this common value must be assumed for the same i and j. That is, there exists (at least) one pair I, J such that $v_1 = v_{IJ} = v_2$. Hence, if each player makes the best of his opportunities, player 1 can use his I^{th} strategy and player 2 his J^{th}. Neither could do better (if the other makes no mistakes*). In a "fair" game, $v_1 = 0 = v_2$.

5. *Mixed strategies:* If $v_1 < v_2$, each player still has a latitude of choice which, however, cannot be exploited (usually) by using any one fixed pure strategy.† Rather either or both of the players must play successive games with different strategies, which must be chosen randomly to prevent the opponent from exploiting

* If I and J are not unique, it behooves each player to choose among them that which takes greatest advantage of any mistakes the opponent might make.

† Compare coin-*matching* games where

$$v = \begin{Vmatrix} 1 & -1 \\ -1 & 1 \end{Vmatrix}$$

any ability to predict the moves in advance. Thus we are lead to consider "mixed strategies" which can be characterized by "vectors" with positive components, thus:

$$\boldsymbol{\alpha} = (\alpha_1, \alpha_2, \cdots, \alpha_N); \qquad \alpha_i \geqslant 0; \qquad \Sigma\, \alpha_i = 1 \tag{20–57}$$

where N is the number of available pure strategies and α_i is the probability that, in any one play of the game, the ith pure strategy will be used.

6. Allowing mixed strategy $\boldsymbol{\alpha}$ for player 1 and $\boldsymbol{\beta}$ for player 2, then the expected average payoff to player 1 is

$$f(\boldsymbol{\alpha}, \boldsymbol{\beta}) = \sum_i \sum_j \alpha_i v_{ij} \beta_j \tag{20–58}$$

As before, player 1 can obtain at least

$$\mathscr{V}_1 = \max_{\boldsymbol{\alpha}} \left\{ \min_{\boldsymbol{\beta}} f(\boldsymbol{\alpha}, \boldsymbol{\beta}) \right\} \tag{20–59}$$

and player 2 need lose no more than

$$\mathscr{V}_2 = \min_{\boldsymbol{\beta}} \left\{ \max_{\boldsymbol{\alpha}} f(\boldsymbol{\alpha}, \boldsymbol{\beta}) \right\} \tag{20–60}$$

7. *Mini-max theorem:* This theorem, (11–45), states that, for all functions of the type (20–58) with variables restricted as in (20–57), there exist $\boldsymbol{\alpha}_0$ and $\boldsymbol{\beta}_0$ such that $\mathscr{V}_1 = f(\boldsymbol{\alpha}_0, \boldsymbol{\beta}_0) = \mathscr{V}_2$.

Thus the players can settle down to these strategies (which may not be unique). Neither could do better *provided* that the other makes the best of his opportunities. Again, if $\boldsymbol{\alpha}_0$ and $\boldsymbol{\beta}_0$ are not unique, it behooves both players to choose among them that which takes greatest advantage of any possible mistakes of the opponent.

8. *Comment:* In some real-life situations, these theories should be applied with caution. Often, full knowledge is not available to both players, and the "optimum" strategy, $\boldsymbol{\alpha}_0$, generally fails to take *greatest* advantage of an opponent's "mistakes". Such "unsafe-but-profitable" strategies are, in fact, often employed in real life.

9. *Computation of $\boldsymbol{\alpha}_0$ and $\boldsymbol{\beta}_0$:* Some methods are:

(a) Direct evaluation of (20–59) or (20–60).

(b) Let b be any square submatrix of $v = \|v_{ij}\|$, let B be the adjoint of b (see (11–10)) and let

$$\sigma = \sum_i \sum_j B_{ij}$$

Then form

$$\alpha_l = \frac{1}{\sigma} \sum_i B_{il}; \qquad \beta_k = \frac{1}{\sigma} \sum_i B_{ki} \tag{20–61}$$

Finally, complete $\boldsymbol{\alpha}$ and $\boldsymbol{\beta}$ by setting equal to zero those components corresponding to rows or columns (respectively) of v which were deleted in forming b. These $\boldsymbol{\alpha}$, $\boldsymbol{\beta}$ need not be solutions but:

As b ranges over all square submatrices of v, those corresponding $\boldsymbol{\alpha}$ and $\boldsymbol{\beta}$ which *are* solutions* form a "basic set" of solutions from which *all* solutions can be obtained by taking ("convex") linear combinations, with non-negative coefficients. The common value of $\mathscr{V}_1$ and $\mathscr{V}_2$ equals $|b|/\sigma$ whenever $\boldsymbol{\alpha}$ and $\boldsymbol{\beta}$ are indeed solutions.

---

* In the sense that $\mathscr{V}_1 = \mathscr{V}_2 = f(\boldsymbol{\alpha}, \boldsymbol{\beta})$. To test $\boldsymbol{\alpha}$, it is sufficient to verify, besides (20–57). that all $f(\boldsymbol{\alpha}, \mathbf{I}) > |b|/\sigma$ where $I_i = \delta_{il}$ (and similarly for $\boldsymbol{\beta}$).

(c) Linear programming: This method is usually simpler but less general than (b). Solve the problem in linear programming (which see):

$$\left.\begin{aligned} &\sum_i \alpha_i v_{i1} - z_1 = \max \\ &\text{with the restrictions,} \\ &z_k - z_1 = \sum_i \alpha_i (v_{ik} - v_{i1}) \\ &\alpha_i \geqslant 0; \qquad \sum \alpha_i = 1; \qquad z_k \geqslant 0 \end{aligned}\right\} \tag{20–62}$$

If $\boldsymbol{\alpha}_0$ is a solution of this problem, then it is an optimum strategy for player 1 and the corresponding maximum in (20–62) is the value, $\mathscr{V}_1 = \mathscr{V}_2$. Similarly, an optimum strategy, $\boldsymbol{\beta}$ for player 2 is found from:

$$\left.\begin{aligned} &z_1 + \sum_j v_{1j}\beta_j = \min \\ &z_k + \sum_j (v_{kj} - v_{1j})\beta_j = z_1 \\ &\beta_i \geqslant 0; \qquad \Sigma\, \beta_i = 1; \qquad z_k \geqslant 0 \end{aligned}\right\} \tag{20–63}$$

In both (20–62) and (20–63) the z_i are variables (on a par with α_i or β_j, even though their final optimizing values are later discarded).

CHAPTER 21

TENSOR ANALYSIS

TENSOR analysis is essentially an extension of classical vector notation to *arbitrary coordinate systems.* A generalization (which, essentially, ignores the "original" space) then leads to *Riemannian geometry.*

Note: *Orthogonal coordinates in ordinary space* (such as cylindrical, spherical, elliptic coordinates, etc.) *are most readily treated by direct geometric arguments*—notably the application of Gauss' or Stoke's theorems to differential volumes as a means of obtaining $\nabla^2\phi$, $\nabla \times \mathbf{a}$, etc.

[This situation arises because orthogonal coordinates allow additional simplifications which are not possible in general and are therefore not readily expressed in the general formalism which follows. Specifically, in terms of the notation below, if the $\mathbf{u}_i$ (and therefore the $\mathbf{v}_j$) are orthogonal, it is convenient to also normalize them ($\mathbf{u}_i \cdot \mathbf{u}_k = \delta_{ik}$) because then all vectors again have only one type of component, the "physical component," $a_I' = \sqrt{\overline{a}^I \overline{a}_I}$, (not summed).]

Notation

Although the reader is urged to keep ordinary 3-space in mind, we shall consider an arbitrary number of dimensions (in the sense explained after (10–68)). The coordinates will be denoted by superscripts,* $x^1, x^2, \cdots, x^n$, for reasons of later consistency. In general, indices for vector or tensor components may occur as either subscripts or superscripts. Also for later consistency, the Kronecker delta will be written in any of four ways:

$$\delta_{ij} = \delta^{ij} = \delta^i_j = g^i_j = \begin{cases} 0, & \text{if } i \neq j \\ 1, & \text{if } i = j \end{cases} \tag{21–1}$$

We shall initially suppose that x^i always denote Cartesian coordinates $[(\Delta \text{ length})^2 = \sum_i dx^i\, dx^i]$ but will later wish to generalize; therefore, *equations which are true only for Cartesian-x^i will carry a "c" over the equality sign.*

Summation Convention

All summation signs will be omitted. Any product of indexed symbols is understood to be preceded by a "$\sum$" symbol in which the summation is over all n possible values of each index which occurs twice in the product. Thus $\sum (x^i)^2$ will be written, $x^i x^i$.

Note: (1) By this convention, the symbol used for a repeated index is arbitrary and may be replaced by any other symbol (which does not already occur elsewhere in the equation). Thus $x^i x^i = x^\alpha x^\alpha = x^j x^j$, etc.

(2) Also by this convention, the Kronecker delta acts on indices as a "substitution operator" (when sums occur over one of its indices). Examples:

$$T^i{}_k \delta^k{}_l B^l = T^i{}_l B^l; \qquad \delta^i_j a^j = a^i$$

Remark: Save for a few exceptions valid only in Cartesian coordinates, summations will always involve one subscript and one superscript. Also, any index symbol

* Ordinary exponents will seldom occur, and there will be no real ambiguity.

when *not* summed will occur in an equation only as a subscript or only as a superscript. [These "rules" are mentioned here since they are a help in reading and remembering later equations; their significance will emerge later.]

Elementary Relations

Consider a new set of coordinates, $\xi^1, \xi^2, \cdots, \xi^n$ which are arbitrary functions of the x^i,

$$\xi^i = \xi^i(x^1, x^2, \cdots, x^n) \tag{21–2}$$

Then, by elementary rules of calculus

$$d\xi^i = \frac{\partial \xi^i}{\partial x^j}\, dx^j; \quad \frac{\partial f}{\partial \xi^i} = \frac{\partial x^k}{\partial \xi^i}\frac{\partial f}{\partial x^k} \tag{21–3}$$

(where f is any function of the x^i). This matrix equation can be inverted (that is, the transformation (21–2) carries distinct points into distinct points) if and only if—in various notations,

$$J = \left|\frac{\partial \xi^i}{\partial x^j}\right| = \text{Det}\left(\frac{\partial \xi^i}{\partial x^j}\right) = \frac{\partial(\xi^1, \xi^2, \cdots, \xi^n)}{\partial(x^1, x^2, \cdots, x^n)} \neq 0 \tag{21–4}$$

and the inverse is then

$$dx^j = \frac{\partial x^j}{\partial \xi^k}\, d\xi^k \tag{21–5}$$

(because):

$$\frac{\partial \xi^l}{\partial x_j}\frac{\partial x^i}{\partial \xi^l} = \frac{\partial x^i}{\partial x_j} = \delta^i_j = \frac{\partial \xi^i}{\partial x^l}\frac{\partial x^l}{\partial \xi^j} \tag{21–6}$$

Volume Element

Since $dV = \prod_1^n dx^i$ can be regarded as the determinant of the diagonal matrix, $\delta_{IJ}\, dx^I$, (where I is *not* summed), it follows from (21–3) that

$$dV_\xi = \prod_1^n d\xi^j = \left|\frac{\partial \xi^i}{\partial x^j}\right| \prod_1^n dx^i = \left|\frac{\partial \xi^i}{\partial x^j}\right| dV_x = J\, dV_x \tag{21–7}$$

(Note that a "singular transformation," with $J \equiv 0$, gives $dV_\xi \equiv 0$; such transformations "collapse" finite volumes.)

Arc Lengths

If the x^i are Cartesian coordinates

$$(ds)^2 \overset{c}{=} dx^i\, dx^i = \frac{\partial x^i}{\partial \xi^k}\frac{\partial x^i}{\partial \xi^l}\, d\xi^k\, d\xi^l \tag{21–8}$$

or

$$\boxed{(ds)^2 = \bar{g}_{ij}\, d\xi^i\, d\xi^j} \tag{21–9}$$

where

$$\bar{g}_{ij} = \bar{g}_{ji} \overset{c}{=} \frac{\partial x^l}{\partial \xi^i}\frac{\partial x^l}{\partial \xi^j} = \frac{\partial x^l}{\partial \xi^i}\frac{\partial x^k}{\partial \xi^j}\delta_{lk} \tag{21–10}$$

From (21–10),

$$\bar{g} \equiv \text{Det}\,(\bar{g}_{ij}) \overset{c}{=} J^2 = \left[\left|\frac{\partial x^i}{\partial \xi^j}\right|\right]^2 \tag{21–11}$$

Vectors

Letting all $\mathrm{d}\xi^i = 0$ except $\mathrm{d}\xi^I$ and regarding (21–5) as $\mathbf{dr} = \dfrac{\partial \mathbf{r}}{\partial \xi^I}\,\mathrm{d}\xi^I$ (not summed), we see that $\partial x^i/\partial \xi^I$ can be regarded as the ith (Cartesian) component of a "local *basis* vector", $\mathbf{u}_I$ which points in the direction of the motion generated when ξ^I alone is changed. The local basis vectors are independent (if $J \neq 0$) but are not in general orthogonal (nor of unit length). It is therefore necessary (compare (10–52)–(10–54)) to introduce also the reciprocal basis vectors, $\mathbf{v}^k$, which, in fact, are given by:

$$\left.\begin{aligned} &\mathbf{v}^k \overset{c}{=} \nabla \xi^k \quad \text{(the normal to the surface, } \xi^k = \text{constant)} \\ &\mathbf{u}_i \overset{c}{=} \frac{\partial}{\partial \xi^i}\,\mathbf{r} \quad \begin{pmatrix}\text{tangent to the curve: } \xi^1 = \text{const}, \cdots, \\ \xi^{i-1} = \text{const}, \xi^{i+1} = \text{const}, \cdots, \xi^n = \text{const}\end{pmatrix} \\ &\mathbf{u}_i \cdot \mathbf{v}^k = \delta_i^{\ k} \end{aligned}\right\} \tag{21–12}$$

Any vector then has two types of components,

$$a_i \hat{x}^i \overset{c}{=} \mathbf{a} = \bar{a}_i \mathbf{v}^i = \bar{a}^i \mathbf{u}_i \tag{21–13}$$

where:

$$\left.\begin{aligned} &\boxed{\bar{a}^i = \frac{\partial \xi^i}{\partial x^k}\,a^k} = \mathbf{a} \cdot \mathbf{v}^i \quad \text{("contravariant components")} \\ &\boxed{\bar{a}_i = \frac{\partial x^l}{\partial \xi^i}\,a_l} = \mathbf{a} \cdot \mathbf{u}_i \quad \text{("covariant components")} \end{aligned}\right\} \tag{21–14}$$

(where, if x^i are Cartesian, $a^k \overset{c}{=} a_k$). Then,

$$|a|^2 = \bar{a}^i \bar{a}_i; \qquad \mathbf{a} \cdot \mathbf{b} = \bar{a}^i \bar{b}_i = \bar{a}_i \bar{b}^i \tag{21–15}$$

and either type of component determines the other:

$$\bar{a}_i = \bar{g}_{ik} \bar{a}^k; \qquad \bar{a}^j = \bar{g}^{jl} \bar{a}_l \tag{21–16}$$

where we have defined

$$\left.\begin{aligned} &\bar{g}^{lj} = \bar{g}^{jl} = \text{matrix inverse of } \bar{g}_{ji} \\ &\bar{g}^{jl} \bar{g}_{lk} = \delta^j_{\ k} \equiv \bar{g}^j_{\ k} \end{aligned}\right\} \tag{21–17}$$

In terms of the basis vectors,

$$\bar{g}_{ik} = \mathbf{u}_i \cdot \mathbf{u}_k; \qquad \bar{g}^{ik} = \mathbf{v}^i \cdot \mathbf{v}^k \overset{c}{=} \nabla \xi^i \cdot \nabla \xi^k$$

A gradient may also be regarded as a vector. Its new components also are of two types:

$$(\overline{\nabla \phi})_i = \frac{\partial \phi}{\partial \xi^i} = \frac{\partial x^k}{\partial \xi^i}\frac{\partial \phi}{\partial x^k}; \qquad \bar{g}^{il}\frac{\partial \phi}{\partial \xi^l} = (\overline{\nabla \phi})^i \tag{21–18}$$

Note that the "free" index is a subscript for the "covariant" components and a superscript for the "contravariant" components, in accord with the convention adopted above.

Tensors

By definition, a tensor of the second order, $T_k^{\ i}$, (Cartesian components, for the moment) has the property that for any vector, $\mathbf{a}$, the quantities, $b_k = T_k^{\ i} a_i$, must always form a vector, **b**. The components, $\bar{T}_k{}^i$, in the ξ-coordinates must satisfy a similar condition,

$$\frac{\partial x^l}{\partial \xi^k} T_l{}^j a_j = \frac{\partial x^l}{\partial \xi^k} b_l = \bar{b}_k = \bar{T}_k{}^i \bar{a}_i = \bar{T}_k{}^i \frac{\partial x^j}{\partial \xi^i} a_j$$

which must hold for arbitrary a_j. (This, indeed, is the meaning of "$\mathbf{a} \cdot \mathfrak{T} = \mathbf{b}$ where **b** is a *vector* for an arbitrary *vector* **a**".) Then, by (21–6),

$$\bar{T}_k{}^j = \frac{\partial x^m}{\partial \xi^k} \frac{\partial \xi^j}{\partial x^n} T_m{}^n \tag{21–19}$$

Corresponding to the free choice of two types of vector-components, the tensor, $\mathfrak{T}$, has a total of four types of components; the other three are, similarly,

$$\left.\begin{aligned} \bar{T}^{ij} = \frac{\partial \xi^i}{\partial x^m} \frac{\partial \xi^j}{\partial x^n} T^{mn}; \qquad \bar{T}^k{}_j = \frac{\partial \xi^k}{\partial x^m} \frac{\partial x^n}{\partial \xi^j} T^m{}_n \\ \bar{T}_{ij} = \frac{\partial x^m}{\partial \xi^i} \frac{\partial x^n}{\partial \xi^j} T_{mn} \end{aligned}\right\} \tag{21–20}$$

where, for Cartesian x^i,

$$T_{mn} \overset{c}{=} T^{mn} \overset{c}{=} T^m{}_n \overset{c}{=} T_m{}^n$$

Note that in all of these relations, T "acts as if" it were a product of vector components $\mathfrak{T} = \mathbf{ab}$. This also extends to the connections between the various components:

$$\bar{T}^{ik} = \bar{g}^{il} \bar{T}_l{}^k; \qquad \bar{T}_i{}^k = \bar{g}_{il} \bar{T}^{lk}; \qquad \text{etc.} \tag{21–21}$$

Convention Given $\bar{T}_{km}$, it is common practice to introduce the symbols, $\bar{T}_k{}^m$, $\bar{T}^k{}_m$, $\bar{T}^{km}$, without explicit definition, it being understood that these are interrelated by multiplication with appropriate $\bar{g}_{ik}$ or $\bar{g}^{ik}$ factors, as in (21–21).

Tensors of general order: Using the *definition** that a scalar product of a tensor of any order with an arbitrary vector always yields a tensor of the next lowest order, it is easily proved by induction that the transformation law is,

$$\bar{T}^{\cdots l \cdots\cdots}_{\cdots\cdots m \cdots} = \cdots \frac{\partial \xi^l}{\partial x^k} \cdots \frac{\partial x^j}{\partial \xi^m} \cdots T^{\cdots k \cdots\cdots}_{\cdots\cdots j \cdots} \tag{21–22}$$

(that is, each index transforms as if it were attached to a vector) and that various possible types of components are interrelated by the "index raising" and "index lowering" operations typified by (21–21).

Compounded Arbitrary Coordinate Transformations

If we introduce the further transformation,

$$\eta^i = \eta^i(\xi^1, \xi^2, \cdots, \xi^n)$$

then it is hardly surprising (and easily checked formally) that all the above equalities (except those written "$\overset{c}{=}$") remain valid between η and ξ as well as between ξ and x.

* In some developments, (21–22) is used as the definition of a tensor and the property here used is called the "quotient theorem"; the two properties are equivalent—indeed each says that a tensor acts like a product of vector components.

In particular, since $(ds)^2$ in (21–9) is, by its very meaning, invariant, it follows that $\bar{g}_{ik}$ is a tensor and that

$$g'_{ik} = \frac{\partial \xi^l}{\partial \eta^i}\frac{\partial \xi^m}{\partial \eta^k}\bar{g}_{lm}$$

and similarly for $\bar{g}^{ik}$ and $\bar{g}^i{}_k = \delta^i{}_k$. Hence:

$$\frac{\sqrt{\pm g'}}{\sqrt{\pm \bar{g}}} = \frac{\partial(\xi^1, \xi^2, \cdots, \xi^n)}{\partial(\eta^1, \eta^2, \cdots, \eta^n)}$$

and therefore (compare (21–11)),

$$dV = \sqrt{\pm \bar{g}}\prod_1^n d\xi^t = \sqrt{\pm g'}\prod_1^n d\eta^j \tag{21–23}$$

is invariant, as of course it must be.

Properties of Tensors

By using the definition or the property (21–22) as required, one easily proves:

(1) The sum of (the same types of components of) two tensors of the same type is again a tensor of the same type.

(2) The (matrix) product, *when* taken over one upper and one lower index, of two tensors of any type is again a tensor.

(3) The ordinary product (without summation) of any two tensors is again a tensor.

(4) If an upper and lower index of a tensor are set equal (and therefore summed), the result is a tensor (whose order is lower by 2). This operation is called "contraction".

(5) Any relation between tensors (built up from the above operations) remains valid (in the new components) under any transformation of coordinates.

(6) $\bar{g}_{ij}$, $\bar{g}^{ij}$, $\delta^i{}_j$ are tensors, whose components in Cartesian coordinates are all δ_{ij}. (Hence, multiplication by $\bar{g}^{ij}$ or $\bar{g}_{ij}$—raising or lower indices—again yields a tensor.)

Property (5) is the basic expression of the "geometric reality" of tensors (at least in ordinary space). In any case, it is very powerful:

If a relation reduces to a true relation in any one set of coordinates and is also a relation between tensors, then it is true in any coordinates.

Covariant Derivatives

Not all "indexed symbols" are tensors. For example, the tensor whose components in Cartesian coordinates are $\partial a_i/\partial x^k$ (for some vector, **a**) will *not* in general have components $\partial \bar{a}_i/\partial \xi^k$ in arbitrary coordinates.

Indeed, by differentiating and rearranging (21–14),

$$\frac{\partial \bar{a}_i}{\partial \xi^k} - \frac{\partial^2 x^s}{\partial \xi^i \partial \xi^k}\frac{\partial \xi^t}{\partial x^s}\bar{a}_t = \frac{\partial x^m}{\partial \xi^i}\frac{\partial x^n}{\partial \xi^k}\frac{\partial a_m}{\partial x^n} \tag{21–24}$$

We are at liberty, however, to define a tensor whose Cartesian coordinates are $\partial a_i/\partial x^k$ and (21–24) then shows that its ξ-components (which we call $\bar{a}_{i;k}$) must be

$$\boxed{\bar{a}_{i;k} = \frac{\partial \bar{a}_i}{\partial \xi^k} - \Gamma^s_{ik}\bar{a}_s} \tag{21–25}$$

where, for Cartesian x^i,

$$\Gamma^s_{ik} \stackrel{c}{=} \frac{\partial \xi^s}{\partial x^l}\frac{\partial^2 x^l}{\partial \xi^i \partial \xi^k} \stackrel{c}{=} \mathbf{v}^s \cdot \frac{\partial \mathbf{u}_i}{\partial \xi^k} \tag{21–26}$$

The Γ^s_{ik} can also be written entirely in terms of $\bar{g}_{ik}$,

$$\boxed{\Gamma^j_{ik} = \Gamma^j_{ki} = \tfrac{1}{2}\bar{g}^{jl}\left(\frac{\partial \bar{g}_{il}}{\partial \xi^k} + \frac{\partial \bar{g}_{kl}}{\partial \xi^i} - \frac{\partial \bar{g}_{ik}}{\partial \xi^l}\right)} \tag{21–27}$$

In (21–24), the two terms on the left are, individually, *not* tensors, but their difference is a tensor, by construction, as may also be readily shown from the transformation law* for the Γ^i_{kl} namely,

$$\Gamma'^j_{ik} = \frac{\partial \xi^r}{\partial \eta^i}\frac{\partial \xi^s}{\partial \eta^k}\frac{\partial \eta^j}{\partial \xi^t}\Gamma^t_{rs} + \frac{\partial \eta^j}{\partial \xi^s}\frac{\partial^2 \xi^s}{\partial \eta^i \partial \eta^k} \tag{21–28}$$

Similarly, another type of component for $\nabla \mathbf{a}$ is

$$\boxed{\bar{a}^i{}_{;k} = \frac{\partial \bar{a}^i}{\partial \xi^k} + \Gamma^i_{kl}\bar{a}^l} \tag{21–29}$$

(The remaining two types of components are seldom used.)

The expressions (21–25) and (21–29) are called the "*covariant derivatives*" of $\bar{a}^i$ and $\bar{a}_i$. Analogously, the covariant derivative of an arbitrary tensor may be derived from the transformation laws and it is found that there is a Γ-term for each index (just as if the tensor were a product of vector components). In analogous notation,†

$$\bar{T}^{\cdots i \cdots}_{\cdots k \cdots ;l} = \frac{\partial}{\partial \xi^l}\bar{T}^{\cdots i \cdots}_{\cdots k \cdots} + \cdots \Gamma^i_{lr}\bar{T}^{\cdots r \cdots}_{\cdots k \cdots} - \cdots \Gamma^r_{kl}\bar{T}^{\cdots i \cdots}_{\cdots r \cdots} \tag{21–30}$$

In particular, even though the Γ^i_{jk} do not vanish, we always have

$$\bar{g}_{ik;l} = 0 = \bar{g}^{ik}{}_{;l} \tag{21–31}$$

From (21–30) and (21–31) it follows that

—Covariant differentiation of a product satisfies the same rule as ordinary differentiation. (For example, $(a^i b_k)_{;j} = a^i{}_{;j}b_k + a^i b_{k;j}$.)

—Indices can be raised or lowered in a covariant derivative without regard to the "nature" of the index. (For example, $\bar{g}^{ik}\bar{a}_{k;m} = \bar{a}^i{}_{;m}$.)

Space Curves

At the risk of confusion, it is common to use x^i or ξ^i to denote also the *functions* of arc length which define the curve (in parametric form):

$$\mathscr{C}: \quad x^i = x^i(s); \quad \xi^j = \xi^j(s)$$

---

* The Γ^i_{kl} are often called the "affine connection" because they do transform like tensors under affine (linear) coordinate transformations.

† A similar notation is often used for ordinary derivatives:

$$\frac{\partial a^i}{\partial x^k} = a^i{}_{,k} = \partial_k a^i.$$

The tangent vector is then

$$\bar{\tau}^i = \frac{d\xi^i}{ds} \tag{21–32}$$

(It is a vector by (21–3).) The curvature vector, often called the "geodesic curvature", is

$$\bar{\kappa}^j = \frac{d\xi^l}{ds}\left(\frac{d\xi^j}{ds}\right)_{;l} = \frac{d^2\xi^j}{ds^2} + \bar{\Gamma}^j_{st}\frac{d\xi^s}{ds}\frac{d\xi^t}{ds} \tag{21–33}$$

(Proof: this expression is correct in Cartesian coordinates—where $\Gamma = 0$—and it is a tensor; therefore it is correct in any coordinates.) The condition, $\bar{\kappa}^j = 0$, is easily shown to be equivalent to the requirement, $\delta\int_1^2 ds = 0$, for any two points on $\mathscr{C}$.

Standard Operators

The Laplace operator is

$$\nabla^2\phi = \bar{g}^{ik}\left(\frac{\partial\phi}{\partial\xi^i}\right)_{;k} \tag{21–34}$$

(reduces to the correct form in Cartesian coordinates and, because it is a tensor, is therefore correct in general). This can also be written,

$$\nabla^2\phi = \frac{1}{\sqrt{\bar{g}}}\frac{\partial}{\partial\xi^j}\left(\bar{g}^{jk}\sqrt{\bar{g}}\,\frac{\partial\phi}{\partial\xi^k}\right) \tag{21–35}$$

by using the relation,

$$\Gamma^i_{ir} = \frac{\partial}{\partial\xi^r}\ln\sqrt{\bar{g}} \tag{21–36}$$

The divergence is similarly

$$\nabla\cdot\mathbf{a} = \bar{a}^i{}_{;i} = \frac{1}{\sqrt{\bar{g}}}\frac{\partial(\sqrt{\bar{g}}\,\bar{a}^i)}{\partial\xi^i} \tag{21–37}$$

Directional derivatives become,

$$\mathbf{c} = (\mathbf{b}\cdot\nabla)\mathbf{a} \quad \text{reads:} \quad \bar{c}^i = \bar{b}^k\bar{a}^i{}_{;k} \quad \text{or} \quad \bar{c}_i = \bar{b}^k\bar{a}_{i;k} \tag{21–38}$$

Curl: In general, this name is used for the second-order tensor,

$$\bar{a}_{i;k} - \bar{a}_{k;i} = \frac{\partial\bar{a}_i}{\partial\xi^k} - \frac{\partial\bar{a}_k}{\partial\xi^i}$$

The analogy lies in the fact that in three dimensions and in Cartesian coordinates, this matrix takes the form,

0	c_z	$-c_y$
$-c_z$	0	c_x
c_y	$-c_x$	0

where $\mathbf{c} = \nabla\times\mathbf{a}$

This identification of an antisymmetric second-order tensor with a vector is possible only in three dimensions. The "vector product" could be similarly generalized, but this is seldom used.

Note on (classical) moving coordinates: The time variable of classical physics plays a *dual* role when moving coordinates are used. It is both a parameter specifying the coordinate-transformation "of the moment" and also a parameter specifying the position (of a mass-point, say) along a space-curve. Thus t is more than merely a fourth coordinate. Moreover, since the metric, $(\mathrm{d}s)^2$, is independent of $\mathrm{d}t$, the metric tensor, g_{ik}, would be singular if an attempt were made to adjoin t as another coordinate. Thus, especially since this picture is used only in classical physics, it is preferable to treat the subject only by classical vector analysis.

RIEMANNIAN GEOMETRY

Up to this point, in order to emphasize the intuitive geometric basis of the concepts, we have been considering arbitrary coordinates in Euclidean space (which is characterized by the possibility of using Cartesian coordinates wherein the Pythagorean theorem, $\mathrm{d}s^2 = \mathrm{d}x_i\, \mathrm{d}x^i$, holds).

Riemannian geometry has its intuitive origins in the properties of two-dimensional curved surfaces in this ordinary three-dimensional space. It is perhaps surprising that the entire geometry of such a surface is described by its "metric tensor", g_{ik}, alone; appeal need not (otherwise) be made to the larger "imbedding" space. The following concepts are then an extension (by analogy, of course) of these ideas of "internal" geometry to "spaces" of any dimension.

A Riemann space is a set of n "coordinates", x^i, with a metric (notion of length) *defined* by

$$(\mathrm{d}s)^2 = g_{ik}\, \mathrm{d}x^i\, \mathrm{d}x^k$$

where the g_{ik} are any specified functions of the x^i. ($\mathrm{d}s$ need not be real; $g_{ik} = g_{ki}$ since any anti-symmetric part would cancel in $\mathrm{d}s$.)

Coordinate transformations can be introduced precisely as before, and it is part of the definition of $\mathrm{d}s$ that it is invariant under such transformations ("$\mathrm{d}s$ is a scalar"). Then the transformation laws, (21–3) and (21–5), are a simple consequence of calculus, and the postulated invariance of $\mathrm{d}s$ can then be used to show that

$$\bar{g}_{ik} = \frac{\partial x^s}{\partial \bar{x}^i}\frac{\partial x^t}{\partial \bar{x}^k} g_{st}$$

g^{ik} is defined as the matrix inverse of g_{ik} and is also a tensor.

A "vector" may then be defined as any set of n quantities which transform according to the same rules as either $\mathrm{d}x^i$ (contravariant) or $g_{ij}\, \mathrm{d}x^j$ (covariant);* and tensors may be defined as any quantities with a transformation law like that of a product of vector components. The entire earlier machinery (except only those relations written "$\overset{c}{=}$") then goes through with these more abstract notions. Indeed, it might appear that the abstract concept is not more general than the concrete, but an important difference arises as follows.

In non-Euclidean spaces, the order of successive covariant differentiations *cannot* be interchanged. Indeed, it is readily shown that

$$a_{n;ij} - a_{n;ji} = a_s R^s{}_{nij} \tag{21–39}$$

where†

$$R^s{}_{nij} = \Gamma^t_{nj}\Gamma^s_{ti} - \Gamma^r_{ni}\Gamma^s_{rj} + \frac{\partial}{\partial \xi^i}\Gamma^s_{jn} - \frac{\partial}{\partial \xi^j}\Gamma^s_{ni} \tag{21–40}$$

is the "Riemann–Christoffel curvature tensor". (It is a tensor since the left side of (21–39) is a tensor and a_s is arbitrary.) In Euclidean spaces, $R^s{}_{nij} \equiv 0$, for this is

* It is common to speak of A^i as "a contravariant vector" but nevertheless, A^i and A_i are to be regarded as two types of components for the *same* "geometric vector", **A**.

† The notation is not standard as regards the order of the indices. (In the standard works on relativity, Tolman and Eddington use (21–40) while Bergman reverses the order and writes $R_{jin}{}^s$ for the right side of (21–40).)

true in Cartesian coordinates and $R^s{}_{nij}$ is a tensor. Conversely, it may be shown that if $R^s{}_{nij} = 0$ then it must be possible to introduce Cartesian coordinates,* so that the space is "flat". (The basic idea of the proof is that $a_{n;ji} = a_{n;ij}$ are the integrability conditions for the set of partial differential equations, $a_{n;j} = 0$.)

It can also be shown that $R^s{}_{ijk}$ (and functions formed from it by standard operations) is the most general tensor which can be formed from g_{ik} and its first two derivatives.

Two (non-trivial) further tensors can be formed from $R^s{}_{ijk}$ by contraction:

$$\left.\begin{aligned} R_{kj} &= R_{jk} = R^s{}_{jks} \\ &= \Gamma^n_{jm}\Gamma^m_{kn} - \frac{\partial}{\partial \xi^m}\Gamma^m_{jk} + \frac{\partial^2}{\partial \xi^j \partial \xi^k}\ln\sqrt{g} - \Gamma^n_{jk}\frac{\partial \ln\sqrt{g}}{\partial \xi^n} \end{aligned}\right\} \tag{21–41}$$

$$R = R^j{}_j = g^{jk}R_{jk} \tag{21–42}$$

("Gaussian curvature"). Of course, $R = 0$ does *not* in general imply $R^s{}_{ijk} = 0$.

Further properties of the curvature tensor are:

$$R^s{}_{ijk} = -R^s{}_{ikj} \tag{21–43}$$

$$R_{mlik} = -R_{lmik} \qquad (= g_{mn}R^n{}_{lik}) \tag{21–44}$$

$$R_{mlik} = R_{ikml} \tag{21–45}$$

$$R^s{}_{ijk} + R^s{}_{jki} + R^s{}_{kij} = 0 \tag{21–46}$$

(Note the cyclic permutation of the lower indices.)

$$R^s{}_{nij;k} + R^s{}_{njk;i} + R^s{}_{nki;j} = 0 \tag{21–47}$$

whence

$$(R^{ls} - \tfrac{1}{2}g^{ls}R)_{;s} = 0 \tag{21–48}$$

The number of independent components of $R^s{}_{ijk}$ in a space of n dimensions is $n^2(n^2 - 1)/12$. Thus, in two dimensions,

$$R^n{}_{lki} = \tfrac{1}{2}(\delta^n_i g_{kl} - \delta^n_k g_{il})R \tag{21–49}$$

and in three dimensions,

$$R^n{}_{lki} = \delta^n_i R_{kl} - \delta^n_k R_{il} + g_{kl}R_i{}^n - g_{il}R_k{}^n - \tfrac{1}{2}(\delta^n_i g_{kl} - \delta^n_k g_{il})R \tag{21–50}$$

Geodesics are curves, $x^i = x^i(s)$ whose curvature vector, κ^i, vanishes everywhere:

$$\frac{d^2x^i}{ds^2} + \Gamma^i_{kl}\frac{dx^k}{ds}\frac{dx^l}{ds} = 0 \tag{21–51}$$

These are also the conditions for the arc-length, $\int_1^2 ds$, between any two points on the curve to be a minimum (or a maximum—compare the great circles on a sphere).

Tensor densities are an occasionally used extension of the tensor concept. A "tensor density of weight, W" is an indexed quantity which transforms according to (21–22) modified by addition of a factor,

$$\left[\operatorname{Det}\frac{\partial x^i}{\partial \bar{x}^j}\right]^W$$

on the right of (21–22).

---

* If $(ds)^2$ can take negative values, then "Cartesian coordinates" are coordinates in which $g_{Ik} = \delta_{Ik}\epsilon_I$ (not summed), where $\epsilon_I = \pm 1$.

EXAMPLE: In three dimensions, the e^{ijk} symbol used in determinant theory, namely,

$$e^{ijk} = \begin{cases} 0, & \text{unless } i, j, k \text{ are all different} \\ \pm 1, & \text{according as } i, j, k \text{ is an } \begin{smallmatrix}\text{even}\\ \text{odd}\end{smallmatrix} \text{ permutation of } 1, 2, 3. \end{cases}$$

is a tensor-density of weight one (note the effect of reversing the x-axis). Consequently, the vector cross-product and curl,

$$\left.\begin{aligned} c^r &= e^{rmn} a_m b_n \qquad (\mathbf{c} = \mathbf{a} \times \mathbf{b}) \\ C^r &= -e^{rst} a_{s;t} \qquad (\mathbf{C} = \nabla \times \mathbf{a}) \end{aligned}\right\} \tag{21–52}$$

are "vector densities of weight one".

Special terminology used in four dimensions:

In four dimensions (*only*):

1. A completely anti-symmetric second-order tensor has six independent elements. This is called a "*six-vector*" or sometimes merely a "tensor" without further explanation.
2. A completely anti-symmetric third-order tensor has four independent components and is often called a "*pseudo-vector*" since these components reverse sign under coordinate reflections. (Compare the three-dimensional vector cross product.)
3. A completely anti-symmetric tensor of the fourth order has but one independent component which also reverses sign under coordinate reflections. This component is called a "*pseudo-scalar*".

NON-RIEMANNIAN GEOMETRY

The process of generalization can be carried still further. In this new abstraction, the existence of the metric tensor, g_{ik}, is not required. (There *is* an intrinsic metric, or notion of length, but this emerges only later.) Rather the "raw material" is:

1. A set of n coordinates (independent variables), $x^1, x^2, \cdots, x^n$.
2. "Vectors" which transform by (21–14)—for example the dx^i.
3. A set of quantities, L^i_{jk} (the "connection") which transform by (21–28) but $L^i_{kj} \neq L^i_{jk}$ in general.

The "geometric" ideas are introduced via the (ad hoc) concept that the covariant ("true") derivative of a contravariant vector is given by

$$a^i{}_{|k} = \frac{\partial a^i}{\partial x^k} + L^i_{lk} a^l \tag{21–53}$$

This is easily proved to be a tensor.

The basic concept is then that of parallel displacement of a vector along a curve, $x^i = x^i(t)$—as motivated by the concept of the covariant derivative. The change in a^i as it is carried along $\mathscr{C}$ is $a^i{}_{|k}\, dx^k/dt$. If the final vector is to be parallel to the old, this change must be a multiple of a^i:

$$f(t) a^i = a^i{}_{|k} \frac{dx^k}{dt} \tag{21–54}$$

or

$$(a^i a^j{}_{|k} - a^j a^i{}_{|k}) \frac{dx^k}{dt} = 0 \tag{21–55}$$

An elementary but involved calculation shows that if the vector is "carried parallel to itself", in this sense, around a small closed loop of sides du, dv the (first order) change ("spherical excess") is

$$\Delta(a^i) = -a^j L^i{}_{jkl} \frac{\partial x^k}{\partial u} \frac{\partial x^l}{\partial v} \, du \, dv + \cdots$$

where

$$L^i{}_{jkl} = \frac{\partial L^i_{jl}}{\partial x^k} - \frac{\partial L^i_{jk}}{\partial x^l} + L^h_{jl} L^i_{hk} - L^h_{jk} L^i_{hl} \tag{21–56}$$

is a tensor—the curvature tensor.

A field of "parallel" vectors, u^i, would satisfy $u^i = \phi U^i$ where $U^i{}_{|k} \equiv 0$ and ϕ is a scalar function of position. Then u^i satisfy (21–55) for all curves, $x^i = x^i(t)$. The integrability-conditions for the equations, $U^i{}_{|k} = 0$ are precisely $L^i{}_{jkm} = 0$, which is thus equivalent to the existence of "Cartesian" coordinates, u^i, or to the "flatness" of the space.

Geodesics may be defined as curves whose tangent vector, dx^i/dt remains parallel to its original direction. In this particular case, (21–54) takes the form:

$$\frac{d^2x^i}{dt^2} + \Gamma^i_{jk} \frac{dx^j}{dt} \frac{dx^k}{dt} = f(t) \frac{dx^i}{dt} \tag{21–57}$$

where Γ is the symmetric part of L:

$$\Gamma^i_{jk} = \tfrac{1}{2}(L^i_{jk} + L^i_{kj}) \tag{21–58}$$

If we fix $f(t)$ in (21–57) to be the same for all geodesics, we can introduce a concept of length by setting

$$ds = dt[c \exp (\textstyle\int f \, dt)] \tag{21–59}$$

Then (21–57) becomes

$$\frac{d^2x^i}{ds^2} + \Gamma^i_{kj} \frac{dx^j}{ds} \frac{dx^k}{ds} = 0 \tag{21–60}$$

Thus s has all the usual properties of arc length (it is invariant since (21–60) is a tensor equation) except only that it need not be expressible in the Riemann form, $(ds)^2 = g_{ik} \, dx^i \, dx^k$; indeed, if $L^i_{jk} \neq L^i_{kj}$, the equations, $g_{ij|k} = 0$ are not even integrable so that a metric *tensor* will not exist even though there is a metric defined.

CHAPTER 22

GROUP THEORY

LIE GROUPS

Definitions

A Lie group is a family of coordinate-transformations,

$$\mathbf{r}' = \mathbf{\Psi}(\mathbf{r}, \boldsymbol{\alpha}); \qquad \text{or} \qquad r_i' = \Psi_i(r_1, \cdots, r_n; \alpha_1, \cdots, \alpha_k) \tag{22–1}$$

(Note that $\boldsymbol{\alpha}$ and $\mathbf{r}$ need not have the same number of components.) The individual transformation of the family is specified by $\boldsymbol{\alpha}$, and the family as a whole by the specific form of the functions, Ψ_i. Various continuity hypotheses are also required for a rigorous theory. We shall assume that $\boldsymbol{\alpha} = 0$ corresponds to the "identity transformation":

$$\mathbf{\Psi}(\mathbf{r}, 0) = \mathbf{r} \tag{22–2}$$

(as may be achieved by a change of the $\boldsymbol{\alpha}$-origin) and that each $\partial\Psi_i/\partial\alpha_j$ does not vanish when $\boldsymbol{\alpha} = 0$ (unless it is identically zero for all $\boldsymbol{\alpha}$); this can also be achieved by changing the α_i variables if necessary.*

Infinitesimal Operator

When $\boldsymbol{\alpha}$ is very small, then because of (22–2), we have for any $f(\mathbf{r})$,

$$f(\mathbf{r}') \doteq f(\mathbf{r}) + \boldsymbol{\alpha} \cdot \mathbf{U}f$$

where

$$\mathbf{U}f(\mathbf{r}) = [\mathbf{\nabla}_\alpha f(\mathbf{r}')]_{\boldsymbol{\alpha}=0} \tag{22–3}$$

That is,

$$\mathbf{U} = (\mathbf{\nabla}_\alpha \mathbf{\Psi})_0 \cdot \mathbf{\nabla}_r; \qquad U_i = \sum_l \left(\frac{\partial \Psi_l}{\partial \alpha_i}\right)_{\boldsymbol{\alpha}=0} \frac{\partial}{\partial r_l} \tag{22–4}$$

This "infinitesimal operator", *does not contain* $\boldsymbol{\alpha}$.

Nevertheless, *the operator* $\mathbf{U}$ *characterizes the entire group of transformations.* Specifically, for any $f(\mathbf{r})$,

$$f(\mathbf{r}') = e^{\boldsymbol{\alpha}\cdot\mathbf{U}} f(\mathbf{r}) = \sum_{n=0}^{\infty} \frac{1}{n!} (\boldsymbol{\alpha} \cdot \mathbf{U})^n f(\mathbf{r}) \tag{22–5}$$

(The exponential function of the operator, $\boldsymbol{\alpha} \cdot \mathbf{U}$, is defined by the last expression, wherein $(\boldsymbol{\alpha} \cdot \mathbf{U})^2 f = \boldsymbol{\alpha} \cdot \mathbf{U}(\boldsymbol{\alpha} \cdot \mathbf{U}f)$, etc.) This relation is readily verified, at least formally, by expanding $f(\mathbf{r}') = f(\mathbf{\Psi}(\mathbf{r}, \boldsymbol{\alpha}))$ in a Taylor's series in $\boldsymbol{\alpha}$. In particular,

$$\mathbf{r}' = e^{\boldsymbol{\alpha}\cdot\mathbf{U}}\, \mathbf{r} \tag{22–6}$$

are the original equations (22–1) which defined the group.†

* A more rigorous treatment of this point may be based on consideration of a general transformation of the family, $\boldsymbol{\alpha}$, and its inverse, $\boldsymbol{\beta}$ (postulated always to exist). Thus when $\boldsymbol{\epsilon}$ vanishes, $\mathbf{\Psi}[\mathbf{\Psi}(\mathbf{r}, \boldsymbol{\alpha}), \boldsymbol{\beta} + \boldsymbol{\epsilon}]$ will equal $\mathbf{r}$. The infinitesimal operator in (22–3) below is then derived by considering very small $\boldsymbol{\epsilon}$.

† We are glossing over a minor point: The relation (22–6) is always equivalent to (22–1), but the parameters, $\boldsymbol{\alpha}$, may not be the same as those originally chosen in (22–1).

The series (22–6), however, is often difficult to sum and it is frequently simpler to set $\boldsymbol{\alpha} = \alpha\mathbf{a}$ where $\mathbf{a}$ is a fixed unit vector; it then follows from the second form in (22–5) that

$$\frac{\partial \mathbf{r}'}{\partial \alpha} = e^{\boldsymbol{\alpha}\cdot\mathbf{U}}\{(\mathbf{a}\cdot\mathbf{U})\mathbf{r}\} = \{(\mathbf{a}\cdot\mathbf{U})\mathbf{r}\}_{\mathbf{r}\to\mathbf{r}'} \tag{22–7}$$

which is a set of ordinary differential equations for r_i' with parameters, a_j. The initial condition, $\mathbf{r}' = \mathbf{r}$ when $\boldsymbol{\alpha} = 0$, brings $\mathbf{r}$ into the solution.

Not all operators of the form, $\mathfrak{X}(\mathbf{r})\cdot\boldsymbol{\nabla}_r$, are necessarily infinitesimal operators of a Lie group of the form (22–1) or (22–6). It can be shown that it is necessary and sufficient that, for all $f(\mathbf{r})$,

$$(U_iU_j - U_jU_i)f(\mathbf{r}) = \sum_k c_{ijk}U_kf(\mathbf{r}) \tag{22–8}$$

where the c's are constants.

Invariant Functions

$$\left.\begin{aligned} f(\mathbf{r}') &= f(\mathbf{r}) && \text{if and only if} \\ U_if(\mathbf{r}) &\equiv 0 && \text{(all } i) \end{aligned}\right\} \tag{22–9}$$

The invariant functions are therefore essentially unique. Conversely, they determine the group.

Invariant Families of Surfaces

$g(\mathbf{r}) = C$ (a constant) implies $g(\mathbf{r}') = C'$ (*another* constant) if and only if the families, $U_ig = C_i$ are each the same as the family, $g = C$.

Invariant Equations

A subtle point is involved here; $U_if(\mathbf{r}) = 0$ is necessary if $f(\mathbf{r}) = 0$ is to imply $f(\mathbf{r}') = 0$, but $U_if = 0$ may be a *consequence* of $f(\mathbf{r}) = 0$—as, for example, when $U_if(\mathbf{r}) = f(\mathbf{r})$. The precise theorem is:

The equation, $f(\mathbf{r}) = 0$, is invariant under all transformations of the group if and only if it is equivalent to a relation of the form,

$$G[f_1(\mathbf{r}), f_2(\mathbf{r}), \cdots, f_k(\mathbf{r})] = 0$$

where the $f_i(\mathbf{r})$ are (independent) solutions of (22–9).

Examples of Lie groups

(1) Translations in space:

$$\mathbf{U} = \boldsymbol{\nabla}; \qquad \boldsymbol{\alpha} = \text{displacement}$$

$$\mathbf{r}' = \mathbf{r} + \boldsymbol{\alpha}$$

Here, equation (22–4) is Taylor's series:

$$f(\mathbf{r} + \boldsymbol{\alpha}) = e^{\boldsymbol{\alpha}\cdot\boldsymbol{\nabla}} f(\mathbf{r}) \tag{22–10}$$

(2) Uniform magnifications:

$$U = \mathbf{r}\cdot\boldsymbol{\nabla}; \qquad \mathbf{r}' = e^{\alpha}\mathbf{r}$$

$$f(e^{\alpha}\mathbf{r}) = e^{\alpha\mathbf{r}\cdot\boldsymbol{\nabla}} f(\mathbf{r}) \tag{22–11}$$

(3) Rotations in space:

$\mathbf{U} = \mathbf{r} \times \nabla$

$\boldsymbol{\alpha}$ = vector along the axis of rotation with $|\boldsymbol{\alpha}|$ = angle of rotation (in radians) clockwise looking out along $\boldsymbol{\alpha}$.

$$\mathbf{r}' = \mathbf{r} + (\boldsymbol{\alpha} \times \mathbf{r}) \frac{\sin \alpha}{\alpha} + \boldsymbol{\alpha} \times (\boldsymbol{\alpha} \times \mathbf{r}) \frac{1 - \cos \alpha}{\alpha^2} = e^{\boldsymbol{\alpha} \cdot (\mathbf{r} \times \nabla)} \mathbf{r} \qquad (22\text{–}12)$$

Note that (since $\mathbf{U}$ contains $\mathbf{r}$), if $\boldsymbol{\alpha}_1$ and $\boldsymbol{\alpha}_2$ are two such transformations, then $\exp(\boldsymbol{\alpha}_1 \cdot \mathbf{U}) \exp(\boldsymbol{\alpha}_2 \cdot \mathbf{U}) \neq \exp[(\boldsymbol{\alpha}_1 + \boldsymbol{\alpha}_2) \cdot \mathbf{U}]$.

(4) The Lorentz group:

$$\mathbf{U} = ct\nabla + \frac{\mathbf{r}}{c} \frac{\partial}{\partial t}; \qquad \boldsymbol{\alpha} = -\frac{\mathbf{v}}{v} \tanh^{-1}\left(\frac{v}{c}\right)$$

$$\left.\begin{aligned} \mathbf{r}' &= \mathbf{r} - \mathbf{v}\left\{\frac{\mathbf{r} \cdot \mathbf{v}}{v^2}\left(1 - \frac{1}{\sqrt{1 - v^2/c^2}}\right) + \frac{t}{\sqrt{1 - v^2/c^2}}\right\} = e^{\boldsymbol{\alpha} \cdot \mathbf{U}}\, \mathbf{r} \\ t' &= \frac{t - \dfrac{(\mathbf{v} \cdot \mathbf{r})}{c^2}}{\sqrt{1 - v^2/c^2}} = e^{\boldsymbol{\alpha} \cdot \mathbf{U}}\, t \end{aligned}\right\} \qquad (22\text{–}13)$$

These have been written in classical three-space notation, but the "basic space" of (22–1) above is really $(\mathbf{r}, t)$; the group is one of rotations in four-space and has three parameters.

(5) Temporal development of time-independent systems:

If

$$\frac{dy_i}{dt} = g_i(y_1, \cdots, y_n)$$

(Recall that higher order equations can be put in this form by (14–14).) And if $y_i(0) = Y_{0i}$ then

$$y_i(t) = e^{tU} Y_{0i}$$

where

$$U = \sum_i g_i(Y_{01}, \cdots, Y_{0n}) \frac{\partial}{\partial Y_{0i}} \qquad (22\text{–}14)$$

The group is one-parameter and effects the transformations $y_i(0) \to y_i(t)$. Note that the g_i must be independent of t.

Improper (Heuristic) Examples

(a) Diffusion equation:

$$\frac{\partial T}{\partial t} = h\nabla^2 T$$

By analogy with (5), we expect

$$T(\mathbf{r}, t) = e^{th\nabla^2} T(\mathbf{r}, 0) \qquad (22\text{–}15)$$

and this is indeed a formal solution.

(b) Wave equation:

$$\frac{\partial^2 \phi}{\partial t^2} = \nabla^2 \phi = \frac{\partial \psi}{\partial t}; \qquad \frac{\partial \phi}{\partial t} = \psi$$

$$\phi(\mathbf{r}, 0) = \phi_0(\mathbf{r})$$

$$\left.\frac{\partial \phi}{\partial t}\right|_{t=0} = \psi_0(\mathbf{r})$$

Formal solution suggested by (5):

$$\left.\begin{aligned}\phi &= \phi_0 + t\psi_0 + \frac{t^2}{2!}\nabla^2\phi_0 + \frac{t^3}{3!}\nabla^2\psi_0 + \cdots \\ &= (\cosh t\nabla)\phi_0 + \left(\frac{\sinh t\nabla}{\nabla}\right)\psi_0\end{aligned}\right\} \tag{22-16}$$

FORMAL GROUP THEORY

Introduction

In its physical applications, group theory may be said (with more brevity than accuracy) to be a formalization and extension of arguments usually dismissed in the phrase, "by symmetry". Its greater precision makes possible deeper arguments and more precise conclusions, often rather surprising ones. It is hardly a panacea, but some results would be virtually inaccessible without it.

The present summary is entirely restricted to aspects found useful in applications. The justification is that the subject and its anciliary concepts range so widely that little more than a brief summary is possible here.

Intuitive examples of a group: The main applications of group theory concern classes of transformations or "motions" such as those which send a crystal or a molecule into a position indistinguishable from its original position (for example, the rotation of a cube by 120° about a main diagonal). The transformations are the "elements" (members) of a group consisting of all such transformations (for a given object). The "product" of two such transformations denotes the overall-transformation generated by the successive application of the individual transformations.

Formal Definitions

1. A group, $\mathscr{G}$, is a set of things $A, B, C, \cdots$ (called "elements") any two of which can be combined by an operation (called "multiplication") to yield a third (called their "product") which, by hypothesis, is always one of the elements of the group. (In general, $AB \neq BA$.)
2. $(AB)C = A(BC)$, which is therefore written simply "ABC".
3. $\mathscr{G}$ contains an element, E, such that $EA = A$ for any A in $\mathscr{G}$. (E is called the "unit" or "identity" element.)
4. For any A in $\mathscr{G}$, there exists an element, A^{-1}, of $\mathscr{G}$ such that $A^{-1}A = E$.

Simple Results

$$A(A^{-1}) = E \tag{22-17}$$

[Proof: $AA^{-1} = EAA^{-1} = (A^{-1})^{-1}A^{-1}AA^{-1} = (A^{-1})^{-1}EA^{-1} = (A^{-1})^{-1}A^{-1} = E$.]

$$(A^{-1})^{-1} = A \tag{22-18}$$

[Proof: $A(A^{-1}) = E$.]

$$AE = A \tag{22-19}$$

[Proof: $AE = A(A^{-1}A) = EA = A$.]

$$E \quad \text{and} \quad A^{-1} \quad \text{(for given } A\text{) are unique.} \tag{22-20}$$

[Proof: If $E'X = X$ for any X, then $E' = XX^{-1} = E$. If $BA = E$ then $A^{-1} = EA^{-1} = BAA^{-1} = BE = B$.]

Rearrangement Theorems

If X runs through all elements of $\mathcal{G}$ then the following also include all elements of $\mathcal{G}$:

$$\left.\begin{matrix} AX \\ XA \end{matrix}\right\} \text{(for any fixed } A \text{ of } \mathcal{G}) \\ X^{-1}$$

[Proof: If B is any element, then take $X = A^{-1}B$ or BA^{-1} or B^{-1} respectively.]

Further Concepts

A "*subgroup*" is any subset of $\mathcal{G}$ which is itself a group (under the same "multiplication" operation). Such groups arise, for example, when alteration of a physical system reduces its symmetry.

The "*direct product*": If $\mathcal{G}$ and $\mathcal{H}$ are two groups with operations denoted by "$\cdot$" and "$\circ$", then the *ordered-pairs*, (G,H), (where G is in $\mathcal{G}$ and H is in $\mathcal{H}$) may be regarded as elements of a group under the operation: $(G_1,H_1)(G_2,H_2) = (G_1 \cdot G_2, H_1 \circ H_2)$. The postulates, 1.–4., above are easily verified. This direct-product group is denoted by $\mathcal{G} \times \mathcal{H}$.

Such groups arise, for example, on regarding two independent physical systems as a single compound system. In such cases, the elements of $\mathcal{G}$ and $\mathcal{H}$ are often independent and one may simply write GH for the elements of $\mathcal{G} \times \mathcal{H}$ and one has: $GH = HG$; $G_1H_1G_2H_2 = (G_1G_2)(H_1H_2)$.

"*Classes*": For any fixed A, the subset of elements generated by the quantities XAX^{-1} as X runs throughout $\mathcal{G}$ is called a "class"—or the class generated by A.

—Two classes are either identical or disjoint.

[Proof: If $ZAZ^{-1} = C = YBY^{-1}$, then $A = Z^{-1}YBY^{-1}Z = (Z^{-1}Y)B(Z^{-1}Y)^{-1}$ and therefore *any* XAX^{-1} equals some XBX^{-1}; similarly for the converse.]

—In a finite group, the number of elements in a class is a divisor of the total number of elements in $\mathcal{G}$.

[Proof: XAX^{-1} "covers" each element of the class (as X runs through $\mathcal{G}$) an equal number of times. Compare the previous proof.]

Thus, for finite groups, if n_i is the number of elements in the class, $\mathcal{C}_i$, if $\mathcal{C}_1, \mathcal{C}_2, \cdots, \mathcal{C}_c$ are all the distinct classes and if g is the "order" of $\mathcal{G}$, that is the total number of elements in $\mathcal{G}$, we have

$$\sum_{i=1}^{c} n_i = g; \qquad \text{each } n_i \text{ is a divisor of } g \tag{22–21}$$

Motivating Digression

Consider the eigenvalue problem (or "wave equation"):

$$L\psi = \lambda\psi \tag{22–22}$$

where L is a linear operator:

$$L(a\psi + b\phi) = aL\psi + bL\phi. \tag{22–23}$$

Let $\psi_{01}, \cdots, \psi_{0n}$ be all linearly independent solutions of (22–22) for $\lambda =$ some fixed value, λ_0.

Let L be invariant under some group, $\mathcal{G}$, of *coordinate transformations*, $R, S, T, \cdots$ (that is $RL = LR$ etc.) and also let the boundary conditions on ψ be invariant.

Then $\psi_{0i}(R\mathbf{r})$ is also a solution of (22-22) for $\lambda = \lambda_0$, but since the ψ_{0i} were all the linearly independent solutions, this new solution must be expressible in terms of the $\psi_{0j}(\mathbf{r})$:

$$\psi_{0i}(R\mathbf{r}) = \sum_j D_{ij}(R)\psi_{0j}(\mathbf{r}) \tag{22–24}$$

Whence it is easily seen that

$$D_{ki}(SR) = \sum_j D_{kj}(S)D_{ji}(R) \tag{22–25}$$

which states that the matrices defined by (22–24) multiply exactly as do the group elements. If the $D(R)$ are all different, this set of matrices is *abstractly identical* with the group $\mathcal{G}$. In general, whether or not the matrices are distinct, one says that such matrices "*represent*" $\mathcal{G}$—though perhaps not "faithfully".

If the ψ_{0i} are orthonormal, the $\psi_{0i}(R\mathbf{r})$ must also be orthonormal* and hence the matrices $D(R)$ are unitary.

It is the property (22–24), namely that the ψ_{0i} "belong to a representation of $\mathcal{G}$", which contains the fundamental reflection of any symmetry of L in the solutions of (22–22). This symmetry shows up directly in solutions for non-degenerate λ (where the D's are all unity), but its effects can be more subtle for the solutions with degenerate λ.

REPRESENTATION THEORY

Definitions

1. A "*representation*" of a group $\mathcal{G}$ is any set of matrices, $D(R)$, for each R in $\mathcal{G}$, which satisfy (22–25)—that is, which multiply in the same way as the corresponding elements of $\mathcal{G}$. In the following we further limit† the name to representations where Det $[D(R)] \neq 0$ and (for infinite groups) the numbers, $D_{ik}(R)$, are bounded. (Note that if any one determinant vanishes then all do.)

2. Two representations, $D(R)$ and $N(R)$, are said to be "*equivalent*" if there exists a matrix, M, such that (for all R in $\mathcal{G}$),

$$D(R) = M \cdot N(R) \cdot M^{-1} \tag{22–26}$$

(corresponding to the change of basis, $\phi_i = \sum_j M_{ij}\psi_j$ in (22–22)–(22–24)).

THEOREM: Any representation (in the restricted sense above) is equivalent to a *unitary* representation (that is, one whose $D(R)$ are all unitary). [Proof: If the Hermitian matrix, $H = \sum_R D(R)D^\dagger(R)$ is diagonalized by U; that is $U^{-1}HU = d$, where $d_{Ij} = h_I\delta_{Ij}$ then $h_I > 0$ and if we let $e_{Ij} = \sqrt{h_I\delta_{Ij}}$ then the matrices, $e^{-1}U^{-1}D(R)Ue$, can be shown to be unitary by using the rearrangement theorem.]

3. A representation D is said to be "*reducible*" (to $D^{(1)}$ and $D^{(2)}$) if it is equivalent to the partitioned form:

$$\begin{Vmatrix} D^{(1)}(R) & 0 \\ 0 & D^{(2)}(R) \end{Vmatrix} \tag{22–27}$$

4. The "*characters*" of a representation $D(R)$ are defined to be the sets of numbers,

$$\chi(R) = \text{Trace } D(R) = \sum_i D_{ii}(R) \tag{22–28}$$

---

* Because a coordinate transformation does not change the value of an integral.

† This limitation is almost always implied, though sometimes not stated in much of the literature.

Note that elements in the same *class* in $\mathscr{G}$ have the same characters, so that *it is sufficient to give only one example $\chi(R)$ from each class.* Since every representation is equivalent to a unitary representation and since equivalent representations have the same characters (Trace $M^{-1}DM =$ Trace D),

$$\chi(R^{-1}) = \chi^*(R) \tag{22–29}$$

If a representation is reducible, as in (22–27), then

$$\chi(R) = \chi^{(1)}(R) + \chi^{(2)}(R) \tag{22–30}$$

where $\chi^{(1)}$ and $\chi^{(2)}$ are the characters for the reduced parts of the representation.

Fundamental Theorem

The characters are of great practical importance because of the following rather surprising theorems:

—*Two representations are equivalent if and only if their character-systems are identical.*

—A representation is irreducible if and only if*

$$\sum_R |\chi(R)|^2 = g \tag{22–31}$$

where g is the order of (number of elements in) the group.

Thus many manipulations can be performed without ever considering the representations themselves; further theorems of this nature will emerge below.

Example of a Representation (for finite groups)

The "regular representation": To simplify the notation, label the rows and columns of the matrices by *elements* of the group. (The matrices are g-by-g where g is the number of elements in the group.) Then set

$$D_{RS}(T) = \begin{cases} 1, \text{ when } R = TS \\ 0, \text{ otherwise} \end{cases} \tag{22–32}$$

It is easily checked that this indeed satisfies (22–25) and in fact is unitary. It is not irreducible, for its characters are:

$$\chi(T) = \begin{cases} g, \text{ when } T = E \\ 0, \text{ otherwise} \end{cases} \tag{22–33}$$

and these do not satisfy (22–31). By (22–37) below, this representation in fact contains all irreducible representations, each of which occurs a number of times equal to its dimension.

A (trivial) example of an irreducible representation is $D(R) = 1$ for all R in $\mathscr{G}$. This is called the identity representation.

Further Theorems

We denote:

$$g = \text{number of elements in } \mathscr{G} = \text{"order of } \mathscr{G}\text{"}$$

The results below can be extended to many cases where $g = \infty$, but for simplicity they are first stated for finite g.

—The number of *non-equivalent* irreducible representations is equal to the number of distinct classes in the group.

* See (22–41)–(22–43) for the modification of (22–31) appropriate to infinite groups.

We denote representative irreducible representations by $d_{ij}^{(l)}(R)$, $l = 1, 2, 3, \cdots, c$. Since these are not uniquely determined (any equivalence transformation may be applied), we use the symbol, Γ_l, to denote the lth irreducible representation generally —or sometimes to denote a typical example.

—If h_l is the dimension of Γ_l (that is, if $d_{ij}^{(l)}(R)$ has h_l^2 components)

$$\left.\begin{array}{ll} h_l \text{ is a divisor of } g & \\ \sum_1^c h_l^2 = g & (c = \text{number of classes}) \end{array}\right\} \tag{22–34}$$

These restrictions will often completely determine the h_l; note also that $\chi^{(l)}(E) = h_l$.

—Among any complete set of non-equivalent, irreducible representations, $d_{ik}^{(l)}(R)$, $l = 1, \cdots, c$,

$$\boxed{\frac{1}{g}\sum_R d_{ik}^{(l)}(R)\, d_{KI}^{(L)}(R^{-1}) = \frac{1}{h_l}\,\delta_{lL}\delta_{iI}\delta_{kK}} \tag{22–35}$$

where h_l is the dimension of $d^{(l)}$. Hence, for the corresponding "irreducible" characters,

$$\frac{1}{g}\sum_R \chi^{(l)}(R)\chi^{(L)}(R^{-1}) = \delta_{lL} \tag{22–36}$$

Note that, since the characters are unchanged by an equivalence transformation, the "irreducible" characters $\chi^{(l)}$ are uniquely determined by specifying Γ_l; they are the same for any $d^{(l)}$.

Equation (22–36) shows how to find the irreducible constituents, Γ_l, of an arbitrary representation, D, (though not how to perform the explicit reduction). Namely if Γ_l (irred.) appears a_l times in D then, since $\chi(R) = \sum_l a_l\chi^{(l)}(R)$, it follows from (22–36) that

$$a_l = \frac{1}{g}\sum_R \chi(R)\chi^{(l)}(R^{-1}) = \frac{1}{g}\sum_R \chi^*(R)\chi^{(l)}(R) \tag{22–37}$$

also:

$$\frac{1}{g}\sum_R \chi(R)\chi(R^{-1}) = \sum_{l=1}^{c} (a_l)^2 \tag{22–38}$$

Thus, as already mentioned, *to within equivalence, the characters determine the representation completely* and also show (even when explicit irreducible representations are not known) whether a given representation is reducible or not.

Note on "Abelian groups": Abelian groups are groups in which $AB = BA$ always. It then follows, since any representation can be made unitary, that any representation can be completely diagonalized. Hence all irreducible representations are one-dimensional—that is the $d^{(l)}$ all reduce to simple numbers of the form e^{ia}. The number of such irreducible representations is equal to the order of the group (the number of elements) according to (22–34).

Direct-product Representations

Type I: If $D(R)$ and $N(R)$ are two representations of the same group, then the direct products of the respective matrices, $D(R) \times N(R)$, are a new representation of $\mathcal{G}$ (which is usually reducible even when D and N are not). Here,

$$\chi_{D\times N}(R) = \chi_D(R)\chi_N(R) \tag{22–39}$$

TYPE II: If $D(G)$ and $N(H)$ are respectively representations of different groups $\mathscr{G}$ and $\mathscr{H}$, then $D(G) \times N(H)$ is a representation of the direct-product group, $\mathscr{G} \times \mathscr{H}$. If D and N run through all irreducible representations of $\mathscr{G}$ and $\mathscr{H}$ respectively, then $D \times N$ runs through all irreducible representations of $\mathscr{G} \times \mathscr{H}$. Here,

$$\chi_{D\times N}((G,H)) = \chi_D(G)\chi_N(H) \tag{22–40}$$

Modifications for Infinite Groups

Aside from the limitation that $D_{ik}(R)$ must be bounded, we must also modify expressions like

$$\frac{1}{g}\sum_R F(R) \tag{22–41}$$

It turns out that, for countably-infinite groups, (22–41) can (for the functions F considered above) be replaced by

$$\lim_{n\to\infty}\frac{1}{n}\sum_{i=0}^{n} F(R_i) \tag{22–42}$$

For continuously-infinite groups (such as all rotations in space), this would still be meaningless; the elements must be specified by continuous parameters: $R = R(x_1, \cdots, x_n)$. We denote the inverse of this connection by $x_i = p_i(R)$. Then the analogue of (22–41) becomes the "Hurwitz integral",

$$\left.\begin{aligned} &\int_{\mathscr{G}} F(R)\,\mathrm{d}R \equiv \int\cdots\int F[R(x_1,\cdots,x_n)]g(x_1,\cdots,x_n)\,\mathrm{d}x_1\cdots\mathrm{d}x_n \\ &\text{where } g \text{ is the Jacobian,} \\ &g(R) = g(x_1,\cdots,x_n) = \lim_{S\to R^{-1}} \frac{\partial(p_1(SR), p_2(SR), \cdots, p_n(SR))}{\partial(x_1, x_2, \cdots, x_n)} \end{aligned}\right\} \tag{22–43}$$

This expression does not always converge (for the simple translation group, it does not) but it exists for many cases of physical interest. If the range of values of the parameters, $x_1, \cdots, x_n$, covers several disconnected regions, then (22–43) is to be interpreted as a sum of the integrals over such regions.

A sometimes more useful expression for the weight function is

$$g(R) = \lim_{U\to E}\left\{\frac{\partial[\cdots p_j(RU)\cdots]}{\partial[\cdots p_k(U)\cdots]}\right\}^{-1}$$

where E is the identity element of the group.

Simple examples:

—Two-dimensional rotation group:

$$g(\phi) = 1$$

(where ϕ is the angle of rotation).

—Three-dimensional rotation group:

$$g(\boldsymbol{\alpha}) = \frac{2(1 - \cos|\alpha|)}{|\alpha|^2}$$

where $\boldsymbol{\alpha}$ is defined in (22–12) except that here $|\alpha| < \pi$.

Expansion Theorems

Let $\mathscr{G}$ be a group of coordinate transformations ($\mathbf{r}' = R\mathbf{r}$, symbolically). An *arbitrary* function, $\phi(\mathbf{r})$, then satisfies,

$$\left.\begin{aligned}\phi(\mathbf{r}) &= \sum_{l=1}^{c}\sum_{k=1}^{h_l}\sum_{\mathscr{G}}\frac{h_l}{g}\,d_{kk}^{(l)}(R)\phi(R\mathbf{r})\\ &= \sum_{l=1}^{c}\sum_{\mathscr{G}}\frac{h_l}{g}\,[\chi^{(l)}(R)]\phi(R\mathbf{r})\end{aligned}\right\} \qquad (22\text{–}44)$$

Also the functions defined by (for any j),

$$\phi_k^{(l)}(\mathbf{r}) = \frac{h_l}{g}\sum_{\mathscr{G}} d_{kj}^{(l)}(R^{-1})\phi(R\mathbf{r}) \qquad (22\text{–}45)$$

satisfy ("belong to the kth row of $d^{(l)}$"),

$$\phi_j^{(l)}(R\mathbf{r}) = \sum_k d_{jk}^{(l)}(R)\,\phi_k^{(l)}(\mathbf{r}) \qquad (22\text{–}46)$$

Warning: We have side-stepped a minor complication. It might appear desirable to adopt the convention, $Rf(\mathbf{r}) = f(R\mathbf{r})$, but this would be inconsistent since it would lead to: $SRf(\mathbf{r}) = Sf(R\mathbf{r}) = f(RS\mathbf{r}) = RSf(\mathbf{r})$ whereas $SR \neq RS$ in general. In much of the literature, therefore, new operators Λ_R are introduced by the definition, $\Lambda_R f(\mathbf{r}) = f(R^{-1}\mathbf{r})$, which is consistent; the Λ_R then form a group isomorphic to $\mathscr{G}$. Equations (22–44)–(22–46) look very different when stated in terms of $\Lambda_R\phi(\mathbf{r})$ rather than in terms of $\phi(R\mathbf{r})$. Also there is then a certain degree of freedom in defining the concept, "$\phi_k(\mathbf{r})$ belongs to the kth row of $d^{(l)}$", and the convention (22–46) is not universal.

REMARKS:

1. From (22–44), since ϕ is arbitrary,

$$\sum_{l=1}^{c}\frac{h_l}{g}\,\chi^{(l)}(R) = \begin{cases}1, \text{ if } R = E\\ 0, \text{ otherwise}\end{cases} \qquad (22\text{–}47)$$

2. For the two-dimensional rotation group, (22–44) is nothing less than the Fourier theorem (recall that "$(1/g)\sum$" is to be replaced by (22–43); also $c = \infty$). Note also that, in this case, (22–44) gives only an expansion in the (polar coordinate) angle ϕ but not in the radius (which is invariant under rotation).

APPLICATIONS

(1) Consider again the eigenvalue problem (22–22), (22–23). The result (22–24) and those just listed show that the degeneracies (number of independent solutions for a given λ) can assume only certain values, namely those of the form, $\sum a_l h_l$. In fact, *in most problems, only degeneracies* $= h_l$ *occur* (that is, the representation (22–25) is irreducible). Other degeneracy-values are called "accidental" since they depend on a numerical "coincidence" having its roots in the analytic details of L and not merely in its symmetry properties. Thus, in general, knowledge of the irreducible representations Γ_l (for the group of transformations interchangeable with L) indicates the types of degeneracies which can occur in (22–22) and some of the properties of the corresponding functions under such transformations, even when the solutions have not been found explicitly. See (5–158) ff.

(2) If an "interaction", P is added to L in (22–22), then (in most physically interesting cases) the symmetry group for the operator, $L + P$, is a subgroup of

the symmetry group for L. The representations (22–25) for the group $\mathscr{G}_L$ are not irreducible representations for $\mathscr{G}_{L+P}$ but, if the character systems are known, (22–37) can be used to determine which irreducible representations $\Gamma^{(l)}_{L+P}$ are contained in each $\Gamma^{(l)}_L$.

This information then determines in what manner the "interaction", P, will lift the degeneracies of L—both the extent to which the λ_i will split and also which types of unperturbed states will contribute to which types of states of the final system. These considerations underly the "vector model" of complex atoms in quantum mechanics and also the various "coupling schemes" in atomic theory, molecular theory, and crystal-state theory.

(3) Matrix elements of certain operators, T, [that is the quantities $T_{ik} = (\psi_i, T\psi_k)$] can be partially evaluated in general *provided that*:

(a) The solutions ψ_i of (22–22) are chosen to be completely orthonormal.

(b) By further unitary transformations (within the ψ_i belonging to each λ_j), certain *specific* irreducible (unitary) representations, $d^{(l)}_{ij}(R)$, are made to appear* in (22–25).

Only a few such results will be quoted here as they are available in standard texts and are pretty much a "once and for all" proposition. The central ideas of the manipulations, however, are as follows.

Let a set of *operators*, $T^{(n)}$, transform under coordinate transformations by an irreducible† representation:

$$R^{-1}T^{(n)}R = \sum_m d^{(l)}_{nm}(R)T^{(m)} \tag{22–48}$$

Since coordinate transformations, R, cannot affect the value of an integral, we also have

$$T^{(n)}_{ik} = (R^{-1}\psi_i, R^{-1}T^{(n)}RR^{-1}\psi_k) = (\psi_i, T^{(n)}\psi_k) \tag{22–49}$$

Combining these two relations and summing over all R in $\mathscr{G}$, one can use (22–25), (22–35) etc. to show that: $T^{(n)}_{ik}$ consists of a factor depending only on λ_i and λ_k and another factor depending *only* on the representations, $d^{(l)}$, to which ψ_i and ψ_k "belong" (in the sense (22–46)). Explicit evaluation of this second factor requires detailed knowledge of the $d^{(l)}$ and a formula for reducing direct-product representations of the form, $d^{(l)} \times d^{(l')}$.

If the operator T is invariant under $\mathscr{G}$, namely $TR = RT$ for all R in the symmetry group of L, then the above steps can be carried through readily for any unspecified group (note $R^{-1}TR = T$). One obtains:

> If T is invariant under the symmetry group of (22–22), then its matrix elements,
>
> $$T_{ik} = (\psi_i, T\psi_k)$$
>
> vanish if ψ_i and ψ_k belong to‡ different *irreducible, unitary* representations or also if ψ_i and ψ_k belong to different rows of the *same*§ irreducible representation. In particular, $(\psi_i, \psi_k) = 0$ under these conditions. (22–50)

* Even if "accidental" degeneracy occurs, the representation (22–25) can still be reduced to a "string" of the chosen $d^{(l)}$; see (4) below.

† If the representation is not irreducible, the set $T^{(n)}$ can be split into subsets with this property; see (4) below.

‡ Definition: see (22–46).

§ *Not* merely "equivalent".

Thus the matrix elements of operators invariant under $\mathcal{G}_L$ will largely vanish. See also (5–159)–(5–160).

(4) *Perturbation theory; Explicit reduction of representations.*

Perturbation theory can lead to very involved calculations when the unperturbed eigenvalues are degenerate (compare (19–71)). Even a partial reduction of the "secular equation" is to be welcomed. This can often be achieved to a very large degree by combining the results of (2) and (3) above: (See also (5–158)–(5–160).)

Namely, the unperturbed eigenfunctions ψ_i are rechosen to "belong to" irreducible representations, *not* of $\mathcal{G}_L$ (the symmetry group of L in (22–22)) but rather of $\mathcal{G}_{L+P}$ (the symmetry group of $L + P$) which is, except for artificial cases, a subgroup of $\mathcal{G}_L$. Then the results (22–50) state that all but very few of the elements of the secular determinant (19–71) for $L + P$ will vanish and the secular equation will therefore factor into several equations of lower degree when these "symmetry-adapted eigenfunctions" are employed.

This observation would be academic without a specific way of achieving the "proper choice" of the ψ_i; therefore consider the situation:

Given a set of ψ_i belonging to a given eigenvalue,* λ_0, of (22–22).

To determine ϕ_i equivalent to (spanning the same "subspace" as) ψ_i but belonging to (transforming by) irreducible representations, Γ_l, of the (sub)group $\mathcal{G}_{P+L}$.

The actual relations (22–24) and (22–25) need not be written out in matrix form; all that is really necessary is to know the effects of the group operations (coordinate transformations) on the ψ_i in one form or another. However, some of the work below can be omitted if the characters of the representation generated by the ψ_i are known, since (22–37) can then be used to indicate which Γ_l will occur. [If the group operations merely permute the ψ_i, then $\chi(R)$ is merely the number of ψ_i for which $\psi_i(R\mathbf{r}) = \psi_i(\mathbf{r})$.]

Consider the functions (R are the operations of $\mathcal{G}$; $\chi^{(l)}$ are the irreducible characters),

$$\eta_i^{(l)} = \sum_R [\chi^{(l)}(R)]^* \psi_i(R\mathbf{r}) \tag{22–51}$$

By (22–45), each $\eta_i^{(l)}$ is a linear combination of functions belonging to Γ_l and *only* to Γ_l. Moreover (summing (22–51) over l and using (22–44) one sees) the $\eta_i^{(l)}$ span the same space† as do the ψ_i. Thus, by picking out linearly independent $\eta_i^{(l)}$ (independent linear combinations of those with the same l), one obtains a set of functions, $\theta_i^{(l)}$, equivalent to the ψ_i but grouped in such a way that the functions in any one group all belong to the same irreducible representation Γ_l.

These $\theta_i^{(l)}$ are not the desired ϕ_i (because repeated occurrences of the same Γ_l may still be "mixed up") but the result (22–50) shows that they already cause a great many of the matrix elements, $L_{ik} + P_{ik}$, to vanish. Moreover, it is remarkable how frequently one is lucky enough to have the $\theta_i^{(l)}$ come out directly as the desired ϕ_i. In any case, if it is desired to complete the process in order to take the fullest advantage of (22–50), the following steps can be taken. (They could have been applied to the ψ_i themselves, but would be far more tedious with the full set of functions.)

Consider only the (not yet fully reduced) $\theta_i^{(l)}$ for some fixed l. Apply (22–45) with $k = j$ to any one of the $\theta_i^{(l)}$ (playing the role of "ϕ") and then re-apply (22–45)

---

* Or more generally an arbitrary set of functions which are known to satisfy relations like (22–24) and (22–25). This can always be achieved by adjoining, if necessary, all (distinct) functions $\psi_i(R\mathbf{r})$ to the original set.

† Hence, if Γ_l does not occur in the representation generated by the ψ_i, then all $\eta^{(l)}$ with that l will be zero. Thus we *need* not know the $\chi(R)$ generated by the ψ_i.

to resulting function, $\phi_j^{(l)}$ to obtain its "partners", $\phi_k^{(l)}$. Then remove these functions $\phi_i^{(l)}$ (Schmidt process) from the set $\theta_i^{(l)}$ to leave a set orthogonal to all the $\phi_i^{(l)}$. Repeat as often as necessary to separate out further occurrences of Γ_l. Do this for each l where necessary.

These last steps require knowledge of explicit $d_{ij}^{(l)}(R)$ whereas the preceding steps required only the characters, $\chi^{(l)}(R)$. The latter are available in tabular form in standard texts on the applications of group theory; the former are less frequently given.

Standard methods for determining the irreducible characters, $\chi^{(l)}$, and some $d^{(l)}$ of Γ_l consist mainly in using (22–44)–(22–46) "in reverse" and in noting that the set $f(R\mathbf{r})$ for any f always generates a representation. The number of distinct "basis-functions" required is useful information in choosing f and is determined by the h_l which are often completely specified by the properties (22–34). Note also that the "regular representation" (22–32) contains all irreducible representations.

INDEX*

* This index is intended to serve in part as a *dictionary*. Consequently, some items have been included even though they may be merely mentioned in the text.

30A—(4 pp.)

31

CONSTANTS

$c = 2.998 \times 10^{10}$ cm/sec

$e = 4.803 \times 10^{-10}$ (erg cm)$^{1/2}$ $= 1.602 \times 10^{-19}$ coulomb $= 3.794$(eV-Å)$^{1/2}$

$$N_0 = \frac{R}{k} = \frac{1.008\text{ g}}{M_H} = \frac{1\text{ g}}{1836.1 m_e} = \frac{F}{e} = 6.025 \times 10^{23}\text{/mole}$$

$h = 6.625 \times 10^{-27}$ erg sec; $\hbar = 1.054 \times 10^{-27}$ g cm^2/sec

$$k = 1.380 \times 10^{-16}\text{ erg/deg} = \frac{1}{11{,}605}\text{ eV/deg}$$

$$R = 8.317 \times 10^{7}\text{ erg/mole deg} = 1.987\text{ cal/mole deg} = 82.06\,\frac{\text{atm cm}^3}{\text{mole deg}}$$

$v_0 = 22.42 \times 10^3$ cm^3/mole $= 0.7916$ ft^3/mole

$L = N_0/v_0 = 2.687 \times 10^{19}$ molec/cm^3

$$\sigma = \frac{0.5669}{10^4}\,\frac{\text{erg}}{\text{cm}^2\text{ sec deg}^4} = \frac{1.355}{(10^3)^4}\,\frac{\text{cal}}{\text{cm}^2\text{ sec deg}^4}$$

(Hence $(4\sigma/c)T^4 = 137(kT_{\text{eV}})^4$ erg/cm^3.)

$$\lambda_{\max} = \frac{2.898\text{ micron}}{(T/1000^\circ)}; \quad h\nu_{\max\,d\lambda} = 5kT; \quad h\nu_{\max\,d\nu} = 3kT$$

$$\alpha = \frac{e^2}{\hbar c} = \frac{1}{137.037}; \quad r_e = \frac{e^2}{m_e c^2} = 2.818 \times 10^{-13}\text{ cm}; \quad \frac{h}{m_e c} = 2.426 \times 10^{-10}\text{ cm}$$

$$a_0 = \frac{\hbar^2}{m_e e^2} = 0.5292\text{ Å}; \quad \frac{e^2}{2a_0} = 13.61\text{ eV}; \quad \frac{8\pi}{3}r^2 = 0.6652\text{ barn}$$

$G = 6.670 \times 10^{-8}$ cm^3/g sec^2 (Newton's gravitational constant)

$g = 980.6$ cm/sec^2 (at 45° latitude)

Speed of sound $= 0.3404$ km/sec (average, sea level air)